INCISED-VALLEY SYSTEMS: ORIGIN AND SEDIMENTARY SEQUENCES

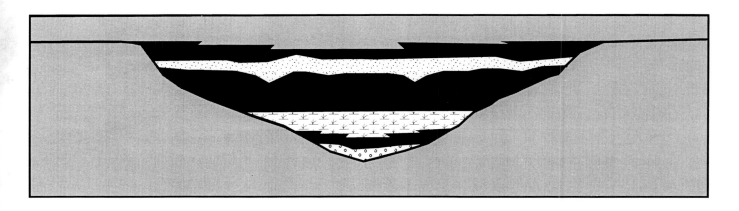

Edited by

Robert W. Dalrymple, Queen's University, Kingston, Ontario, Canada
Ron Boyd, University of Newcastle, Newcastle, Australia
and
Brian A. Zaitlin, PanCanadian Petroleum Limited, Calgary, Alberta, Canada

Peter A. Scholle, Editor of Special Publications
Special Publication No. 51

Tulsa, Oklahoma, U.S.A.   *December, 1994*

A Publication of

SEPM (Society for Sedimentary Geology)

ISBN 1-56576-015-8

© 1994 by
SEPM (Society for Sedimentary Geology)
P.O. Box 4756
Tulsa, Oklahoma 74131

Printed in the United States of America

PREFACE

Incised valleys were not widely recognized prior to the 1980's, although there are notable exceptions. Most early workers forced the isolated, incised-valley deposits along an unconformity into a single continuous unit, ignored them by including them within larger stratigraphic units, or interpreted them as deltaic distributaries or non-incised fluvial channels. In the last decade, intense interest in the influence that changes in accommodation space have on stratigraphic organization has focused attention on incised-valley systems, because they are one of the most visible records of major decreases in accommodation. In practical terms, they are also a significant key to the identification of sequence-bounding unconformities. As a result, many successions have been re-examined, and incised-valley fills are being found in rapidly growing numbers.

This enthusiasm for incised valleys is also fuelled by the recognition that incised-valley deposits contain significant hydrocarbon reserves in basins around the world. Thus, there is a powerful economic incentive to understand how allocyclic and autocyclic factors interact to determine the nature and organization of facies within incised-valley systems. Modern, incised-valley estuarine environments are among the most heavily populated settings on the planet. Thus, an accurate and detailed understanding of their response to changing sea level is essential to predicting their response to global warming.

This volume is an outgrowth of this widespread interest in incised-valley sedimentation. Many of the papers were initially presented at the popular Special Session on the "Recognition and Facies of Incised Valley Fills" held at the AAPG-SEPM Annual Meeting (Calgary) in June, 1992. We have also solicited additional papers in order to give the broadest possible coverage of the origin and shape of incised valleys and of the facies and stratigraphic organization of valley-fill successions.

Given that incised-valley systems have not been the subject of systematic study in the past, one of our objectives in preparing this compilation was to provide an integrated examination of these systems. It is obviously impossible,

however, to produce a truly integrated presentation within the context of a volume such as this, given the lack of a pre-existing framework for comparison and the rapidly evolving nature of the field. To compensate, we have used our editorial perogative to organize the case studies into groups with similar (paleo-) geographic settings and geologic histories, based on our perception of the fundamental organization of incised-valley systems that formed in response to changes in relative sea level. Only future research will tell to what extent we have succeeded at capturing the true "essence" of incised-valley systems in this model.

As might be expected, some form of sequence stratigraphy features prominently in most of the contributions. Due to the terminological problems which plague the field, we have asked that authors utilize widely accepted terms wherever possible, clearly indicating the source and justifying any departures from common usage. Uniformity has not been achieved, and readers must be cautious when comparing the various contributions. Hopefully this diversity of approach stimulates constructive thought rather than frustration.

In the preparation of this volume we have been assisted by many people in addition to the authors whose efforts are the basis of the volume. Therefore, we offer our sincere thanks to: our current and former employers (RWD-Queen's University; RB-University of Newcastle; BAZ-Pan-Canadian Petroleum Ltd. and Imperial Oil Resources) for the considerable logistical and financial support provided, particularly with regard to the voluminous international correspondence required (RWD specifically thanks the Ocean Sciences Institute, Department of Geology and Geophysics, University of Sydney, for their hospitality and support during the preparation of the volume, and the Advisory Research Committee, Queen's University, for a grant to help defray editorial expenses); SEPM Council for allowing this venture to proceed; Barbara Lidz, Dana Ulmer-Scholle and Peter Scholle for their editorial assistance; and the many scientists listed below for their insightful reviews of the manuscripts.

Phil Allen	John Anderson	Bill Arnott
Gail Ashley	John Barwis	Chris Beaumont
Tony Belperio	Michael Blum	Doug Cant
Rick Cheel	Ed Clifton	Norm Corbett
Trevor Elliott	Ken Ericksson	Frank Ethridge
Chris Fielding	Duncan Fitzgerald	Steven Flint
Don Forbes	Jim Gardiner	Martin Gibling
Victor Gostin	John Grotzinger	Peter Homewood
John Hopkins	David James	Jocke Keene
Lee Krystinik	Dale Leckie	Bruce Levell
John Lindsay	Gerry Middleton	Molly Miller
Tom Moslow	Maynard Nichols	Dag Nummedal
Chris Paola	Ron Pickerill	Guy Plint
Gerry Reinson	Brian Ricketts	Peter Roy
John Shaw	Rudy Slingerland	Derald Smith

John Suter   Tony Tankard   Bruce Thom
Rod Tillman   John VanWagoner   Chris von der Borsch
Roger Walker   Gary Willgoose   Colin Woodroffe

Robert W. Dalrymple,
Ron Boyd, and
Brian A. Zaitlin, Editors
December, 1993

CONTENTS

INTRODUCTION AND GENERAL CONCEPTS

HISTORY OF RESEARCH, TYPES AND INTERNAL ORGANISATION OF INCISED-VALLEY SYSTEMS: INTRODUCTION TO THE VOLUME

ROBERT W. DALRYMPLE
Department of Geological Sciences, Queen's University, Kingston, Ontario K7L 3N6, Canada
RON BOYD
Department of Geology, University of Newcastle, Newcastle, N.S.W. 2308, Australia
AND
BRIAN A. ZAITLIN
PanCanadian Petroleum Limited, Calgary, Alberta T2P 2S5, Canada

ABSTRACT: The study of unconformities has a long and distinguished history, and incised valleys have been recognized for more than 70 years. Early descriptions of incised-valley deposits lacked detail, with fluvial and deltaic interpretations predominating. Estuarine deposits were largely unrecognised until advances in our understanding of estuarine sedimentation permitted more sophisticated treatment of the fluvial-marine transition. Interest in incised-valley systems has increased dramatically in the last decade due to widespread application of sequence-stratigraphic concepts.

Following standard definitions, we urge that the term "incised valley" be restricted to fluvially eroded features that are larger than a single channel. A loss of accommodation space and the resulting formation of incised valleys may occur in response to factors unrelated to changes in relative sea level; however, all but one of the examples described in the volume are believed to be associated with a drop of relative sea level. Thus, the model proposed by Zaitlin and others (this volume) for this type of incised-valley system is used to group the papers according to which portion of an incised-valley system the deposits represent: *segment 1*—the portion between the mouth of the valley and the initial highstand shoreline, which is transgressed and overlain by marine deposits; *segment 2*—the region occupied by the drowned-valley estuary at the time of maximum transgression; and *segment 3*—the incised valley landward of the limit of marine/estuarine facies, which contains and is overlain exclusively by fluvial deposits. Each segment displays a predictable succession of environments and stratigraphic surfaces, but differences exist between the examples due to the poorly understood influence of such factors as the rate of sediment input and the magnitude and duration of the relative sea-level fall and rise.

INTRODUCTION

Incised-valley systems, which are considered in this volume to consist of an incised valley and its sedimentary fill, are a volumetrically minor but scientifically and economically important component of the stratigraphic record. The current interest in incised-valley fills is due in large measure to the recent popularization of sequence stratigraphy. In the Exxon version, which is the template most widely used by those working with incised-valley systems, type 1 unconformities are commonly marked by the presence of incised valleys that were eroded by fluvial action during the relative sea-level fall and lowstand (e.g., Posamentier and Vail, 1988; Van Wagoner and others, 1990). Thus, the recognition of incised-valley systems is an important criterion for the identification of sequence boundaries. As a consequence, incised-valley systems are being recognized in rapidly increasing numbers and are being found to contain significant hydrocarbon reserves (e.g., Howard and Whitaker, 1990; Van Wagoner and others, 1990; Zaitlin and Shultz, 1990; Dolson and others, 1991; Brown, 1993). At the same time, the potential for sea-level rise as a result of global warming has increased the need to understand the transgressive history of modern, drowned-valley estuaries, which serve as harbours, fisheries, waste-disposal sites and recreational areas for a significant fraction of the world's population.

The combined influence of these factors has produced a dramatic increase in research on both modern and ancient incised-valley systems. This volume is one expression of this interest. Because there has been no systematic study of incised valleys, current work lacks a conceptual framework, and case studies commonly stand in isolation. For this reason, we have gathered together in this volume a set of modern and ancient examples, in order to develop a better understanding of the complex stratigraphy of incised-valley systems.

As background to the following contributions, this introduction will review several general topics that provide a framework for assessing the relationships between the individual examples. These topics include: a review of early work on incised-valley deposits; a discussion of what does and does not constitute an incised valley; an overview of the key components of an incised-valley system; and an outline of the contents of the volume.

HISTORICAL REVIEW

Although incised-valley systems have not been studied intensely until recently, there is an extensive history of research on the subject. Prior to the development of radiometric dating, geologists were very interested in terrestrial-valley formation, because they believed that the observed rates of incision could be used to estimate the age of the earth (e.g., Lyell, 1853; Dana, 1880). Perhaps as a result of this belief, erosional unconformities have long been recognised as significant features of the rock record, and an enormous and at times deeply philosophical literature exists on their recognition, classification, and significance (e.g., Grabau, 1906; Blackwelder, 1909; Schuchert, 1927; Twenhofel, 1936; Krumbein, 1942; Shrock, 1948; Wheeler, 1958; Weller, 1960; Sloss, 1963; Weimer, 1984).

Despite this interest in unconformities, relatively little attention was directed specifically at incised valleys or their fill. For instance, erosional relief and stratal truncation, two of the key elements in the recognition of incised valleys (Van Wagoner and others, 1990; Zaitlin and others, this volume), are only two of 35 criteria listed by Krumbein (1942) as possible indicators of unconformities. Nevertheless, a brief review of North American literature indicates that ancient incised-valley systems were recognised and described by a number of early workers. Most of these examples appear to have been discovered in the course of regional mapping, and their descriptions are buried in geological-survey reports (e.g., Wanless, 1931a; Lee and others, 1938; Pepper and others, 1954). Relatively few were described in widely circulated journals (e.g., Wanless, 1931b; Wilson, 1948; Siever, 1951). Weller's (1960) textbook is the only one to consider incised valleys. Then as now, the impetus to document incised-valley deposits was economic, as many of the early examples were hydrocarbon reservoirs.

The three-dimensional geometry of the sediment body was of primary interest in much of this early work, with most incised-valley fills being classified as "shoestring" or "channel" sands. Indeed, some of these studies provide superb documentation of the plan geometry of the channel network, particularly notable examples being Siever's (1951) study of the geometry of the Mississippian-Pennsylvanian unconformity in southern Illinois and Pepper and others' (1954) examination of sandstone distribution in the Bedford and Berea Formations (Mississippian) of northern Ohio. By contrast, relatively little attention was paid to the depositional environment(s) in which the valley fill accumulated. In many instances, "channel sand" was deemed sufficient. In addition, little effort was made to distinguish between channels in an unbroken progradational succession and incised valleys formed in response to a base-level fall (e.g., Wanless and others, 1970). In almost all cases where a specific environment was suggested, the valley fill was treated as a single, undifferentiated entity. Prior to the 1970's, fluvial (e.g., Siever, 1951; Stokes, 1961; Harms, 1966) and deltaic (e.g., Pepper and others, 1954; MacKenzie, 1965) interpretations predominated due in part to the influence of Fisk's (1944; Fisk and others 1954) seminal work on the Mississippi River incised valley and delta. In the case of deltaic interpretations, the confined nature of the deposits led to some unrealistic paleogeographic reconstructions (Fig. 1).

One of the notable exceptions to the foregoing is Wilson's (1948) description of Upper Ordovician, valley-fill deposits in Tennessee. Based largely on paleocurrent information, he proposed that the sediment moved up-valley from a marine source and inferred a tidally-influenced, estuarine origin for the fill (Fig. 2). Although aspects of this interpretation are open to question (e.g., why there are no fluvial deposits in a fluvially-cut valley), the reconstruction is very modern in appearance and is easily reinterpreted in sequence-stratigraphic terms (Fig. 2). For many years, however, this remained one of the few estuarine interpretations of an incised-valley fill.

From the mid 1960's to early 1980's, the focus of sedimentological research moved away from stratigraphic studies and concentrated instead on the development of "static" facies models (Walker, 1992), which emphasised the role of autocyclic processes and largely ignored the influence of relative sea-level changes. Perhaps as a result, there are fewer studies of incised-valley systems from this period. The publication of American Association of Petroleum Geologists Memoir 26 (Payton, 1977) and subsequent elaboration of the Exxon school of sequence stratigraphy (e.g., Wilgus and others, 1988; Van Wagoner and others, 1990)

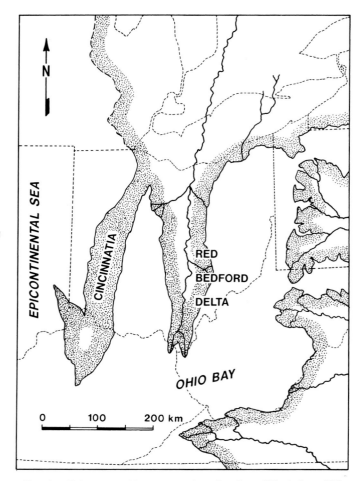

FIG. 1.—Paleogeographic reconstruction of northern Ohio during middle Bedford Shale (Early Mississippian) time. Failure to fully appreciate the incised-valley setting of the unit has led to the unrealistically elongate form of the inferred "Red Bedford Delta." The areas shown as submerged on either side of the delta were probably emergent during deposition of the "channel sands." After Pepper and others (1954, Plate 13C).

fundamentally changed the focus of research and ushered in the current phase of work on incised-valley deposits. Throughout the history of incised-valley research, valley incision has generally been ascribed to a drop in relative sea level, but this interpretation has become more explicit in the last fifteen years.

At the same time, our ability to recognize estuarine deposits, which are an important component of many incised-valley systems, took a large step forward. At the small scale, Visser (1980) demonstrated the existence of tidal bundles and neap-spring cyclicity in cross-bedded sands, thereby providing a means of recognizing the tidal signature that characterizes many estuarine deposits. On the large scale, Roy and others (1980) and Roy (1984), following earlier work by Oomkens and Terwindt (1960), Allen and others (1970), Nelson and Bray (1970), and Reinson (1977) popularised the now widely-used, tripartite facies model for wave-dominated estuaries. This model, which was the first to encompass the entire length of an estuarine system, has since been extended to all estuaries (Dalrymple and others, 1992). Studies by Kraft and associates (e.g., Kraft and others, 1973;

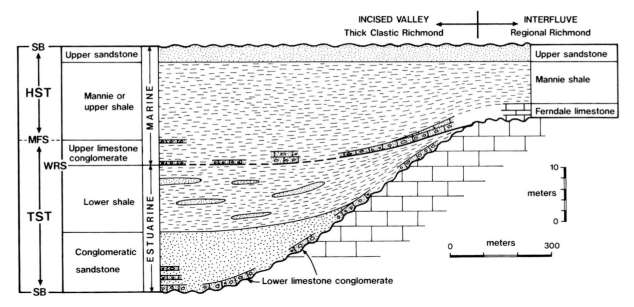

FIG. 2.—Diagrammatic cross section showing distribution of facies and depositional environments within a late Ordovician incised valley, central Tennessee (after Wilson, 1948, Fig. 3), with the inferred sequence-stratigraphic interpretation (left margin). SB = sequence boundary; TST = transgressive systems tract; HST = highstand systems tract; WRS = wave ravinement surface; MFS = maximum flooding surface. The Mannie shale thickens over the valley due to differential compaction and remaining (unfilled) relief. The inferred absence of fluvial sediments at the base is intriguing, and it may be that parts of the Lower limestone conglomerate and Conglomeratic sandstone are lowstand to transgressive fluvial deposits. The position of transgressive surface is unclear.

Belknap and Kraft, 1985; Kraft and others, 1987) in Delaware estuaries provided important information on the stratigraphic organisation and preservation potential of estuarine facies in transgressive settings.

The first application of the tripartite model to preserved deposits appears to have been by Nelson and Bray (1970) in their description of Holocene valley-fill sediments in the ancestral Sabine River on the Texas shelf (see Nichol and others, and Thomas and Anderson, this volume, for further discussion of this area). More recently, Rahmani's (1988) work on an incised-valley deposit in the Cretaceous of Alberta did much to bring this model to widespread attention (see Ainsworth and Walker, this volume, for a new look at this unit). Numerous estuarine deposits have now been documented, many of them comprising portions of incised-valley systems (e.g., Zaitlin and Shultz, 1984, 1990; Reinson and others, 1988; Howard and Whitaker, 1990; Leckie and Singh, 1991; Ricketts, 1991).

As the number of documented incised-valley deposits has increased in the last few years, significant variability has emerged with respect to the facies present and their stratigraphic complexity. For example, some incised valleys contain no fluvial sediment at their base (the fill is entirely estuarine and marine), despite the inference that the valley was cut by rivers (e.g., Reinson and others, 1988; Pattison, 1991), while others are largely to entirely filled with fluvial deposits (e.g., Dolson and others, 1991; Shanley and McCabe, 1991). Some valleys are filled by a single depositional sequence (defined as a *simple fill* by Zaitlin and others, this volume), whereas others are interpreted to contain multiple sequences (a *compound fill*). Organising the flood of new observations into a unified model or models will be a key challenge of future research. The important

elements of one such model are discussed briefly below, but before doing this, it is necessary to examine the range of features which might be considered as an incised valley. Only by restricting discussion to a clearly-defined set of features with a common origin will it be possible to develop a model that depicts the anticipated stratigraphy accurately.

TYPES OF INCISED VALLEY

It follows from the common definition of "valley" (e.g., Gray and others, 1972) that incised valleys are elongate erosional features that are larger than a single channel. It is also explicitly stated in most definitions that the erosion is caused by rivers. This concept is implicit in all of the papers in this volume (with glacial modification in some cases) and is an overriding theme in previous work on incised valleys.

It does not follow, however, that all fluvially eroded valleys have equal stratigraphic significance. Indeed, two fundamental classes of incised fluvial valleys should be recognized: (1) those which are eroded in response to a fall of relative sea level (i.e., due to a eustatic sea-level fall or tectonic uplift of the coastal zone); and (2) those which are not related to relative sea-level change (i.e., erosion is due to tectonic uplift of an inland area, or to an increase in fluvial discharge caused by climatic change; Schumm and others, 1987; Blum, 1992).

Incised valleys belonging to the first class are associated with sequence-bounding unconformities (*sensu* Van Wagoner and others, 1990), and are influenced by marine processes along some of their length. Most previously described incised valleys, modern and ancient, including all but one example in this volume (Fraser, this volume), are either inferred or assumed to belong to this category. Thus, most papers in this volume implicitly or explicitly (see Zaitlin and others, this volume) define an *incised-valley system* as consisting of: (1) an erosional valley, which is formed by river action during a relative sea-level fall; and (2) the valley fill, which may begin to accumulate near the end of the lowstand, but which typically contains sediments deposited during the succeeding base-level rise. Deposits of the following highstand and subsequent sea-level cycles may also be present within the fill. It is inherent in this definition that the valley is larger than a single channel and that the erosion surface has regional extent. The basal deposits of the fill should (ideally) show an abrupt seaward shift of facies relative to those beneath the erosion surface (Van Wagoner and others, 1988, 1990; Zaitlin and others, this volume). In this type of valley the fill typically contains a complex assemblage of fluvial, estuarine, deltaic and fully-marine facies; however, as discussed briefly below (see also Zaitlin and others, this volume), these deposits have a predictable organisation due to changes in accommodation space during infilling.

Although incised valleys in the second class are also common at present, few workers have studied them (e.g., Blum, 1992; Fraser, this volume), and valleys of this type have not been widely identified in older successions. Indeed, their recognition may be difficult, as they are likely to occur within fluvial successions and to be filled by terrestrial deposits. Unlike those of the first category, such incised valleys have no sequence-stratigraphic significance in the sense of Van Wagoner and others (1990). Nevertheless, systematic changes in fluvial style may occur during filling, due to cyclic changes in accommodation space caused by tectonics and/or climate. Further work is needed to determine the characteristics and abundance of this type of incised-valley fill.

In ancient successions, many features which do not fall into either of the above categories may be confused with incised valleys. Erosionally based, fluvial-channel deposits that have the dimensions of a single channel (10's to many 100's of meters wide and up to 10+ m deep) should not be classified as an incised valley, as they typically result of autocyclic processes such as channel avulsion, stream capture, or normal coastal progradation (Van Wagoner and others, 1990; Schumm, 1993). Thus, they do not imply regional changes in accommodation space. Tidally-eroded features, including shore-normal, tidal-inlet scours (the tidal ravinement surface of Allen, 1991 and Allen and Posamentier, 1993), also rarely fulfill the definition of a valley. In most cases, they form in response to an increase (not a decrease) in accommodation space, and although they are commonly associated with a fluvially produced valley (Allen and Posamentier, this volume; Ashley and Sheridan, this volume), they need not be. The Schelde estuaries in The Netherlands, which were created by tidal scour during the Holocene transgression and captured the Schelde River (Zagwijn, 1986; P. Vos, pers. commun., 1992), are an example of this. Similarly, shelf-edge canyons and gulleys formed by slumping and mass flows should not be classified as incised valleys because they may not be associated with a fluvial system and need not be linked to changes in

relative sea level (e.g., Jansen and others, 1987; Bouma and others, 1992). Therefore, great care must be taken before an incised-valley origin is ascribed to an elongate erosional feature.

INCISED-VALLEY SYSTEMS ASSOCIATED WITH RELATIVE SEA-LEVEL CHANGES

As indicated above, all but one of the case studies in this volume deal with incised valleys caused by a fall of relative sea level. Despite this, the examples are extremely diverse in terms of the nature and stratigraphic organization of the facies within the valley fill. Zaitlin and others (this volume) have attempted to synthesize these studies and previous descriptions into a general model for this type of incised-valley system. This model provides a framework which helps to integrate the described examples; therefore, we have used it to organize the contributions into groups with similar depositional settings. As background to what follows, we briefly summarise the main elements of the model here. Readers are referred to Zaitlin and others (this volume) for details.

The model is developed for a simple incised-valley system, in which the valley is cut during a single, relative sea-level fall and fills completely during the ensuing transgression and highstand. Thus, the fill consists of a single depositional sequence, such as might be formed in a relatively small valley during a high-frequency, sea-level cycle.

Erosion of the valley will be initiated in the region exposed by the relative sea-level fall, and incision will propagate headward with time. If the lowstand is relatively short, incision will not extend all the way to the mountainous hinterland, and the incised valley will pass landward into a non-incised fluvial system that is not influenced by the base-level fall (cf. Schumm and others, 1987; Schumm, 1993). During the subsequent base-level rise, fluvial sediment supply is commonly less than the rate of creation of accommodation space, and a drowned-valley estuary is generated at the seaward end of the incised valley. This estuary and its associated shoreline migrates landward throughout the transgression, stabilizing only as the rate of relative sea-level rise decreases to zero at the beginning of the next highstand. From this time on, fluvial and marine sediment input leads to deltaic or coastal-plain progradation, such that highstand deposits fill any remaining space within the incised valley.

Based on this succession of events, Zaitlin and others (this volume) identify four key points along the length of an incised valley (Fig. 3): (1) the seaward limit of the incised valley, which corresponds approximately with the landward limit of the lowstand wedge; (2) the seaward limit of the estuary at the time of maximum transgression, which corresponds with the shoreline position at the beginning of the highstand; (3) the landward limit of marine influence (the landward end of the estuary; Dalrymple and others, 1992) at the time of maximum transgression; and (4) the landward limit of incision during the lowstand.

These points in turn define three valley segments, each of which experiences a different depositional history and has a distinct stratigraphy (Fig. 3; Zaitlin and others, this volume, Fig. 6; see also Dalrymple and others, 1992, Figs.

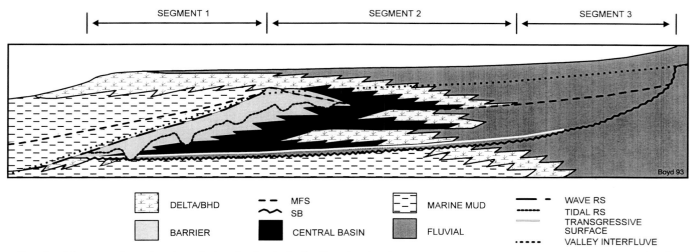

FIG. 3.—Diagrammatic section along the length of an incised valley, showing the valley segments, facies, and surfaces comprising an idealized, simple, incised-valley system. Great vertical exaggeration, but no particular vertical or horizontal scale implied. See text and Zaitlin and others (this volume) for further discussion.

13, 14). The most seaward portion (*segment 1*) initially experiences fluvial and estuarine deposition, but is transgressed by the shoreline so that the estuarine deposits are overlain by marine sediments. The middle portion (*segment 2*) of the valley is the zone occupied by the drowned-valley estuary at the time of maximum transgression. The lower part of the valley fill consists of a transgressive, fluvial to estuarine succession like that in segment 1, but is overlain by a progradational, estuarine to fluvial succession which accumulates as the estuary fills at the beginning of the highstand. The most landward portion of the valley (*segment 3*) lies beyond the limit of estuarine/marine influence. It remains fluvial throughout its history, and is overlain by terrestrial deposits. The extent to which the changes in base level are reflected in the facies of the fluvial fill of this segment depends on river gradient and distance from the marine limit, with the base-level signal decreasing in strength inland (e.g., Blum, 1992). The relative lengths of these three segments will vary from example to example (cf. Zaitlin and others, this volume), but segment 2 is likely to be the shortest of the three (although it could be tens to hundreds of kilometers long; Dalrymple and others, 1992).

Because the incision is caused by a relative sea-level fall, the basal erosion surface represents a *sequence boundary*. The assignment of the overlying valley fill to systems tracts is scale dependent. In work pertaining to thick, low-frequency sequences, the entire valley fill was placed in the lowstand systems tract (e.g., Van Wagoner and others, 1988). In the model (Fig. 3), by contrast, the fill contains sediments belonging to the lowstand, transgressive and highstand systems tracts of a high-frequency sequence. Consequently, the *transgressive surface* and *maximum flooding surface* are present within the fill (Allen and Posamentier, this volume; Zaitlin and others, this volume), although they may not be easily identified. Erosional surfaces produced by the tidal inlet and associated channels at the mouth of the estuary (the *tidal ravinement surface*; Allen, 1991) and by fluvial channels at the head of the estuary

(the *bayhead diastem*; Nichol and others, this volume) are likely to be more prominent, and care is needed not to confuse them with sequence boundaries. A *wave ravinement surface* produced by landward retreat of the shoreface (Swift, 1968) marks the top of the estuarine deposits in segment 1 of wave-dominated and mixed-energy settings.

No generalized model can reflect the variability that exists between real examples. However, the above model (Fig. 3) provides a basis that makes it possible to identify several of the more significant causes of variation.

1. The model developed by Zaitlin and others (this volume) emphasises the allocyclic controls on sedimentation, because they determine the basic organisation of the deposits. The nature of the individual facies and the expression of the various surfaces are determined, however, by environmental variables such as the relative intensity of waves, tides and river currents (Coleman and Wright, 1975; Dalrymple and others, 1992), alluvial-plain gradient, and sediment grain size (cf. Orton and Reading, 1993).

2. The relative amounts of fluvial and estuarine facies depend on the rate of sediment supply by fluvial and marine processes, relative to the rate of transgression. Thus, the thickness and proportion of fluvial deposits in segments 1 and 2 will increase as the rate of fluvial sedimentation increases and the rate of relative sea-level rise decreases. It remains to be determined, however, whether the absence of fluvial deposits in features interpreted as fluvially-cut valleys (e.g., Fig. 3; Wilson, 1948; Rahmani, 1988; Pattison, 1991; Ainsworth and Walker, this volume) can be accounted for by rapid transgression and a low rate of fluvial sedimentation. Such an explanation appears appropriate for small tributary valleys (Ashley and Sheridan, and Belknap and others, this volume) but is less likely in larger trunk systems (Colman and Mixon, 1988; Ashley and Sheridan, this volume).

3. The stratigraphic complexity of the valley fill, including the number of parasequences in a simple fill or of se-

quences in a compound fill, depends on the depth of incision, deeper valleys being less likely to fill in a single sea-level cycle. Lower rates of sediment input also favor the presence of multiple sequences, as does the superposition of high-frequency, sea-level oscillations on a longer-period fall and rise. For example, the Quaternary fill of the Chesapeake Bay incised valley contains several nested sequences (Colman and Mixon, 1988), each of which lacks the upper, regression portion because of the short duration of the glacio-eustatic highstands and the relatively low rate of fluvial sediment input.

CONTENTS OF THE VOLUME

The papers in this volume provide a wide-ranging overview of incised-valley origin, morphology, and sedimentary successions and illustrate the variability and complexity of incised-valley deposits. The first section of the volume contains papers of a general nature that examine the historical context of present work, address the issues of incised-valley origin and morphology, and develop an idealized model for the stratigraphic organization of incised-valley fills associated with changes in relative sea level. The following 18 papers report individual case studies, with the examples ranging in age from Precambrian to Modern (Table 1). All three of the valley segments discussed above (Fig. 3) are represented, and the papers are organized according to our assessment of the segment which figures most prominently in the contribution. In many of the modern examples, the study involves both segments 1 and 2 (present-day shelf and adjacent estuary), and the assignment to a section of the volume is arbitrary to some extent. Within a section, the papers are ordered by the geological age of the deposits. Examination of these examples (Table 1), together with the comprehensive compilation of previous descriptions prepared by J.E. Barclay and F.F. Krause (1993, pers. commun.), reveals some interesting points about the age and valley-segment distribution of incised-valley fills.

Firstly, most documented examples are from Quaternary, Cretaceous and Carboniferous successions. This clearly represents a sampling bias driven by interest in modern shelf and coastal areas and economic considerations. The presence of large numbers of incised-valley systems in deposits of both glacial (Quaternary and Carboniferous) and nonglacial (Cretaceous) times indicates that the formation of incised valleys is not particularly favoured by high-frequency and large-magnitude, glacio-eustatic, sea-level changes. One would expect that the duration and magnitude of the sea-level oscillation has an influence on the nature of the incised-valley systems, but too few well-documented examples exist to permit discussion of any differences.

Secondly, the largest number of documented examples comes from valley segment 1 (the valley fill is overlain by marine sediments). Numerous examples of segment 2 also exist, but this is due largely to the intense interest in modern estuaries. Ancient examples of estuaries at the transgressive limit are uncommon (e.g., Zaitlin and Shultz, 1990), presumably because of the relatively short length of this

TABLE 1.—SUMMARY OF THE INCISED-VALLEY SYSTEMS DISCUSSED BY PAPERS IN THIS VOLUME. "VALLEY SEGMENT" REFERS TO (1) THE PORTION WHICH EXPERIENCED MARINE TRANSGRESSION, (2) THE DROWNED-VALLEY ESTUARY AT THE TRANSGRESSIVE LIMIT, AND (3) THE SECTION THAT REMAINED FLUVIAL THROUGHOUT (FIG. 3). "SIMPLE" AND "COMPOUND" INDICATE WHETHER THE FILL CONSISTS OF ONE OR MORE SEQUENCES, RESPECTIVELY

Authors	Age	Location	Depositional Environments	Valley Segment	Simple/Compound
Quaternary					
Allen and Posamentier	Pleistocene-Holocene	SW France	fluvial, estuarine	2	simple
Ashley and Sheridan	Pleistocene-Holocene	U.S. East Coast	fluvial, estuarine, marine	1/2	simple
Belknap and others	Holocene	U.S. East Coast	fluvial, estuarine	1/2	simple
Clifton	Pleistocene-Holocene	U.S. West Coast	fluvial, estuarine	2	compound
Fraser	Pleistocene-Holocene	Ohio, U.S.A.	fluvial, lacustrine	—*	compound
Harris	Pleistocene-Holocene	Northern Australia	fluvial, deltaic, marine	1	simple
Kindinger and others	Pleistocene-Holocene	U.S. Gulf Coast	fluvial, estuarine, marine	1/2	simple
Nichol and others	Pleistocene-Holocene	U.S. Gulf Coast	fluvial, estuarine	2	simple and compound
Roy	Holocene	SW Australia	fluvial, estuarine	2	simple
Thomas and Anderson	Pleistocene-Holocene	U.S. Gulf Coast	fluvial, estuarine	1/2	simple and compound
Mesozoic					
Ainsworth and Walker	Cretaceous	Alberta, Canada	estuarine	1/2	simple?
Martinsen	Cretaceous	Wyoming, U.S.A.	fluvial, estuarine, deltaic	1	simple
MacEachern and Pemberton	Cretaceous	Alberta, Canada	fluvial, estuarine	1	compound
Paleozoic					
Aitken and Flint	Pennsylvanian	Kentucky, U.S.A.	fluvial, estuarine?	3	compound
Archer and others	Pennsylvanian	Kansas, U.S.A.	fluvial, estuarine	1	simple
Kvale and Barnhill	Pennsylvanian	Indiana, U.S.A.	fluvial, estuarine	1/2	simple
Precambrian					
Dyson and von der Borsch	Proterozoic	South Australia	fluvial, estuarine, marine	1	simple?
Levy and others	Proterozoic	Idaho and Utah, U.S.A.	fluvial, estuarine?	3	simple?

*The incised-valley systems described by Fraser were formed in response to fluvial-discharge variations and are not a result of changes in relative sea level. Thus, the segment model proposed by Zaitlin and others (this volume) is not applicable. However, because the valley fill is entirely terrestrial in origin, this case study is grouped with the other examples of segment 3 in this volume.

segment. The small number of examples of segment 3 (fluvially filled valleys in a fluvial succession) is perhaps surprising, as one might expect this valley segment to be of considerable length. Whatever the reason, this valley segment is the least well documented of the three and deserves further study.

Finally, simple fills slightly outnumber compound fills in the examples documented in this volume, but further work is needed to determine whether this is a valid generalization. Many more examples of compound fill must be described before the factors controlling their distribution become clear.

CONCLUDING STATEMENT

The study of incised-valley systems is one of the major outgrowths of sequence stratigraphy, and significant advances in our knowledge of these complex environments have occurred over the last ten years. Nevertheless, our understanding remains imperfect. Because incised-valley systems are a direct response to cyclic changes in accommodation space, any facies model(s) which may be developed will differ conceptually from earlier, static facies models in which the organisation is imparted largely by fluid-mechanical processes. Although the framework for a model is beginning to emerge for incised valleys created by relative sea-level falls, the relative importance of the many allocyclic and autocyclic factors which influence incised-valley sedimentation remain poorly known. Furthermore, almost nothing is known about other types of incised-valley deposits. Hopefully the contributions in this volume will provide the stimulus for further systematic study.

ACKNOWLEDGMENTS

We thank our respective employers (Queen's University, University of Newcastle and PanCanadian Petroleum Ltd.) for their support of our effort on this volume. The initial draft of this paper was prepared while RWD was on sabbatical at the University of Sydney. The hospitality and logistical support provided by the Ocean Sciences Institute, the Department of Geology and Geophysics, and Drs. Peter Harris and Peter Davies are gratefully acknowledged. Jim Gardiner and Jock Keene are thanked for their constructive reviews.

REFERENCES

ALLEN, G. P., 1991, Sedimentary processes and facies in the Gironde estuary: A recent model of macrotidal estuarine systems, in Smith, D. G., Reinson, G. E., Zaitlin, B. A., and Rahmani, R. A., eds., Clastic Tidal Sedimentology: Calgary, Canadian Society of Petroleum Geologists Memoir 16, p. 29–39.

ALLEN, G. P., CASTAING, P., FERAL, A., KLINGEBIEL, A., AND VIGNEAUX, M., 1970, Contribution à l'etude des facies de comblement et interpretation paléogéographique de l'evolution des milieux sédimentaires recents et actuels de l'estuaire de la Gironde: Bulletin de l'Institut de Geologie du Bassin d'Aquitaine, v. 8, p. 99–155.

ALLEN, G. P., AND POSAMENTIER, H. W., 1993, Sequence stratigraphy and facies model of an incised valley fill: The Gironde Estuary, France: Journal of Sedimentary Petrology, v. 63, p. 378–391.

BELKNAP, D. F., AND KRAFT, J. C., 1985, Influence of antecedent geology on the stratigraphic preservation potential and evolution of Delaware's barrier system: Marine Geology, v. 63, p. 235–262.

BLACKWELDER, E., 1909, The valuation of unconformities: Journal of Geology, v. 17, p. 289–300.

BLUM, M. D., 1992, Climatic and eustatic controls on Gulf coastal plain sedimentation: An example from the late Quaternary of the Colorado River, in Armentrout, J. M., and Perkins, R.F., eds., Sequence Stratigraphy as an Exploration Tool: Concepts and Practices in the Gulf Coast, Eleventh Annual Research Conference: Houston, Gulf Coast Section, Society of Economic Paleontologists and Mineralogists Foundation, p. 71–84.

BOUMA, A. H., ROBERTS, H. H., AND COLEMAN, J. M., 1992, Late Neogene Louisiana continental margin construction timed by sea-level fluctuations, in Watkins, J. S., Zhiqiang, F., and McMillen, K. J., eds., Geology and Geophysics of Continental Margins: Tulsa, American Association of Petroleum Geologists Memoir 53, p. 333–341.

BROWN, L. F., JR., 1993, Seismic and Sequence Stratigraphy: Its Current Status and Growing Role in Exploration and Development: New Orleans, New Orleans Geological Society Short Course No. 5, American Association of Petroleum Geologists 78th Annual Convention, unpaginated.

COLEMAN, J. M., AND WRIGHT, L. D., 1975, Modern river deltas: Variability of processes and sand bodies, in Broussard, M. L., ed., Deltas—Models for Exploration: Houston, Houston Geological Society, p. 99–149.

COLMAN, S. M., AND MIXON, R. B., 1988, The record of major Quaternary sea-level changes in a large coastal plain estuary, Chesapeake Bay, eastern United States: Palaeogeography, Palaeoclimatology, Palaeoecology, v. 68, p. 99–116.

DALRYMPLE, R. W., ZAITLIN, B. A., AND BOYD, R., 1992, Estuarine facies models: Conceptual basis and stratigraphic implications: Journal of Sedimentary Petrology, v. 62, p. 1130–1146.

DANA, J. D., 1880, Manual of Geology: Treating of the Principles of the Science with Special Reference to American Geological History (3rd ed.): New York, Ivison, Blakeman, Taylor and Company, 911 p.

DOLSON, J., MULLER, D., EVETTS, M. J., AND STEIN, J. A., 1991, Regional paleotopographic trends and production, Muddy Sandstone (Lower Cretaceous), central and northern Rocky Mountains: American Association of Petroleum Geologists Bulletin, v. 75, p. 409–435.

FISK, H. N., 1944, Geological investigation of the alluvial valley of the lower Mississippi River: Vicksburg, United States Army Corps of Engineers, Mississippi River Commission, 78 p.

FISK, H. N, MCFARLAN, E., JR., KOLB, C. R., AND WILBERT, L. J., 1954, Sedimentary framework of the modern Mississippi delta: Journal of Sedimentary Petrology, v. 24, p. 76–99.

GRABAU, A. W., 1906, Types of sedimentary overlap: Geological Society of America Bulletin, v. 17, p. 567–636.

GRAY, M., MCAFEE, R., JR., AND WOLF, C. L., eds., 1972, Glossary of Geology: Washington, D. C., American Geological Institute, 805 p.

HARMS, J. C., 1966, Stratigraphic traps in a valley-fill, western Nebraska: American Association of Petroleum Geologists Bulletin, v. 50, p. 2119–2149.

HOWARD, R. H., AND WHITAKER, S. T., 1990, Fluvial-estuarine valley fill at the Mississippian-Pennsylvanian unconformity, Main Consolidated Field, Illinois, in Barwis, J. H., McPherson, J., and Studlick, J. R. J., eds., Sandstone Petroleum Reservoirs: New York, Springer-Verlag, p. 319–341.

JANSEN, E., BEFRING, S., BUGGE, T., EIDVIN, T., HOLTEDAHL, H., AND SEJRUP, H. P., 1987, Large submarine slides on the Norwegian continental margin: Sediments, transport and timing: Marine Geology, v. 78, p. 77–107.

KRAFT, J. C., BIGGS, R. B., AND HALSEY, S. D., 1973, Morphology and vertical sedimentary sequence models in Holocene transgressive barrier systems, in Coates, D. R., ed., Coastal Geomorphology: Binghamton, State University of New York, p. 321–354.

KRAFT, J. C., CHRZASTOWSKI, M. J., BELKNAP, D. F., TOSCANO, M. A., AND FLETCHER, C. H., III, 1987, The transgressive barrier-lagoon coast of Delaware; Morphostratigraphy, sedimentary sequences and responses to relative rise in sea level, in Nummedal, D., Pilkey, O. H., and Howard, J. D., eds., Sea-level Fluctuation and Coastal Evolution: Tulsa, Society of Economic Paleontologists and Mineralogists Special Publication 41, p. 129–143.

KRUMBEIN, W. C., 1942, Criteria for subsurface recognition of unconformities: American Association of Petroleum Geologists Bulletin, v. 26, p. 36–62.

LECKIE, D. A., AND SINGH, C., 1991, Estuarine deposits of the Albian Paddy Member (Peace River Formation), and lowermost Shaftsbury Formation, Alberta: Journal of Sedimentary Petrology, v. 61, p. 825–850.

LEE, W., NICKELL, C. O., WILLIAMS, J. S., AND HENBEST, L. G., 1938, Stratigraphic and paleontologic studies of the Pennsylvanian and Permian rocks in north-central Texas: Austin, University of Texas, Bureau of Economic Geology Publication 3801, 252 p.

LYELL, SIR C., 1853, Principles of Geology; or, the Modern Changes of the Earth and its Inhabitants Considered as Illustrations of Geology (9th ed.): Boston, Little, Brown, and Company, 835 p.

MACKENZIE, D. B., 1965, Depositional environments of Muddy Sandstone, western Denver Basin, Colorado: American Association of Petroleum Geologists Bulletin, v. 49, p. 186–206.

NELSON, H. F., AND BRAY, E. E., 1970, Stratigraphy and history of the Holocene sediments in the Sabine-High Island area, Gulf of Mexico, *in* Morgan, J. P., and Shaver, R. H., eds., Deltaic Sedimentation Modern and Ancient: Tulsa, Society of Economic Paleontologists and Mineralogists Special Publication 15, p. 48–77.

OOMKENS, E., AND TERWINDT, J. H. J., 1960, Inshore estuarine sediments of the Haringvleit (Netherlands): Geologie en Mijnbouw, v. 39, p. 701–710.

ORTON, G. J., AND READING, H. G., 1993, Variability of deltaic processes in terms of sediment supply, with particular reference to grain size: Sedimentology, v. 40, p. 475–512.

PATTISON, S. A., 1991, Crystal, Sundance and Edson valley fill deposits, *in* Leckie, D. A., Posamentier, H. W., and Lovell, R. R., eds., 1991 NUNA Conference on High Resolution Sequence Stratigraphy, Program, Proceedings and Guidebook: Calgary, Geological Association of Canada, p. 44–46.

PAYTON, C. E., ed., 1977, Seismic Stratigraphy- Applications to Hydrocarbon Exploration: Tulsa, American Association of Petroleum Geologists Memoir 26, 516 p.

PEPPER, J. F., DEWITT, W., JR., AND DEMAREST, D. F., 1954, Geology of the Bedford Shale and Berea Sandstone in the Appalachian Basin: Washington, D. C., United States Geological Survey, Professional Paper 259, 109 p.

POSAMENTIER, H. W., AND VAIL, P. R., 1988, Eustatic controls on clastic sedimentation II— Sequence and systems tract models, *in* Wilgus, C. K., Hastings, B. S., Ross, C. A., Posamentier, H. W., Van Wagoner, J., and Kendall, C. G. St. C., eds., Sea-level Changes: An Integrated Approach: Tulsa, Society of Economic Paleontologists and Mineralogists Special Publication 42, p. 125–154.

RAHMANI, R. A., 1988, Estuarine tidal channel and nearshore sedimentation of a Late Cretaceous epicontinental sea, Drumheller, Alberta, Canada, *in* de Boer, P. L., van Gelder, A., and Nio, S. D., eds., Tide-influenced Sedimentary Environments and Facies: Boston, Reidel Publishing, p. 433–481.

REINSON, G. E., 1977, Hydrology and sediments of a temperate estuary— Mallacoota Inlet, Victoria: Australian Bureau of Mineral Resources, Geology and Geophysics, Bulletin 178, 91 p.

REINSON, G. E., CLARK, J. E., AND FOSCOLOS, A. E., 1988, Reservoir geology of Crystal Viking field, Lower Cretaceous estuarine tidal channel-bay complex, south-central Alberta: American Association of Petroleum Geologists Bulletin, v. 72, p. 1270–1294.

RICKETTS, B. D., 1991, Lower Paleocene drowned valley and barred estuaries, Canadian Arctic Islands: aspects of their geomorphological and sedimentological evolution, *in* Smith, D. G., Reinson, G. E., Zaitlin, B. A., and Rahmani, R. A., eds., Clastic Tidal Sedimentology: Calgary, Canadian Society of Petroleum Geologists Memoir 16, p. 81–106.

ROY, P. S., 1984, New South Wales estuaries: their origin and evolution, *in* Thom, B. G., ed., Coastal Geomorphology in Australia: New York, Academic Press, p. 99–121.

ROY, P. S., THOM, B. G., AND WRIGHT, L. D., 1980, Holocene sequences on an embayed high energy coast: An evolutionary model: Sedimentary Geology, v. 26, p. 1–19.

SCHUCHERT, C., 1927, Unconformities as seen in disconformities and diastems: American Journal of Science, v. 13, p. 260–262.

SCHUMM, S. A., 1993, River response to baselevel change: implications for sequence stratigraphy: Journal of Geology, v. 101, p. 279–294.

SCHUMM, S. A., MOSLEY, M. P., AND WEAVER, W. E., 1987, Experimental Fluvial Geomorphology: New York, Wiley, 413 p.

SHANLEY, K. W., AND MCCABE, P. J., 1991, Predicting facies architecture through sequence stratigraphy— an example from the Kaiparowits Plateau, Utah: Geology, v. 19, p. 742–745.

SHROCK, R. R., 1948, Sequence in Layered Rocks: New York, McGraw-Hill, 507 p.

SIEVER, R., 1951, The Mississippian-Pennsylvanian unconformity in southern Illinois: American Association of Petroleum Geologists Bulletin, v. 35, p. 542–581.

SLOSS, L. L., 1963, Sequences in cratonic interior of North America: Geological Society of America Bulletin, v. 74, p. 93–114.

STOKES, W. L., 1961, Fluvial and eolian sandstone bodies in Colorado Plateau. *in* Peterson, J. A., and Osmond, J. C., eds., Geometry of Sandstone Bodies: Tulsa, American Association of Petroleum Geologists, p. 151–178.

SWIFT, D. J. P., 1968, Coastal erosion and transgressive stratigraphy: Journal of Geology, v. 76, p. 444–456.

TWENHOFEL, W. H., 1936, Marine unconformities, marine conglomerates, and thickness of strata: American Association of Petroleum Geologists Bulletin, v. 20, p. 677–703.

VAN WAGONER, J. C., POSAMENTIER, H. W., MITCHUM, R. M., VAIL, P. R., SARG, J. F., LOUTIT, T. S., AND HARDENBOL, J., 1988, An overview of the fundamentals of sequence stratigraphy and key definitions, *in* Wilgus, C. K., Hastings, B. S., Posamentier, H. W., Ross, C. A., Van Wagoner, J., and Kendall, C. G. St. C., eds., Sea-level Changes: An Integrated Approach: Tulsa, Society of Economic Paleontologists and Mineralogists Special Publication 42, p. 39–45.

VAN WAGONER, J. C., MITCHUM, R. M., CAMPION, K. M., AND RAHMANIAN, V. D., 1990, Siliciclastic Sequence Stratigraphy in Well Logs, Cores, and Outcrops: Concepts of High-resolution Correlation of Time and Facies: Tulsa, American Association of Petroleum Geologists, Methods in Exploration Series 7, 55 p.

VISSER, M. J., 1980, Neap-spring cycles reflected in Holocene subtidal large-scale bedform deposits: A preliminary note: Geology, v. 8, p. 543–546.

WALKER, R. G., 1992, Facies, facies models and modern stratigraphic concepts, *in* Walker, R. G., and James, N. P., eds., Facies Models-Response to Sea Level Change: St. John's, Geological Association of Canada, p. 1–14.

WANLESS, H. R., 1931a, Pennsylvanian cycles in western Illinois: Illinois State Geological Survey, Bulletin 60, p. 179–193.

WANLESS, H. R., 1931b, Pennsylvanian section in western Illinois: Geological Society of America Bulletin, v. 42, p. 801–812.

WANLESS, H. R., BAROFFIO, J. R., GAMBLE, J. C., HORNE, J. C., ORLAPP, D. R., ROCHA-CAMPOS, A., SOUTER, J. E., TRESCOTT, P. C., VAIL, R. S., AND WRIGHT, C. R., 1970, Late Paleozoic deltas in the central and eastern United States, *in* Morgan, J. P. and Shaver, R. H., eds., Deltaic Sedimentation Modern and Ancient: Tulsa, Society of Economic Paleontologists and Mineralogists Special Publication 15, p. 215–245.

WEIMER, R. J., 1984, Relation of unconformities, tectonics, and sea-level changes, Cretaceous of Western Interior, *in* Schlee, J. S., ed., Interregional Unconformities and Hydrocarbon Accumulation: Tulsa, American Association of Petroleum Geologists Memoir 36, p. 7–35.

WELLER, J. M., 1960, Stratigraphic Principles and Practice: New York, Harper, 725 p.

WHEELER, H. E., 1958, Time-stratigraphy: American Association of Petroleum Geologists Bulletin, v. 42, p. 1047–1063.

WILGUS, C. K., HASTINGS, B. S., POSAMENTIER, H. W., ROSS, C. A., VAN WAGONER, J., AND KENDALL, C. G. St. C., eds., 1988, Sea-level Changes: An Integrated Approach: Tulsa, Society of Economic Paleontologists and Mineralogists Special Publication 42, 407 p.

WILSON, C. W., 1948, Channels and channel-filling sediments of Richmond age in south-central Tennessee: Geological Society of America Bulletin, v. 59, p. 733–766.

ZAGWIJN, W. H., 1986, Geologie van Nederland, Deel 1: Nederland in het Holocene: Haarlem, Rijks Geologische Dienst, 's-Gravenhage, Staatsuitgeverij, 46 p.

ZAITLIN, B. A., AND SHULTZ, B. C., 1984, An estuarine-embayment fill model from the Lower Cretaceous Mannville Group, west-central Saskatchewan, *in* Scott, D. F., and Glass, D. J., eds., Mesozoic of Middle North America: Calgary, Canadian Society of Petroleum Geologists Memoir 9, p. 455–469.

ZAITLIN, B. A., AND SHULTZ, B. C., 1990, Wave-influenced estuarine sandbody: the Senlac Heavy Oil Pool, Saskatchewan, *in* Barwis, J. H., McPherson, J., and Studlick, J. R. J., eds., Sandstone Petroleum Reservoirs: New York, Springer-Verlag, p. 363–387.

ORIGIN, EVOLUTION AND MORPHOLOGY OF FLUVIAL VALLEYS

STANLEY A. SCHUMM AND FRANK G. ETHRIDGE

Colorado State University, Fort Collins, Colorado 80523

ABSTRACT: Valleys are formed by both erosional and tectonic forces, although the former is the most common. Most valleys form by channel incision, and they follow an evolutionary sequence of deepening and widening that is controlled by the lithologic and structural character of the valley perimeter and the erosive power of the river that is eroding the valley. Usually valleys are single features that are contained by valley walls, but on alluvial plains a complex anastomosing network of multiple valleys can develop as a result of channel avulsion.

In general, valley dimensions increase down valley, and older valleys are larger than younger valleys, but the main characteristic is great variability both in cross section and longitudinally. Unlike stream channels formed in relatively homogeneous alluvium that reflect hydrologic and hydraulic variables, valley morphology also reflects lithologic and structural controls. Valley-fill deposits should also reflect this variability to a lesser extent, as channel morphology varies in response to variations of valley slope and to tributary influences.

INTRODUCTION

Valleys are ubiquitous features of the earth's surface that are defined as follows (Bates and Jackson, 1987): "Any low-lying land bordered by higher ground; specially an elongate, relatively large, gently sloping depression of the Earth's surface, commonly situated between two mountains or between ranges of hills or mountains, and often containing a stream with an outlet. It is usually developed by stream erosion, but may be formed by faulting."

Valleys played an important role in the great geologic debates of the 19th century. If the earth was only 6,000 years old then valleys probably were formed by faulting and subsequently occupied by rivers. However, if the earth was very old, then the slow processes of fluvial and valley-side erosion could form valleys (Gregory, 1918; Chorley and others, 1964). Even the famous statement of Playfair (1802, p. 102) did not resolve the controversy; nevertheless, his reasoning was impressive, as follows:

> "Every river appears to consist of a main trunk, fed from a variety of branches, each running in a valley proportioned to its size, and all of them together forming a system of valleys, communicating with one another, and having such a nice adjustment of their declivities, that none of them join the principal valley, either on too high or too low a level; a circumstance which would be infinitely improbable, if each of these valleys were not the work of the stream that flows in it."

Unlike rivers, valleys have not received detailed scrutiny by geomorphologists. A reason for this is that valleys are bedrock paleoforms. Valley morphology probably developed under climatic and hydrologic conditions that were different from the present, and it is difficult to obtain data on the subsurface configurations of the valley floor and walls. Hence, attempts to relate valley morphology to modern hydrologic data are few. In addition, most studies have been of valleys in continental interiors that are unlikely to be preserved in the rock record. Nevertheless, this review is an attempt to develop some general statements concerning valleys that have been formed primarily by fluvial processes.

ORIGIN AND EVOLUTION

Valleys originate when faulting, uplift, baselevel lowering or the concentration of flow causes channel incision.

If a valley is a graben, its shape and dimensions are determined by faulting. Although the margins of this structural valley can be modified by lateral stream erosion, mass wasting, and runoff, its character will be fault dominated. However, a fluvial valley undergoes an evolution from incising channel to valley by a combination of fluvial and valley-side slope processes. Time is an important element that determines the stage of erosional evolution. For example, in a study of valley characteristics in Iowa, Tuttle and others (1966) showed that old valleys are larger than young valleys, and that valleys become more rectangular and less triangular with time. Retreat of valley walls with time can form an enormous valley of the Grand Canyon type (Fig. 1). Tuttle and others (1966) also conclude that valleys have a more triangular shape in resistant rocks, and they are more rectangular in weak rocks. Also, valley size decreases with increasing rock resistance.

Figure 2 illustrates the origin of a valley in more detail. The initial vertical incision produces a narrow deep channel that widens by lateral erosion and bank failure. Increased sediment delivery from upstream in the widening channel causes deposition and eventually a new floodplain is formed in a new valley, or the valley could be completely filled if deposition continues. Although this example is of a valley that formed in alluvium and erosive Tertiary sediments, the processes are the same in bedrock. Variations of bedrock character, of course, will cause irregularities of the valley walls, and the resistance of the rock and the energy of the stream will determine the rate of change (Table 1). For example, the changes illustrated by Figure 2A-E occurred during only 40 years, whereas, the changes in Figure 1 may require millions of years.

Valleys originate when streams incise. The incision is the result of an increase of potential energy following baselevel lowering or uplift, or an increase of kinetic energy following concentration of flow on an erosive surface. Most valleys reflect either baselevel change or uplift or both. Incision will occur in existing channels, or if the surface is newly exposed, incision will occur where water is concentrated. For example, an experimental study of drainage network development showed that channels and valleys are formed where flow is concentrated in depressions on a relatively smooth surface (McLane, 1978; see Schumm and others, 1987).

The amount of incision depends upon the amount of baselevel change and uplift. During experimental studies,

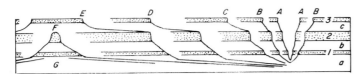

FIG. 1.—Profiles showing progressive widening of a valley. Initial incision into strata of different resistance produces an irregular cross section (A-C). Continued valley-wall retreat (B-E) produces a Grand Canyon type profile (from Davis, 1908; see King and Schumm, 1980).

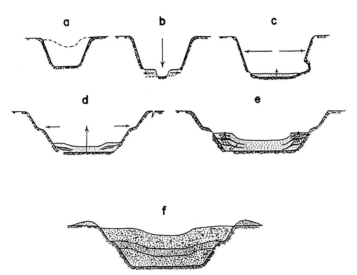

FIG. 2.—Evolution of valley from initial channel incision (a,b) through widening by lateral migration and valley-wall failure (c,d), to aggradation (d,e), followed by valley filling as a result of climate or baselevel change (f). This sequence was documented as streams adjusted to channelization in Mississippi (from Schumm and others, 1984).

TABLE 1.—RATES OF VALLEY INCISION

Rate (mm/1000 yr)	Rock Type	Location	Source
240	granite	SE Australia	Brittlebank, 1900
96	basalt	SE Australia	Brittlebank, 1900
95	conglomerate	Arizona	Rice, 1980
248	sandstone	Arizona	Rice, 1980
300	sedimentary rock	Colorado	Larsen and others, 1975
70	metamorphic rock	Colorado	Scott, 1975
370	limestone and basalt	Utah	Hamblin and others, 1981
26	limestone and basalt	Utah	Hamblin and others, 1981
87	granite	Sierra Nevada Mtns., CA	Huber, 1981

an entire drainage network can be rejuvenated by major baselevel lowering (Schumm and others, 1987). However, field investigations (Saucier, 1991; Blum, 1992) and theoretical considerations (Schumm, 1993) suggest that the upvalley influence of sea-level change is limited to the lower drainage system.

Climate change affects the quantity of discharge and sediment loads, which can significantly affect the morphology of rivers, but the effect upon valleys will probably be minor unless erosion of the valley walls is accelerated.

In summary, valleys that are formed by fluvial processes are initiated by channel incision. Deepening is followed by widening, and the form of the valley can be significantly influenced by the nature of the material exposed in the floor and walls of the valley.

RATES OF VALLEY FORMATION

In weak material, river incision and valley widening can be very rapid (Fig. 2), but many valleys form in more resistant rocks, and the rates of incision depend upon the energy of the river and the resistance of the materials that it is eroding (Table 1). According to Pitty (1971), an average rate of bedrock incision in middle latitudes is roughly 15 cm/1000 years. The bulk of information on the rate of river incision is based on the position of the river below a dated stratum. For example, Rice (1980) calculated a rate of incision of 95 m per million years by the Little Colorado River in Arizona as it incised below dated lava flows. Hamblin and others (1981) used dated lava flows along the Hurricane Fault in western Utah to determine that the Virgin River incised 128 m through limestone and basalt in about 290,000 years (1 m/2270 yr). A nearby ephemeral stream eroded a 130-m deep and 2-km long canyon in less than 0.44 million years. In the Sierra Nevada Mountains, 900 m of uplift occurred between 10 and 3 my ago. During that time, 700 m of downcutting occurred (Huber, 1981). The disparity between uplift and incision indicates that adjustment of streams lag, as the increased stream gradients and steeper valley-side slopes provide larger sediment loads of larger grain size, which retard the incision rate. However, in weak rocks incision can be rapid, and it may keep pace with uplift. For example, channel incision into coastal-plain sediments could keep pace with uplift or baselevel lowering unless the stream was unable to remove all of the sediment delivered to it by rejuvenated and incising tributaries. During experimental studies, rapid incision of a drainage network into unconsolidated sediments was followed by valley widening and aggradation (Schumm, and others, 1987). This sequence of events has been documented in channelized streams of the southeast (Fig. 2) and arroyos of the southwest (Schumm, and others, 1984).

Valley widening is not entirely the result of erosion and mass failure of valley walls by gravitational processes. It can also occur by lateral planation. Suzuki (1982) determined that the width of the Iwaki River valley in northwestern Honshu, Japan is a function of a ratio between an index of erosive energy of the river, and an index of rock resistance (Fig. 3). Suzuki and others (1983) continued this investigation in four other valleys. Using archaeological and tephrochronological data they found that rates of valley widening ranged from about 0.01 to 0.5 meters per year.

These studies confirm the qualitative conclusions of Tuttle and others (1966) concerning the effects of rock resistance on valley size and the assumption that big rivers will have big valleys. Nevertheless, it is clear that valley formation will be a relatively slow process.

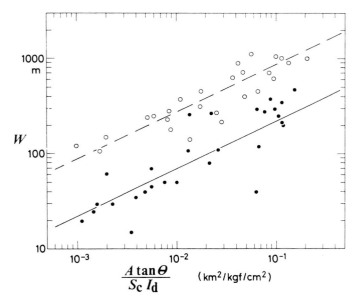

FIG. 3.—Relation between floodplain (black dots) and terrace (open circles) width and Suzuki's ratio between erosive force and rock resistance. The sum of floodplain and terrace widths equal valley width that was formed by lateral planation (A = drainage area; $\tan q$ = valley slope; Sc = mean compressive strength of bedrock; I_d = ratio between longitudinal waves in bedrock and in a cylindrical specimen of the same rock; W = width).

VALLEY MORPHOLOGY

Dimensions

Size is one of many criteria for distinguishing between paleochannels and paleovalleys. Channels are in general much smaller than the valleys in which they flow. The largest modern river, the Amazon, at Obidos is 2.3 km wide and 61 m deep. The world's fourth largest river, the Mississippi, is approximately 0.6 km wide and 18 m deep at Vicksburg (Schumm, 1977). Most modern rivers are much smaller than these giants. The modern Guadalupe River, an average river on the Texas Coastal Plain, is 0.06 km wide and 7 m deep. Data on the dimensions of some inferred paleovalleys (Table 2) reveals that many are smaller than the largest modern rivers, but most are larger by an order

of magnitude than the average modern coastal-plain stream. Obviously, modern valleys range in size from tiny incisions in badlands to major river valleys like the Nile and Mississippi.

Valleys usually increase in size in the downstream direction as drainage area and discharge increase. For example, Tuttle and others (1966) conclude from studies of streams in Iowa that valley size increases with discharge. This conclusion supports Playfair's (1802) statement that every river flows in a valley proportional to its size.

Salisbury and others (1968) collected data on valley width in 26 drainage basins in Iowa. Because of a lack of drill hole or seismic data, total valley depth was unknown. Width, as measured by Salisbury and others (1968), is the width of the valley bottom at the floodplain level rather than the maximum width at the valley top. Hence, it is not known where within the total valley cross section the measurement was made. Although this measurement may reflect modern conditions, it can also reflect past, perhaps Pleistocene, hydrologic conditions. For example, the low, but in a few cases, significant correlation coefficients indicate that there is no general relation between valley width and modern hydrology. Although channel width shows a reasonable correlation with mean annual flood, valley width does not. Correlations between valley and channel width, and between valley width and drainage basin area are also poor. The conclusion from this aspect of their investigation is that the occurrence of bedrock at some gaging stations, glacial meltwater floods and different Pleistocene sediment loads explains the poor correlations with modern hydrologic conditions. However, the plotting of data from 26 different rivers is likely to obscure or weaken the expected relations because of the differences that exist among rivers. In another study, Bhowmik and Stall (1979) found good relations between average valley (floodplain) width and stream order. An example is the Susquehanna River (Fig. 4). The averaging of widths for a number of valleys of the same order significantly reduces the scatter of data. Nevertheless, a progressive increase of average width with stream order does not always occur, as the Little Wabash River demonstrates (Fig. 4), especially when such rivers enter a different geologic terrain.

It may be more meaningful to consider variations of valley width along single streams. This was done by compar-

TABLE 2.—PALEOVALLEY DIMENSIONS

Age	Location	Max Width or Range (km)	Max Thickness or Range (m)	Reference
Middle Miocene	Louisiana Gulf Coast	1.6–64.0	73–82	Van Wagoner and others, 1990
L. Cret. (Fall River)	Eastern Powder River Basin	?	18	Knox, 1989
L. Cret. (Muddy SS)	Powder River Basin, Wyoming	9.6	18	Van Wagoner and others, 1990
L. Cret. (J SS)	Western Nebraska	0.5	20	Harms, 1966
L. Cret. (J SS or Muddy)	Denver Basin, Colorado	3.0–15.0	40	Weismer, 1991; Dolson, unpublish.
L. Cret. (Cutbank)	N-Central Montana	10's	35	Hayes, 1991; James and Elliott, 1991
L. Cret. (Viking)	Alberta Canada	7.0–12.0	32	Pattison, 1991a, b
Upper Penn.	Northeastern Kansas	22.5	31	LINS, 1950
Middle Penn.	Indiana	0.8	15	Friedman, 1960
Penn. (Tyler)	Central Montana	15.0	100	Kranzler, 1966
Early Penn. (Morrow)	E. Colorado W. Kansas	0.8–3.2	15–24	Krystinik and Blakeney, 1990
Lower Penn.	S. Eastern Illinois	32.0	91	Howard and Whitaker, 1990
Miss. (Berea SS)	West Virginia	5.0	8?	Heck, 1941

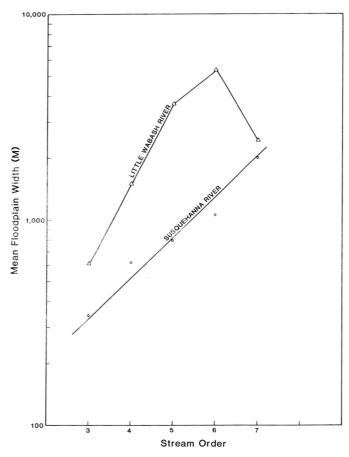

FIG. 4.—Relation between floodplain (valley) width and stream order for Susquehanna River, New York and Pennsylvania and Little Wabash River, Illinois (after Bhowmik and Stall, 1979).

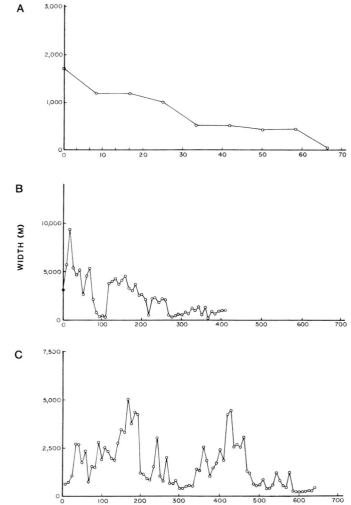

FIG. 5.—Variability of valley width for three Iowa rivers. Distance is kilometers upstream from a gaging station at kilometer zero (from Salisbury and others, 1968). (A) South River, (B) Iowa River, and (C) Des Moines River.

ing valley size with increasing distance upstream from a gage (Salisbury and others, 1968). Three of these valleys were selected as examples (Fig. 5).

The South River valley (Fig. 5A) displays an almost perfect example of upstream decrease of valley width ($r = -0.96$). The high coefficient of correlation between valley width and distance is exactly what one would predict for a decrease of valley size with decreasing drainage area and discharge. The South River developed its valley in Kansan-age glacial drift. Bedrock is present locally along the valley walls throughout its middle and lower course, and it is highly likely that the constriction at about kilometer 7 and 35 owes its existence to such outcrops. Nevertheless, the variation of valley width along the South River is minimal, and with a few measurements of width in a paleovalley of this type the flow direction could be relatively easily determined.

The Iowa River (Fig. 5B) is a stream with headwaters developed on young glacial deposits and a lower course on old glacial deposits. Valley width decreases upstream but with pronounced variability. The wide valley at kilometer 10 is associated with unconsolidated sediments in the left valley wall. The extreme narrowing at about kilometer 100 is associated with a bedrock gorge. Upstream the valley

widens again as it passes through a region of unconsolidated Kansan-aged drift capped with beds of loess and sand. A fairly consistent upstream decrease of width is observed in this reach until at kilometer 210 there is an abrupt narrowing at a bedrock high. The stream reverts back to a valley-width trend normal for the entire valley from kilometer 215 to 260. Narrowing occurs in a sandstone-limestone gorge from kilometer 260 to 290. Beyond kilometer 290 bedrock is locally at or close to the surface. The variability of valley width along the Iowa River valley would at some locations cause an error in estimating flow direction, and this possibility should be considered when interpreting paleovalley dimensions from limited data.

The Des Moines River (Fig. 5C) has its headwaters in young glacial deposits, but it flows for a considerable distance through older rocks in southern Iowa. Because the Des Moines River is so long, crosses such varied topography, and receives tributary flow from so many different kinds of streams, it is not surprising that its width-distance plot is erratic. The coefficient of correlation is insignificant. Differences in resistance to erosion explain the major valley-width variations. In general, the very narrow reaches of the valley are carved in limestone, the broader reaches are in coal measures or Pennsylvanian sandstones and shales. Within the latter, the predominance of shales in a section leads to a broad valley. The great variability of the Des Moines River is an example of how river behavior and valley-wall materials can greatly affect valley morphology. Lithologic variations play a major role in determining valley widths.

Experimental studies on the effect of tributary discharge and sediment load (Mosley, 1976) demonstrate clearly that lateral shift of the main channel can be expected when tributary contributions are large. Mosley's observations help to explain the position of a river within its valley; for example, the upper Mississippi River between St. Louis, Missouri, and St. Paul, Minnesota, is strongly influenced by large tributaries that have pushed the main channel to the opposite side of the valley The persistence of this effect may well create a marked asymmetry of the bedrock valley at such locations. In addition, the experiments also indicate that valley width may increase significantly at tributary junctions and then narrow again, an observation, also made by Salisbury and others (1968).

Valley Shape

Usually little is known about valley cross sections and the bedrock floor of a valley and; therefore, when sketches of a valley profile or cross section are made, a relatively smooth-floored profile is drawn. The smoothness of the valley floor, as sketched, is usually a reflection of ignorance. For example, Figure 6 is a cross section of the James River Valley in southern North Dakota. Based on only three drill holes, the cross section of the James River Valley is highly generalized and provides little information on details of the valley floor. Nevertheless, it is obvious that variations of valley-side lithology will greatly affect the character of a valley (Fig. 7). In addition, if uplift and baselevel change is intermittent, or if there are distinct episodes of incision, the valley may develop a valley-in-valley form (Fig. 8A), or it may contain multiple bedrock terraces (Fig. 8B), which further complicate the morphology of an already complex landform.

The cross section of the James River valley (Fig. 6) is interesting because the James River is located on the left side of the valley, where the depth of alluvium below the channel is very shallow. The deepest part of the valley does not lie directly beneath the river. However, there are locations where a river has a preferred position in a valley as a result of tributary influence or location at a valley bend. Palmquist (1975) found that the probability of the active channel being located at any given point on the valley floor tended to be proportional to the depth to bedrock at that point (Fig. 9), that is, the channel tends to be over the deepest part of the valley. Noting also that the depth of scour by an alluvial river is approximately twice the "normal" bank height, he suggested that the asymmetric cross-profile of the bedrock surface in a valley meander might simply be related to the proportion of time that the river is located at the outside of the bend.

Valley asymmetry can be produced by a variety of causes (Wilson, 1968; Shepherd, 1972a). For example, lateral erosion by a river can preferentially steepen one valley wall at the apex of a bend in contrast to the gentler slip-off slope inside the bend (Fig. 9). A tributary may force the main channel to a position against the opposite valley wall, steepening it. Also, there can be preferential erosion of one valley wall owing to different microclimatic conditions on opposite sides of a valley. For example, in the western U. S., the higher moisture content of rocks on north-facing slopes maintains more vegetation, less erosion and a steeper slope in contrast to south-facing slopes.

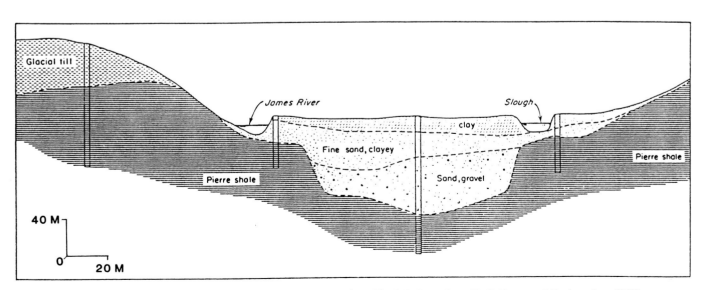

FIG. 6.—Cross-section of James River at site of Jamestown dam, North Dakota (from U. S. Bureau of Reclamation, 1957).

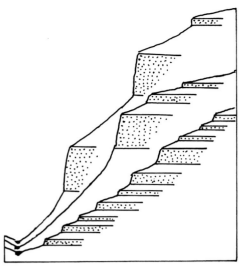

FIG. 7.—Effect of lithology on valley-wall morphology (from Davis, 1908; see King and Schumm, 1980).

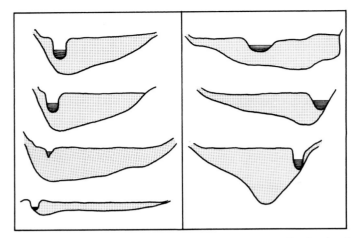

FIG. 9.—Asymmetry of the bedrock surface across valley bends of selected English rivers, looking downstream (from Dury, 1964b). (Note: varying horizontal scale; vertical exaggeration 5× throughout)

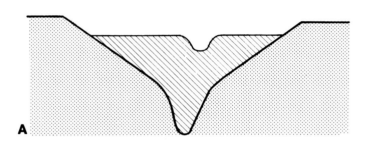

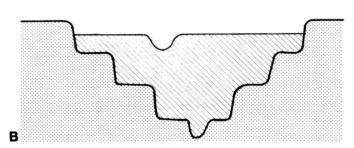

FIG. 8.—Sketches showing valley-in-valley profiles (A) and valley with multiple terraces (B). (Not to scale)

An ancient example is the asymmetrical valley filled with the Berea Sandstone in Ohio (Fig. 10A). Contours of the valley floor show that the deepest and most asymmetrical part of the valley floor is at the narrowest part of the valley. Below and above the apex of the bend the valley floor is broadly concave and relatively symmetrical, and the depth of the valley is 30.5 m less than that at the bend. Changing hydraulic conditions, as the valley narrows and widens, cause these variations in depth of scour.

The work of Siever (1951) in delineating ancient valleys and of Howard and Whitaker (1988, 1990) in characterizing the fluvial-estuarine valley fill on the Mississippian-Pennsylvanian unconformity of southern Illinois provide additional examples of cross-section irregularity (Fig. 10B). Several hills are conspicuous in their cross sections, and Siever (1951) suggests that these are meander cores abandoned as bedrock meanders were cut off. He also identifies bedrock terraces at several levels in the valley. Obviously the morphology of valleys is much more variable than the usual cross section indicates (Fig. 6).

Valley Floor Morphology

It is common to find a narrow inner channel in both modern and ancient fluvial valleys. Matthews (1917) described long, linear "deeps" cut into the bedrock floor of the Susquehanna River that were revealed during a survey for a power plant. Bretz (1924) observed a similar inner channel at The Dalles on the Columbia River, where the river has incised 35 m below sea level 305 km from the sea. Similarly, a field study of Tertiary gravel-filled valleys in California revealed inner channels that contained rich gold deposits (Peterson and others, 1968). An example of this type of valley-floor configuration is provided by the Mississippi River below its junction with the Missouri River at St. Louis (Fig. 11). The maximum depth of alluvium is in excess of 49 m in what appears to be an inner channel. This inner channel, approximately 12 m deep and 3 km wide, is delineated by the 37-m (120-ft) isopach.

Evidence for valley-floor irregularity and the presence of inner channels was also discovered during experimental studies (Shepherd, 1972b; Gardner, 1973; see Schumm and others, 1987). Fluvial incision was studied in straight channels cut into the surface of a fine sand and kaolinite mixture which simulated bedrock in a flume. These channels were about 0.4 m wide and 0.03 m deep, and erosion was initiated by increasing the slope of the flume. In two straight channels, the same general sequence of erosional events was

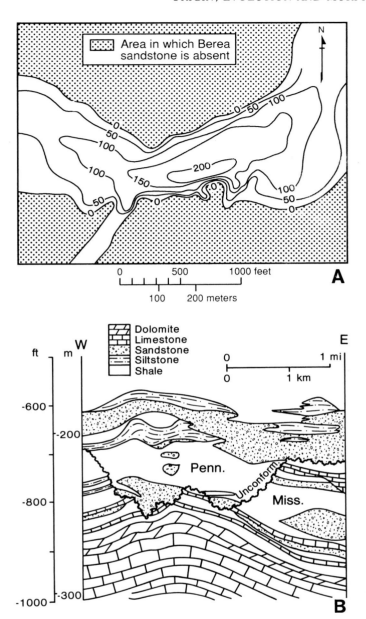

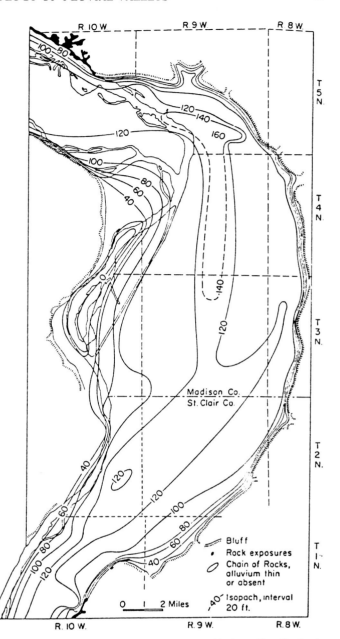

FIG. 10.—(A) Isopach map showing thickness of Mississippian, Berea Sandstone in paleovalley, South Amherst, Ohio (from Pepper and others, 1954). (B) Generalized east-west cross-section showing configuration of Pennsylvanian-Mississippian unconformity and paleovalley, southern Illinois (modified from Howard and Whitaker, 1990).

FIG. 11.—Thickness of Mississippi valley alluvium, East St. Louis, Illinois (from Bergstrom and Walker, 1956).

observed (Fig. 12). The two most obvious features of this sequence are the irregularity of the valley floor and the development of an inner channel. This latter feature formed by enlargement of one of the many elongate troughs that formed in the valley floor. Theoretical and experimental studies by Ashida and Sawai (1976) show that shear distribution on the floor of a channel is irregular, which leads to the development of parallel troughs and ridges (Fig. 12). Such assemblages of linear features appear to be an intermediate erosional state, and eventually a single inner channel becomes dominant as suggested by Bretz (1924).

In summary, there is remarkable agreement between field and experimental studies regarding the irregular nature of valley floors, the scour patterns, and the presence of an inner channel.

Longitudinal Profiles

Long profiles of rivers are usually shown as being relatively smooth. There are changes of slope relating to tributary junctions, bedrock influences and active tectonics, but the tendency of the river is to smooth its profile. This tendency exists in a bedrock channel also, but the energy of

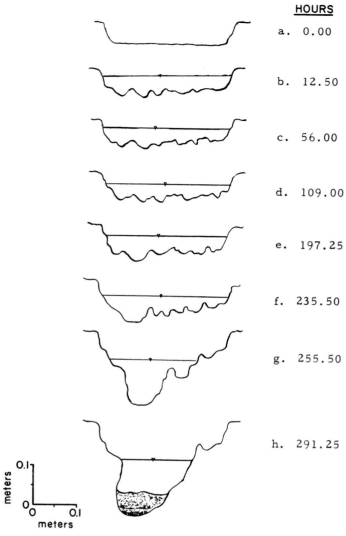

HOURS

a. 0.00

b. 12.50

c. 56.00

d. 109.00

e. 197.25

f. 235.50

g. 255.50

h. 291.25

Fig. 12.—Series of transverse profiles obtained during experimental study of incision into simulated bedrock (from Shepherd, 1972a).

the boundaries of Reaches 5 and 6 and of 9 and 10. Therefore, it should not be surprising to find that some of the variability of Mississippi River channel characteristics is a result of these geological influences, which undoubtedly are a reflection of valley-floor variability.

Where information is available, most surveys suggest that the longitudinal profile of valley floors is very irregular. For example, a seismic refraction survey of the lower Illinois River valley reveals a very irregular bedrock valley floor (Fig. 15). The high reaches reflect resistant rocks; whereas, weaker rocks have been deeply eroded (Heigold and Ringler, 1979). The 30.5-m variations seem extreme and may be a result of Pleistocene megafloods or the fact that the survey did not follow the bedrock thalweg.

Experimental studies (Shepherd and Schumm, 1974) produced irregular valley-floor profiles. During incision, "bedrock" was eroded below baselevel (Fig. 16), and the profile of the bedrock inner channel did not slope smoothly in a downstream direction. It was irregular, but the spacing of highs and lows appeared regular. The incised channel was markedly narrower at points of maximum scour and wider at crests between scour holes so that flow cross-sectional area and water surface slope were maintained. Keller and Melhorn (1978) report a regularity of bedrock pools with a good relation between bedrock-pool spacing and channel width in natural bedrock channels. Even in homogeneous bedrock, the floor of a valley will be irregular. The irregularity will be increased by tectonic effects. Deformation of the bedrock floor of a valley is indicated by bedrock configuration and the thickness of overlying alluvium. For example, Kowalski and Radzikowska (1968) note that alluvium will be thickest over down faulted blocks (grabens) and thinnest over areas of uplift, as expected. In areas of subsidence, streams may have broad valleys with well-developed floodplains and meandering channels (Sizkov and Zfumster, 1967).

In summary, field and laboratory studies suggest that the longitudinal profiles of valleys are as variable as the cross sections, and many of the changes can be related to bedrock variability and to active tectonics.

Patterns

The most detailed investigation of single-valley patterns was performed by Dury (1964a, 1964b, 1965) whose purpose was to estimate past discharge from the dimensions of valley meanders. He showed that the wavelength of valley meanders is about one order of magnitude greater than the meander wavelength of modern stream meanders, when both are plotted against drainage area, which is a substitute for hydrologic data.

The patterns of valley networks (dendritic, parallel, trellis, etc.) are obviously established by streams, and therefore, stream patterns are, in fact, valley patterns that are related to structure and to the inclination of the surface upon which the pattern formed (Howard, 1967). It is well known that the texture of river and valley patterns is a function of erodibility, that is, shales have a finer-textured pattern than resistant sandstone or igneous rocks. Also the inclination of the surface upon which a channel and valley network

the river may be insufficient to erode irregularities created by outcrops of resistant rocks in the bed. Therefore, it can be assumed that a relatively smooth channel or floodplain profile need not mirror the bedrock profile beneath the valley-fill sediments.

Investigations of the variability of alluvial river morphology have shown that valley surfaces are not smooth. Rather most rivers can be divided into reaches that reflect tributary, bedrock and tectonic controls. For example, the Mississippi River can be divided into at least 24 reaches between Cairo, Illinois and Old River, Louisiana (Fig. 13). The reaches are different morphologically, and river behavior is different with some reaches being more active through time (Fig. 14). For the most part, the river is reflecting the character of the bedrock-valley bottom because the river crosses at least two zones of surface deformation (Lake County Uplift-Reaches 2, 3, 4, and Monroe Uplift-Reaches 18, 19; Burnett and Schumm, 1983) and faults at

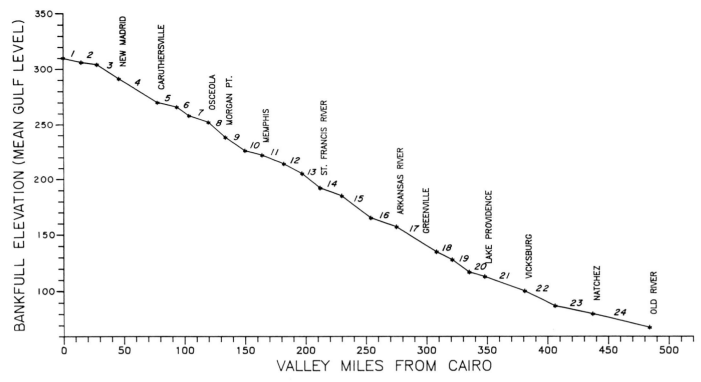

FIG. 13.—Longitudinal profile of the Mississippi River alluvial valley showing 24 reaches identified between Cairo, Illinois and Old River. Elevation is 1880 water level, and distance is valley miles paralleling the river course.

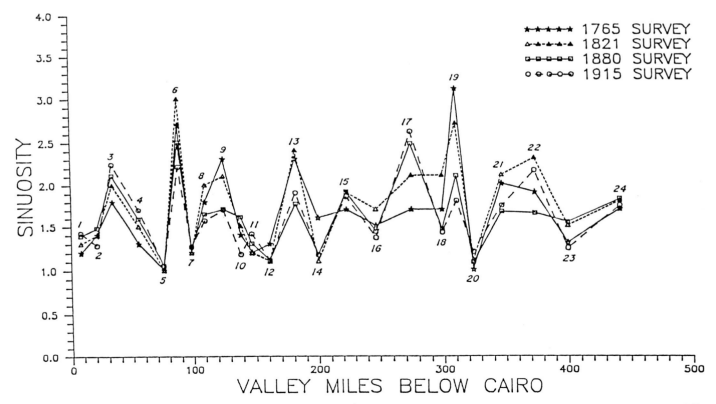

FIG. 14.—Variability of Mississippi River sinuosity (ratio of channel length to valley length) for 24 reaches (shown in Fig. 14) between 1765 and 1915.

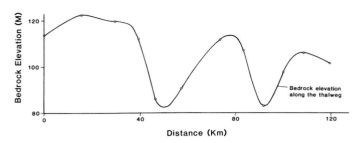

FIG. 15.—Thalweg profile of the lower Illinois bedrock valley based on seismic refraction data (elevation datum: m.s.l.; from Heigold and Ringler, 1979).

develops significantly influences the texture of the network expressed as drainage density (ratio of total channel length to drainage area). Obviously, more channels and valleys form on steeper surfaces (Mosley, 1974).

Mosley (1974) also found that the ratio of maximum width to length of small drainage basins decreased from 0.3 to 0.1 with an increase of surface slope. That is, watersheds were more elongated on steeper initial slopes. Phillips and Schumm (1987) demonstrated experimentally that the angle of junction of tributaries with the main channel decreased significantly from about 60° to 40° at a slope of about 3 percent. These results indicate that a larger number of elongate, infrequently branching valleys form on steeper surfaces. Also, it is important to recognize that tributary junction angles are usually much less than 90°. That is, the tributary joins the main valley in a direction consistent with the direction of flow in the main channel. However, exceptions occur when structural controls on tributary location dominate.

In summary, valley-meander characteristics can be related to drainage area, which is obviously a control of hydrologic variables. A valley network will have a higher

drainage density on erodible rocks and on steeper surfaces than on resistant rocks and gentle surfaces. It also appears that at least the initial pattern will be parallel on slopes steeper than about 3 percent, but below that value patterns will be more dendritic.

Multiple Valleys

The discussion to this point relates to single valleys and valley networks that are bounded by relatively resistant valley walls. However, multiple valleys form as channels avulse and incise on alluvial plains (Fig. 17), alluvial fans, deltas, and exposed continental shelves. This means that at the same stratigraphic level, very long valley segments that enter the sea at different points may join up valley. The present Mississippi-Atchafalaya complex provides a good example of this situation, as do the Brazos and Colorado rivers on the Texas Coastal Plain (Bernard and others, 1970). The end result is an interconnecting network of channels and valleys in three dimensions.

There is another type of avulsive change that involves only reaches of channels. The formation and abandonment of these anabranches form a complex anastomosing channel and valley network. This type of channel and valley network will be considered here in some detail because it has received less attention than distributary or dendritic patterns, and because of the problem of differentiating channels from valleys in rock record. Ancient examples will be reviewed and one will be compared to a modern analog.

Ancient anastomosing "channels," which are really valley networks have been described in South Africa (Cairncross, 1980), the U. S. A. (Flores and Hanley, 1989), and especially in Canada (Putnam, 1982, 1983; Rust and Legun, 1983; Smith and Putnam, 1980). Putnam described an impressive anastomosing valley pattern in the Mannville Group of lower Cretaceous age in eastern Alberta, that is 80 km wide and 300 km long. These linear sandstones are

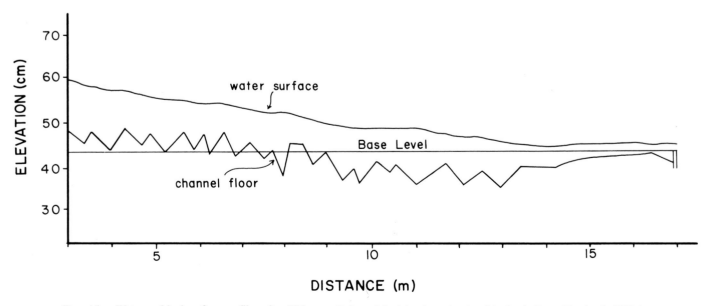

FIG. 16.—Water and bed surface profiles after 65 hours of channel incision into simulated bedrock (from Shepherd, 1972a).

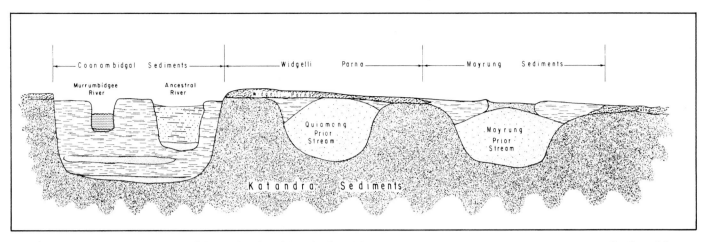

Fig. 17.—Cross section showing surficial stratigraphy of the Riverine Plain, New South Wales and Victoria, southeastern Australia (from Schumm, 1968; after Butler, 1958). Not drawn to scale. The Murrumbidgee River is about 61 m wide and 6 m deep. The Ancestral River is about 137 m wide and 11 m deep. The paleovalley that contains these two rivers ranges from 914 to 1830 m wide but depth is unknown to the authors. Paleochannels that can be observed on the surface of the Riverine Plain (Mayrung) or that are buried by aeolian sediment (Widgelli Parna) are about 152 m wide and 3 m deep. Paleovalleys that contain these paleochannels are approximately 305 m wide and up to 9 m deep, although their dimensions vary greatly.

"thick, narrow, elongate bodies that can be as narrow as 300 m and as thick as 35 m" (Putnam, 1983, p. 521). These "channel" sandstones form major hydrocarbon reservoirs. The bases of the sandstones are at different elevations, and the valley-fill sediments are composed of several fining-upward cycles that are from 2 to 6 m thick (Tilley and Last, 1980). These sandstone bodies form a three-dimensional anastomosing network. The development of such a pattern can be illustrated by a Holocene Australian example.

Figure 18 shows an anastomosing network on the Riverine Plain of southeastern Australia. The Riverine Plain of Australia includes the coalescing low-angle, wet alluvial fans of the Murray, Murrumbidgee, Goulburn and Lachlan Rivers and their tributaries in southern New South Wales and northern Victoria, an area of about 77,000 km² (Butler, 1950, 1958; Butler and others, 1973; Bowler, 1978). The Quaternary deposits of the Riverine Plain are about 45 m thick, and are composed primarily of alluvium with some eolian deposits (Fig. 17). The anastomosing pattern (Fig. 18), however, is comprised of channels of very different ages. For example, the Gum Creek channel still carries flood flows, whereas the Prior Stream channel has not been active in more than 45,000 years (Page and others, 1989). Therefore, the anastomosing channel network comprises an anastomosing pattern of multiple channels of different ages rather than an anastomosing river of currently-active multiple channels. Borings reveal more channels at depth, and there are at least five generations of channels on the Riverine Plain (Fig. 17). Although the features exposed on the surface of the Riverine Plain are channels, they represent only the last stages of deposition in valleys that were incised to depths of 15 m. Each channel occupies a valley of its own making (Fig. 17).

Recent studies in the Ovens and King River valleys of northern Victoria, Australia illustrate the morphology and behavior of anastomosing channels which lead to a system of anastomosing valleys. In the wide valleys of the King and Ovens Rivers, which are tributaries to the Murray River, there are at least 4 channels, and it is clear that the channels are of different ages (Figs. 19, 20). The oldest (4 on Fig. 19) consists of a series of sinuous pools that fill during floods, but are not active flood channels. The next youngest (3) is a highly sinuous and inefficient channel also perched on an alluvial ridge that only carries water during floods. The present Ovens and King Rivers convey the bulk of the annual flow through relatively efficient channels (2), and the youngest channel (1) is a developing anabranch that is incising in order to bypass inefficient reaches of the main channel.

Each channel becomes progressively less efficient hydraulically through time. This inefficiency occurs as the channels become more sinuous, and the fine sediments that comprise the floodplains or the banks of the channels inhibit rapid lateral migration. Hence, as sinuosity increases, the channel becomes less efficient, and overbank flooding occurs more frequently. Natural levees and alluvial ridges form, and the main channel can actually occupy the highest parts of the floodplain before avulsion occurs. Figure 20 shows conditions in the valley after this type of avulsion occurred. Overbank flows scour a channel through the natural levee, and because the overbank flows carry a small sediment load, the channel is extended down valley. The flood waters concentrate in the lowest part of the floodplain, and they also incise where they enter a channel downvalley. This new, down-valley channel extends headward until it joins the upvalley channel to form a new anabranch. The anabranch channel becomes a valley by further incision and widening (Fig. 2). This model is generally supported by the research of Taylor and Woodyer (1978), Riley and Taylor (1978), Woodyer (1978), Woodyer and others (1979), and Schumann (1989) on modern anastomosing channels, although they stress the importance of

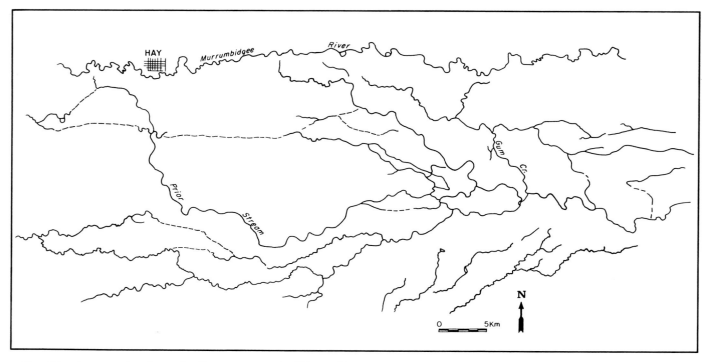

FIG. 18.—Anastomosing river and valley patterns south of Murrumbidgee River near Hay, New South Wales, Australia. Flow direction is to the west.

sediment deposition, bench formation, tree growth, and log jams as triggers of avulsion. These Australian anastomosing channels differ significantly from the Canadian and Columbian anastomosing channels described by Smith (1983, 1986).

As new channels incise deeply and form a valley, they could intersect older valleys that were completely infilled, abandoned, and buried beneath the surface of the plain. In this way, the three dimensional network of anastomosing valleys develop. Not only is there an anastomosing pattern on the surface of the alluvial plain, but the incision associated with new anabranches insures that there is a three dimensional pattern of fluvial-channel deposits making up the alluvial plain.

One can conclude that an anastomosing pattern covering large areas of an alluvial plain is probably not composed of valleys that functioned contemporaneously, rather the pattern is composed of valleys of different ages. In fact, reaches of the same valley may be of different ages, as demonstrated for the Ovens and the King Rivers (Fig. 19). This presumably makes little difference to the sedimentologist or petroleum geologist who is concerned more with the interconnectedness of the valleys and the ability of fluids to move through the valley fills. However, if there is a high suspended load moving through the incised channel and valley, the connection between the new and old valleys may be sealed by fine suspended-load sediments, which would hinder or prevent fluid migration from the new to the old or vice versa. For example, groundwater is contained in many of the Riverine Plain paleovalleys, but others are isolated and dry as a result of these permeability barriers.

Another way that multiple valleys of different dimensions can form is by the integration of drainage networks by stream capture. This is the usual course of events as parallel drainages evolve to form a dendritic drainage network. For example, it seems probable that as a continental shelf is exposed by falling sea level, a series of shallow parallel channels will form (Fig. 21A). As tributaries develop (Fig. 21B), some channels become dominant and capture the drainage of adjacent, less effective channels (Fig. 21C). The increased discharge in the captor stream will cause channel incision, deepening and widening, while captured streams will retain their relatively narrow, shallow valleys. The results are valleys of different dimensions, each of which follow the evolutionary sequence outlined in Figure 2. Multiple-valley development similar to that described here was documented in a flume study of the effects of baselevel change on coastal plain-shelf systems (Koss, 1992).

In summary, when not confined by valley walls, multiple channels and valleys can develop on alluvial plains and continental shelves. The result can be an interconnected network of anastomosing channels and valleys of different ages and different dimensions.

VALLEY-FILL SEDIMENTS

A valley is a sediment container, and while this chapter deals primarily with the container, a few final words about the valley-fill sediments are in order. Valley filling takes place in three ways, depending on the nature of the control that causes deposition (Schumm, 1977):

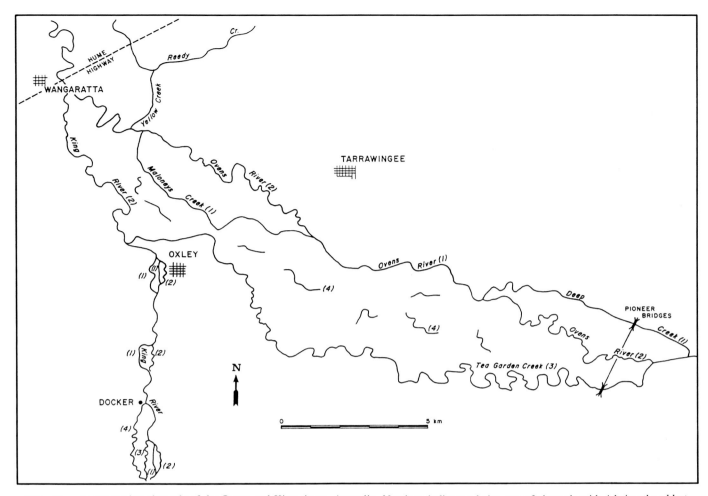

FIG. 19.—Anastomosing channels of the Ovens and King rivers, Australia. Numbers indicate relative age of channels with 4 being the oldest.

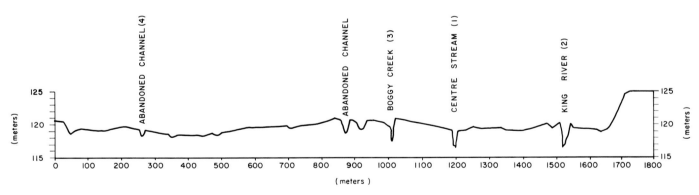

FIG. 20.—Valley cross section of King River, Victoria, Australia. Numbers indicate relative age of channels with 4 being the oldest.

1. Progressive backfilling of a valley (in most cases with predominantly marine or brackish sediments) will usually result from a significant rise in baselevel.
2. Progressive downfilling of the valley will probably result from uplift in the source area or change in climate, such that a significant increase in sediment production results.

3. Vertical aggradation (filling) may result from a significant increase in sediment production from numerous tributaries that are associated with a climate change. Under these conditions a more or less uniform raising of the level of the valley floor may result.

These differences in the nature of valley fills should be apparent in ancient paleovalley deposits, but in all cases,

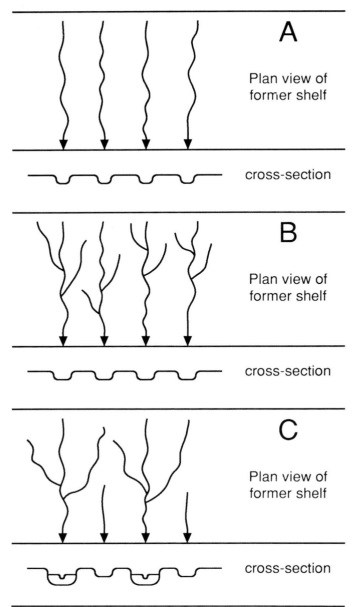

FIG. 21.—Integration of drainage networks on a former continental shelf. Plan and profile of initial parallel drainage (A), development and expansion of patterns (B) leading to stream capture and development of large valleys (C) (Not to scale).

the variability of the sediments on the valley floor and in the alluvial valley fill will be large (Schumm, 1977). In most cases, more than one type of deposit will probably be present in a single paleovalley. For example, Lower Cretaceous valley-fill successions are dominated by fluvial facies in southern Alberta and Saskatchewan, mud-filled estuarine deposits in south-central Alberta, and tidally-influenced sand-dominated deposits in east-central Alberta and west-central Saskatchewan (James, 1985, 1986; James and Elliott, 1991). Another example is illustrated by the Cretaceous Dakota paleovalley fill that is dominated by fluvial

facies in northwestern New Mexico-southwestern Colorado and by paralic and marginal marine facies in eastern Colorado (Aubrey, 1989).

An excellent example of backfilling of an incised valley by estuarine deposits is described by Zaitlin and Shultz (1990). These deposits comprise the Lloydminister Member, Mannville Group (Lower Cretaceous) at the Senlac heavy-oil pool in west-central Saskatchewan. The effects of rates of baselevel change on valley-fill deposits are reviewed by Wood and others (1993).

Dominantly non-marine, fluvial paleovalley fills are recognized in Lower Cretaceous Lytle deposits along the northern Colorado Front Range (Dolson and Nibbelink, 1985; Dolson and others, 1991) and in Upper Cretaceous (Turonian through Campanian) strata of the Kaiparowits Plateau, southern Utah (Shanley and McCabe, 1991). Both successions were probably formed by either downfilling or vertical aggradation.

Finally, it is important to note that because channel morphology varies with the slope of the valley floor (Figs. 13, 14), the character of the sedimentary deposits should also vary significantly. For example, reaches 1, 2, 5, 7, 10, 11, 12, and 20 of the Mississippi River have been relatively straight since 1765, whereas reaches 3, 6, 9, 13, 17, 19, 21, and 22 have been sinuous. Valley-fill deposits should reflect these differences and should show characteristics of straight or braided channels at one location and meandering elsewhere. Hence, limited exposure of paleovalley deposits could lead to erroneous interpretations of the nature of the channel system.

CONCLUSIONS

Information on valley morphology is scarce in contrast to that available for river channels because most valley characteristics are obscured by valley-fill deposits. Nevertheless, this review has, at least, produced the general conclusion that valley morphology is highly variable.

Valleys formed by channel incision follow an evolutionary sequence of deepening and widening through time that, of course, is modified by the lithologic and structural character of the valley perimeter. Rates of valley formation vary greatly depending upon the erosional forces and rock resistance. Therefore, valley size also depends on these variables and time.

Valleys increase in dimensions downvalley, but the increase can be highly variable and the reverse can occur. Valley-floor gradient should decrease downvalley, but it is locally variable and can be reversed. Both in cross section and longitudinally, there may be great irregularity of valley profiles as a result of lithologic variability, the variability of hydraulic scour patterns, and the effect of tributaries.

Valley patterns range from straight to sinuous, and multiple patterns can develop by anastomosis. The integration of drainage networks can lead to valleys of different dimensions on the same erosional surface. Valley-fill deposits will vary vertically and longitudinally depending on the manner of sediment deposition that can occur by backfilling, downfilling, or by vertical aggradation.

ACKNOWLEDGMENTS

The discussion of the King and Ovens Rivers was based on field work of the senior author and Wayne Erskine of the University of New South Wales; National Science Foundation Grant EAR-8712287. The Mississippi River discussion was based on research by the senior author and Ian Rutherford, Monash University and John Brooks, the U. S. Army Corps of Engineers, Vicksburg, Mississippi. The authors are thankful to Zeev Berger, Esso Resources Canada, Ltd. who encouraged a critical review of valley morphology and sedimentology. This paper has benefited greatly by constructive reviews of an earlier manuscript by Doug Cant and Mike Blum. During preparation of this paper, the senior author was supported by the U. S. Army Research Office Project 24608-GS-UIR.

REFERENCES

ASHIDA, K., AND SAWAI, K., 1976, Erosion and cross section on the cohesive stream bed: Disaster Prevention Research Institute, Kyoto University, Bulletin 26, p. 145–161.

AUBREY, W. M., 1989, Mid-Cretaceous alluvial-plain incision related to eustasy, southern Colorado Plateau: Geological Society of America Bulletin, v. 101, p. 443–449.

BATES, R. L., AND JACKSON, J. A., 1987, Glossary of Geology: Alexandria, American Geological Institute, 788 p.

BERGSTROM, R. F., AND WALKER, T. R., 1956, Groundwater geology of the East St. Louis area, Illinois: Champaigne, Illinois State Geological Survey Report of Investigations 191, 44 p.

BERNARD, H. A, MAJOR, D. F, JR., PARROTT, B. S., AND LEBLANC, R. J., SR., 1970, Recent sediments of southeast Texas. A Field Guide to the Brazos Alluvial and Deltaic Plains and the Galveston Barrier Island Complex: Austin, Bureau of Economic Geology, The University of Texas at Austin Guidebook No. 11 (not paginated).

BHOWMIK, N. G., AND STALL, J. B., 1979, Hydraulic geometry and carrying capacity of floodplains: Champaigne, Water Resources Center, University Illinois, Research Report 145, 147 p.

BLUM, M. D., 1992, Modern depositional environments and recent alluvial history of the lower Colorado River, Gulf Coastal Plain of Texas: Unpublished Ph.D. Dissertation, University of Texas at Austin, Austin, 280 p.

BOWLER, J. M., 1978, Quaternary climate and tectonics in the evolution of the Riverine Plain, southeastern Australia, in Davies, J. L., and Williams, A. J., eds., Landform Evolution in Australia: Canberra, Australian National University Press, p. 70–112.

BRETZ, J. H., 1924, The Dalles type of river channel: Journal Geology, v. 24, p. 129–149.

BRITTLEBANK, C. C., 1900, The rate of erosion of some river valleys: Geological Magazine, v. 7, p. 320–322.

BURNETT, A. W., AND SCHUMM, S. A., 1983, Alluvial river response to neotectonic deformation in Louisiana and Mississippi: Science, v. 222, p. 49–50.

BUTLER, B. E., 1950, A theory of prior streams as a causal factor of soil occurrence in the Riverine Plain of southeastern Australia: Australian Journal Agricultural Research, v. 1, p. 231–257.

BUTLER, B. E., 1958, Depositional systems of the Riverine Plain in relation to soils: Melbourne, Soil Publication No. 10, Commonwealth Scientific Industrial Research Organization, 35 p.

BUTLER, B. E., BLACKBURN, G., BOWLER, J. M., LAWRENCE, C. R., NEWELL, J. W., AND PELS, S., 1973, A geomorphic map of the Riverine Plain of southeastern Australia: Canberra, Australian National University Press, 39 p.

CAIRNCROSS, B., 1980, Anastomosing river deposits: Paleo-environmental control on coal quality and distribution, northern Karoo Basin: Geological Society of South Africa, Transactions, v. 83, p. 327–332.

CHORLEY, R. J., DUNN, A. J., AND BECKINSALE, R. P., 1964, The History of the Study of Landforms: London, Methuen, 678 p.

DAVIS, W. M., 1908, Practical Exercises in Physical Geography: Boston, Ginn and Company, 148 p.

DOLSON, J., AND NIBBELINK, K. A., 1985, Cretaceous depositional systems, northern D-J (Cheyenne) basin: Examples from the Dakota Group and Laramie-Fox Hills Formation, in Macke, D. L., and Maughan, E. K., eds., Rocky Mountain Section Field Trip Guide—1985: Denver, Rocky Mountain Section American Association Petroleum Geologist, Rocky Mountain Section Society of Economic Paleontologists and Mineralogists, National Energy Minerals Division and Rocky Mountain Association of Geologists, p. 1–40.

DOLSON, J. C., MULLER, DAVE, EVETTS, M. J., AND STEIN, J. A., 1991, Regional paleotopographic trends and production, Muddy Sandstone (Lower Cretaceous), Central and Northern Rocky Mountains: American Association Petroleum Geology Bulletin, v. 75, p. 409–435.

DURY, G. H., 1964a, Principles of underfit streams: Washington, D. C., United States Geological Survey Professional Paper 452-A, 67 p.

DURY, G. H., 1964b, Subsurface exploration and chronology of underfit streams: Washington, D. C., United States Geological Survey Professional Paper 352-B, 56 p.

DURY, G. H., 1965, Theoretical implications of underfit streams: Washington, D. C., United States Geological Survey Professional Paper 452-C, 48 p.

FLORES, R. M., AND HANLEY, J. H., 1984, Anastomosed and associated coal-bearing fluvial deposits: Upper Tongue River Member, Palaeocene Fort Union Formation, northern Powder River basin, Wyoming, USA, in Rahmani, R. A., and Flores, R. M., eds., Sedimentology of Coal and Coal-Bearing Sequences: Oxford, International Association of Sedimentologists Special Publication 7, p. 85–103.

FRIEDMAN, S. A., 1960, Channel-fill sandstones in the Middle Pennsylvanian rocks of Indiana: Indiana Geological Survey Report of Progress 23, 59 p.

GARDNER, T. W., 1973, Experimental study of knickpoint and longitudinal profile evolution in cohesive homogeneous material: Geological Society of America Bulletin, v. 94, p. 664–672.

GREGORY, H. E., 1918, Steps of progress in the interpretation of landforms: American Journal Science, v. 46, p. 104–131.

HAMBLIN, W. K., DAMON, P. E., AND BULL, W. B., 1981, Estimates of vertical crustal strain rates along the western margins of the Colorado Plateau: Geology, v. 9, p. 293–298.

HARMS, J. C., 1966, Stratigraphic traps in a valley fill, western Nebraska: American Association of Petroleum Geologists Bulletin, v. 50, p. 2119–2149.

HAYES, B. J. R., 1968, Stratigraphy of the basal Cretaceolus lower Mannville Formation, southern Alberta and north-central Montana: Bulletin of Canadian Society of Petroleum Geologists, v. 34, p. 30–48.

HECK, E. T., 1941, Gay-Spencer-Richardson oil and gas trend, Jackson, Roane and Calhoun Counties, West Virginia, in Levorsen, A. I, ed., Stratigraphic Type Oil Fields: Tulsa, American Association of Petroleum Geologists, p. 806–829.

HEIGOLD, P. C., AND RINGLER, R. W., 1979, A seismic refraction survey of the lower Illinois valley bottomland: Champaigne, Illinois State Geological Survey Circular 507, 18 p.

HOWARD, A. D., 1967, Drainage analysis in geologic interpretation: American Association of Petroleum Geologists Bulletin, v. 51, p. 2246–2259.

HOWARD, R. H., AND WHITAKER, S. T., 1988, Hydrocarbon accumulation in a paleovalley at Mississippian-Pennsylvanian unconformity near Crawford Country, Illinois: a model paleogeomorphic trap: Champaigne, Department of Energy and Natural Resources, Illinois State Geological Survey, Illinois Petroleum 129, 26 p.

HOWARD, R. H., AND WHITAKER, S. T., 1990, Fluvial-estuarine valley fill at the Mississippian-Pennsylvanian unconformity, Main Consolidated field, Illinois, in Barwis, J. H., McPherson, J. G., and Studlick, J. R. J., eds., Sandstone Petroleum Reservoirs: New York, Springer-Verlag, p. 319–341.

HUBER, N. K., 1981, Amount and timing of Late Cenozoic uplift and tilt of the central Sierra Nevada, California: Washington, D. C., United States Geological Survey Professional Paper 1197, 28 p.

JAMES, D. P., 1985, Sedimentology, paleogeography and reservoir quality of the Mannville Group, southwestern Alberta: implications for exploration: Bulletin of Canadian Society of Petroleum Geology, v. 12, p. 2–3.

JAMES, D. P., 1986, Depositional History of the Lower Cretaceous Blairmore and Mannville Strata in Southern Alberta: Calgary, Canadian Society Petroleum Geology Field Trip Guide No. 2, 97 p.

JAMES, D. P., AND ELLIOTT, TREVOR (Compilers), 1991, Aspects of high resolution sequence stratigraphy—A working Document: Banff, Alberta, NUNA Conference on High Resolution Sequence Stratigraphy, 24 p. + illustrations.

KELLER, E. A., AND MELHORN, W. N., 1978, Rhythmic spacing and origin of pools and riffles: Geological Society of America Bulletin, v. 89, p. 723–730.

KING, P. B. AND SCHUMM, S. A., 1980, The Physical Geography of William Morris Davis: Norwich, Geo Books, 217 p.

KNOX, P. R., 1989, Depositional environments, sequence stratigraphy, and petroleum geology of the Lower Cretaceous Fall River Sandstone in Donkey Creek and Coyote Creek Oil Fields, Eastern Powder River Basin, Wyoming: Unpublished M.S. Thesis, California State University, Long Beach, 308 p.

KOSS, J. E., 1992, Effects of sea-level change on fluvial and coastal plain system: an experimental approach: Unpublished M.S. Thesis, Colorado State University, Fort Collins, 157 p.

KOWALSKI, W. C. AND RADZIKOWSKA, H., 1968, The influence of neotectonic movements on the formation of alluvial deposits and its engineering-geological estimation: Proceedings 23rd International Geological Congress, Prague Czechsolovakia, Section 12, p. 197–203.

KRANZLER, I., 1966, Origin of oil in lower member of Tyler Formation of central Montana: American Association of Petroleum Geologists Bulletin, v. 50, p. 2245–2259.

KRYSTINIK, L. F., AND BLAKENEY, B. A., 1990, Sedimentology of the upper Morrow Formation in eastern Colorado and western Kansas, in Sonnenberg, S. A., Shannon, L. T., Rader, K., Von Drehle, W. F., and Martin, G. W., eds., Morrow Sandstones of Southeast Colorado and Adjacent Areas: Denver, Rocky Mountain Association of Geologists, p. 37–50.

LARSON, E. E., OZIMA, M., AND BRADLEY, W. C., 1975, Late Cenozoic basic volcanism in northwestern Colorado and its implications concerning tectonism and the origin of the Colorado River system, in Curtis, B. F. ed., Cenozoic History of the Southern Rocky Mountaina: Boulder, Geological Society America Memoir 144, p. 155–178.

LINS, T. W., 1950, Origin and environment of the Tonganoxie sandstone in northeastern Kansas: Kansas Geological Survey Bulletin No. 86, p. 105–190.

MATTHEWS, E. B., 1917, Submerged "deeps" in the Susquehanna River: Geological Society of America Bulletin, v. 28, p. 335–346.

MCLANE, C. F., III, 1978, Channel network growth: an experimental study: Unpublished M.S. Thesis, Colorado State University, Fort Collins, 100 p.

MOSLEY, M. P., 1974, Experimental study of rill erosion: American Society Agricultural Engineers, Transaction, 1984, p. 909–913.

MOSLEY, M. P., 1976, An experimental study of channel confluences: Journal Geology, v. 84, p. 535–562.

PAGE, K. J., PRICE, D. M., AND NANSON, G.C., 1989, Thermoluminescence chronology of late Quaternary sediments of the Riverine Plain, southeastern Australia: Melbourne, Australian and New Zealand Geomorphology Group, 4th Conference., Monash University, p. 28–29.

PALMQUIST, R. C., 1975, Preferred position model and subsurface symmetry of valleys: Geological Society of America Bulletin, v. 86, p. 1392–1398.

PATTISON, S. A. J., 1991a, Viking Formation overview, in Leckie, D. A., Posamenteir, H. W., and Lovell, R. W. W., eds., NUNA Conference on High Resoultion Sequence Stratigraphy: Calgary, Geological Association of Canada Programme/Proceedings/Guidebook, p. 40–43.

PATTISON, S. A. J., 1991b, Crystal Sundance and Edison valley-fill deposits, in Leckie, D. A., Posamenteir, H. W., and Lovell, R. W. W., eds., NUNA Conference on High Resolution Sequence Stratigraphy: Calgary, Geological Association of Canada Programme/Proceedings/Guidebook, p. 44–47.

PEPPER, J. G., DEWITT, W., JR., AND DEMAREST, D. F., 1954, Geology of the Bedford Shale and Berea Sandstone in the Appalachian Region: Washington, D. C., United States Geological Survey Professional Paper 259, 109 p.

PETERSON, D. W., YEEND, W. E., OLIVER, H. W., AND MATTICK, R. E., 1968, Tertiary gold-bearing channel gravel in northern Nevada County, California: Washington, D. C., United States Geological Survey Circular 566, 22 p.

PHILLIPS, L. AND SCHUMM, S. A., 1987, Effect of regional slope on drainage networks: Geology, v. 15, p. 813–816.

PITTY, A. F., 1971, Introduction to Geomorphology: London, Methuen, 526 p.

PLAYFAIR, J., 1802, Illustrations of the Huttonian Theory of the Earth: Edinburgh, William Creech, 528 p.

PUTNAM, P. E., 1982, Fluvial channel sandstones within Upper Mannville (Albian) of Lloydminster area, Canada—Geometry, petrography and paleogeographic implications: American Association of Petroleum Geologists Bulletin, v. 66, p. 436–459.

PUTNAM, P. E. 1983, Fluvial deposits and hydrocarbon accumulations: Examples from the Lloydminister area, Canada, in Collinson, J. D., and Lewin, J., eds., Modern and Ancient Fluvial Systems: Oxford, International Association of Sedimentologists Special Publication 6, p. 517–532.

RICE, R. J. 1980, Rates of erosion in the Little Colorado River valley, Arizona, in Cullingford, R. A., Davidson, D. A., and Lewin, J., eds., Timescales in Geomorphology: New York, Wiley Interscience, p. 317–331.

RILEY, S. J., AND TAYLOR, G., 1978, The geomorphology of the upper Darling River system with special reference to the present fluvial system: Royal Society of Victoria Proceedings, v. 90, pt. 1, p. 89–102.

RUST, B. R., AND LEGUN, A. S., 1983, Modern anastomosing fluvial deposits in arid central Australia and a Carboniferous analogue in New Brunswick, Canada, in Collinson, J. D., and Lewin, J., eds., Modern and Ancient Fluvial Systems: Oxford, International Association of Sedimentologists Special Publication 6, p. 385–392.

SALISBURY, N. E., KNOX, J. C., AND STEPHENSON, R. A., 1968, The valleys of Iowa-1: Valley width and stream discharge relationships in the major streams, Iowa: Iowa City, Studies in Geography 5, University of Iowa, 107 p.

SAUCIER, R. T., 1991, Geomorphology, stratigraphy, and chronology, in Morrison, P. B., ed., Quaternary Non Glacial Geology: Continental U. S.: Geological Society of America, The Geology of North America, v. K-L, p. 550–563.

SCHUMANN, R. R., 1989, Morphology of Red Creek, Wyoming, an arid-region anastomosing channel system: Earth Surface Processes and Landforms, v. 14, p. 277–288.

SCHUMM, S. A., 1968, River adjustment to altered hydrologic regimen, Murrumbidgee River and paleochannels, Australia: Washington, D .C., United States Geological Survey Professional Paper 598, 65 p.

SCHUMM, S. A., 1977, The Fluvial System: New York, John Wiley, 338 p.

SCHUMM, S. A., 1993, River response to baselevel changes: Implications for sequence stratigraphy: Journal of Geology, v. 101, p. 279–294.

SCHUMM, S. A., HARVEY, M. D., AND WATSON, C. C., 1984, Incised Channels: Morphology dynamics and control: Littleton, Water Resources Publications, 200 p.

SCHUMM, S. A., MOSLEY, M. P., AND WEAVER, W. E., 1987, Experimental Fluvial Geomorphology, New York, John Wiley, 413 p.

SCOTT, G. R., 1975, Cenozoic surfaces and deposits in the southern Rocky Mountains, in Curtis, B. F., ed., Cenozoic History of the Southern Rocky Mountains: Boulder, Geological Society of America Memoir 144, p. 227–248.

SHANLEY, K. W., AND MCCABE, P. J., 1991, Predicting facies architecture through sequence stratigraphy, an example from the Kaiparowits Plateau, Utah: Geology, v. 19, p. 742–745.

SHEPHERD, R. G., 1972a, A model study of river incision: Unpublished M.S. Thesis, Colorado State University, Fort Collins, 135 p.

SHEPHERD, R. G., 1972b, Incised river meanders: Evolution in simulated bedrock: Science, v. 178, p. 409–411.

SHEPHERD, R. G., AND SCHUMM, S. A., 1974, Experimental study of river incision, Geological Society of America Bulletin, v. 85, p. 257–268.

SIEVER, R., 1951, The Mississippian-Pennsylvanian unconformity in southern Illinois: American Association of Petroleum Geologists Bulletin, v. 35, p. 542–581.

SIZKOV, A., AND ZFUMSTER, 1967, Role of neotectonics in the formation of the river drainage in central Transbarkalia: Akademiya Nauk SSSR, Seriya Geographic, v.4, p. 113–117.

SMITH, D. G., 1983, Anastomosed fluvial deposits: Modern examples from western Canada, in Collinson, J. D., and Lewin, J., eds., Modern and Ancient Fluvial Systems: Oxford, International Association of Sedimentologists Special Publication 6, p. 155–168.

SMITH, D. G., 1986, Anastomosing river deposits, sedimentation rates and basin subsidence, Magdalena River, northern Columbia, South America: Sedimentary Geology, v. 46, p. 177–196.

SMITH, D. G., AND PUTNAM, P. E., 1980, Anastomosed river deposits: modern and ancient examples in Alberta, Canada: Canadian Journal of Earth Science, v. 17, p. 1396–1406.

SUZUKI, T., 1982, Rate of lateral planation by Iwaki River, Japan: Japanese Geomorphologic Union, Transactions, v. 3, p. 1–24.

SUZUKI, T., NODA, H., AND ABE, Y., 1983, Rate of lateral planation by rivers in Japan: Japanese Geomorphologic Union, Transactions, v. 4, p. 33–47 (in Japanese).

TAYLOR, G., AND WOODYER, K. D., 1978, Bank deposition in suspended-load streams: Bulletin of Canadian Society of Petroleum Geology, v. 26, p. 257–275.

TILLEY, B. J., AND LAST, W. M., 1980, Upper Mannville fluvial channels in east-central Albert, *in* Beck, L. S., Christopher, J. D., and Kent, D. M., eds., Lloydminister and Beyond: Geology of Mannville Hydrocarbon Reservoirs: Regina, Saskatchewan Geological Society, Special Publication 5, 217 p.

TUTTLE, S. D., MILLING, M. E., AND RUSNAK, R. S, 1966, Comparisons of stream sizes (discharge) with valley sizes and shapes: Geological Society of America Special Paper 101, 225 p.

UNITED STATES BUREAU OF RECLAMATION, 1957, Technical record of design and construction, Johnstown Dam: Denver, United States Bureau of Reclamation, 86 p.

VAN WAGONER, J. C., MITCHUM, R. M., CAMPION, K. M., AND RAHMANIAN, V. D., 1990, Siliciclastic Sequence Stratigraphy in Well Logs, Cores, and Outcrops: Concepts for High-Resolution Correlation of Time and Facies: Tulsa, American Association of Petroleum Geologists, Methods in Exploration Series 7, 55 p.

WEIMER, R. J., 1991, Sequence stratigraphy of the Muddy (Viking) Sandstone (Lower Cretaceous), Rocky Mountain Region, USA: Illustrated by core data from the Denver basin, Colorado, *in* Leckie, D. A., Posamentier, H. W., and Lovell, R. W. W., eds., 1991 NUNA Conference on High Resolution Sequence Stratigraphy: Calgary, Geological Association of Canada Programme/Proceedings/Guidebook, p. 116–135.

WILSON, L., 1968, Asymmetric valleys, *in* Fairbridge, R. W., ed., The Encyclopedia of Geomorphology: New York, Reinhold, p. 30–34.

WOOD, L. J., ETHRIDGE, F. G., AND SCHUMM, S. A., 1993, The effects of rate of base-level fluctuation on coastal-plain, shelf, and slope depositional systems: an experimental approach, *in* Posamentier, H. W., Summerhayes, C. P., Haq, B. U., and Allen, G. P., eds., Sequence Stratigraphy and Facies Associations: Oxford, International Association of Sedimentologists Special Publication No. 18, p. 43–59.

WOODYER, K. D., 1978, Sediment regime of the Darling River: Royal Society Victoria Proceedings, v. 90, pt. 1, p. 139–147.

WOODYER, K. D., TAYLOR, G., AND CROOK, K. A. W., 1979, Depositional processes along a very low gradient suspended-load stream: the Barwon River, New South Wales: Sedimentary Geology, v. 22, p. 97–120.

ZAITLIN, B. A., AND SHULTZ, B. C., 1990, Wave-influenced estuarine sand body, Senlac heavy oil pool, Saskatchewan, Canada, *in* Barwis, J. H., McPherson, J. G., and Studlick, J. R. J., eds., Sandstone Petroleum Reservoirs: New York, Springer-Verlag, p. 363–387.

CONSTRAINTS ON RIVERINE VALLEY INCISION AND THE RESPONSE TO SEA-LEVEL CHANGE BASED ON FLUID MECHANICS

JULIAN THORNE

Chevron Petroleum Technology Company, La Habra, CA 90633

ABSTRACT: The response of naturally occurring river systems to changes in regional controls such as base level or climate involves a complex response by many factors. These include changes at different reaches within the drainage network of: (1) river width, depth, slope, and type (e.g., braided vs. meandering); (2) bedload to suspended load ratio; (3) bed friction factors; (4) vegetation; (5) bed and bank grain-size distribution; (6) evaporation and runoff potential; (7) discharge flashiness; (8) drainage system plan form and density; (9) avulsion frequency; (10) meander migration speed and wavelength; (11) average drainage-basin size for each order of stream; and (12) valley broadening.

The complexities of an evolving river system are somewhat simplified by considering a self-similar drainage network of tributaries such that tributaries themselves have tributaries. In such a self-similar network, the various factors considered above change in a theoretically predictable fashion such that the lowest-order (alluvial-valley) streams are dominantly erosional while the highest-order (coastal-plain) streams are dominantly depositional. Primary among changes from the alluvial valley to coastal plain are changes in discharge flashiness, flood-stage frequency, the rate of overbank deposition, and sediment delivery ratio. These changes are theoretically derived from an advective-diffusive-wave equation for flood-wave travel in a tributary network obeying Horton's Laws.

Base-level, tectonic, and climatic changes can act as perturbations to this homeostatic, self-similar drainage system. A qualitative response model is proposed based on the above theoretical work that links these forcing factors to their depositional response. Stratigraphic examples of incised-valley formation and fill are used to test the implications of this model. Both this theoretical model and field observations suggest that: (1) broad valley erosion occurs with a seaward shift of the dominantly erosional alluvial valley, which makes up the upper reaches of the drainage network; (2) incised alluvial valleys formed during periods of slow sea-level fall preferentially incise into lower coastal-plain sediments and, thus, the expected fill of these valleys is transitional, estuarine, or marine sediment; (3) entrenched channels formed during periods of slow sea-level fall preferentially incise into lower alluvial-valley sediments and, thus, the expected fill of these channels is fluvial rather than transitional or marine sediment; and (4) entrenched channels formed during periods of rapid sea-level fall preferentially incise into lower coastal-plain sediments and, thus, the expected fill of these channels is transitional, estuarine, or marine sediment.

INTRODUCTION

There are two fundamentally different erosional modes of fluvial response to base-level fall and seaward shift of the coastline: the first is broad valley erosion of the previous coastal-plain deposits while the second is deep entrenchment of coastal-plain rivers. Recognizing these two alternatives in subsurface stratigraphic data is critical to the hydrocarbon potential of interpreted incised-valley deposits. Furthermore, understanding the different modes of fluvial response to base-level change is critical to environmental and engineering projects that attempt to forecast changing river and drainage-basin conditions in the near future. This study is an attempt to lay the groundwork necessary to understand theoretically the two modes of fluvial erosional response. Though much further work remains to be done, a qualitative response model will be proposed that suggests how eustatic, tectonic, and climatic changes act to produce either broad valley erosion or entrenched-channel formation.

BROAD VALLEY EROSION AND CHANNEL ENTRENCHMENT

The term incised valley has come to encompass a broad spectrum of topographic and paleotopographic features which are formed by fluvial erosion. In its original meaning, however, *incised* was synonymous with *entrenched*. These terms both referred to a stream flowing in a narrow, steep-sided valley, whose course is inherited from a earlier stage of erosion and, thus, does not appreciably change with time (Bates and Jackson, 1980). VanWagoner and others (1990) in an influential monograph defined *incised valleys* as entrenched fluvial systems. However, the examples of incised valleys cited by this study (e.g., the Mississippi valley),

though erosional, are not formed by entrenched channels in the geomorphic sense. The alluvial valley of the Mississippi is, in places, 120 mi (195 km) wide (Fisk, 1944) and is formed by the avulsion and lateral migration of successive channels rather than by erosion caused by a single entrenched channel which is fixed in place. In the original sense, therefore, the Grand Canyon in Arizona is an incised valley, but many of the erosional valleys described in this volume are not. Moreover, in the sense used by VanWagoner and others (1990), the distinction between broad valley erosion and channel entrenchment is confused.

In order to clarify the distinction between a feature formed by broad valley erosion versus channel entrenchment, in this study I will refer to the former as an incised alluvial valley and the later as an entrenched channel. The term incised valley will be a general term referring to either an incised alluvial valley or an entrenched channel. It is recognized that incised valleys may undergo a complicated evolution with various degrees of entrenchment occurring and reoccurring. Moreover, incised valleys may be entrenched in one segment but not in another. In view of these complications, I hope the remainder of this study can serve as a basis for interpretation and classification.

QUALITATIVE DESCRIPTION OF MODEL

Much of this study is a theoretical derivation of the fluid mechanical behavior of episodic flow in self-similar drainage networks. The intended audience for this volume, however, is largely interested in a conceptual and more intuitive understanding of fluvial processes as an aid in interpreting the stratigraphic rock record. It is this audience that can provide the critical tests for the hypothesis proposed here.

To accommodate this more general audience, the theoretical arguments made in this study will first be presented in a qualitative, intuitive fashion. "Equations" in this section are not mathematically rigorous but are only intended to give a sense of which geologic factors are important in controlling the potential to develop entrenched channels. Theoretical steps in the quantitative section are based on deductive reasoning in which the final conclusion is derived at length as the last step in the "proof." In this section, to provide the reader with a better understanding of the thread of argument used in this "proof," I start with the hypothesis and work backwards. An analogy is also used in this section between river drainage and the flow of traffic along highways and city streets. Though this analogy is not mathematically rigorous, it does provide a good intuitive grasp of the results derived in this study.

Entrenched-channel Potential Predicted from Metastable Accumulation Potential

The potential for the formation of entrenched channels is relatively high where there are long periods of time between river avulsion events. In this case, continued erosion over the same river course increases the depth of the river and lowers the average elevation of the drainage. These changes in river depth and elevation, in turn, make it even more unlikely that subsequent avulsion can occur. In contrast, broad valley formation is favored by frequent avulsion which makes it relatively likely that any position in the valley will be eroded by a subsequent channel (Mackey and Bridge, 1992). This relationship between the potential for entrenched-channel formation and avulsion frequency can be written:

$$\text{avulsion frequency} \propto \frac{1}{\text{entrenched-channel potential}} \quad (1)$$

A necessary condition for avulsion is that the active river course is in a topographically metastable position. Rivers become topographically metastable when their course runs over an area of relatively high elevation compared to a nearby area. This process occurs even in drainage basins in which, averaged over a relatively long period of time, there is no net accumulation. The rivers in such a drainage basin are still sites of *metastable accumulation* in which certain reaches accumulate sediment in the short term. A river becomes increasingly subject to avulsion when the channel bottom elevation becomes higher than the elevation of the surrounding area adjacent to the river levees ($\xi > 0$ in Fig. 1). During the period between avulsions, potential sites for avulsion accumulate sediment metastably until these areas are topographically above surrounding areas. The length of time this process takes: (1) increases with the initial depth of a new channel that is formed by an avulsion event (δ in Fig. 1) and (2) decreases with the rate of accumulation. The avulsion frequency is, therefore, some function of the ratio of the metastable accumulation potential divided by the channel-form erosion potential of avulsion events:

avulsion frequency

$$= f\left[\frac{\text{metastable accumulation potential}}{\text{channel-form erosion potential}}\right] \quad (2)$$

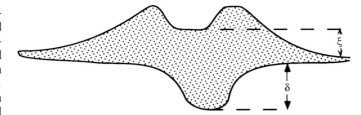

FIG. 1.—Depositional geometry of a river channel fill with levee deposits. δ is the original incision depth of the channel below the elevation of the surrounding area. ξ is the height of a topographically metastable channel above the elevation of the surrounding area.

Both the metastable accumulation potential and the channel-form erosion potential characteristically change from the upper to lower reaches of a drainage basin. In fact, geologists recognize three distinct depositional environments (the erosional uplands, alluvial valley and coastal plain) which are distinguished by these two factors. The erosional uplands are characterized by very little metastable accumulation and net erosion, whereas the coastal plain is characterized by a tendency to accumulate sediment metastably even in the absence of long-term accommodation potential provided by rising relative sea level. The alluvial valley has transitional qualities of both the erosional uplands and coastal plain. In the theoretical sections that follow, a quantitative explanation of this observation is derived from fluid mechanical constraints in river networks. This theory predicts that the potential of any given reach of a river to entrench is a function of: (1) the concavity of valley/river profile and (2) and its position within the drainage network of erosional uplands, alluvial-valley, or coastal-plain environments. This relationship can be written:

entrenched-channel potential =

f [concavity of valley profile; position in erosional uplands, alluvial valley or coastal plain]   (3)

Equations 2 and 3 indicate that to understand incised-valley formation and avulsion frequency a fluid-mechanical theory must be developed for metastable accumulation potential and channel-form erosion potential. In the development that follows, a series of theoretical steps leads to a predicted form for characteristic changes in a downstream direction of metastable accumulation potential and channel-form erosion potential. The ratio of these two potentials, as in equation 2, allows a prediction of downstream changes in avulsion frequency and entrenched-channel potential.

Metastable Accumulation is Predicted from Sediment Transport Capacity

A high potential for metastable accumulation occurs in a valley segment where there is a greater ability to bring in sediment from the upstream direction compared to the ability to carry sediment further down the valley. The gradient of downstream change in *sediment transport capacity* per unit valley width is a measure of this contrast. In the following analysis sediment transport *capacity* is used instead of sediment transport *mobility* to understand *metastable* accumulation. Capacity measures the maximum potential for sediment transport which only under rare, short-lived, circumstances is a good predictor of the actual sediment transport. Mobility, in contrast, is a time-averaged estimate of the mean sediment transport. Metastable accumulation occurs because there is a difference between the sediment budget controlled by sediment transport mobility and that determined by sediment transport capacity. This contrast leads to the defining nature of metastable accumulation; it is likely to be eroded after initial deposition. Conceptually, metastable accumulation occurs during a short-lived episode in which sediment transport is controlled by the maximum sediment transport capacity; the long-term sediment budget is reestablished with the removal of metastable sedimentary features.

Transport Capacity is Predicted from Frequency vs. Magnitude of Discharge

Sediment transport capacity varies greatly with river discharge such that rare high magnitude discharge events can account for the bulk of sediment transport during an episode of metastable accumulation. Thus, a time-averaged sediment transport capacity must be evaluated as the net effect of frequent small events and rare large events (i.e., by integrating over the probability distribution of discharge with a given magnitude-frequency relationship).

Frequency vs. Magnitude of Discharge is Predicted from River Flashiness

The frequency of small vs. large discharge events in a drainage basin is controlled by: (1) the relative frequency of small and large precipitation/snow-melt events in the basin and (2) the capacity of the river network to integrate the effects of multiple, localized, high-magnitude precipitation events occurring at differing times and places in the drainage basin into a single downstream flood. The first of these factors and the role of changes in precipitation in incised-valley formation is beyond the scope of this study. The second factor is related to river *flashiness*. A flood event in a flashy river is short-lived, rises and falls quickly, and is localized to the immediate area of high-magnitude precipitation. A flood event in a well-integrated drainage basin (the opposite of flashy) is long-lived, rises and falls slowly, and is of regional extent. High-magnitude discharge is extremely rare in a river reach dominated by localized floods (flashy conditions). High-magnitude discharge is relatively more common in a river reach dominated by regional flooding (non-flashy conditions).

River Flashiness is Predicted from Downstream Changes in Hydraulic Geometry

The capacity of a river network to collect multiple upstream floods into a downstream, integrated flood can be predicted from the solution to the advective-diffusive wave equation for flood-wave travel along a river channel (see Eqs. 18–21). These equations predict that flashy river reaches are largely fed by water that has dropped only a short distance (compared to the river depth). In contrast, well-integrated rivers collect precipitation that originally fell at much higher elevations than the trunk river channel.

The average elevation change between the precipitation source area and the trunk channel (normalized by channel depth) can be predicted using semi-empirical relationships for downstream changes in the hydraulic geometry of rivers as a function discharge. Downstream changes in flashiness, sediment transport capacity per unit valley width, metastable accumulation potential, and channel-form erosion potential can be predicted from the hydraulic geometry of regime rivers. In a self-similar, branching drainage network the successive downstream depositional environments of erosional upland, alluvial valley, coastal plain, and distributary are linked to increasing discharge and stream order.

Hydraulic Geometry is Linked to Sea-level Change

Subtly different concavities of the stream profile can have profoundly different effects on river flashiness and its downstream changes. Thorne and Swift (1991) show, based on geomorphological regime theory, that periods of rapid sea-level fall cause the topographic slope of the fluvial plain (alluvial valley here) to increase and the topographic slope of the coastal plain to decrease. Thus during rapid sea-level fall, longitudinal stream profiles are of higher concavity than during periods of slow sea-level fall. In this scenario, a "bottle neck" of high metastable accumulation rate is created at the junction between the relatively steep alluvial valley and the relatively flat coastal plain caused by the rapid decrease in sediment transport capacity per unit valley width at this location. The high rate of metastable accumulation increases the avulsion frequency and suppresses the tendency for entrenched-channel formation. The relatively flat coastal plain has a decreased rate of metastable sediment accumulation. Accumulation in this location changes to long-term degradation caused by sea-level fall with consequent formation of entrenched channels.

Traffic-flow Analogy to Fluid-mechanical Model

The theoretical predictions of this study regarding avulsion frequency and entrenched-channel potential, given below, can be grasped intuitively by using an analogy to the flow of traffic along highways and city streets (Fig. 2). In this analogy, the progression from rural to suburban to urban highways is analogous to the progression from the sedimentary environments of the erosional uplands to the alluvial valley and coastal plain. The power of this analogy is that the factors that lead to high, peak-flow traffic conditions are analogous to the factors that lead to high, peak-flow sediment transport conditions.

Rural highways are characterized by high speed limits, few traffic lanes, and a dominance of local travellers on the roads. Analogously, the streams of the erosional upland environment are characterized by high gradients and shallow channels and are fed by local drainage. These factors make high volume flows (of traffic or sediment) very unlikely. Using the traffic analogy, the small number of traffic lanes reduces the chances for high-volume traffic flow, and the

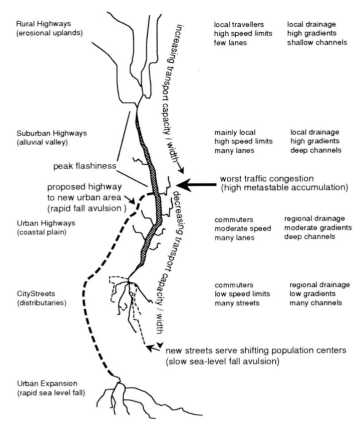

FIG. 2.—The flow of traffic along an integrated road system is a useful analogy to the flow of water along an integrated river system. The progression from rural to urban roads is analogous to the progression of the sedimentary environments from the erosional uplands to the distributary system. Road conditions are characterized by: (1) local travellers vs. commuters, (2) high vs. low speed limits, and (3) few or many lanes. Analogously, rivers are characterized by: (1) local vs. regional drainage, (2) high vs. low gradients, and (3) shallow vs. deep channels. The analogy helps explain (1) why alluvial-valley rivers are flashy, (2) why metastable accumulation is greatest in the upper coastal plain, and (3) why there are differing sites for frequent avulsion during rapid vs. slow sea-level fall (see text).

dominance of local travellers precludes a high volume of flow.

Suburban highways are characterized by high speed limits, many traffic lanes, and a mixture of local and long-distance travellers on the roads. Analogously, the streams of the alluvial valley are characterized by high gradients and deep channels and are fed largely by local drainage with the addition of some regional drainage. These factors make high volume flows (of traffic or sediment) more likely than in the upstream case. The suburban highway (analogous to the alluvial valley) is characterized by moderately flashy traffic (flow) conditions in which periods of well-regulated traffic flow are occasionally interrupted by the convergence of large numbers of long-distance travellers (regional water discharge).

Urban highways are characterized by moderate speed limits, many traffic lanes, and a dominance of long-distance travellers (commuters) who enter the highway on nu-

merous adjoining suburban highways. Analogously, the streams of the upper coastal plain are characterized by moderate gradients and deep channels and are fed largely by regional drainage of many tributaries. These factors lead to well-integrated, non-flashy flow conditions. As each suburban highway joins with the urban highway, the capacity to handle the additional traffic is diminished, and the potential for traffic congestion increases. This decreasing capacity to handle traffic in the downstream direction and the resultant traffic jams translates to a high potential for metastable sediment accumulation in rivers.

City streets are characterized by low speed limits, many alternative streets, and a mixture of some locals and many commuters on the roads. Analogously, the distributary streams are characterized by low gradients and alternative channels and are fed largely by regional drainage. To avoid traffic congestion, a well-managed city-street system must continually modify the street system in response to shifting business and residential needs. Analogously, the flow in distributaries shifts on rapid time scales.

The river-system/traffic-system analogy can also be used to consider the effects of sea-level change on river systems. Sea-level fall adds exposed land in a downstream direction. This is analogous to urbanization of new tracts of land. When urbanization is rapid (analogous to rapid sea-level fall), the urban area expands leaving behind a street system that is no longer maintained as construction funds are diverted to build new highways from the suburbs to the new urban areas. Analogously, during rapid sea-level fall, the coastal plain expands leaving behind entrenched channels that no longer avulse as water discharge is diverted to upstream avulsion in the alluvial valley and upper coastal plain.

When urbanization is slow (analogous to slow sea-level fall), the urban area gradually relocates as population centers shift. Urban highways, which once served active communities, serve less and less people and are not maintained as road construction funds are diverted to build new streets in the relocated urban areas. Analogously, slow sea-level fall causes a gradual seaward shift of the alluvial valley and coastal plain. With this shift of environment, rivers transform from coastal-plain to alluvial-valley conditions and consequently become incised.

QUANTITATIVE DESCRIPTION OF MODEL

When attempting to quantitatively model the complicated evolution of a river and valley drainage system, it is sometimes difficult to avoid mixing physical processes that do not apply to the same spatial and temporal scales. I begin the development of this quantitative model for riverine valley incision, therefore, with a more general quantitative discussion of sediment budget in such a system and the spatial and temporal scales of sediment accumulation. This general discussion provides the basis for the more specific application that follows.

The Sediment Budget of the Alluvial Valley and Coastal Plain

The response of naturally-occurring river systems to changes in regional controls such as base level or climate involves a complex response by many factors (e.g., Leopold and others, 1964; Gregory and Walling, 1973; Chorley and others, 1984). These include changes at different reaches within the drainage network of: (1) river width, depth, slope, and type (e.g., braided vs. meandering); (2) bedload to suspended load ratio; (3) bed friction factors; (4) vegetation; (5) bed and bank grain-size distribution; (6) evaporation and runoff potential; (7) discharge flashiness; (8) drainage system plan form and density; (9) avulsion frequency; (10) meander migration speed and wavelength; (11) average drainage basin size for each order of stream; and (12) valley broadening.

This complex system can be understood most readily by realizing that, in the most general sense, erosional valleys form in response to a negative sediment budget, i.e., when more sediment is being transported out than is being brought into a particular segment of a drainage basin. The sediment budget can be expressed in terms of the average rates of all fluxes of sediment into the valley at a given reach of length Δx of it's trunk river as:

$$\frac{\partial L_{\text{trib}}}{\partial t} - \Delta x \cdot \frac{\partial L_{\text{trunk}}}{\partial x \partial t} + \frac{\partial L_{\text{mig}}}{\partial t} + \frac{\partial L_{\text{ovb}}}{\partial t} - \frac{\partial L_{\text{hslp}}}{\partial t}$$

$$= -\frac{1}{1-\phi} \frac{\partial (A_r - A_1 + A_v)}{\partial t} + \mathring{a} \cdot w + \varepsilon \quad (4)$$

where t is time; x is downstream distance, $\partial L_{\text{trib}}/\partial t$, $\partial L_{\text{mig}}/\partial t$, $\partial L_{\text{ovb}}/\partial t$, and $\partial L_{\text{hslp}}/\partial t$ are the sediment fluxes per unit length from tributaries, river migration/avulsion, overbank deposits, and valley hillslope/sheet flood erosion, L_{trunk} is the sediment transported by the trunk river; ϕ is the sediment porosity; A_r, A_l, and A_v are the cross-sectional areas of the active trunk river, river levees, and valley; $\mathring{a}$ is the long-term regional accumulation rate (measured in compacted units of sediment); w is the width of the valley; and ε is the change in topography not accounted for by A_r, A_l, and A_v. Equation 4, as it stands, is not very useful because it combines average fluxes which operate over different time scales. For example, river profile and cross-sectional adjustments occur on the scale of decades (Knighton, 1987) while long-term, regional accumulation rates characterize periods on the order of a millennium to a million years.

Spatial and Temporal Scales of Accumulation

The functional form of sediment accumulation in tributary and trunk rivers can be decoupled into three parts representing the self-organized chaotic, metastable equilibrium, and long-term equilibrium profile components of the sediment budget. These differing components arise out of three differing forms of geomorphologic dynamic equilibrium that are, in a sense, competing to control drainage-basin morphology. Each form of dynamic equilibrium represents a different type of balance between water discharge, topographic slope, and sediment transport (Table 1). Moreover, each of these components is characterized by fundamentally different responses to the external forcing factors that affect drainage basins such as sea-level change, climate, or tectonics.

TABLE 1.—FORMS OF DYNAMIC EQUILIBRIUM IN A FLUVIAL SYSTEM

Type of Equilibrium	Function of Slope	Function of Discharge	Dominant Factor
self-organized chaotic	local	local	transport mobility ratio
metastable	regional	local	transport capacity
long-term	local	regional	transport mobility

Self-organized chaotic behavior arises out of the non-linear feedbacks between the local topographic slope, the local water discharge, and the high transport mobility of water compared to the low transport mobility of sediment. Fluvial examples of this type of sediment accumulation are well described in sandbox experiments that exhibit changing patterns of drainage-basin morphology (Schumm and others, 1987). Theoretical studies on the self-organized chaotic behavior of granular materials (Bak and others, 1988; Chris Paola, pers. commun., 1992) as well as computer models of drainage network evolution (Willgoose and others, 1991) indicate that much work remains to be done using the mathematics of chaos theory to document the statistical forms of equilibrium that characterize this type of system. Functionally this component of the sediment budget can be expressed as:

$$L^{\text{self-organized}} \propto \text{transport mobility ratio}$$
$$[\text{slope}(x), \text{discharge}(x)] \quad (5)$$

The metastable component of sediment accumulation involves temporary changes in local slope that are a response to changes in sediment transport capacity as a function of local water discharge and regional slope. Mathematical models of this component of fluvial sedimentation have been used to predict river reaches subject to potential erosion and deposition and the magnitude-frequency relationship of sand delivery to the coast (Stow and Chang, 1987). A key to this type of model is the magnitude-frequency relationship of water discharge at different reaches within the drainage basin. Functionally this component of the sediment budget can be expressed as:

$$L^{\text{metastable}} \propto f(\text{regional slope})$$
$$\cdot \text{transport capacity}[\text{discharge}(x)] \quad (6)$$

The long-term component of sediment accumulation/erosion involves adjustments of local slope and sediment mobility so that regional changes in sediment supply are in dynamic equilibrium with the accommodation space created by base-level change. The relaxation time scale of this process is controlled by a regional function of water discharge. Mathematical models of this component of fluvial sedimentation have been used to predict the rate of downstream fining as a function of basin subsidence (Paola, 1990), the form of stream-profile adjustment to crustal warping (Slingerland and Snow, 1988; Snow and Slingerland, 1990), and the morphology of a large number of landscape features that are a response to base-level change (e.g., Scheidegger, 1961).

$$L^{\text{long-term}} \propto f(\text{regional discharge})$$
$$\cdot \text{transport mobility}[\text{slope}(x)] \quad (7)$$

A complete model of drainage-basin evolution would include self-organized, metastable, and long-term components of sediment accumulation. In this paper, we simplify the problem by considering only metastable accumulation which, as discussed earlier, is a dominant factor in controlling avulsion frequency and entrenched-channel formation.

Equation 4 can be decoupled into three equations representing the dynamic equilibrium of the self-organized chaotic, metastable, and long-term sediment budget as follows:

self-organized chaotic accumulation rate—

$$\frac{\partial L_{\text{trib}}^{\text{self-organized}}}{\partial t} - \Delta x \cdot \frac{\partial L_{\text{trunk}}^{\text{self-organized}}}{\partial x \partial t} = \varepsilon \qquad (8)$$

metastable accumulation rate—

$$\frac{\partial L_{\text{trib}}^{\text{metastable}}}{\partial t} - \Delta x \cdot \frac{\partial^2 L_{\text{trunk}}^{\text{metastable}}}{\partial x \partial t} + (1 - sd)$$
$$\cdot \left[\frac{\partial L_{\text{mig}}}{\partial t} + \frac{\partial L_{\text{ovb}}}{\partial t} - \frac{\partial L_{\text{hslp}}}{\partial t} \right] = \frac{1}{1 - \phi} \frac{\partial (A_l - A_r)}{\partial t} \qquad (9)$$

long-term accumulation rate—

$$\frac{\partial L_{\text{trib}}^{\text{long-term}}}{\partial t} - \Delta x \cdot \frac{\partial^2 L_{\text{trunk}}^{\text{long-term}}}{\partial x \partial t} + sd$$
$$\cdot \left[\frac{\partial L_{\text{mig}}}{\partial t} + \frac{\partial L_{\text{ovb}}}{\partial t} - \frac{\partial L_{\text{hslp}}}{\partial t} \right] = \mathring{a} \cdot w - \frac{1}{1 - \phi} \frac{\partial A_v}{\partial t} \qquad (10)$$

where *sd* is a *sediment delivery ratio* that represents the percentage of the total material locally eroded from the drainage basin that is removed at the trunk-river outlet (assuming a negligible long-term accumulation rate).

Sedimentary accumulation rates are, generally, orders of magnitude larger when measured over durations of decades than when measured over durations of millennia (Sadler, 1981). Thus we can use the approximation:

$$\frac{1}{1 - \phi} \left| \frac{\partial (A_1 - A_r)}{\partial t} \right| \gg \left| \mathring{a} \cdot w - \frac{1}{1 - \phi} \frac{\partial A_v}{\partial t} \right| \qquad (11)$$

Using equations 10 and 11 in equation 9 gives (for sd in the observed range 0.05–0.95; Walling, 1983):

$$\frac{1}{1 - \phi} \frac{\partial (A_1 - A_r)}{\partial t} = -\Delta x \cdot \frac{\partial^2 L_{trunk}}{\partial x \partial t} \qquad (12)$$

Sediment Transport Capacity of a River

Sediment discharge in a given reach of a river, L_{trunk}, will vary greatly with time. A large amount of observational data (e.g., Leopold and others, 1964; Gregory and Walling, 1973) shows that sediment-load transport capacity, $\partial L / \partial t$, increases at a given river reach as a power law with water discharge, Q, as follows:

$$\frac{\partial L}{\partial t} = \begin{bmatrix} \sim 0, & Q \leq Q_p \\ kQ^m, & Q_P < Q \end{bmatrix} \qquad (13)$$

where Q_P is the most probable river discharge, k is a proportionality constant depending on the grain-size distribution of the sediments, and m is an exponent which is observationally ~ 3. To find the average load transported, the load is integrated for each discharge level, Q, weighted by the percentage of time the river is between discharge Q and $Q + dQ$.

It is found for a large number of natural rivers that, if only flows larger than Q_p are considered, the frequency of a given discharge per dQ, $f(Q)$, is given by (Schubert and Lingenfelter, 1974):

$$f(Q) = (s - 1)Q_P^{s-1} Q^{-s} \qquad (14)$$

where s is an exponent that depends on the 'flashiness' of the river and $f(Q) \cdot dQ$ is a dimensionless product. If flows of all sizes are considered, equation 14 can be modified to:

$$f(Q) = \frac{(s + 1)(s - 1)}{2s} Q^{-s} Q_p^{s-1} \quad Q > Q_p \qquad (15a)$$

$$f(Q) = \frac{(s + 1)(s - 1)}{2s} Q^{-s} Q_p^{-s-1} \quad Q < Q_p \qquad (15b)$$

If observations of discharge are made at equally spaced time intervals, the probability that a given observation exceeds a magnitude, Q, is shown in Figure 3 for two representative values of flashiness exponents. For flashy rivers ($s = 2.5$), the frequency of extreme discharges is far lower than for rivers which are not flashy ($s = 1.3$).

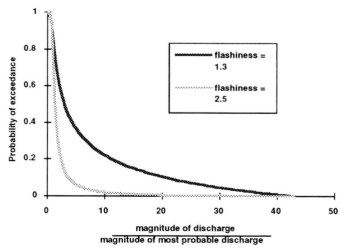

Fig. 3.—The probability that a given observation exceeds a magnitude, Q, is shown for two representative values of flashiness exponent, s, based on observations of discharge made at equally-spaced time intervals. The curves are derived by integrating equation 15 with respect to Q.

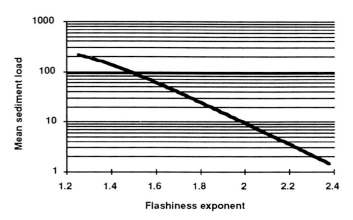

FIG. 4.—Mean sediment load ($\Psi 10^{-4}$) from equation 16 as a function of flashiness exponent s, using equation 15 with $k = 1$, $m = 3$, $Q_p = 1$, and $Q_{max} = 500$.

Using equations 13 and 14 or 13 and 15, the mean sediment load is given by:

$$\frac{\partial \overline{L}}{\partial t} = \int_{Q_P}^{Q_{max}} kQ^m f(Q) \, dQ \qquad (16)$$

The extreme sensitivity of the mean sediment load to the flashiness exponent, s, is illustrated in Figure 4. Flashy rivers are orders of magnitude less efficient in transporting sediment because extreme flows, which can carry a lot of sediment, are rare in these systems.

The flashiness also determines the percentage of time that flows are less than Q_p and, thus, from equation 13 are below the threshold of sediment movement. Figure 5 shows that the percentage of time that channel sediment is immobile increases with the flashiness exponent, s (Ephemeral rivers are not considered in this calculation).

Fluid Mechanics in a Self-similar Drainage Network

In this section, I present a theoretical derivation of the expected flashiness exponent, s, and its variation along the

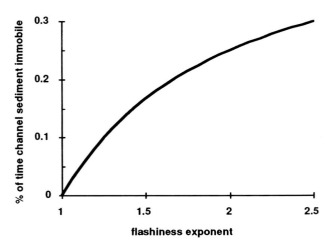

FIG. 5.—The percentage of time that channel sediment is immobile as a function of the flashiness exponent s.

length of a river which is part of a integrated, self-similar, drainage system. The basic starting point for this derivation is the observation by Schubert and Lingenfelter (1974) that the exponent s is related to the recession decay curve of individual floods, $Q(t)$, by:

$$Q(t) \propto (t - t_0)^{1/(1-s)} \quad \text{for } t > t_m \qquad (17)$$

where t_0 is the start of the flood and t_m is the time of maximum discharge rate. This relationship follows from the fact that, in the rivers studied, the percentage of time spent at a high discharge is determined mainly by how fast floods decay rather than by how often floods occur. These relationships will not hold for ephemeral rivers where this may not be the case. It is assumed that the rivers modelled here are not ephemeral.

The decay curve of the unit flood hydrograph can be predicted from theoretical results for the dispersion of a unit flood pulse traveling through a river network. In general, the farther the distance between source and observer the more dispersed the flood effects will be in time. Moore (1984) gives an appropriate convolution operator which operates on the input flow at the source $g(t)$ to give the flow at the downstream observer:

$$Q(t) = \int_0^t g(\tau) f(t - \tau) \, d\tau \qquad (18)$$

The function $f(t)$ is given by:

$$f(t) = \left(\frac{\lambda}{2\pi t^3}\right)^{1/2} \exp\left\{\frac{-\lambda(t - \mu)^2}{2\mu^2 t}\right\} \qquad (19)$$

$$\mu = \frac{2\overline{X} \cdot A_r}{3Q(t)} \qquad (20)$$

$$\lambda = \frac{L^2 Q(t)}{A_r C^2 H^2} \qquad (21)$$

where H and A_r are the river depth and cross-sectional area, C is the Chezy coefficient and $\overline{X}$ is the mean distance from the source to the observer. The time of peak flow occurs when $f(t)$ reaches a maximum in equation 19:

$$t_m = \frac{\mu}{2\lambda}((4\lambda^2 + 9\mu^2)^{0.5} - 3\mu) \qquad (22)$$

The values of s in equation 17 that best fit equation 18 for various values of μ and λ can be determined by numerical experimentation for times between t_m and $3t_m$. It is found that to a sufficient degree of accuracy the value of s is given by:

$$s = \frac{(5.0 + \lambda/\mu)}{(1.9 + \lambda/\mu)} \qquad (23)$$

where the ratio λ/μ simplifies to:

$$\lambda/\mu = \frac{3\overline{X}S}{2H} \qquad (24)$$

where S is the river-bottom slope and the approximation has been made that the hydraulic radius is equal to the channel depth. A plot of the unit flood hydrograph for two different values of flashiness exponent, s, is shown in Figure 6. A flashy flood ($s = 2.5$) rises abruptly while a flood with a low flashiness exponent ($s = 1.3$) is spread out over a longer duration. The dependance of flashiness s on the ratio λ/μ from equation 23 is shown in Figure 7.

The value of flashiness s given by equation 23 at a given reach depends on the value of $\overline{X}$ as seen by each water particle on its way from source to observer. We are not particularly interested in the background flow in the trunk river which is fed by a river's sources at all lower stream orders, as well as by groundwater seepage. Rather, we assume that significant flood events are superimposed on the background flow which may vary seasonally. The source of water for these flood events is then, largely, from the drainage basin of the trunk river itself and the tributaries feeding the trunk river. These tributaries are of different orders and of different lengths; however, the average dis-

tance water flows on tributaries to the trunk stream can be assessed for a random topological stream network. On a topologically-random network, the average number of tributaries of order u to a stream of order is 2^{-u-1} (Shreve, 1967). Furthermore, given a typical trunk-to-tributary length ratio of 2 (Abrahams, 1984), the drainage area, A_d, of each tributary can be assessed from the fractal relationship between drainage area and length of the trunk river, X, (Hack, 1957; Shreve, 1974; Mandelbrot, 1977; Robert and Roy, 1990).

$$A_d \propto X^q \tag{25}$$

where q is the fractal dimension of the drainage basin.

The contribution to the total discharge by each tributary increases with drainage area according to a relationship first proposed by Hack (1957):

$$Q \propto A_d^v \tag{26}$$

The coefficient v in equation 26 typically lies between 0.7 and 1.0 (Hack, 1957; Knighton, 1987). Using equations 25 and 26, with exponent $v = 1$, a summation is performed over the travel distance of each tributary order u, weighted by its expected contribution to the total drainage:

$$\overline{X} = \frac{X}{2}\left[X^q - 2\left(\frac{X}{2}\right)^q\right] + 2\left[\frac{X}{2} + \frac{X}{4}\right]\left\{\left[\frac{X}{2}\right]^q - 2\left[\frac{X}{4}\right]^q\right\}$$
$$+ 4\left[\frac{X}{2} + \frac{X}{4} + \frac{X}{8}\right]\left\{\left[\frac{X}{4}\right]^q - 2\left[\frac{X}{8}\right]^q\right\}\cdots\Big/X^q$$
$$= \left[\frac{2^{q-1}}{2^q - 1}\right]X \tag{27}$$

where $\overline{X}$ is the average distance of travel of water particles on tributaries feeding the trunk river, and X is the length of the trunk river. The dependency of $\overline{X}$ on q, the fractal dimension of the drainage basin, is shown in Figure 8. The dependency of $\overline{X}$ on fractal dimension q is not high. Thus,

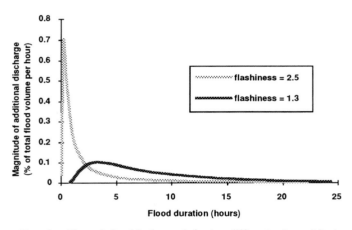

FIG. 6.—The unit-flood hydrograph for two different values of flashiness exponent s shows the history of flood stages at a downstream location caused by a single, short episode of water discharge into an upstream location.

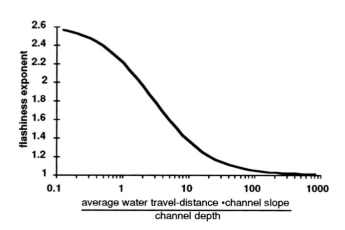

FIG. 7.—The dependence of flashiness s on the ratio λ/μ from equation 23.

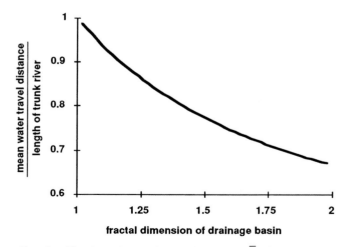

FIG. 8.—The dependence of the ratio between $\overline{X}$, the mean water-travel distance in a self-similar river network, and the trunk-river length L, on q, the fractal dimension of the drainage basin (relationship from equation 27).

the theoretical results of this study should be generally applicable to integrated drainage basins which are not, strictly, self-similar.

River Hydraulic Geometry as a Function of Discharge and Stream Order

A large number of empirical studies have examined downstream changes in the hydraulic geometry of rivers as a function discharge (e.g., Leopold and Maddock, 1953; Leopold and others, 1964; Smith, 1974; Church and Rood, 1983; Knighton, 1987; Rhodes, 1987). These studies indicate that the downstream variation of discharge (of a given return period) is the single most dominating independent variable controlling river geometry. Using standard notation, the river width, W, depth, H, and slope, S, are expressed as power-law functions of discharge Q:

$$W \propto Q^b \tag{28}$$

$$H \propto Q^f \tag{29}$$

$$S \propto Q^z \tag{30}$$

Downstream changes in discharge can serve as a conceptual indicator of position within a integrated drainage network. The lowest-order streams in the erosional uplands of the river network have small drainage areas. The highest-order stream in the coastal plain of the river network has the largest drainage area. Thus, from equation 26, discharge increases in a predictable fashion as a function of location in fluvial system.

In this paper, Horton's stream order (Horton, 1945) is adopted as a semi-quantitative proxy for depositional environment and its expected changes as a function of position within an integrated drainage network. Equations 28–30 indicate that hydraulic geometry changes downstream as a function of discharge. This variation in discharge is transformed to a variation in drainage area and stream length through equations 25 and 26. Stream length in a tributary system is related to stream order through (Horton, 1945):

$$R_L{}^{u-1} = \frac{X}{X_0} \tag{31}$$

where R_L is the trunk-to-tributary length ratio and X_0 is the average length of an order 1 stream. The length ratio for natural river networks varies between 1.5 and 3.5 (Abrahams, 1984). Thus, the expected number of stream orders in a river network of a given average length from river headwaters to river outlet depends strongly on R_L (Fig. 9). For Figures 11–16, R_L is set to 2 and the product vq is set to 1.26 (Knighton, 1987). Using other values for these parameters will change the scale of the stream-order axis in these figures but does not conceptually change the results of this study.

The exponents b, f, and z that determine hydraulic geometry (equations 28–30) are normally derived for a limited range of discharges (Rhodes, 1987). To extend the usefulness of these approximations to the full range of discharges considered in this study, the exponents z and f are allowed

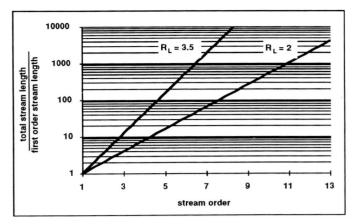

FIG. 9.—The expected number of stream orders in a river network of a given average length from river headwater to river outlet, as a function of R_L, the trunk-to-tributary length ratio in a self-similar drainage network.

to vary with Q:

$$z = -0.2 - concavity \cdot \ln\left(\frac{Q}{Q_0}\right) \tag{32}$$

$$f = 0.26 + 0.035 \cdot \ln\left(\frac{Q}{Q_0}\right) \tag{33}$$

The coefficients in equations 32 and 33 are constrained by the data in Rhodes (1987) and Church and Rood (1983). The coefficient, concavity, on the right-hand side of equation 32 is particularly important to the results of this study. Figure 10 shows the computed stream elevation as a function of distance along two drainage networks, one of concavity 0.01 and the other of concavity 0.02. The profile with a higher concavity coefficient has a more concave shape.

Metastable Sediment Accumulation as a Function of Stream Order

The results of the previous sections can be used to develop a theory for metastable sediment accumulation as a

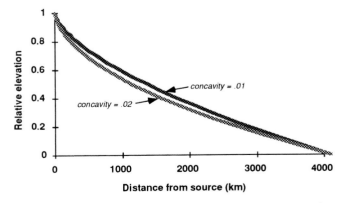

FIG. 10.—Computed stream elevation as a function of distance along two drainage networks, one of concavity 0.01 and the other of concavity 0.02. See equation 32 for the definition of concavity.

function of depositional environment in an integrated drainage system (or its proxy—stream order). Using equations 25–31 in equation 24 results in:

$$\lambda/\mu = c\left[\frac{2^{q-1}}{2^q - 1}\right]X^{1+vq[z-f]} \qquad (34)$$

with c being a proportionality constant.

In Figure 11, the flashiness exponent s is shown as a function of stream order from equation 23 using equations 32–34. Though the absolute magnitude of the flashiness exponent s cannot be predicted with certainty, both estimates show a clearly defined minimum value of s between stream orders 7 and 8 ($\sim$ order 4 for $R_L = 3.5$). This minimum reflects the contribution of two opposing tendencies. First, there is a tendency towards well-regulated (non-flashy) flow in higher-order streams which collect discharge from the integrated sum of their upstream tributaries. In contrast, there is a tendency towards flashy flow in streams which have low longitudinal gradients. These opposing tendencies combine to produce the net effect shown in Figure 11. The form of the flashiness vs. stream-order relationship shown in Figure 11 is supported by the historical record of modern floods (Thorne, unpublished manuscript; analysis of data in Rodier and Roche, 1984).

Using equations 13, 15, 23, 32, 33, and 34, the sediment-load transport capacity, time-averaged over a long interval of observation, is:

$$\frac{\partial \overline{L}_{\text{trunk}}}{\partial t} = \frac{k(s-1)(s+1)}{2s(1-s+m)F_{\text{max}}}$$
$$\cdot \left\{\left[\frac{2(1-F_{\text{max}})\cdot s}{(1+s)}\right]^{(1-s+m)/(1-s)} - 1\right\} \qquad (35)$$

where

$$F_{\text{max}} = \int_0^{Q_{\text{max}}} f(Q)\, dQ \qquad (36)$$

and Q_{max} is the maximum discharge during the period of observation.

Downstream changes in sediment transport capacity per unit valley width determine the likelihood for metastable accumulation in any segment of the valley system. Metastable accumulation is most likely in segments where there is a downstream decrease in the sediment transport capacity per unit valley width. The sediment transport capacity from equation 35 is plotted per unit valley width, w, in Figure 12 for two values of exponent m (assuming that valley width is roughly proportional to river width; Bhowmik and Stall, 1979). Four distinct zones are predicted to occur from low-to-high order streams. The lowest stream orders are characterized by increasing sediment transport capacity in the downstream direction. This zone, the erosional uplands, is, therefore, characterized by metastable erosion.[1] Proceeding in the downstream direction, the next zone is characterized by approximately constant sediment transport capacity. This zone, the alluvial valley, is characterized by sediment bypass. The next zone shows a decreasing sediment transport capacity in the downstream direction. Thus, the coastal plain is characterized by a tendency for metastable accumulation even in the absence of long-term accommodation potential. The fourth zone, at the seaward limit of the integrated drainage system, is characterized by an extremely low magnitude of sediment transport capacity per unit channel width. It is beyond the scope of this paper to elaborate on the theoretical reasons why this low transport capacity leads to the formation of multiple channels in a distributary form.

Equations 9, 10, 13, 15, 23, and 32–35 can be used to predict the sediment delivery ratio as a function of basin

---

[1]Long-term deposition is still possible in this zone if long-term subsidence (accommodation potential) is present.

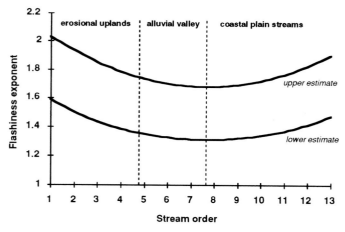

FIG. 11.—Flashiness exponent s as a function of stream order from equation 23 using equations 32–34. Parameters values are: $v = 0.85$, $q = 1.6$, $b = 0.5$, concavity $= 0.015$, lower estimate $c = 1$, upper estimate $c = 3$. Estimates of c are chosen so that predicted values of exponent s fall in the range observed in natural rivers (Schubert and Lingenfelter, 1974).

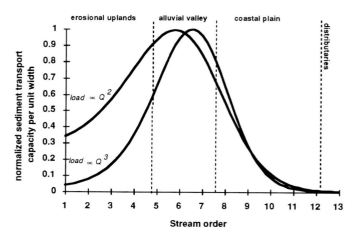

FIG. 12.—Sediment transport capacity per unit valley width, w, as a function of stream order (relationship from equation 35).

drainage area for basins that are under steady-state conditions (Appendix 1). The results of these calculations are in excellent agreement with measured field data of sediment delivery ratios.

Equation 12 gives the net, time-averaged, metastable accumulation/erosion rate as a function of the longitudinal gradient of the sediment-load transport capacity. The potential for a short-lived episode of metasable accumulation must take into account random deviations around the time-averaged rate. Thus, short-term episodes of metastable *accumulation* are still possible in river reaches undergoing net *degradation* (Fig. 13). The likelihood of these short term episodes controls avulsion frequency. Assuming a Poisson distribution of sediment accumulation/erosion events (Nishiwaki, 1978), the short-term, metastable accumulation potential is related to the net rate of accumulation/erosion by:

metastable accumulation potential $\propto$

$$\exp\left\{-c_2 \frac{\partial\left[\dfrac{\overline{L}_{\text{trunk}}}{w}\right]}{\partial x \partial t}\right\} \quad (37)$$

alluvial valley and upper coastal plain (Fig. 14). There is virtually no metastable accumulation potential in the upland erosional environment.

As previously indicated by equation 2, avulsion frequency is inversely related to channel-form erosion potential. Smith and Bretherton (1972), in a theoretical study based on a sediment transport capacity function which is a general function of discharge and slope, demonstrated that channel-form erosion potential depends on the longitudinal curvature of the topographic surface over which drainage is occurring. It was found that concave surfaces have a high channel-form erosion potential because small topographic perturbations will tend to grow rapidly to form a channelized surface. In contrast, convex surfaces do not have channel-form erosion potential because channels tend to disappear with continued deposition. Thus, based on this work,

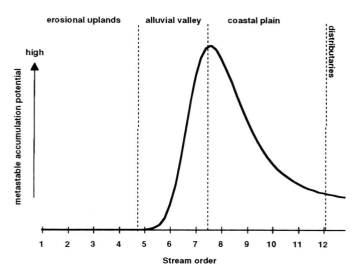

FIG. 14.—Metastable accumulation potential (based on equation 37) as a function of stream order (depositional environment).

the channel-form erosion potential is given by:

$$\text{channel-form erosion potential} \propto \frac{\partial S}{\partial x} \quad (38)$$

Equation 38 predicts that channel-form erosion potential decreases systematically with stream order (Fig. 15).

A QUALITATIVE RESPONSE MODEL:
VALLEY EROSION VS. CHANNEL ENTRENCHMENT

Thorne and Swift (1991) discuss the control of paleogeographic variables on long-term equilibrium profiles of

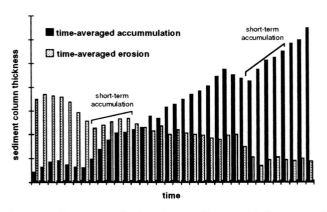

FIG. 13.—Short-term episodes of metastable accumulation are possible in river reaches undergoing either net (time-average) accumulation or erosion. An hypothetical sediment column is shown at successive times. Random episodes of erosion or deposition (following a Poisson distribution) occur at each step.

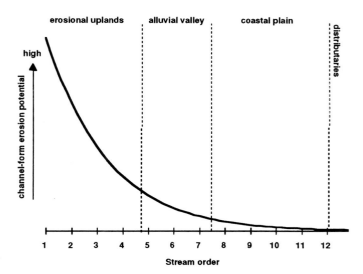

FIG. 15.—Channel-form erosion potential (derived from equation 38) decreases systematically with stream order.

fluvial and marine environments. Following the pioneering work of Sloss (1962); the fundamental paleogeographic variables considered are: **R**, the rate of relative sea-level change (combining eustatic, tectonic, isostatic, and compactional components); **D**, the rate of sediment transport; $\mathbf{Q_s}$, the rate of sediment supply; and **M**, the sediment grain size. Thorne and Swift (1991) demonstrate that the product $f_1(\mathbf{Q_s})f_2(\mathbf{M})$ is a function for effective sediment supply where f_1 and f_2 are positive-valued functions that monotonically increase with $\mathbf{Q_s}$ and **M** respectively. Similarly, the product $f_3(\mathbf{R})f_4(\mathbf{D})$ is a function for effective accommodation potential where f_3 and f_4 are positive-valued functions that monotonically increase with **R** and **D** respectively.

A qualitative response model for valley erosion and channel entrenchment can be based on the observation of Thorne and Swift (1991) that the ratio of sediment accommodation to supply, defined as $¥ = f_3(\mathbf{R})f_4(\mathbf{D})/f_1(\mathbf{Q_s})f_2(\mathbf{M})$, is inversely proportional to the concavity of the long-term, equilibrium, alluvial-valley/coastal-plain longitudinal profile. For example, if the rate of relative sea-level fall increases, $f_3(\mathbf{R})$ and $¥$ decrease leading to an increase of the concavity of the alluvial-valley/coastal-plain longitudinal profile. Equivalently, if there is an increase in the rate of sediment supply, $¥$ also decreases leading to an increase of the concavity of the alluvial-valley/coastal-plain longitudinal profile.

The changes of entrenched-channel potential and avulsion frequency along an integrated stream network are a strong function of the parameter *concavity* from equation 32. A high concavity of 0.02 characterizes low values of the accommodation to supply ratio, $¥$, while a low concavity of 0.01 characterizes conditions of high $¥$. In Figure 16, the entrenched-channel potential as a function of stream order is computed (from equations 2, 3, 32, 37, and 38) for both fast and slow rates of sea-level fall. It is assumed in this calculation that the variation of $¥$, due to the dif-

fering magnitudes of the rate of fall of sea level, is not compensated for by any variation in **D**, $\mathbf{Q_s}$, or **M**.

The theoretical results shown in Figure 16 suggest that entrenched channels that incise lower coastal-plain sediments are preferentially formed during periods of fast sea-level fall. The fill of this type of channel is expected to contain transitional and marine sediments deposited during subsequent transgression. In contrast, entrenched channels formed by periods of slow sea-level fall occur preferentially into the lower alluvial valley and upper coastal plain. This type of entrenched channel is far removed from marine environments and, thus, is subsequently filled by fluvial sediment.

STRATIGRAPHIC EXAMPLES

A review of ancient examples of incised valleys can test the predictions of the previous section. In Table 2, I have classified 15 examples of ancient incised valleys as either entrenched channels or incised alluvial valleys. This classification is based on the valley width and valley meander wavelength (where data is available). The later criterion is useful because channel meander wavelengths are smaller than alluvial-valley meander wavelengths (Dury, 1965). One representative Holocene example is included in Table 2 for comparative purposes. Example 14 is left unclassified because the valley width is not diagnostic by itself, and the valley meander wavelength is poorly constrained. The last column in Table 2 indicates a "fast" rate of sea-level fall for periods of glacial eustasy (Paleozoic eustasy from Ross and Ross, 1988).

The examples in Table 2 clearly show a correspondance between the type of valley fill, the type of incised valley, and the rate of sea-level fall. First, incised alluvial valleys formed during periods of slow (non-glacial) sea-level fall (examples 1–5) are filled by fully marine, estuarine, or transitional environment sediments. Second, entrenched channels formed during periods of slow sea-level fall (examples 6–13) are filled by fluvial (non-marine) sediments. Third, entrenched channels formed during periods of fast sea-level fall (examples 15–17) are at least partially filled by deltaic or estuarine sediments. The preserved stratigraphy of this last type of channel is apparently complicated by superposition of successive stages of channel entrenchment during subsequent periods of glacial fall.

These three observations concerning the correspondance between the type of valley fill, the type of incised valley, and the rate of sea-level fall are in excellent agreement with the theoretical results of this study as summarized in Figure 16. These results predict, in agreement with observation, that: (1) incised alluvial valleys formed during periods of slow sea-level fall preferentially incise into lower coastal-plain sediments, and, thus, the expected fill of these valleys is transitional, estuarine, or marine sediment; (2) entrenched channels formed during periods of slow sea-level fall preferentially incise into lower alluvial-valley sediments, and, thus, the expected fill of these channels is fluvial rather than transitional or marine sediment; and (3) entrenched channels formed during periods of rapid sea-level fall preferentially incise into lower coastal-plain sediments,

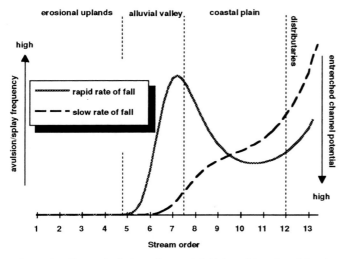

FIG. 16.—Entrenched-channel potential (right axis) and avulsion frequency (left axis): as a function of stream order, computed from equations 2, 3, 32, 37, and 38 for fast and slow rates of sea-level fall. Parameter concavity from equation 32 is 0.01 and 0.02 for slow and fast rates of sea-level fall respectively.

TABLE 2.—GEOMETRY AND FACIES OF INCISED-VALLEY FILLS. EACH INCISED VALLEY (WITH ONE EXCEPTION) IS CLASSIFIED AS AN INCISED ALLUVIAL VALLEY OR ENTRENCHED CHANNEL. THE RATE OF SEA-LEVEL FALL IS CLASSIFIED AS "FAST" FOR PERIODS OF GLACIAL EUSTACY

No.	Reference	Year	Age	Valley Width	Strata Cut Into	Valley Depth	Valley Fill	Meander Wavelength	Incised-Alluvial Valley/ Entrenched Channel	Sea-Level Fall
1	Weimer	1984	100–98[1] Ma	20–50 km	fluvial	20 m	marine		incised alluvial valley	slow
2	Weimer	1984	97 Ma	90 km	marine	40 m	transitional	50 km	incised alluvial valley	slow
3	Reinson & others	1988	L. Albian	6 km	marine	10 m	estuarine	25 km	incised alluvial valley	slow
4	Rahmani	1988	72 Ma	10 km	transitional	20 m	estuarine	20 km	incised alluvial valley	slow
5	Barclay	1988	Lower Carbonif.	5–10 km	transitional/ marine	25 m	transitional	>25 km	incised alluvial valley	slow
6	Weimer	1984	100–98 Ma	5–12 km	fluvial	20 m	fluvial		entrenched channel	slow
7	Weimer	1984	96 Ma	10 km	transitional	15 m	fluvial		entrenched channel	slow
8	Rahmani	1988	72 Ma	1 km	transitional	10 m	fluvial	4 km	entrenched channel	slow
9	Pryer and Potter	1979	upper Mississippian	4 km	marine	50 m	fluvial	10 km	entrenched channel	slow
10	Kraus and Middleton	1987	Upper Triassic	~0.1 km	fluvial	15 m	fluvial		entrenched channel	slow
11	Hradsky and Griffin	1984	Lower Cretaceous	10 km	transitional/ marine	25 m	fluvial	10 km	entrenched channel	slow
12	Harms	1966	Albian	1–2 km	marine	20 m	fluvial	3 km/straight	entrenched channel	slow
13	Levy and others	this volume	upper Proterozoic	20–200 m	fluvial	40 m	fluvial		entrenched channel	slow
14	Zaitlin and Shultz	1984	Lower Albian	5 km	fluvial	25 m	transitional/ estuarine	10 km?	?	slow
15	Sonnenberg	1985	Morrow	2 km	transitional	15 m	deltaic remnants	3 km	entrenched channel	fast
16	Palmer and others	1979	Desmoinesian	3 km	shallow marine	75 m	deltaic remnants	10 km	entrenched channel	fast
17	Kraft and others	1987	Holocene	2 km	transitional	20 m	estuarine	5 km	entrenched channel	fast

[1]Stratigraphic ages use the Van Hinte (1976) Cretaceous time scale

and, thus, the expected fill of these channels is transitional, estuarine, or marine sediment.

CONCLUSIONS

The response of naturally-occurring river systems to changes in regional controls such as base level or climate involves a complex response by many factors which are competing to control drainage-basin morphology. This study recognizes that there are, in a general sense, three differing forms of geomorphologic dynamic equilibrium (self-organized chaotic, metastable equilibrium, and long-term equilibrium profile) that operate on different spatial and temporal scales. It is the second of these forms of equilibrium, the metastable, that dominatly controls the potential for entrenched channel formation and its counterpart — avulsion frequency. This study applies the theory of metastable equilibrium to the formation of two type of incised valleys: incised alluvial valleys and entrenched channels.

Both the metastable accumulation potential and the channel-form erosion potential characteristically change from the upper to lower reaches of a drainage basin. Primary among changes from the alluvial valley to coastal plain are changes in discharge flashiness, flood stage frequency, the rate of overbank deposition, and sediment delivery ratio. These changes can be theoretically derived from an advective-diffusive equation for flood-wave travel in self-similar drainage network.

Base-level, tectonic, and climatic changes can act as perturbations to this homeostatic, self-similar drainage system. The qualitative response model of Thorne and Swift (1991)

suggests that the ratio of sediment accommodation potential to supply controls the concavity of the long-term, equilibrium, alluvial-valley/coastal-plain longitudinal profile. By analysing the potential for channel avulsion on self-similar drainage networks of varying longitudinal concavity, the fluid- mechanical theory predicts: (1) incised alluvial valleys formed during periods of slow sea-level fall preferentially incise into lower coastal-plain sediments, and, thus, the expected fill of these valleys is transitional, estuarine, or marine sediment; (2) entrenched channels formed during periods of slow sea-level fall preferentially incise into lower alluvial-valley sediments, and, thus, the expected fill of these channels are fluvial rather than transitional or marine sediment; and (3) entrenched channels formed during periods of rapid sea-level fall preferentially incise into lower coastal-plain sediments, and, thus, the expected fill of these channels is transitional, estuarine, or marine sediment. These three predictions are consistent with stratigraphic observations made in 15 examples of ancient incised-valley fill.

REFERENCES

ABRAHAMS, A. D., 1984, Channel networks: a geomorphical perspective: Water Resources Research, v. 20, p. 161–168.

BAK, P., TANG, C., AND WIESENFELD, K., 1988, Self-organized criticality: Physical Review A, v. 38, p. 364–374.

BARCLAY, J. E., 1988, The Lower Carboniferous Golata Formation of the Western Canada Basin, in the context of sequence stratigraphy, *in* James, D. and Leckie, D., eds., Sequences, Sedimentology, Surface and Subsurface: Calgary, Canadian Society of Petroleum Geology Memoir 15, p. 1–13.

BATES, R. L., AND JACKSON, J. A., eds., 1980, Glossary of Geology: Falls Church, American Geological Institute, 751 p.

BHOWMIK, N. G., AND STALL, J. B., 1979, Hydraulic geometry and carry capacity of floodplains: University of Illinois, Water Resources Center, Research Report 145, 52 p.

CHORLEY, R. J., SCHUMM, S. A., AND SUGDEN, D. E., 1984, Geomorphology: New York, Methuen, 498 p.

CHURCH, M., AND ROOD, K., 1983, Catalogue of alluvial river channel regime data—Edition 1.0: Department of Geography, University of British Columbia, unnumbered publication, 99 p.

DURY, G. H., 1965, Theoretical implications of underfit streams: Washington, D. C., United States Geological Survey Professional Paper, 452-A, 43 p.

FISK, H. N., 1944, Geological investigation of the alluvial valley of the lower Mississippi river: Vicksburg, Mississippi: Vicksburg, United States Army Corps of Engineers, Mississippi River Commission, 78 p.

GREGORY, K. J., AND WALLING, D. E., 1973, Drainage Basin Form and Process: A Geomorphological Approach: New York, Wiley & Sons, 456 p.

HACK, J. T., 1957, Studies of longitudinal stream profiles in Virginia and Maryland: Washington D. C., United States Geological Survey Professional Paper 294-B, p. 45–94.

HARMS, J. C., 1966, Stratigraphic traps in a valley-fill, western Nebraska: American Association of Petroleum Geologists Bulletin, v. 50, p. 2119–2149.

HORTON, R. E., 1945, Erosional development of streams and their drainage patterns: hydrophysical approach to quantitative morphology: Geologic Society of America Bulletin, v. 56, p. 275–370.

HRADSKY, M., AND GRIFFIN, M., 1984, Sandstone body geometry, reservoir quality and trapping mechanisms in Lower Cretaceous Mannville Group, Taber/Turin area southern Alberta, in Scott, D., and Glass, D., eds., The Mesozoic of Middle North America: Calgary, Canadian Society of Petroleum Geology Memoir 9, p. 401–411.

KNIGHTON, A. D., 1987, River channel adjustment — the downstream dimension, in Richards, K., ed., River Channels: Environment and Process: Oxford, Basil Blackwell Ltd., p. 95–128.

KRAFT, J. C., CHRZASTOWSKI, M. J., BELKNAP, D. F., TOSCANO, M. A. AND FLETCHER, C. F., 1987, The transgressive barrier lagoon coast of Delaware: morphostratigraphy, sedimentary sequences and responses to relative rise in sea level, in Nummedal, D., Pilkey, O., and Howard, J. D., eds., Sea Level Fluctuations and Coastal Evolution: Tulsa, Society of Economic Paleontology and Mineralogy Special Publication 41, p. 129–145.

KRAUS, M., AND MIDDLETON, L., 1987, Dissected paleotopography and base-level changes in a Triassic fluvial sequence: Geology, v. 15, p. 18–21.

LEOPOLD, L., AND MADDOCK, T., JR., 1953, The hydraulic geometry of stream channels and some physiographic implications: Washington D.C., United States Geological Survey Professional Paper 252, 56 p.

LEOPOLD, L. B., WOLMAN, M. G., AND MILLER, J. P., 1964, Fluvial Processes in Geomorphology: San Francisco, W. H. Freeman, 522 p.

MACKEY, S. D., AND BRIDGE, J. S., 1992, A revised Fortran program to simulate alluvial stratigraphy: Computers and Geosciences, v. 18, p. 119–181.

MACKIN, J. H., 1948, Concept of the graded river: Geologic Society of America Bulletin, v. 59, p. 463–511.

MANDELBROT, B. B., 1977, Fractals: Form, Chance and Dimension: New York, W. H. Freeman.

MOORE, R. J., 1984, A dynamic model of basin sediment yield: Water Resources Research, v. 20, p. 89–103.

NISHIWAKI, N., 1978, Simulation of bed-thickness distribution based on waiting time in the Poisson process, in Gill, D., and Merriam, D. F., eds., Geomathematical and Petrophysical Studies in Sedimentology: Oxford, Pergammon Press, p. 17–31.

PALMER, J., JACOBSON, R., AND TRASK, B., 1979, Depositional environments of strata of late Desmoinesian age overlying the Herrin Coal Member in south-western Illinois, in: Palmer, J., and Dutcher, R., eds., Depositional and Structural History of the Pennsylvanian Sytstem of the Illinois Basin, Part 2, Field Trip 9: Urbana, Ninth International Congress of Carboniferous Stratigraphy and Geology, p. 49–62.

PAOLA, C., 1990, A simple basin-filling model for coarse-grained alluvial systems, in Cross, T., ed., Quantitative Dynamic Stratigraphy: Englewood Cliffs, Prentice Hall, p. 363–374.

PRYOR, W., AND POTTER, P., 1979, Sedimentology of a paleovalley fill: Pennsylvanian Kyrock Sandstone in Edmonten and Hart Counties,

Kentucky, in Palmer, J., and Dutcher, R., eds., Depositional and Structural History of the Pennsylvanian Sytstem of the Illinois Basin, Part 2, Field Trip 9: Urbana, Ninth International Congress of Carboniferous Stratigraphy and Geology, p. 49–62.

RAHMANI, R., 1988, Estuarine tidal channel and nearshore sedimentation of late Cretaceous epicontinental sea, Drumheller, Alberta, Canada, in deBoer, P., van Gelder, A., and Nio, S., eds., Tide-Influenced Sedimentary Environments and Facies: Boston, Reidel Publishing Company, p. 433–481.

REINSON, G., CLARK, J., AND FOSCOLOS, A., 1988, Reservoir geology of Crystal Viking field, Lower Cretaceous estuarine tidal channel-bay complex, south-central Alberta: American Association of Petroleum Geologists Bulletin, v. 72, p. 1270–1294.

RHODES, D., 1987, The b-f-m diagram for downstream hydraulic geometry: Geografiska Annaler, v. 69A, p. 147–161.

ROBERT, A., AND ROY, A., 1990, On the fractal interpretation of the mainstream length-drainage area relationship: Water Resources Research, v. 26, p. 839–842.

RODIER, J. A. AND ROCHE, M., 1984, World Catalogue of Maximum Observed Floods: Wallingford, International Association Hydrologic Sciences, Publication 143, 354 p.

ROSS, C. A., AND ROSS, J. R. P., 1988, Late Paleozoic transgressive-regressive deposition, in Wilguss, C., Hastings, B., Kendall, C. G., Posamentier, H., Ross, C., and Van Wagoner, J., eds., Sea-level Changes: An Integrated Approach: Tulsa, Society of Economic Paleontology and Mineralogy Special Publication 42, p. 228–247.

SADLER, P., 1981, Sedimentation rates and the completeness of stratigraphic sections: Journal of Geolology, v. 89, p. 569–584.

SCHEIDEGGER, A. E., 1961, Theoretical Geomorphology: Berlin, Springer-Verlag, 334 p.

SCHUBERT, G., AND LINGENFELTER, R. E., 1974, Power law dependence on time of river flood decay and its relationship to long-term discharge frequency distribution: Water Resources Research, v. 10, p. 98–102.

SCHUMM, S., MOSELY, M., AND WEAVER, W., 1987, Experimental Fluvial Geomorphology: New York, John Wiley and Sons, 413 p.

SHREVE, R. L., 1974, Variation of mainstream length with basin area in river networks: Water Resources Research, v. 10, p. 1167–1177.

SLINGERLAND, R., AND SNOW, R., 1988, Stability analysis of a rejuvenated fluvial system: Zeitschrift für Geomorphologie, v. 67, p. 93–102.

SLOSS, L. L., 1962, Stratigraphic models in exploration: Journal of Sedimentary Petrology, v. 32, p. 415–422.

SMITH, T. R., 1974, Derivation of the hydraulic geometry of steady-state channels from conservation principles and sediment transport laws: Journal of Geology, v. 82, p. 98–104.

SMITH, T. R., AND BRETHERTON, F. P., 1972, Stability and conservation of mass in drainage basin evolution: Water Resources Research, v. 8, p. 1506–1529.

SNOW, R., AND SLINGERLAND, R., 1990, Stream profile adjustment to crustal warping: Journal of Geology, v. 98, p. 699–708.

SONNENBERG, S., 1985, Tectonic and sedimentation model for Morrow Sandstone deposition, Sorrento Field area, Denver Basin, Colorado: The Mountain Geologist, v. 22, p. 180–191.

STOW, D., AND CHANG, H., 1987, Magnitude-frequency relationship of coastal sand delivery by a southern California stream: Geo-Marine Letters, v. 7, p. 217–222.

THORNE, J. A., AND SWIFT, D. J. P., 1991, Sedimentation on continental margins, VI: a regime model for depositional sequences, their component system tracts, and bounding surfaces, in Swift, D. J. P., Oertel, G. F., Tillman, R.W., and Thorne, J. A., eds., Shelf Sand and Sandstone Bodies: Geometry, Facies and Sequence Stratigraphy: Oxford, International Association of Sedimentologists Special Publication 14, p. 189–255.

VAN HINTE, J. E., 1976, A Cretaceous time scale: American Association of Petroleum Geologists Bulletin, v. 60, p. 498–516.

VAN WAGONER, J. C., MITCHUM, R. M., CAMPION, K. M., AND RAHMANIAN, V. D., 1990, Siliciclastic Sequence Stratigraphy in Well Logs, Cores, and Outcrops: Tulsa, American Association of Petroleum Geologists Methods in Exploration Series, 7, 55 p.

WALLING, D. E., 1983, The sediment delivery problem: Journal of Hydrology, v. 65, p. 209–237.

WEIMER, R., 1984, Relation of unconformities, tectonics and sea-level changes, Cretaceous of Western the Interior, in Schlee, J., ed., Interregional Unconformities and Hydrocarbon Accumulations: Tulsa, American Association of Petroleum Geologists Memoir 36, p. 7–35.

WILLGOOSE, G., BRAS, R., AND RODRIGUEZ-ITURBE, I., 1991, Results from a new model of river basin evolution: Earth Surface Processes and Landforms, v. 16, p. 237–254.

ZAITLIN, B., AND SCHULTZ, B., 1984, An estuarine embayment fill model from the Lower Cretaceous Mannville Group, west-central Saskatchewan, Canada, *in* Scott, D., and Glass, D., eds., The Mesozoic of Middle North America: Calgary, Canadian Society of Petroleum Geology Memoir 9, p. 455–469.

APPENDIX 1: STEADY STATE DRAINAGE SYSTEMS

The concept of grade has long been applied to rivers that have adjusted their morphology so that no net deposition or erosion occurs along their longitudinal profiles (Mackin, 1948). This concept can be extended to integrated drainage systems by considering systems in which the areas A_r, A_l, and A_v do not change with time, i.e.:

$$\frac{\partial A_v}{\partial t} = \frac{\partial A_r}{\partial t} = \frac{\partial A_1}{\partial t} = 0 \qquad (a1)$$

where A_r, A_l, and A_v are as defined in equation 4. Substituting expressions 10 and a1 into expression 9,

$$\frac{\partial L_{\text{trib}}}{\partial t} - \Delta x \cdot \frac{\partial L_{\text{trunk}}}{\partial x \partial t} + (1 - sd_{\text{graded}}) \cdot \mathring{a} \cdot w / sd_{\text{graded}} = 0 \qquad (a2)$$

Neglecting the first term involving tributaries, this reduces to:

$$sd_{\text{graded}} = \frac{\mathring{a} \cdot w}{\Delta x \cdot \dfrac{\partial L_{\text{trunk}}}{\partial x \partial t} + \mathring{a} \cdot w} \qquad (a3)$$

Figure A1 shows the predicted sediment delivery ratio as a function of drainage area from equation a3. The predicted variation of sediment delivery is in excellent agreement with the worldwide data compiled by Walling (1983).

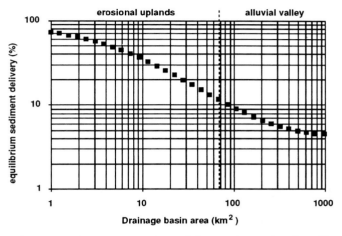

FIG. A1.—The predicted sediment delivery ratio as a function of basin-drainage area for basins that are under steady-state conditions (see Appendix 1).

THE STRATIGRAPHIC ORGANIZATION OF INCISED-VALLEY SYSTEMS ASSOCIATED WITH RELATIVE SEA-LEVEL CHANGE

BRIAN A. ZAITLIN
PanCanadian Petroleum Ltd., Calgary, Alberta T2P 2S5 Canada
ROBERT W. DALRYMPLE
Department of Geological Sciences, Queen's University, Kingston, Ontario K7L 3N6, Canada
AND
RON BOYD
Department of Geology, University of Newcastle, Newcastle, New South Wales 2308, Australia

ABSTRACT: The most common form of incised-valley system develops during a lowering in base level associated with a fall in relative sea level. This form of incised-valley system provides the most complete, and at times, the only evidence of lowstand to early-transgressive deposition in shelf and/or shallow ramp depositional settings. Incised-valley systems of this type are characterized by a fluvially-eroded, elongate paleotopographic low, generally larger than a single channel, which displays an abrupt basinward shift of facies at its base. The valley fill typically begins to accumulate during base-level rise, and may contain deposits of the following highstand and subsequent sea-level cycles.

Two major varieties of incised valley occur during a lowering of sea level: (i) incised-valley systems that have their headwaters in a (mountainous) hinterland and cross a "fall line" (or knickpoint) are here considered to be *piedmont incised-valley systems*, and (ii) incised-valley systems that are localized within low-gradient coastal plains and that do not cross a "fall line" are here termed *coastal-plain incised-valley systems*. An incised-valley system that is filled during one depositional sequence is termed a *simple fill*, whereas a *compound fill* records multiple cycles of incision and deposition.

The fill of an incised-valley system that forms in response to a lowering of base level is divisible into three segments: (i) the seaward reaches of the incised valley (SEGMENT 1) is characterized by backstepping (lowstand to transgressive) fluvial and estuarine deposits, overlain by transgressive marine sands and shelf muds; (ii) the middle reach of the incised valley (SEGMENT 2) consists of the drowned-valley estuarine complex that is developed at the time of maximum transgression, overlying a lowstand to transgressive succession of fluvial and estuarine deposits like those in segment 1; and (iii) the innermost reach of the incised valley (SEGMENT 3) lies headward of the transgressive estuarine limit, and extends to the point where changes in relative sea level no longer control fluvial style. Segment 3 is characterized by fluvial deposits throughout its depositional history; however, the fluvial style may change systematically due to changes in base level and the rate of creation of accommodation space.

The stratigraphic organization of these incised-valley systems is characterized by a number of stratigraphically-significant surfaces that differ greatly in their origin, geographic extent, and chronostratigraphic significance. Filling of the valley may begin during the lowstand, but typically continues through the succeeding transgression. Thus, the *transgressive surface* (i.e., the flooding surface separating the Lowstand Systems Tract and the Transgressive Systems Tract) should be present in the lower portion of the fill. It may occur within fluvial deposits or at the fluvial-estuarine contact in segments 1 and 2, and at a correlative change in fluvial depositional style in segment 3. Erosion by tidal currents in tidal inlets or other tidal channels creates a *tidal ravinement surface* which is confined to the incised valley in segment 1 and the seaward part of segment 2. More regional erosion by waves at the retreating shoreface produces a *wave ravinement surface* that separates fluvial and/or estuarine sediments from overlying marine deposits in segment 1. Both of these surfaces are diachronous, and could become amalgamated with the sequence boundary. In the idealized case, a *maximum flooding surface* may extend throughout the incised-valley fill, passing from its typical position within marine shales in segment 1, through the center of the estuarine deposits in segment 2, into fluvial sediments in segment 3. However, rapid relative sea-level fall after the end of the transgression, or renewed sea-level rise after valley filling (but before the onset of significant progradation), may prevent development of the maximum flooding surface. Compound valley fills may contain multiple sets of these surfaces.

INTRODUCTION

An *incised-valley system* consists of both an incised valley and its depositional fill, and may provide the most complete (and at times, only) evidence of lowstand to transgressive deposition in shelf-slope and/or shallow-ramp, marine depositional settings (Suter and others, 1987; Van Wagoner and others, 1990; Allen and Posamentier, this volume; Belknap and others, this volume; Thomas and Anderson, this volume; Fig. 1). Incised valleys have been recognized for many years (e.g., Fisk, 1944), and are known throughout the geologic record, from the Precambrian (e.g., Dyson and von der Borch, this volume; Levy and others, this volume) through to the Quaternary and modern units (e.g., Allen and Posamentier, this volume; Ashley and Sheridan, this volume; Belknap and others, this volume; Kindinger and others, this volume; Roy, this volume; Thomas and Anderson, this volume). See Dalrymple and others (this volume) for a more complete historical summary.

Interest in incised-valley systems is based upon their increasing significance in three related contexts.

1) Recent application of sequence-stratigraphic principles to the stratigraphic record, and the recognition of the association between incised valleys and regionally mappable unconformity (i.e., sequence-bounding) surfaces. When recognized, these surfaces are a major key to the development of a chronostratigraphic framework that provides a better understanding of reservoir distribution in shallow-marine and non-marine depositional environments (e.g., Vail and others, 1977; Weimer, 1983, 1984; Posamentier and Vail, 1988; Posamentier and others, 1988; Van Wagoner and others, 1988, 1990; Galloway, 1989). Thus, the recognition of incised valleys is an important tool in the correct subdivision of the stratigraphic record.

2) The recognition that economically-significant quantities of hydrocarbons are produced from reservoirs hosted by the fill of incised-valley systems (e.g., Harms, 1966; Berg, 1976; Van Wagoner and others, 1990; Zaitlin and Shultz, 1990; Dolson and others, 1991; Brown, 1993). Indeed, Brown (1993) has estimated that approximately

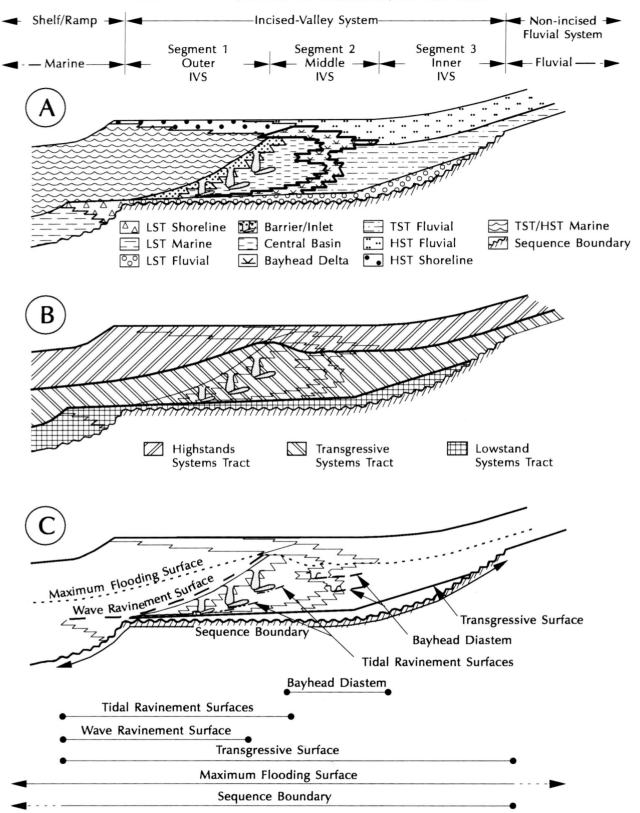

FIG. 1.—Idealized longitudinal section of a simple incised-valley system showing the distribution of: (**A**) depositional environments; (**B**) system tracts; and (**C**) key stratigraphic surfaces. See text for discussion of the segments and surfaces. Note that segments 1 and 3 are typically much longer than segment 2, and are compressed here for ease of presentation. LST = lowstand systems tract; TST = transgressive systems tract; HST = highstand systems tract.

25% of all off-structure clastic reservoirs containing conventional hydrocarbons, world-wide, are produced from lowstand to transgressive, incised-valley deposits. Thus, the internal facies architecture of incised-valley fills is of critical importance to both the exploration for, and exploitation of, hydrocarbon reserves.

3) Finally, there is heightened concern about global warming and the associated rise of sea level that will flood low-lying and heavily-populated, coastal-valley areas (Komar and Enfield, 1987; Davis and Clifton, 1987; Demarest and Kraft, 1987). An increased understanding of the evolutionary changes that occur within incised-valley systems, based on the integrated study of modern, Quaternary and ancient analogs, may allow better prediction of the environmental effects and permit a better response to future sea-level change.

Objectives

The factors discussed above indicate that incised-valley systems are of greater importance than their volumetric contribution to the stratigraphic record would suggest. Despite this, there have been no attempts to develop a "generalized" facies model (cf. Walker, 1992) for the entire incised-valley system; models that do exist concentrate on specific segments of, or depositional styles within, incised-valley systems (e.g., Roy, 1984, this volume; Allen, 1991; Allen and Posamentier, 1993, this volume; Dalrymple and others, 1992; Reinson, 1992; Schumm and Ethridge, this volume; Thomas and Anderson, this volume). The aim of this paper is to present an idealized facies model for an incised-valley system that is produced by fluvial incision associated with a drop in relative sea level (Figs. 1, 2). The model will be presented in a sequence-stratigraphic context, generally following the methodology of Van Wagoner and others (1988, 1990). The model will incorporate a synthesis of the papers published in this volume, and original work stemming from research in modern and ancient incised-valley systems. We recognize that our knowledge of incised-valley systems is incomplete, and acknowledge that our model will require refinement as additional data become available.

Two separate (but inter-connected) issues arise when one is attempting to develop a generalized model for incised-valley systems. The first issue is the establishment of criteria by which an incised-valley system may be recognized in the stratigraphic record. The second issue is the description of the (predictable) stratigraphic organization of the incised-valley fill. This paper will start by defining the nature of an incised-valley system, and will then summarize the recognition criteria that stem from this definition, and address the nature and stratigraphic organization of the incised-valley fill. The paper will conclude by commenting on aspects of the variability and preservation potential of deposits within incised-valley systems.

BASIC ATTRIBUTES OF INCISED-VALLEY SYSTEMS

Schumm and Ethridge (this volume) and Thorne (this volume) have noted that several factors promote fluvial incision, including (but not limited to): (i) *eustatic sea-level*

fall and (ii) *tectonic uplift*, both of which result in relative base-level fall (and commonly an increase in stream gradient); (iii) *climatic change* resulting in increased discharge; and (iv) *stream capture* that increases discharge in the combined system. Despite the multiplicity of causes of incision, we will limit our discussion to incised-valley systems that develop as a result of fluvial incision caused by relative sea-level fall (factors (i) and (ii) above), because such systems are associated with sequence boundaries and appear to be the most common type preserved in the geological record.

Definition

In this context, an **incised-valley system** is here defined as a "*fluvially-eroded, elongate topographic low that is typically larger than a single channel form, and is characterized by an abrupt seaward shift of depositional facies across a regionally mappable sequence boundary at its base. The fill typically begins to accumulate during the next base-level rise, and may contain deposits of the following highstand and subsequent sea-level cycles.*" Although exceptions may exist, incised-valley systems that occur in shallow-gradient, shelf/ramp settings typically extend landward from a lowstand delta at the mouth of the incised-valley, to a point beyond which relative sea-level change no longer influences fluvial erosion and deposition (Van Wagoner and others, 1990; Figs. 1, 2B). Above this point we consider that no incised valley (in the sense of the definition proposed above) exists; instead, a *non-incised, fluvial-channel system* feeds into the incised valley, producing a through-going fluvial network (Figs. 1, 2). In the case where sea level falls below the shelf/slope break, the incised-valley may traverse the entire shelf/ramp and transport sediment to the slope, so that the mouth of the incised valley feeds directly into a submarine canyon-fan complex (e.g., Van Wagoner and others, 1988, 1990; Posamentier and Erskin, 1991).

Fundamental Characteristics of Incised-Valley Systems

The criteria for the recognition of an incised-valley system represent the initial step in defining a generalized facies model. In light of the definition and preceding discussion, the following criteria can be identified (Fig. 3; Van Wagoner and others, 1988, 1990). (i) The valley is a negative (i.e., erosional) paleotopographic feature, the base of which truncates underlying strata including any regional markers that may be present. (ii) The base and walls of the incised-valley system represent a sequence boundary that may be correlated to an erosional (or hiatal) surface outside the valley (i.e., on the interfluve areas). This erosional surface may be modified by later transgression, forming an E/T surface (Plint and others, 1992), or a combined flooding surface and sequence boundary (an FS/SB surface; Van Wagoner and others, 1990). The sequence boundary may be mantled by a pebble lag, and/or characterized by burrows belonging to the *Glossifungites* ichnofacies (MacEachern and others, 1992; MacEachern and Pemberton, this volume). On the interfluves, the exposure surface may be characterized by a soil or rooted horizon (Leckie and Singh,

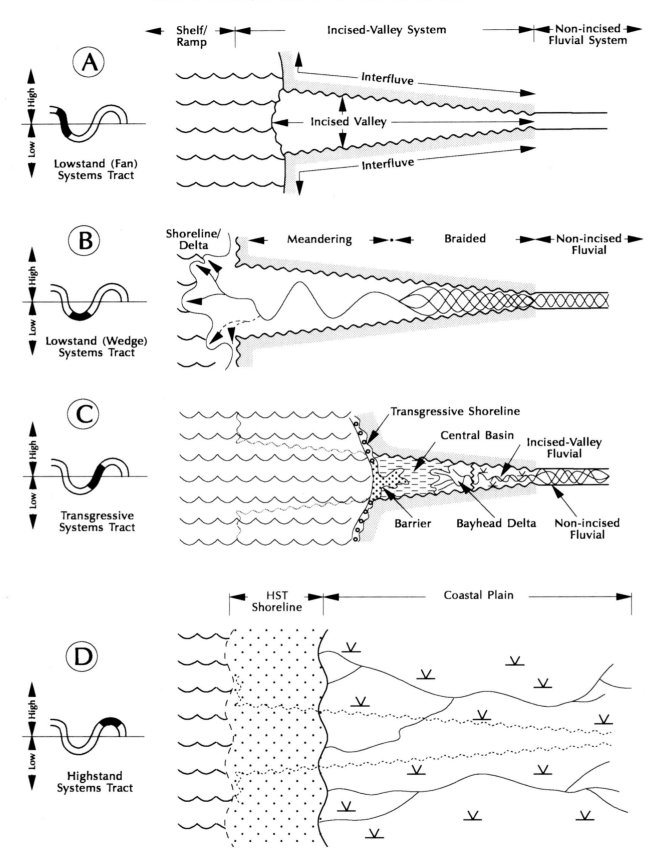

1991). (iii) The base of the incised-valley fill exhibits an erosional juxtaposition of more proximal (landward) facies over more distal deposits (i.e., a "basinward shift in facies," *sensu* Van Wagoner and others, 1990). Finally, (iv) depositional markers within the deposits of the incised-valley fill will *onlap* the valley walls.

It is critical when identifying the extent of the incised-valley system to document the geometry of the sequence boundary, both within and outside of the incised valley. The paleotopography of the incised-valley network may allow one to determine the paleodrainage direction as an aid in paleogeographic reconstruction. A variety of techniques have been employed to identify and map paleovalleys, including: (i) seismic or geological structural mapping of the erosional surface from wireline logs (e.g., Zaitlin and Shultz, 1984, 1990; Van Wagoner and others, 1990); (ii) third- or higher-order residual mapping of the erosional surface in areas affected by post-depositional structuring (e.g., Zaitlin and Shultz, 1984, 1990); and (iii) detailed isopach mapping of the interpreted fill, or of an interval between the unconformity and an overlying horizontal marker that extends over the interfluves, to locate anomalously thick sections confined to the paleotopographic lows (e.g., Seiver, 1951; Van Wagoner and others, 1990).

Piedmont and Coastal Plain Incised-Valley Systems

Incised-valley systems may reach lengths in excess of 100's of kilometers, widths to 10's of kilometers, and depths to 100's of meters (e.g., Christie-Blick and others, 1990; Leckie and Singh, 1991; Ricketts, 1991; Ashley and Sheriden, this volume). These systems may cross physiographic, lithologic and/or tectonic boundaries which may have significant affects on fluvial style (Miall, 1992; Schumm, 1993, Schumm and Ethridge, this volume), but nevertheless, two major physiographic types of incised valley occur in the stratigraphic record (Fig. 4). Incised-valley systems that have their headwaters in a (mountainous) hinterland, and that cross a "fall line" where there is a significant reduction in gradient, are here considered to be *piedmont incised-valley systems*. Incised-valley systems that are confined to low-gradient coastal plains and that do not cross a "fall line" are termed *coastal-plain incised-valley systems*.

Piedmont incised-valley systems are characterized by a longer fluvial reach than coastal-plain systems, and are commonly associated spatially with underlying structural features in the hinterland. As a result, these river systems may be longer lived than coastal-plain systems. Also, piedmont systems more commonly contain coarse-grained, immature, fluvially-derived sediment, whereas coastal-plain systems are usually filled by finer-grained and more mature

deposits recycled from coastal-plain sediments. In both piedmont and coastal-plain systems, marine-derived sediment is preserved in the estuarine portion of the valley fill (see below). It is possible to have coastal-plain and piedmont incised-valley systems adjacent to each other in coastal areas (e.g., Hayes and Sexton, 1989; Fig. 4).

Simple and Compound Incised-Valley Fills

The fill of any incised-valley system may be classed as either *simple* or *compound* depending on the absence or presence, respectively, of multiple, internal sequence boundaries (Fig. 5; see Dalrymple and others, this volume). If the valley is filled completely during one lowstand-transgressive-highstand sequence, the fill is termed a "simple fill" (e.g., Rahmani, 1988; Wood and Hopkins, 1989; Fig. 5A). A "compound fill" records multiple cycles of incision and deposition resulting from fluctuations in base level, and is therefore punctuated by one or more sequence boundaries in addition to the main sequence boundary at the base of the incised valley (e.g., Clark and Reinson, 1990; Fig. 5B). Due to the presence of structural control on their location, piedmont river systems commonly exist through more than one sequence of sea-level fall and rise; thus, their incised valleys commonly contain a compound fill. Coastal-plain systems are more likely to exist through only one regressive-transgression cycle and typically have a simple fill.

MODEL FOR A SIMPLE INCISED-VALLEY FILL

Although many incised-valley systems are characterized by compound fills (e.g., Suter and Berryhill, 1985; Suter and others, 1987; Ainsworth and Walker, this volume; Archer and others, this volume; Clifton, this volume), for simplicity and ease of discussion we will consider here the case of a piedmont incised-valley system, which is cut and filled in a single cycle of 4th or 5th order (Van Wagoner and others, 1988, 1990). We will also assume that fluvial sediment supply and the rate of transgression are constant. These assumptions will allow us to model an idealized fill without adding unnecessary complexity. We believe that, by understanding the geometry of this type of fill, it will then be easier to appreciate and predict variations in facies architecture associated with more complex, compound fills. In addition, we assume that waves are more significant than tides in the coastal zone, and that any estuaries that develop are wave-dominated (*sensu* Dalrymple and others, 1992), as this is the situation most commonly documented in ancient incised-valley systems.

Stratigraphic Organization: Overview

Following Dalrymple and others (this volume), a threefold, longitudinal subdivision is proposed for the incised-

---

Fɪɢ. 2.—Idealized plan view of a simple, piedmont incised-valley system showing its evolution over one complete sea-level cycle (sea-level fall to subsequent highstand). (**A**) Lowstand (fan) time showing the incised-valley system passing headward into a non-incised fluvial-channel system. The junction between the two is the knickpoint. (**B**) Lowstand (wedge) time showing a lowstand delta at the mouth of the incised valley, and the beginning of fluvial deposition throughout the incised-valley system. (**C**) Transgressive systems tract time showing development of a tripartite, wave-dominated estuarine system within the incised valley. (**D**) Highstand time with a progradational shoreface and alluvial plain that extends beyond the margins of the buried incised valley.

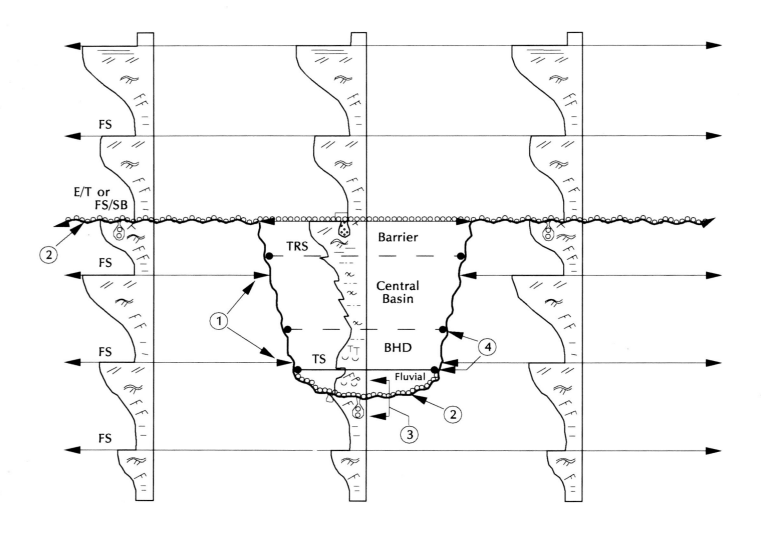

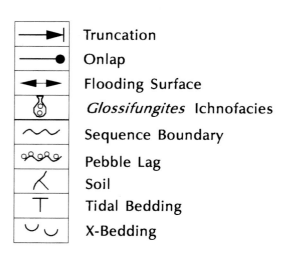

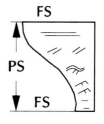

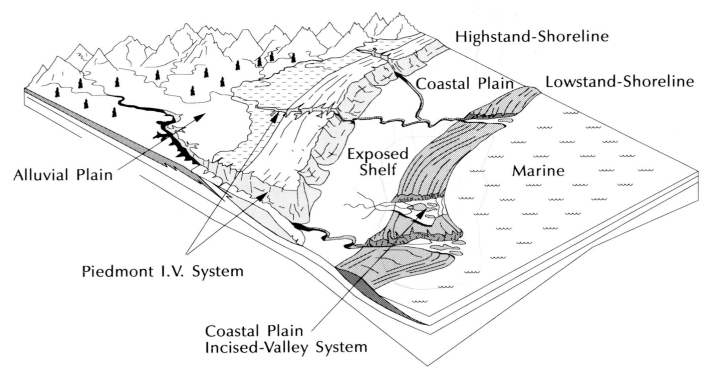

FIG. 4.—Schematic view of a coastal zone showing the distinction between piedmont and coastal-plain incised-valley systems. Modified after Rosenthal (1988) paleogeographic interpretation of the Lower Cretaceous Glauconitic Sandstone in Alberta, Canada.

valley fill (Figs. 1, 2, 6). This three-fold subdivision reflects the unique depositional/stratigraphic organization which results from transgression followed by highstand deposition.

As relative sea level falls, the entire length of the incised valley is characterized by (net) fluvial erosion which creates the basal sequence boundary (Fig. 2A). When relative sea level reaches its lowest level and starts to rise, fluvial deposition begins at the mouth of the incised-valley system (Fig. 2B), and will extend progressively further up the valley as the transgression proceeds (e.g., Belknap and others, this volume; Thomas and Anderson, this volume). It is possible, therefore, to have continuing erosion and sediment bypass in the upper (headward) regions of the incised valley as deposition is occurring in the lower (seaward) reaches during "lowstand time."

Ideally, the fill of the seaward portion of the incised-valley (Fig. 1, segment 1) is characterized by backstepping (lowstand to transgressive) fluvial and estuarine deposits, overlain by transgressive marine sands and/or shelf muds (e.g., Thomas and Anderson, this volume). The middle reach of the incised valley (Fig. 1, segment 2) consists of the

drowned-valley estuarine complex that existed at the time of maximum transgression, overlying a lowstand to transgressive succession of fluvial and estuarine deposits like those in segment 1. The innermost reach of the incised valley (Fig. 1, segment 3) is developed headward of the transgressive estuarine limit and extends to the landward limit of fluvial incision (i.e., the knickpoint; Schumm, 1993). This segment is characterized by fluvial deposits throughout its depositional history; however, the fluvial style will change systematically due to changes in the rate of change of base level (Gibling, 1991; Wright and Marriott, 1993). The effect of base-level change will decrease inland until eventually climatic, tectonic and sediment-supply factors become the dominant controls on the nature of the fluvial system. The following sections will present in more detail the characteristics of each of these three segments (Figs. 1, 2, 6).

Segment 1—Outer Incised Valley

The outer incised valley (segment 1) extends from the lowstand mouth of the incised valley to the point where the

FIG. 3.—Schematic diagram illustrating the criteria for the recognition of an incised-valley system: 1—truncation of underlying regional markers by a sequence boundary; 2—regional correlation of the sequence boundary from the base of the incised valley onto the interfluves; 3—a basinward ("downward") shift in facies across sequence boundary; and 4—onlap of surfaces within the incised valley onto the sequence boundary. SB = sequence boundary; FS = flooding surface; P.S. = parasequence; E/T = surface of subaerial erosion and transgression; FS/SB = flooding surface/sequence boundary; TS = transgressive surface; TRS = tidal ravinement surface; BHD = bayhead delta; HCS = hummocky cross-stratification.

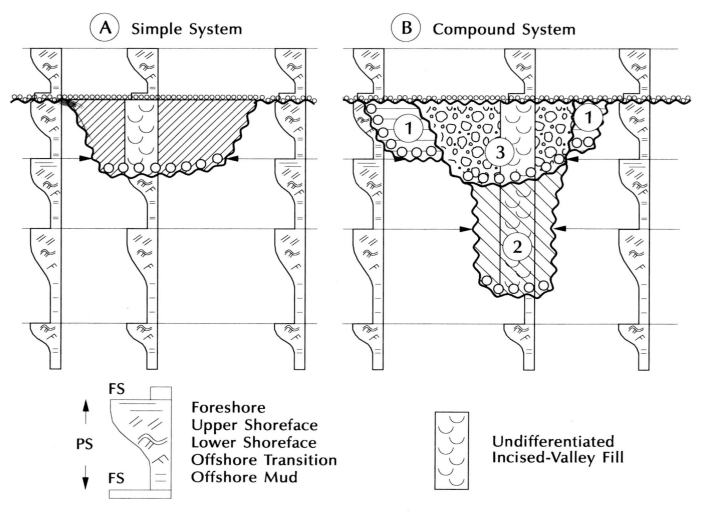

Ⓐ Simple System　　　　　　Ⓑ Compound System

FS

PS

FS

Foreshore
Upper Shoreface
Lower Shoreface
Offshore Transition
Offshore Mud

Undifferentiated
Incised-Valley Fill

FIG. 5.—Schematic diagram illustrating (A) simple and (B) compound incised-valley systems. Numbers 1–3 refer to successive episodes of erosion and deposition within the incised valley. PS = parasequence; FS = flooding surface.

shoreline stabilizes at the beginning of highstand progradation (Figs. 1, 6). As in the other segments, this reach of the valley initially undergoes fluvial incision with the lowering of base level (Figs. 2A, B). Sediment is by-passed to the mouth of the valley where it is deposited as either a lowstand delta and/or prograding shoreline (Fig. 2B). Within segment 1, this period is represented by the sequence boundary, which may be overlain by lowstand fluvial deposits (Fig. 6, profile 1). As sea level begins to rise and the lower reaches of the system are transgressed, the incised valley changes from being a conduit for fluvially-eroded sediment, to the site of fluvial, and (subsequently) estuarine deposition (Fig. 2C). Fluvial deposition, although initiated during the late lowstand, continues during the early stages of transgression, with the locus of deposition shifting landward as relative sea level rises and the shoreline transgresses (Wright and Marriott, 1993; Wescott, 1993). Thus, the boundary between the lowstand and transgressive systems tracts (i.e., the transgressive surface) may lie within the fluvial deposits rather than at their top (cf. Allen and Posamentier, 1993, this volume).

The fluvial style (i.e., braided, meandering, anastomosed, or straight) within the incised valley is dependent on a variety of factors including the sediment supply, grain size, discharge, valley gradient, and rate of transgression (Schumm, 1977, 1993; Schumm and Ethridge, this volume). These variables will likely change during the rise in sea level associated with the marine transgression (Gibling, 1991; Wright and Marriott, 1993; Törquist, 1993). Thus, in the simplest case where all other factors remain constant, the character of the lowstand to transgressive fluvial sediments should change vertically as the depositional gradient and capacity of the fluvial system decreases as the shoreline approaches. This change would most likely result in an overall upward-fining fluvial succession, with a change from higher-energy (sandy braided?) to lower-energy (mixed sand/mud meandering?) fluvial deposits. An excellent example of this is provided by the Quaternary sediments in the Mississippi River incised valley (Fisk, 1944). Abrupt changes in style within this succession may correlate with marine flooding surfaces developed farther seaward in the valley.

The thickness of the basal fluvial succession, and the extent to which the predicted changes in fluvial style are developed, may be variable along the length of segment 1. The ultimate thickness is controlled by the accommodation space developed during the rise in sea level (Jervey, 1988), with the major factor being the ratio between the rate of fluvial-sediment input and the rate of sea-level rise. In the situation where sea-level rise greatly outpaces fluvial input, transgression is rapid, and the thickness of the fluvial deposits will be less than in the case where rapid fluvial input occurs during a slow rise in sea level. In the special case where sediment input matches sea-level rise, the fluvial deposits will aggrade vertically. In all cases, the preserved thickness of the fluvial succession may be affected by subsequent erosion associated with transgression.

As the transgression proceeds, the estuarine conditions which are established in the seaward end of the valley migrate landward. In a wave-dominated estuarine setting, the first estuarine deposits over the fluvial sediments will be *bayhead-delta* (distributary channel, levee, and inter-distributary bay) deposits (Figs. 2, 6, profile 1). Due to continued transgression, *central-basin* deposits will then overlie the bayhead delta with a gradational facies contact. The central-basin deposits will in turn be overlain by the *estuarine barrier* (cf. Boyd and others, 1992; Dalrymple and others, 1992). This contact may be gradational, but is equally likely to coincide with the erosional base of a tidal (inlet) channel. In the latter case, it is referred to as a *tidal ravinement surface* (Allen and Posamentier, 1993).

As transgression proceeds, the shoreface passes the former location of the estuary. Wave erosion associated with shoreface retreat produces a *wave ravinement surface* which will truncate the underlying estuarine deposits (e.g., Ashley and Sheridan, this volume; Belknap and others, this volume; Kindinger and others, this volume; Thomas and Anderson, this volume; Fig. 6, profile 1). This surface may then be overlain by transgressive shoreface to nearshore sands. Finally, the valley will be capped by open-marine mudstones associated with the succeeding highstand. The landward limit of these mudstones is an indicator of the inner end of segment 1.

Segment 2—Middle Incised Valley

Segment 2 lies between the inner end of segment 1 and the marine/estuarine limit at the time of maximum flooding (Figs. 1, 6); it therefore corresponds to the area occupied by the drowned-valley estuary at the end of the transgression (Fig. 2C). In this segment, the sequence boundary is overlain by lowstand to early transgressive fluvial deposits similar to those in segment 1 (Fig. 6). These are in turn overlain by transgressive estuarine facies, but in this segment the nature of the overlying estuarine succession varies along the length of the segment (cf. Dalrymple and others, 1992, their Figure 13) because the estuarine facies are (ideally) preserved with the spatial distribution they would have had in the contemporaneous estuary.

Near its seaward end, the succession is similar to that in segment 1, with bayhead-delta sediments overlain by central-basin deposits that are in turn capped by estuary-mouth, barrier sands. Because open-marine conditions do not transgress into this segment, the barrier sediments are overlain by highstand fluvial deposits (Fig. 6, profile 2). In the middle portion of segment 2, barrier sands are absent, and central-basin deposits coarsen upwards into progradational, bayhead delta and fluvial sediments of the succeeding highstand (Fig. 6, profile 3). At the headward end of segment 2, central-basin sediments are absent, and the bayhead delta is overlain directly by highstand fluvial deposits (Fig. 6, profile 4). The most landward limit of detectable marine influence (tidal features or brackish-water traces) is taken as the inner end of segment 2. This point corresponds with the inner end of the estuary as defined by Dalrymple and others (1992), and also with the "bayline" of Posamentier and others (1988) and Allen and Posamentier (1993).

Segment 3—Inner Incised Valley

The innermost segment (Segment 3) of the incised-valley system lies between the transgressive marine/estuarine limit and the landward limit of incision (Figs. 1, 2, 6). This segment may extend for 10's to 100's of kilometers above the limit of marine/estuarine influence (Shanley and others, 1992; Schumm, 1993; Levy and others, this volume). The fill of this segment will be entirely fluvial, and may be braided, meandering, anastomosed and/or straight in character, depending on a variety of factors including sediment supply, gradient, discharge, sediment size, etc.. However, relative sea-level and accommodation changes associated with the lowstand-transgression-highstand cycle influence sedimentation, and may produce a predictable vertical succession of fluvial styles (Fig. 6, profile 5; Gibling, 1991; Wright and Marriott, 1993). Lowstand fluvial deposits would be expected to be relatively thin as the fluvial system would have been erosional, or have acted as a transport conduit (a bypass zone) at that time. Late lowstand to early transgressive deposits at the base of the fill may be characterized by relatively coarse-grained, amalgamated channel deposits. As transgression proceeds, an overall upward-fining succession would be expected to develop as the gradient and stream capacity decrease. The deposits which accumulated during times of rising base level should contain more isolated, channel-sandstone bodies, interbedded with a higher percentage of overbank deposits (e.g., Törquist, 1993). Freshwater organic facies (e.g., peat or lacustrine carbonates) might be abundant and the soils less mature than those associated with the lowstand (Cross, 1988). The overlying highstand deposits may be expected to coarsen upward, due to progradation in response to decreasing rates of base-level rise and accommodation creation (Schumm, 1993).

Summary

As the foregoing idealized model illustrates, *the fill of an incised valley may be extremely complex*, even in the case where many simplifying assumptions are introduced. No single facies succession (i.e., upward-coarsening, upward-fining, blocky, etc.) occurs along the entire length of the system (Fig. 6). Data compiled by J. Barclay and F. Krause (pers. commun., 1993) suggest that transgressive successions containing estuarine deposits capped by marine shales are the most common expression of an incised-valley fill.

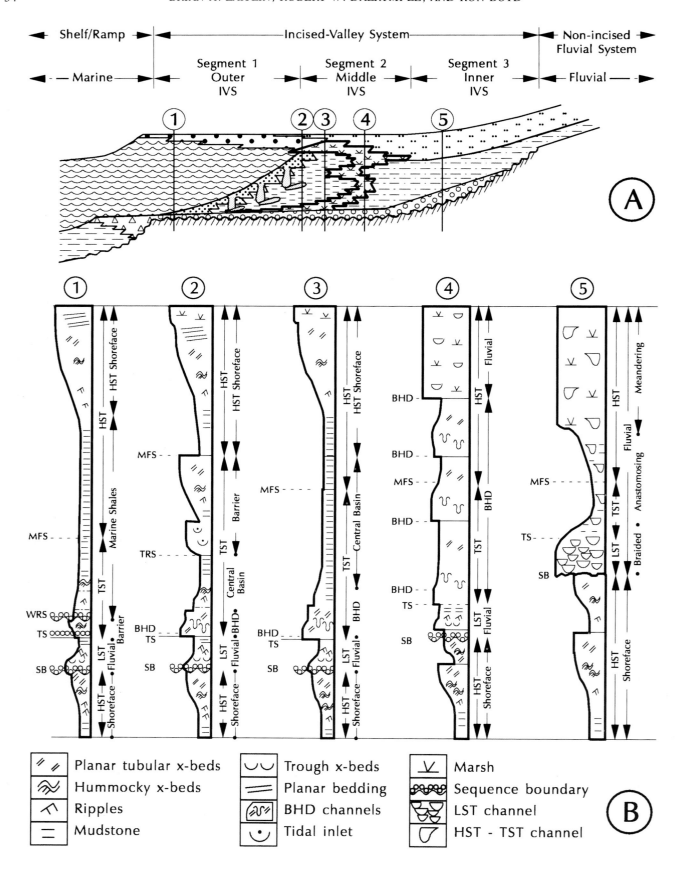

Possible reasons for this are: (i) segment 1, where such successions form, is longer than segments 2 and 3 in most cases and (ii) the deposits of segment 3 have not been fully recognized as incised-valley deposits.

STRATIGRAPHIC SURFACES

The infill of incised-valley systems is characterized by a number of stratigraphically-significant surfaces (Figs. 1C, 6). The surface that defines the valley form is the most regionally extensive of these. It is the *sequence boundary*, which develops through a combination of fluvial incision within the valley form and subaerial exposure of the interfluves. The specific facies expression of the sequence boundary depends, in part, on the location with respect to the valley form (see Van Wagoner and others, 1988, 1990).

In the general case, the sediments immediately overlying the sequence boundary consist of lowstand fluvial deposits. Commonly, however, a large part of the valley fill is deposited in response to rising base levels, and thus belongs to the transgressive systems tract. Consequently, the *transgressive surface*, which is defined as the flooding surface separating the progradational or aggradational, lowstand systems tract from the retrogradational, transgressive systems tract (Van Wagoner and others, 1988), should occur low in the incised-valley fill. This transgressive surface may lie within the basal fluvial deposits, especially in cases where these deposits are relatively thick (e.g., Nichols and others, this volume; Thomas and Anderson, this volume). Another important horizon low in the fill in segments 1 and 2 is the estuarine-fluvial contact, which commonly represents the first, or *initial flooding surface*. Allen and Posamentier (1993, this volume) have utilized this surface as the transgressive surface because little fluvial sediment accumulated in the Gironde valley during the rapid Holocene transgression. In the general case, however, this surface is a facies boundary (Figs. 1, 6), and has limited chronostratigraphic significance. Thus, great care is needed to define the transgressive surface within incised-valley systems.

If the transgression was intermittent, due to variations in the rate of sea-level rise or sediment supply, backstepping parasequences may be developed within the transgressive estuarine and marine portions of the valley fill in segments 1 and 2 (Thomas and Anderson, this volume). These "stillstand," progradational episodes will be separated by additional *flooding surfaces*, which may or may not be recognizable in the fluvial deposits of segment 3.

In segment 1 and the seaward portion of segment 2 of the incised valley, the next higher surface is the *tidal ravinement surface* (Allen, 1991; Allen and Posamentier, 1993, this volume; Belknap and others, this volume; "tidal-inlet diastem" of Nichols and others, this volume), which is produced by erosion in the base of the deepest tidal inlet or other tidal channel. Typically, these channels are associated with the estuary-mouth, barrier/flood-tidal-delta complex of wave-dominated estuaries, or with the sand bars and flats which extend along the length of tide-dominated estuaries. In tide-dominated shelf settings, tidal ravinement may also take place on the shelf (Dalrymple, 1992; Harris, this volume). Note that this surface is diachronous, becoming younger up the valley. Special care is needed not to confuse this surface with a fluvially-incised sequence boundary. Unlike the sequence boundary, this surface is generally confined to the incised valley (Allen and Posamentier, this volume) and cannot be correlated regionally.

As transgression continues, the *wave ravinement surface* is developed as the shoreface migrates up-system and erodes pre-existing barrier sediments (Swift, 1968), and perhaps also central-basin, bayhead-delta and fluvial deposits if wave base is sufficiently deep (Allen and Posamentier, this volume; Ashley and Sheridan, this volume; Belknap and others, this volume). Unlike the tidal ravinement surface which has a channelized morphology and is generally localized within the incised valley, the wave ravinement surface is relatively planar and of regional extent, extending over both the incised valley and the interfluves (Fig. 1). This surface is typically overlain by an upward-fining (transgressive) succession, possibly containing retrogradationally-stacked parasequences. Because the wave ravinement surface forms at the shoreface, it is only present in segment 1. It is not present in tide-dominated settings, although a tidal erosion surface formed on the shelf may take its place (Dalrymple, 1992).

The *maximum flooding surface* (MFS), which corresponds to the time of maximum transgression, is the next higher surface in the succession (Fig. 1C, 6). Its physical expression varies markedly between the three segments. In segment 1, it occurs within the marine shales which overlie the wave ravinement surface. As discussed by Loutit and others (1988), the MFS on the shelf is commonly a condensed section, with abundant biogenic carbonate, phosphate and above-normal levels of radioactive material. The MFS passes landward through the sands of the estuary-mouth barrier and initial highstand shoreline, and into the estuarine deposits of segment 2. In the central part of segment 2, it lies within the central-basin deposits where they are sandwiched between the underlying transgressive, and overlying regressive, bayhead-delta sediments (Fig. 6, profile 3). Within segment 3, the MFS may be difficult to recognize, but it may be associated with the fluvial sediments that have the most distal character and are the finest grained (Fig. 6, profile 5).

Nichol and others (this volume) and Roy (this volume) describe a *fluvial-channel diastem* (or bay-head diastem) located at the base of the distributary channels in the bayhead

---

FIG. 6.—(A) Idealized longitudinal section of a simple, incised-valley system showing the location of the schematic vertical profiles illustrated in (B). LST = lowstand systems tract; TST = transgressive systems tract; HST = highstand systems tract; SB = sequence boundary; TS = transgressive surface; WRS = wave ravinement surface; MFS = maximum flooding surface; FCD = fluvial channel diastem; TRS = tidal ravinement surface; BHD = bayhead delta. No particular horizontal or vertical scale intended.

delta (Figs. 1C, 6, profiles 2–4). The fluvial erosion which produces this surface can cause coarse-grained fluvial sediments to directly overlie bayhead-delta or central-basin estuarine deposits. In the extreme case, this surface can cut down through transgressive and lowstand fluvial deposits and amalgamate with, or modify, the sequence boundary. This surface may occur in the landward parts of backstepping parasequences in segment 1, or beneath fluvial deposits of the early highstand in segment 2. Channel switching may not be 100% effective in cutting down to a common level so that this surface may have significant topographic relief and limited lateral continuity. Thus, it may be difficult to correlate.

PRESERVATION POTENTIAL

Two separate issues exist when considering the preservation potential of incised-valley systems: (1) the preservation of the various facies within the incised valley and (2) the preservation potential of the incised valley itself.

In segment 1 of any incised-valley system, erosion by tidal- and wave-ravinement processes during transgression is a major control on preservation potential of transgressive estuarine and lowstand to early transgressive fluvial deposits. Scour in tidal inlets and channels may remove some or all of the underlying, transgressive, central-basin sediments, and may extend deeply enough to remove bayhead-delta and underlying fluvial deposits. In extreme cases, the tidal ravinement surface may amalgamate with the basal sequence boundary and modify it. The factors determining the depth of tidal incision are not completely understood, but it is likely that incision is greatest in mixed-energy settings such as the Gironde estuary (Allen and Posamentier, 1993, this volume); in strongly wave-dominated estuarine systems, there may be insufficient tidal energy to cause erosion, while in strongly tide-dominated estuaries a constriction is not created by waves and the tidal flow is spread over a wider area (Dalrymple and others, 1990).

Wave ravinement in segment 1 commonly removes all but the deepest portions (e.g., tidal-inlet fills) of the estuary-mouth barrier complex. The underlying deposits of the central basin, bayhead delta and fluvial system typically escape erosion in deeper valleys, provided they not been eroded previously by tidal scour, but may be removed from shallow valleys in easily-eroded, coastal-plain areas (see above). Marine erosion may also occur in tidally-dominated shelf areas (Dalrymple, 1992). For example, Harris (this volume) discusses the possibility that tidal currents have exhumed incised-valley systems, removing fluvial, estuarine and deltaic deposits, leaving the valley open, to be filled later by shelf sands and muds.

In wave-dominant settings, the preservation potential of the incised valley itself is dependent primarily on the effectiveness and depth of the wave-ravinement process during transgression (Ashley and Sheridan, this volume; Belknap and others, this volume). The depth of the incised valley relative to the depth of wave base will determine how much (if any) of the valley form will be preserved (Swift, 1968). In cases where the incised valley has been eroded into soft or semi-consolidated sediment, as is commonly the case in coastal-plain settings, it is easier for the wave-ravinement process to completely erode the incised valley. This is common in areas like the Texas Gulf Coast (Thomas and Anderson, this volume), the Louisiana coast (Suter and Berryhill, 1985, Suter and others, 1987), or the portions of the U. S. east coast that are not bedrock controlled (Ashley and Sheridan, this volume; Belknap and others, this volume). The preservation potential of incised-valley systems is greater in areas of bedrock control because the interfluves are not as easily eroded. Examples of this occur along the modern Eastern Shore of Nova Scotia (Boyd and Honig, 1992), the New England Coast (Belknap and Kraft, 1981; Belknap and others, this volume), and the coast of New South Wales (Roy, 1984, this volume). Tidal ravinement may also occur on the shelf (Dalrymple, 1992; Harris, this volume), but tidal currents are usually channelized parallel to the axis of the incised valley, as opposed to being spread uniformly along the shoreline as wave action is. Thus, tidal ravinement on the shelf tends not to obliterate valleys, and may even enhance the valley form.

In compound incised-valley fills, the multiple cut-and-fill events associated with different orders of lowstand fluvial incision are an important additional control on preservation potential (Fig. 5B). As shown by Thomas and Anderson (this volume), incised-valley systems formed by high-frequency lowstands in the early stages of an overall sea-level fall are subject to erosional removal during subsequent, lower lowstands. In comparison, preservation of paleovalley systems and their infill is enhanced during overall rising sea level, because accommodation space is being created (rather than lost). Thus, compound incised-valley fills are more likely to be preserved in low-order, transgressive systems tracts.

VARIATIONS ON THE PROPOSED MODEL

The model proposed above corresponds closely to the essential features of most simple, incised-valley systems that have been described; however, many incised-valley systems exhibit deviations from this model, as would be expected because of differing site- and time-specific factors (Walker, 1992). In this section, we will examine some of the effects of valley shape, depositional gradient, sediment supply and magnitude of sea-level change, in order to illustrate the variations that can be accommodated in the model.

Valley Shape and the Relative Influence of Waves and Tides

The shape of the incised valley has an important control on the zonation, extent and depositional style of each segment, particularly in the early stages of infilling, prior to depositional modification of the original geometry (e.g., Dalrymple and others, 1992). The shape of the incised valley may result in the amplification or damping of tidal action during transgression of the paleovalley (Salomon and Allen, 1983; Nichols and Biggs, 1985). In situations of irregular valley morphology, tidal amplification is unlikely and the estuaries tend to be hyposynchronous and wave-dominated (Dalrymple and others, 1992), with the formation of a barrier bar at a local constriction (Boyd and others, 1987). Incised-valley systems which have a more regular, funnel-shaped geometry are more likely to be hypersynchronous (Salomon and Allen, 1983) and tide-dominated (Dalrymple and others, 1992). Thus, the nature of the estuarine component of segments 1 and 2 is controlled in part by the original shape of the valley. This in turn influences the nature of the facies and stratigraphic surfaces, and the extent to which the fill escapes erosion by wave and tidal ravinement processes.

As tidal range increases, the widespread distribution of strong tidal currents may modify the shape of the incised valley to form the funnel shape which typifies macrotidal systems such as the Cobequid Bay-Salmon River Estuary (Dalrymple and Zaitlin, 1989; Dalrymple and others, 1990). During transgression, this estuarine funnel will deepen and widen, and migrate up the valley. This will be accompanied by erosion of adjacent and underlying sediments by tidal currents in the channels. As a result, the transgressing estuarine funnel will be bounded on its sides and base by a tidal ravinement surface which has a very different geometry and greater extent than the equivalent surface in wave-dominated systems.

Depositional Gradient, Sea-level Change and Sediment Supply

The length of the entire incised valley is a function of the magnitude and duration of the sea-level fall, and of the coastal-zone gradient. Large sea-level falls are more likely to take the shoreline beyond the shelf edge, thereby increasing river gradients and promoting incision. Longer-duration falls provide more time for incision and headward retreat of any knickpoint; consequently, incised valleys associated with longer falls may have a greater length than those associated with short falls. Coastal zones with steep gradients are more prone to incision than gently-inclined coastal plains (Schumm, 1993), but the coastal zone is typically narrower in the former case, and the incised valleys may be shorter than those on broad coastal plains.

The length of segment 2 is as long as the estuary which exists at the end of the transgression, which in turn is strongly dependent on the coastal-zone gradient, with longer estuaries occurring in lower-gradient settings (Dalrymple and others, 1992). The rate of fluvial sediment input, relative to the rate of sea-level rise, also has an influence, the estuary being shorter as the ability of the fluvial system to offset transgression increases. The relative lengths of segments 1 and 3 are influenced primarily by the amount of transgression (segment 1 lengthens at the expense of segment 3 as the transgression proceeds), which is in turn a function of the amount of relative sea-level rise, with larger rises producing a longer segment 1, all other factors being equal, than smaller rises.

In addition, however, the ratio between the rates of sea-level rise and fluvial sedimentation has a significant influence on the length of the segments. In the case where sediment supply by the river equals or exceeds the amount of relative sea-level rise, it is possible for the entire fill of the incised valley to be fluvial and aggradational in character.

Transgression would not occur until the interfluves were inundated, and an incised-valley estuary would not be developed. Thus, the tidal and wave ravinement surfaces would not be present within the incised-valley fill, and the wave ravinement surface and transgressive surface would coincide with the top of the incised-valley system. On the other hand, if the fluvial sediment supply is small relative to the rate of sea-level rise, then there would be significant flooding of the valley and the proportion of estuarine and marine deposits in the fill would increase as the amount of fluvial input decreases. The situation shown in Figures 1 and 6, which typifies many Holocene and Cretaceous incised-valley systems we have examined, is representative of situations with relatively low fluvial input and/or a rapid sea-level rise.

SUMMARY AND CONCLUSIONS

The majority of incised valleys preserved in the stratigraphic record have formed in response either to a fall of relative sea level caused by a eustatic fall or tectonic uplift, or to an increase in fluvial discharge due to climatic change or stream capture (Schumm, 1993). Changes in discharge do not involve a change in relative sea level, and the resulting incised valleys are probably filled entirely with fluvial sediments. Relatively few incised valleys have been attributed to this cause. In contrast, many modern and ancient incised-valley systems are known or believed to have resulted from a lowering of relative sea level. Thus, in this paper, we have considered only this type of incised valley, which is, by definition, associated with the development of a sequence boundary. Such incised valleys are eroded by fluvial action during the relative sea-level fall and lowstand (Fig. 2C). Infilling commences during the late lowstand and/or early transgression, as relative sea level rises and the shoreline transgresses up the valley system. If the valley is completely filled during the transgression and succeeding highstand, the fill is here termed *simple* because it consists of a single sequence (Fig. 5A). If the valley is re-incised during one or more subsequent sea-level falls so that the fill contains two or more sequence, the fill is termed *compound* (Fig. 5B). Compound fills are more likely to occur in larger, piedmont river systems, whose position is commonly controlled by structure, than in smaller, coastal-plain systems (Fig. 4).

In a simple incised-valley fill, or in one phase of a compound fill, the incised valley can be subdivided into three idealized segments (Figs. 1, 6). The inner (landward) segment of the incised valley (segment 3) never experiences marine influence and remains fluvial throughout infilling. This segment reflects changes in relative sea level through changes in the style of fluvial deposition. The middle segment (segment 2) corresponds to the incised-valley estuary at the time of maximum transgression. Here, lowstand to transgressive fluvial and estuarine deposits are overlain by progradational (highstand) fluvial sediments. The outer segment (segment 1) of the incised valley is transgressed by the shoreline and contains a transgressive succession of fluvial and estuarine facies, overlain by marine sands and shales.

The absolute and relative length of these segments depends on a complex interaction of several variables, the most important being the particular sea-level history, the coastal-zone gradient and the rate of fluvial sediment input. The relative intensity of waves and tidal currents determines the nature of the facies, and the physical expression of the stratigraphically-significant surfaces within the incised-valley fill.

The various surfaces differ greatly in their origin, geographic extent (Figs. 1C, 6), and chronostratigraphic significance. A *sequence boundary* is present at the base of the incised valley throughout its length, and is correlative with the exposure surface on the interfluves. In situations where fluvial sediment supply is moderate to low relative to the rate of transgression, the *transgressive surface* typically lies low in the incised-valley fill. The fluvial-estuarine contact, which is commonly the *initial flooding surface*, is a diachronous facies boundary, and may not provide a useful boundary between the lowstand and transgressive systems tracts along its entire length. The stacking pattern of parasequence-scale units may be the only reliable criterion for recognizing systems tracts, especially in segment 3. In systems with mixed wave and tidal influence, two different ravinement surfaces may occur higher in the fill, but only in segment 1 and the outer portion of segment 2. Erosion by tidal currents in tidal inlets or other tidal channels creates a *tidal ravinement surface* which is typically confined to the incised valley. It could be mistaken for a second sequence boundary because it is typically overlain by coarse-grained, channel deposits. More regional erosion by waves at the retreating shoreface produces a *wave ravinement surface* that separates fluvial and/or estuarine sediment below from overlying marine deposits. Both of these surfaces are diachronous, and could become amalgamated with the sequence boundary. In the idealized case, a *maximum flooding surface* may extend throughout the incised-valley fill, passing from its typical position within marine shales in segment 1, through the center of the estuarine deposits in segment 2, into fluvial sediments in segment 3. However, rapid relative sea-level fall after the end of the transgression, or renewed sea-level rise after valley filling (but before the onset of significant progradation), may preclude development of the maximum flooding surface. Compound valley fills contain multiple sets of surfaces.

ACKNOWLEDGMENTS

The ideas presented here have resulted from our respective research in modern and ancient incised-valley and estuarine systems in Canada, the Gulf Coast and Australia, supported by discussions with colleagues in the field, and the ideas and well-documented case studies contained in this volume. B. A. Z. thanks PanCanadian Petroleum Limited both for their logistical support and for permission to publish this paper; and R. Jameus for the expert drafting of the diagrams. B. A. Z. also acknowledges the contributions of colleagues at Imperial Oil (ESSO) Resources and EXXON Production Research Company. Others who have freely shared there ideas include P. Roy, B. Thom, A. Short and S. Nichol (University of Sydney), and C. Amos, D. Leckie, and G. Reinson (Geological Survey of Canada), H. Posamentier (ARCO), G. Allen (TOTAL), and K. Bohacs and J. Suter (EXXON). Work by B. A. Z. and R. W. D. was funded by NSERC Operating Grant A7553, the Advisory Research Committee of Queen's University, Imperial Oil Limited, Gulf Canada Limited, Mobil Oil Limited, Shell Oil Limited, and Canterra Energy Limited. R. W. D. also thanks Drs. Peter Harris and Peter Davies, Department of Geology and Geophysics, University of Sydney, for their hospitality while on sabbatical. R. B. acknowledges NSERC (Operating Grant A8452), the Canadian Department of Energy Mines and Resources, and the Australian Research Council for funding his research on coastal depositional systems. We are grateful to D. Cant, N. Corbett, and D. Leckie for their constructive and timely comments on the manuscript.

REFERENCES

ALLEN, G. P., 1991, Sedimentary processes and facies in the Gironde estuary: a recent model of macrotidal estuarine systems, in Smith, D. G., Reinson, G. E., Zaitlin, B. A., and Rahmani, R., eds., Clastic Tidal Sedimentology: Calgary, Canadian Society of Petroleum Geologists Memoir 16, p. 29–39.

ALLEN, G. P., AND POSAMENTIER, H. W., 1993, Sequence stratigraphy and facies model of an incised valley fill: the Gironde Estuary, France: Journal of Sedimentary Petrology, v. 63, p. 378–391.

BELKNAP, D. F., AND KRAFT, J. C., 1981, Preservation potential of transgressive coastal lithosomes on the United States Atlantic shelf: Marine Geology, v. 42, p. 429–442.

BERG, R. R., 1976, Trapping mechanisms for oil in Lower Cretaceous Muddy Sandstone at Recluse Field, Wyoming: Wyoming Geological Association Guidebook, p. 261–272.

BOYD, R., BOWEN, A. J., AND HALL, R. K., 1987, An evolutionary model for transgressive sedimentation on the Eastern Shore of Nova Scotia, in Fitzgerald, D. M., and Rosen, P. S. eds., Glaciated Coasts: New York, Academic Press, p. 88–114.

BOYD, R., DALRYMPLE, R. W., AND ZAITLIN, B. A., 1992, Classification of coastal sedimentary environments: Sedimentary Geology, v. 80, p. 139–150.

BOYD, R., AND HONIG, C., 1992, Estuarine sedimentation on the Eastern Shore of Nova Scotia: Journal of Sedimentary Petrology, v. 62, p. 569–583.

BROWN, L. F., JR., 1993, Seismic and sequence stratigraphy: its current status and growing role in exploration and development: New Orleans, New Orleans Geological Society Short Course No. 5, American Association of Petroleum Geologists 78th Annual Convention, unpaginated.

CHRISTIE-BLICK, N., VON DER BORCH, C. C., AND DIBONA, P. A., 1990, Working hypothesis for the origin of the Wonaka Canyons (Neoproterozoic), South Australia: American Journal of Science, v. 290A, p. 295–332.

CLARK, J. E., AND REINSON, G. E., 1990, Continuity and performance of an estuarine reservoir, Crystal field, Alberta, Canada, in Barwis, J. H., McPherson, J., and Studlick, J. R. J., eds., Sandstone Petroleum Reservoirs: New York, Springer-Verlag, p. 342–362.

CROSS, T. A., 1988, Controls on coal distribution in transgressive-regressive cycles, Upper Cretaceous, Western Interior, U. S. A., in Wilgus, C. K., Hastings, B. S., Kendall, C. G. St. C., Posamentier, H. W., Ross, C. A., and Van Wagoner, J. C., eds., Sea-level Changes: An Integrated Approach: Tulsa, Society of Economic Paleontologists and Mineralogists Special Publication 42, p. 371–380.

DALRYMPLE, R. W., 1992, Tidal depositional systems, in Walker, R. G., and James, N. P., eds., Facies Models, Response to Sea-Level Change: St. John's, Geological Association of Canada, p. 195–218.

DALRYMPLE, R. W., AND ZAITLIN, B. A., 1989, Tidal sedimentation in the macrotidal, Cobequid Bay-Salmon River estuary, Bay of Fundy: Calgary, Canadian Society of Petroleum Geologists Field Guide, Second International Symposium on Clastic Tidal Deposits, 84 p.

DALRYMPLE, R. W., KNIGHT, R. J., ZAITLIN, B. A., AND MIDDLETON, G. V., 1990, Dynamics and facies model of a macrotidal sand-bar complex, Cobequid Bay-Salmon River estuary (Bay of Fundy): Sedimentology, v. 37, p. 577–612.

DALRYMPLE, R. W., ZAITLIN, B. A., AND BOYD, R., 1992, Estuarine facies models: conceptual basis and stratigraphic implications: Journal of Sedimentary Petrology, v. 62, p. 1130–1146.

DAVIS, R. A., Jr., AND CLIFTON, H. E., 1987, Sea-level change and the preservation potential of wave-dominated and tide-dominated coastal sequences, in Nummendal, D., Pilkey, O. H., and Howard, J. D., eds., Sea-level Fluctuation and Coastal Evolution: Tulsa, Society of Economic Paleontologists and Mineralogists Special Publication 41, p. 167–178

DEMAREST, J. M., II AND KRAFT, J. C., 1987, Stratigraphic record of Quaternary sea levels: implication for more ancient strata, in Nummendal, D., Pilkey, O. H., and Howard, J. D., eds., Sea-level Fluctuation and Coastal Evolution: Tulsa, Society of Economic Paleontologists and Mineralogists Special Publication 41, p. 223–239.

DOLSON, J., MULLER, D., EVETTS, M. J., AND STEIN, J. A., 1991, Regional paleotopographic trends and production, Muddy Sandstone (Lower Cretaceous), central and northern Rocky Mountains: American Association of Petroleum Geologists Bulletin, v. 75, p. 409–435.

FISK, H. N., 1944, Geological investigation of the alluvial valley of the lower Mississippi River: Vicksburg, United States Army Corps of Engineers, Mississippi River Commission, 78 p.

GALLOWAY, W. E., 1989, Genetic stratigraphic sequences in basin analysis I: architecture and genesis of flooding-surface bounded depositional units: American Association of Petroleum Geologists Bulletin, v. 73, p. 125–142.

GIBLING, M. R., 1991, Sequence analysis of alluvial-dominated cyclothems in the Sydney Basin, Nova Scotia, in Leckie, D. A., Posamentier, H. W., and Lovell, R. W. W., eds., 1991 NUNA Conference on High Resolution Sequence Stratigraphy, Program, Proceedings, Guidebook: Calgary, Geological Association of Canada, p. 15–19.

HARMS, J. C, 1966, Stratigraphic traps in a valley fill, western Nebraska: American Association of Petroleum Geologists Bulletin, v. 50, p. 2119–2149.

HAYES, M. O., AND SEXTON, W. L., 1989, Modern clastic depositional environments, South Carolina: Washington, D.C., American Geophysical Conference Field Trip Guidebook T-371, 85 p.

JERVEY, M. T., 1988, Quantitative geological modeling of siliciclastic sequences and their seismic expressions, in Wilgus, C. K., Hastings, B. S., Kendall, C. G. St. C., Posamentier, H. W., Ross, C. A., and Van Wagoner, J. C., eds., Sea-level Changes: An Integrated Approach: Tulsa, Society of Economic Paleontologists and Mineralogists Special Publication 42, p. 47–69.

KOMAR, P. D., AND ENFIELD, D. B., 1987, Short-term sea-level changes and coastal erosion, in Nummendal, D., Pilkey, O. H., and Howard, J. D., eds., Sea-level Fluctuation and Coastal Evolution: Tulsa, Society of Economic Paleontologists and Mineralogists Special Publication 41, p. 17–27.

LECKIE, D. A., AND SINGH, C., 1991, Estuarine deposits of the Albian Paddy Member (Peace River Formation) and lowermost Shaftsbury Formation, Alberta, Canada: Journal of Sedimentary Petrography, v. 61, p. 825–849.

LOUTIT, T. S., HARDENBOL, J., VAIL, P. R., AND BAUM, G. R., 1988, Condensed sections: the key to age dating and correlation of continental margin sequences, in Wilgus, C. K., Hastings, B. S., Kindle, C. G. St. C., Posamentier, H. W., Ross, C. A. and Van Wagoner, J. C., eds., Sea-level Changes: An Integrated Approach: Tulsa, Society of Economic Paleontologists and Mineralogists Special Publication 42, p. 183–216.

MACEACHERN, J. A., RAYCHAUDURI, I., AND PEMBERTON, S. G., 1992, Stratigraphic applications of the Glossifungites ichnofacies: delineating discontinuities in the rock record, in Pemberton, S. G., ed., Applications of Ichnology to Petroleum Exploration: Tulsa, SEPM (Society of Sedimentary Geology) Core Workshop 17, p. 169–198.

MIALL, A. D., 1992, Alluvial Deposits, in Walker, R. G., and James, N. P., eds., Facies Models: Response to Sea-level Change: St. John's, Geological Association of Canada, p. 119–142.

NICHOLS, M. M., AND BIGGS, R. B., 1985, Estuaries, in Davis, R. A., Jr., ed., Coastal Sedimentary Environments (2nd ed.): New York, Springer-Verlag, p. 77–142.

PLINT, A. G., EYLES, N., EYLES, C. H., AND WALKER, R. G., 1992, Control of sea-level change, in Walker, R. G., and James, N. P., eds.,

Facies Models, Response to Sea-Level Change: St. John's, Geological Association of Canada, p. 15–26.

POSAMENTIER, H. W., AND ERSKIN, R. D., 1991, Seismic expression and recognition criteria of ancient submarine fans, in Weimer, P., and Link, M. M., eds., Seismic Facies and Sedimentary Processes of Submarine Fans and Turbidite Systems: New York, Springer-Verlag, p. 197–222.

POSAMENTIER, H. W., JERVEY, M. T., AND VAIL, P. R., 1988, Eustatic controls on clastic deposition I—conceptual framework, in Wilgus, C. K., Hastings, B. S., Kendall, C. G. St. C., Posamentier, H. W., Ross, C. A., and Van Wagoner, J. C., eds., Sea-level Changes: An Integrated Approach: Tulsa, Society of Economic Paleontologists and Mineralogists Special Publication 42, p. 109–124.

POSAMENTIER, H. W., AND VAIL, P. R., 1988, Eustatic controls on clastic deposition II- sequence and systems tract models, in Wilgus, C. K., Hastings, B. S., Kendall, C. G. St. C., Posamentier, H. W., Ross, C. A., and Van Wagoner, J. C., eds., Sea-level Changes: An Integrated Approach: Tulsa, Society of Economic Paleontologists and Mineralogists Special Publication 42, p. 125–154.

RAHMANI, R. A., 1988, Estuarine tidal channel and nearshore sedimentation of a late Cretaceous epicontinental sea, Drumheller, Alberta, Canada, in de Boer, P. L., Van Gelder, A., and Nio, S.D., ed., Tide-influenced Sedimentary Environments and Facies: Dordrecht, D. Reidel Publishing Company, p. 433–471.

REINSON, G. E., 1992, Transgressive barrier island and estuarine systems, in Walker, R. G., and James, N. P., eds., Facies Models: Response to Sea-level Change: St. John's, Geological Association of Canada, p. 179–194.

RICKETTS, B. R., 1991, Lower Paleocene drowned valley and barred estuaries, Canadian Arctic Islands: aspects of their geomorphological and sedimentological evolution, in Smith, D. G., Reinson, G. E., Zaitlin, B. A., and Rahmani, R., eds., Clastic Tidal Sedimentology: Calgary, Canadian Society of Petroleum Geologists Memoir 16, p. 91–106.

ROSENTHAL, L., 1988, Wave-dominated shorelines and incised valley trends: Lower Cretaceous Glauconite Formation, west-central Alberta, in James, D. P., and Leckie, D. A., eds., Sequences, Stratigraphy, Sedimentology: Surface and Subsurface: Calgary, Canadian Society of Petroleum Geologists Memoir 15, p. 207–220.

ROY, P. S., 1984, New South Wales Estuaries: their origin and evolution, in Thom, B. G., ed., Coastal Geomorphology in Australia: Sydney, Academic Press, p. 99–121.

SALOMON, J. C., AND ALLEN, G. P., 1983, Role sédimentologique de la marée dans les estuaries a fort mornage: Paris, Compagnie Française des Petroles Notes et Mémoires, v. 18, p. 35–44.

SCHUMM, S. A., 1977, The Fluvial System: New York, John Wiley and Sons, 338 p.

SCHUMM, S. A., 1993, River response to baselevel change: implications for sequence stratigraphy: Journal of Geology, v. 101, p. 279–294.

SEIVER, R., 1951, The Mississippian-Pennsylvanian unconformity in southern Illinois: American Association of Petroleum Geologists, v. 35, p. 542–581.

SHANLEY, K. W., MCCABE, P. J., AND HETTINGER, R. D., 1992, Tidal influence in Cretaceous fluvial strata from Utah, U. S. A.: A key to sequence stratigraphic interpretation: Sedimentology, v. 39, p. 905–930.

SUTER, J. R., AND BERRYHILL, H. L., JR., 1985, Late Quaternary shelf margin deltas, Northwest Gulf of Mexico: American Association of Petroleum Geologists Bulletin, v. 69, p. 77–91.

SUTER, J. R., BERRYHILL, H. L., JR., AND PENLAND, S., 1987, Late Quaternary sea-level fluctuations and depositional sequences, southwest Louisiana continental shelf, in Nummendal, D., Pilkey, O. H., and Howard, J. D., eds., Sea-level Fluctuation and Coastal Evolution: Tulsa, Society of Economic Paleontologists and Mineralogists Special Publication 41, p. 199–219.

SWIFT, D. J. P., 1968, Coastal erosion and transgressive stratigraphy: Journal of Geology, v. 76, p. 444–456.

TÖRQUIST, T. E., 1993, Holocene alternation of meandering and anastomozing fluvial systems in the Rhine-Meuse Delta (central Netherlands) controlled by sea-level rise and subsoil erodibility: Journal of Sedimentary Petrology, v. 63, p. 683–693.

VAIL, P. R., MITCHUM, R. M., AND THOMPSON, S., III, 1977, Seismic stratigraphy and global changes of sea level, part 3: relative changes of sea level from coastal onlap, in Payton, C. W., ed., Seismic Stratigraphy Applications to Hydrocarbon Exploration: Tulsa, American Association of Petroleum Geologists Memoir 26, p. 63–97.

VAN WAGONER, J. C., MITCHUM, R. M., CAMPION, K. M., AND RAHMANIAN, V. D., 1990, Siliciclastic sequence stratigraphy in well logs, cores, and outcrops: concepts for high resolution correlation of time and facies: Tulsa, American Association of Petroleum Geologists Methods in Exploration 7, 55 p.

VAN WAGONER, J. C., POSAMENTIER, H. W., MITCHUM, R. M., VAIL, P. R., SARG, R, LOUTIT, T. S., AND HARDENBOL, J., 1988, An overview of sequence stratigraphy and key definitions, in Wilgus, C. K., Hastings, B. S., Kendall, C. G. St. C., Posamentier, H. W., Ross, C. A., and Van Wagoner, J. C., eds., Sea-level Changes: An Integrated Approach: Tulsa, Society of Economic Paleontologists and Mineralogists Special Publication 42, p. 39–45.

WALKER, R. G., 1992, Facies, facies models, and modern stratigraphic concepts, in Walker, R. G., and James, N. P., eds., Facies Models: Response to Sea-level Change: St. Johns, Geological Association of Canada, p. 1–14.

WEIMER, R. J., 1983, Relation of unconformities, tectonism and sea level changes, Cretaceous of the Denver Basin and adjacent areas, in Reynolds, M. W., and Dolly, E. D., eds., Mesozoic paleogeography of West Central United States: Denver, Rocky Mountain Section, Society of Economic Paleontologist and Mineralogists Rocky Mountain Paleogeography 2, p. 359–376.

WEIMER, R. J., 1984, Relation of unconformities, tectonism and sea level changes, Cretaceous of the Western Interior, in Schlep J., ed., Interregional Unconformities and Hydrocarbon Accumulations: Tulsa, American Association of Petroleum Geologists Memoir 36, p. 7–35.

WESCOTT, W. A., 1993, Geomorphic thresholds and complex response of fluvial systems- some implications for sequence stratigraphy: American Association of Petroleum Geologists Bulletin, v. 77, p. 1208–1218.

WOOD, J. M., AND HOPKINS, J. C., 1989, Reservoir sandstone bodies in estuarine valley fill: Lower Cretaceous Glauconitic Member, Little Bow Field, Alberta, Canada: American Association of Petroleum Geologists Bulletin, v. 73, p. 1361–1382.

WRIGHT, V. P., AND MARRIOTT, S. B., 1993, The sequence stratigraphy of fluvial depositional systems: the role of floodplain sediment storage: Sedimentary Geology, v. 86, p. 203–210.

ZAITLIN, B. A., AND SHULTZ, B. C., 1990, Wave-influenced estuarine sandbody: the Senlac Heavy Oil Pool, Saskatchewan, in Barwis, J. H., McPherson, J. and Studlick, J. R. J., eds., Sandstone Petroleum Reservoirs: Ney York, Springer-Verlag, p. 363–387.

ZAITLIN, B. A. AND SHULTZ, B. C., 1984, An Estuarine-embayment fill model from the Lower Cretaceous Mannville Group, West-Central Saskatchewan, in Stott, D. F., and Glass, D. J., eds., Mesozoic of Middle North America: Calgary, Canadian Society of Petroleum Geologists Memoir 9, p. 455–469.

SEGMENT 1—TRANSGRESSED, SHELF VALLEYS

SEA-LEVEL CONTROLS ON THE FACIES ARCHITECTURE OF THE TRINITY/SABINE INCISED-VALLEY SYSTEM, TEXAS CONTINENTAL SHELF

MARK A. THOMAS
Geology Research, Shell Development Company, Houston, Texas, 77001
AND
JOHN B. ANDERSON
Department of Geology and Geophysics, Rice University, Houston, Texas 77251

ABSTRACT: Over 1,000 km of high-resolution seismic profiles and nearly 200 cores were interpreted to document the evolution of the Trinity/Sabine incised-valley system, which lies offshore of Galveston Bay and Sabine Pass. Long-term sea-level fluctuations, related to Wisconsinan ice-sheet growth, caused multiple cycles of incision and valley-filling that are preserved as terraced fluvial deposits. The oldest incision began approximately 110 ka ($\delta^{18}O$ stage 5d). Age estimates are possible because the unconformities which bound the fluvial terraces are traceable laterally and bound offlapping sequences (probably deltaic) on the adjacent interfluves. The sequence stratigraphy of the interfluves suggests each offlapping sequence correlates to an isotope substage (20 ka in duration). The terraced fluvial deposits represent the lowstand and transgressive phase of each 20 ka cycle, and the offlapping sequences represent the highstand phase.

Short-term changes in the rate of sea-level rise during the Holocene transgression affected the facies architecture of the incised-valley fill. There are three parasequences recognized, and they step landward within the incised valley, thus the distribution of valley-fill facies is discontinuous. Parasequences formed during sea-level stillstands and consist of paired upper-bay and tidal inlet facies. Periods of rapid rise are manifested as flooding surfaces that bound each parasequence. Large shelf sand banks situated adjacent to the incised valley are associated with each stillstand parasequence but were extensively reworked and isolated by subsequent sea-level rises. The younger parasequences show decreased preservation of lower bay facies, attributed to the slowing of sea-level rise (therefore, decreasing accommodation) about 6 ka.

INTRODUCTION

Studies of late Quaternary estuaries have understandably focused on the modern coastal systems because of ease of access. Because these studies were limited to the estuaries themselves and the nearshore zone, they either documented the latest Holocene portion of the last transgression (Rehkemper, 1969; Wilkinson and Byrne, 1977; Fletcher and others, 1990; Allen and Posamentier, 1993) or recorded previous highstand estuaries (Shidler, 1986; Colman and Mixon, 1988). This investigation of the Trinity/Sabine river-valley system is significant in terms of its scope because the data presented extend from the present shoreline to the mid-shelf (Fig. 1), and, therefore, the interpretations span an extensive period of the valley's history (from ≈120 ka to ≈50 ka and ≈10 ka to the present). This study is one part of a regional examination of the north Texas continental shelf. A logical and ongoing continuation of this study is the mapping of the Trinity/Sabine valley on the outer shelf, which will capture the valley's history over a complete glacial cycle and address the relationship between the incised-valley and shelf-margin deltas (Sarzalejo and others, 1993).

Companion studies offshore of the Brazos Delta (Abdulah and Anderson, 1991; Bartek and others, 1991) and Matagorda Bay (Thomas and others, 1991) demonstrate the variety of late Quaternary valley types and valley-fill facies. Differences in sediment supply rates appear to exert a major control on valley-fill facies, as is suggested by the present coastal physiography. Bays occur in the upper portions of the Trinity/Sabine incised valley (Fig. 1), which are being filled with fine-grained estuarine muds, whereas the Brazos and Colorado rivers have filled their incised valleys to form a deltaic headland (Fig. 1).

The late Quaternary valley-fill deposits on the continental shelf show similar variations that can be attributed to differing sediment-supply regimes. Low to moderate sediment-supply systems (e.g., the Trinity, Sabine, and Lavaca rivers) are characterized by mud-dominated estuarine facies and by sedimentation that is primarily confined within the lowstand incised valley (Thomas and others, 1991). In contrast, the high sediment-supply systems (e.g., the Brazos and Colorado rivers) are characterized by sand-dominated fluvial facies and by deposition in shallow channels on regional interfluves (Abdulah and Anderson, 1991; Bartek and others, 1991).

Because of its mud-dominated fill, the Trinity/Sabine valley system lends itself to high-resolution geophysical examination. The internal and external geometries of seismic facies are very similar to depositional facies. Likewise, the scale and resolution of seismic profiles is analogous to large and continuous outcrops. Sequence-stratigraphic analysis helps to develop a chronostratigraphic and architectural framework of the incised-valley fill.

Previous Work

Several authors have addressed the late Quaternary stratigraphy of the Texas and Louisiana continental shelves (Winker, 1979; Suter, 1986; Suter and others, 1987; Coleman and Roberts, 1988; McFarlan and LeRoy, 1988). Suter (1986) demonstrated that incised fluvial valleys are a major element of shelf stratigraphy. Coleman and Roberts (1988) and Winker (1979) showed that the shelf stratigraphy generally reflects the eustatic record inferred from $\delta^{18}O$ curves of deep-sea sediments and, in particular, that the sea-level fall from the last highstand ($\delta^{18}O$ stage 5e) was not monotonic and was expressed as offlapping depositional sequences.

Two key papers concern the nature of the last transgression and resulting sedimentary deposits of the Texas shelf. Frazier (1974) proposed that sea level rose in a step-like manner (a series of rapid rises and stillstands). He radiocarbon-dated sand banks and shoals on the Texas and Lou-

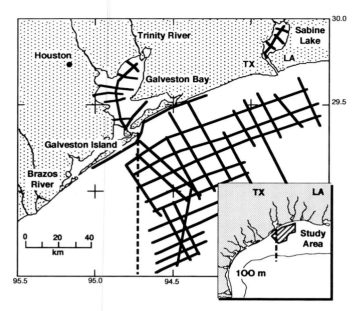

FIG. 1.—Regional geography of the study area and location of Rice University Uniboom profiles (solid lines). Dashed line is regional sparker profile from Winker (1979) which extends to the shelf edge (inset).

isiana continental shelf and interpreted them as former shoreline positions during stillstands. Nelson and Bray (1970) studied the offshore portion of the Sabine incised valley and adjacent Sabine Bank. They documented a thick (35 m of incision relative to the modern sea floor) valley-fill succession which included fluvial, estuarine, and marine deposits. The estuarine portion was interpreted as representing continuous transgressive deposition although Nelson and Bray (1970) suggested that a minor sea-level fall occurred, based on the graphed age and elevation of freshwater peats. Another key observation made by Nelson and Bray (1970) was that the sands of Sabine Bank interfingered with marine sediments on its landward side, which suggests the bank is in part a marine shelf sand. Their work illustrates the potential for misinterpreting all sand banks as former shorelines and, in turn, the potential inaccuracy of using sand banks as an estimate of former sea level.

Objectives

This paper addresses the Trinity/Sabine valley evolution at two scales of time and detail. The first section concerns the long-term history of the valley, which is interpreted as reflecting sea-level changes of 25–50 m in magnitude over 20–100 ka periods. These interpretations rely on correlating erosional surfaces within the valley to regional sequence boundaries. The origin of terraced, fluvial valley-fill deposits (which are probably Wisconsinan in age and represent early filling episodes) is also addressed.

The second section focuses on the facies architecture and sequence stratigraphy of the late Wisconsinan-Holocene transgressive valley fill. These deposits record fluctuations in the rate of sea-level rise (maximum rate 5–10 m per 1 ka) during the transgression. There are several large shelf

sand banks adjacent to the Trinity/Sabine incised valley (e.g., Sabine, Heald, and Shepard Banks); thus, this area optimizes the ability to relate the valley-fill stratigraphy to the shelf stratigraphy studied by Frazier (1974).

METHODS AND DATA

Over 1000 km of high-resolution seismic profiles (Fig. 1) were collected for this study with the Rice University research vessels, the R/V Matagorda and R/V Lone Star. The sound source was an EG&G Model 230 Uniboom. Analog tape and thermal printers recorded the data. Navigation was accomplished with Loran C and SatNav instruments; accuracy of shot-point locations is plus or minus 100 m. Seismic data from other sources included shallow hazard surveys of several offshore blocks (3.5 kHz data), a Uniboom survey of the nearshore zone (Williams and others, 1979), and a regional sparker profile from Winker (1979) that extends from Galveston Bay to the shelf edge (Fig. 1). Correlation of seismic profiles to nearby geotechnical borings yielded an average interval velocity of 1550 m/s for the late Wisconsinan-Holocene sediments.

A variety of data sources provide lithologic "ground truth" for the seismic interpretations. These data sources consist of two categories: cores with associated sediment samples and core descriptions alone.

Cores with samples included ten vibracores (maximum length 3 m), 130 3 m piston cores, and ten 6.5 m piston cores collected over the Trinity/Sabine valley. Seventy-four vibracores (up to 10 m long) were collected for an archaeological study of the offshore Sabine Valley by Coastal Environments Inc. for the Minerals Management Service (Pearson and others, 1986). Thirty-five vibracores (up to 6 m long) were from the Williams and others (1979) study of the inner continental shelf. Grain size analysis, radiocarbon dates, and lithologic and faunal descriptions were done or were available for all these data sets.

Lithologic data (no samples available) exists in previously published and proprietary reports. Studies by Rehkemper (1969), McEwen (1969) which focused on Galveston Bay, and by Nelson and Bray (1970) in the Sabine River, Heald Bank, and Sabine Bank areas are particularly relevant to this study and contribute radiocarbon age control. Core descriptions of U. S. Army Corps of Engineers' borings from navigation channel construction projects were obtained for Galveston Bay and Sabine Lake.

On the continental shelf, geotechnical borings from foundation studies for drilling rigs and production platforms form a large yet under-used lithologic data set. Fugro-McClelland Engineers of Houston allowed examination of their geotechnical boring files; the appropriate oil companies released the boring descriptions published here. Significantly, the geotechnical borings commonly exceed 100 m in depth thereby yielding complete penetrations of the incised valleys. Because the lithologic descriptions are general and simple, they can rarely be used to identify sedimentary facies. However, physical-property analysis of the sediments (water content, shear strength, and compressive strength) aid in recognizing discontinuities (sequence boundaries and condensed sections) where the lithology is uniform. Nearly 200 geotechnical borings were examined in the course of this project.

Radiocarbon Dates

The nine radiocarbon dates obtained during this study (Thomas, 1990), when combined with previously published dates (Rehkemper, 1969; Nelson and Bray, 1970; Frazier, 1974; Williams and others, 1979), provide a chronologic framework for the transgressive valley-fill deposits. Rather than relying on the age and elevation relationship of peats as a sea-level indicator, this study emphasizes the relationship of dates to key flooding surfaces (e.g., the bayline and ravinement surfaces).

INCISION OF THE TRINITY/SABINE VALLEY: THE EFFECT OF LONG-TERM SEA-LEVEL CHANGES

The eustatic record for the late Pleistocene is approximated by oxygen isotope variations measured in deep-sea cores. The $\delta^{18}O$ proxy for ice volume indicates glacial cycles occurred at 100 ka intervals over at least the last 800 ka (Emiliani, 1958; Shackleton, 1967; Hays and others, 1976; Imbrie and others, 1984). The asymmetric (sawtooth) pattern of $\delta^{18}O$ curves suggests that ice sheets build slowly in 20 ka cycles, then rapidly deglaciate (Fig. 2). The 100 ka and 20 ka cycles controlled incision of the Trinity/Sabine valley system.

The $\delta^{18}O$ curve provides a conceptual and chronological framework for the interpretation of late Pleistocene seismic sequences. As a convention, the even-numbered, low sea-level stages designate sequence boundaries (labeled "SB" with an isotope-stage subscript), and the odd-numbered, high sea-level stages designate deposits (labeled "SQ" with an isotope-stage subscript) between sequence boundaries (where

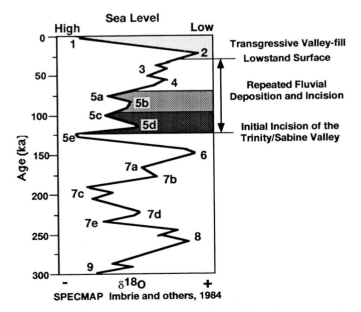

FIG. 2.—$\delta^{18}O$ curve from Imbrie and others (1984). Shaded areas indicate interpreted age of fluvial deposits within the Trinity/Sabine incised-valley study area (see Figure 6).

stage 5 substages are identified, 5b and 5d are the sequence boundaries and 5a, 5c, and 5e are the deposits). Unfortunately, this convention lumps all deposits between sequence boundaries even though there may be significant age differences among them. For example, fluvial deposits formed during the stage 2 lowstand are named stage 1 fluvial (because they are above the stage 2 sequence boundary) and are not differentiated from stage 1 transgressive or highstand fluvial deposits.

Several methods were used to constrain the relative ages of seismic sequences identified in the study. The regional sparker profile (Winker, 1979) shows four offlapping highstand units, which in number and areal distribution generally match the shape of $\delta^{18}O$ curves from stage 5e to 2 (Thomas, 1990; Thomas and Anderson, 1991). We surmise that each offlapping unit represents a 20 ka glacial stage or substage (Fig. 2). Internally, the offlapping units contain prograding clinoformal reflectors and are likely deltaic deposits. On the inner shelf, the oldest offlapping unit (SQ_{5e}) downlaps onto a distinctive and regionally mappable surface. The downlap surface (DLS) is characterized by a high-amplitude doublet.

Indirectly, the DLS can be correlated to $\delta^{18}O$ stage 5 in analyzed wells from the Louisiana slope (Coleman and Roberts, 1988). This correlation is accomplished by tying the Rice seismic data to published seismic data from the Louisiana shelf (Berryhill and others, 1986; Suter and others, 1987) and by tying Coleman and Roberts' (1988) isotope analysis to the same Louisiana shelf seismic data. Additionally, ongoing $\delta^{18}O$ analysis of a boring from the Texas shelf margin suggests the DLS correlates to stage 5e (K. Abdulah, pers. commun., 1993). Therefore, the DLS is interpreted as the stage 5e downlap surface ($\approx$120 ka, Fig. 2) and hence designated as DLS_{5e}. DLS_{5e} becomes the key horizon for estimating the age of overlying and underlying units.

Three regional erosion surfaces below DLS_{5e} show channels 15 to 20 m deep, with modification of the interfluves by ravinement. These incisions likely correlate to previous lowstands (stages 6, 7d, and 8, Fig. 2) and represent older drainages of the Sabine and Trinity rivers (Fig. 3).

There are two erosional surfaces above DLS_{5e} within the study area. The lower, named SB_{5d}, represents the initial incision of the Trinity/Sabine valley, which began as sea level fell from the stage 5e highstand (Sangamonian) approximately 120 ka (Fig. 4). The SB_{5d} incision truncates DLS_{5e}, SB_6, SB_{7d}, and SB_8 (Fig. 4). The SB_{5d} sequence boundary at the base of the incised channel can be traced out of the incision and laterally to where it is the base of the next younger offlapping highstand unit, sequence 5c (SQ_{5c}) (line 9 eastern section, Fig. 5). This interfingering relationship between the incised sequence boundaries and the offlapping units permits relative age determinations. Our proposed correlation of offlapping units to $\delta^{18}O$ stages enables estimation of the incision ages (Fig. 2).

The SB_{5d} incision filled during the stage 5d lowstand and stage 5c interglacial. To date, within this sequence only fluvial valley-fill deposits are interpreted from seismic and core control. The SQ_{5c} fluvial complexes are preserved along the valley margin (Fig. 6). Internally, the fluvial complexes

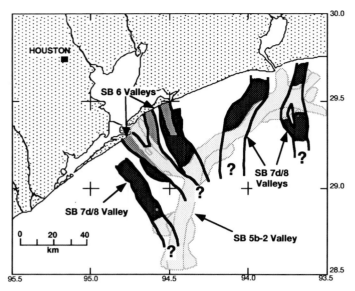

FIG. 3.—Distribution of incised valleys associated with older sequence boundaries 6 and undifferentiated 7d plus 8. For reference, the incised valley for stages 5d through 2 is shown in the lightest gray shade. The older valleys are darker gray shades. Seismic data for older valleys is obscured where they underlie the 5d-2 incision.

display a range of seismic responses from cut and fill geometries (Fig. 4) to high-angle, chaotic reflectors (line 9, western section, Fig. 5).

The next lowstand ($\delta^{18}O$ stage 5b) reoccupied the same valley and eroded all 5c estuarine and most 5c fluvial deposits from the valley fill. Presently, SB_2 is the upper boundary of the 5c fluvial complexes due to its amalgamation with previous sequence boundaries (SB_{5b} and SB_4). The surfaces of the 5c fluvial complexes are oxidized and terraced (offset 2 to 5 m below the SB_2 interfluvial surface). Fluvial terraces that are intermediate in height between the Beaumont Formation (probably SQ_{5e}) and the present floodplain of the Trinity and Sabine rivers are likely the onshore equivalent of the 5c fluvial complexes.

The 5c offlapping unit (SQ_{5c}) is adjacent to the valley and bounded by the same unconformities (SB_{5d} and SB_2) as the 5c fluvial complex. Therefore, they are generally the same age (within the same sequence), although there must be a flooding surface (bayline or ravinement) that separates the fluvial from paralic deposits. The landward pinchout of SQ_{5c} occurs near the present shoreline. An infinite radiocarbon age (>26 ka, CERC core #7, Williams and others, 1979) on a *Rangia* shell from this sequence confirms, at least, that these are pre-$\delta^{18}O$, stage 2 lowstand (20 ka) deposits. The highstand shoreline position within SQ_{5c} is poorly constrained by core control but is estimated to be a maximum of 50 km from the present shoreline and a maximum of 26 m below present sea level.

The next cycle of valley filling (5a deposits) is manifested only as a remnant of a stage 5a fluvial complex (line 9, western section, Fig. 5). The SQ_{5a} offlapping unit, though identified on regional seismic profiles, must pinchout near the outer edge of the study area as it is not recognized within

it. Likewise, stage 3 deposits do not occur within the study area. Regional seismic profiles show that the stage 3 offlapping unit (SQ_3) pinches out at approximately −40 m on the outer shelf.

SB_2, representing the ultimate lowstand, forms the deepest incision of the Trinity/Sabine valley. The SB_2 valley base is not well imaged on seismic profiles because of the large acoustic-impedance contrast associated with the overlying stage 1 estuarine-fluvial contact. However, numerous geotechnical borings indicate the SB_2 incision averages 35 m below the sea floor (Fig. 7) thus truncating previous fluvial complexes and sequence boundaries. On the interfluves, SB_2 amalgamates with (or truncates) SB_{5b} and SB_4 on the inner shelf. Deposits above SB_2 are younger than 20 ka, and can be radiocarbon dated.

In summary, we consider the Wisconsinan history of the Trinity/Sabine incised-valley system to reflect sea-level changes associated with ice-sheet growth and decay. Fluvial complexes preserved along the valley margin and their offlapping sequence counterparts correlate to long-term (20 ka), high amplitude (25–50 m) sea-level fluctuations. Two periods of valley incision (SB_{5d} and SB_{5b}) and filling (stage 5c and 5a deposits) prior to the ultimate SB_2 lowstand incision are recognized in the study area.

Discussion of Long-term Sea-level Effects

The terraced fluvial complexes and their corresponding offlapping units are unconformity-bounded sequences that represent 20 ka sea-level cycles. Vail and others (1977) define sequences of this duration as fifth-order sequences. Offlapping fifth-order sequences ($\delta^{18}O$ stages 5e to 3) form the highstand systems tract of a fourth-order sequence ($\delta^{18}O$ stages 6 to 2) (Fig. 8). The incised-valley fills are the lowstand and transgressive systems tracts of each fifth-order sequence, while the offlapping sequences are the highstand component.

At a fourth-order scale, the Trinity/Sabine valley's evolution spans the time from highstand through lowstand and sequence boundary development to the transgressive phase of the next sequence. Because of this long-lived temporal setting and high preservation potential, the shelfal record of incised-valleys can yield clues about lowstand deposition on the shelf margin and slope. The apparent re-occupation and re-incision the Trinity/Sabine valley suggests it efficiently provided sand-rich sediment to the shelf during early highstand and to the shelf margin during late highstand and lowstand. Flushing of the previous fluvial-valley fills by early highstand, sea-level falls (SB_{5d} and SB_{5b}) could potentially have produced sandy "perched lowstand" (Posamentier and Vail, 1988) deposits (thin deltas or beaches) on the mid to outer shelf. The late highstand fall (SB_4) probably delivered sand to the shelf margin and slope prior to the ultimate lowstand (SB_2).

Fisk (1944) proposed the concept of linked coastal and fluvial aggradation/degradation in response to glacial eustasy. In general, our observation of sequences composed of both fluvial and offlapping (probably deltaic) facies supports Fisk's concept. As alluded to previously, the fluvial complexes on the continental shelf are separated from the

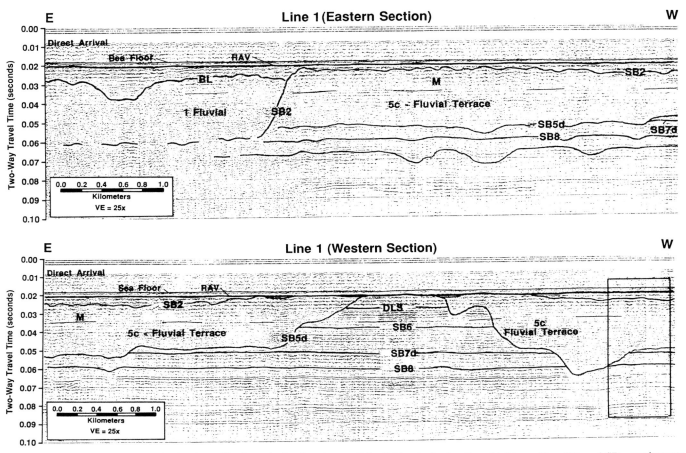

FIG. 4.—Line 1, strike-oriented seismic profile from the landward part of the Sabine incised valley. At this position SB$_2$ and SB$_{5d}$ amalgamate in the interfluves, and so the 5c offlapping sequence (SQ$_{5c}$) is not preserved. SB$_2$ and SB$_{5d}$ bound the 5c fluvial complex. At the eastern end, SB$_2$ truncates the 5c fluvial complex and forms the base of the stage 1 fluvial deposits. BL—bayline, M—sea-floor multiple, RAV—ravinement surface, DLS—Stage 5e downlap surface, SB—sequence boundary. See Figure 6 for location.

offlapping units by a transgressive flooding surface (bayline or ravinement) so that fluvial and coastal aggradation is not simultaneous but occurs within the same sea-level cycle.

An interesting question to pose is how far inland does fluvial aggradation occur in response to base-level rise. A rough estimate of this distance is possible with the current data if one accepts our tentative correlation of the 5c terraced fluvial complexes offshore to the Deweyville Terraces onshore. In the type area along the Sabine River described by Bernard (1950), the Deweyville Terrace lies about 4 m above the Holocene (stage 1) floodplain and also about 4 m below the Beaumont Terrace (probably SQ$_{5e}$). Similarly, just offshore, Line 1 (Fig. 4) shows comparable (3–4 m) offsets between the upper surfaces of stage 1 fluvial, 5c fluvial, and SQ$_{5e}$ interfluve deposits. The stage 5c highstand shoreline was about 50 km offshore from the present shoreline. Gagliano and Thom (1967) reported that the Deweyville Terrace extends 35 to 45 km inland from the head of Trinity Bay (70 to 80 km from the present shoreline). Therefore, stage 5c base-level rise may have influenced fluvial deposition up to 130 km inland from the stage 5c highstand shoreline. Other factors (climate, discharge changes, and basinward equilibrium profile shifts) also in-

fluence fluvial aggradation, but their role has not been evaluated in the Trinity/Sabine system.

LATE WISCONSINAN-HOLOCENE TRANSGRESSIVE INCISED-VALLEY FILL: THE EFFECT OF SHORT-TERM SEA-LEVEL CHANGES

Sea level began to rise at about 20 ka from the stage 2 lowstand, which was 120 m below present sea level (Fairbanks, 1989). A key to understanding the facies architecture of the Trinity/Sabine valley system is to adopt the concept that during the stage 1 transgression the rate of sea-level rise fluctuated dramatically (Frazier, 1974; Penland and others, 1988; Anderson and Thomas, 1991). The range in rates of sea-level rise span from stillstand to 5–10 m per one thousand years. We will demonstrate that the fluctuating rate of sea-level rise produced a greater facies complexity within the Trinity/Sabine incised valley than would result from a steady continuous rise.

Key Surfaces and Depositional Facies

The following surfaces and depositional facies are recognized.

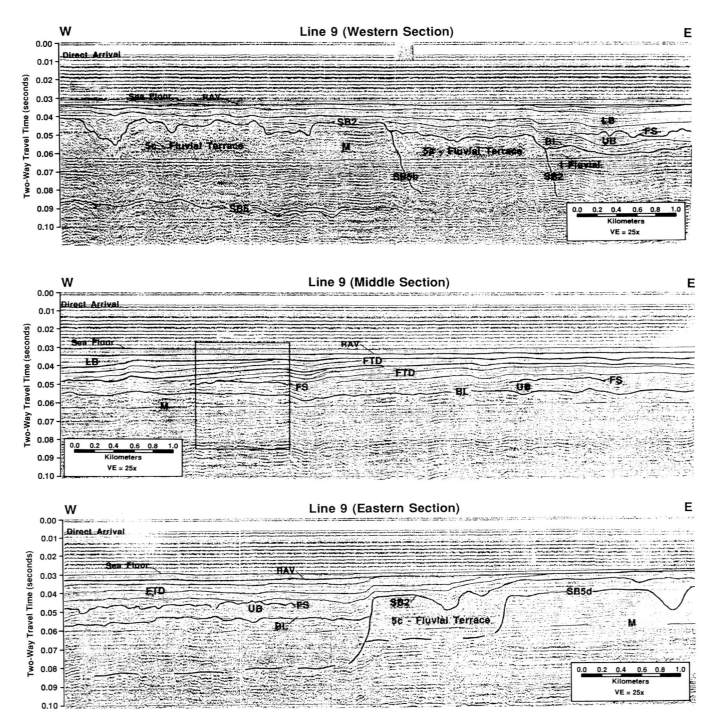

FIG. 5.—Line 9, at this location the 5c offlapping sequence (SQ$_{5c}$) occurs adjacent to the Trinity/Sabine incised valley (east end of line). The unconformities which bound the 5c fluvial complex also bound the 5c offlapping sequence. The interpretation of the 5a fluvial complex remnant is based on the height offset of the terrace surface. Flood-tidal facies within the estuarine section prograde landward, oblique to the valley axis (northwest). M—sea-floor multiple, FTD—flood-tidal delta, UB—upper bay, BL—bayline, FS—flooding surface, LB—lower bay, RAV—ravinement surface, DLS—stage 5e downlap surface, SB—sequence boundary. See Figure 6 for location.

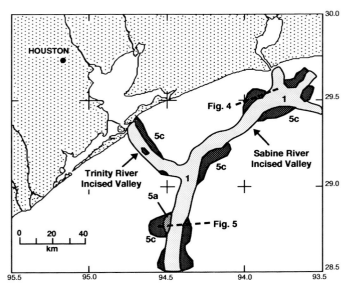

FIG. 6.—The Trinity/Sabine incised-valley system, showing the stage 5c and probable stage 5a fluvial complexes preserved along the valley margin.

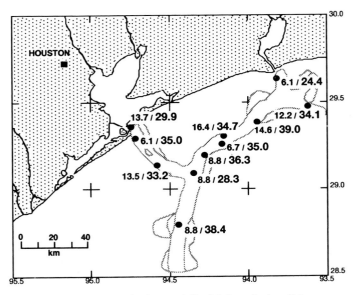

FIG. 7.—Thickness (m) of stage 1 fluvial deposits (small type, preceding slash) and depth (m) of incision (large type, following slash) below the sea floor for the Trinity/Sabine incised valley, based on geotechnical borings.

Sequence Boundary SB_2.—

SB_2 forms the base of the stage 1 valley fill, and the incision is 35 to 40 m below the sea floor throughout the study area (Fig. 7). SB_2 truncates older sequence boundaries and overlying deposits onlap against it. In the interfluvial areas, ravinement modified SB_2, so the sequence boundary and ravinement surface amalgamate.

Bayline Surface.—

The bayline surface is the fluvial-estuarine contact, which appears as a broad, high-amplitude reflector (Fig. 9). Pearson and others (1986) reported a similar seismic response on 3.5 kHz profiles and found organic intervals associated with that reflector. Analysis of those intervals showed organic content of 50 to 80% with large fragments of cypress wood (Pearson and others, 1986). The minor relief of several meters on this surface is attributed to the drowned topography of the former floodplain. By analogy, meander-belt topography of the modern Trinity River floodplain has up to two meters of relief.

Regionally, the bayline surface has a uniform slope with an average gradient of 0.0030 at the top of the stage 1 fluvial deposits (Fig. 10). Locally, however, the bayline surface steepens and forms steps of 7 to 10 m. The largest bayline steps occur within Galveston Bay where they are defined by core control.

Upper Bay Flooding Surface.—

As commonly observed within the Trinity/Sabine valley, the upper-bay flooding surface (UBFS) separates truncated horizontal reflectors of the upper-bay/bayhead-delta facies from onlapping horizontal reflectors of middle-bay deposits. Although this contact between successive transgressive facies may seem conformable, evidence from core and seismic records suggests these contacts represent discontinuities in the valley-fill succession (Figs. 9, 11). We suspect that the erosional relief below the UBFS is drowned topography and not a process of the flooding phase. In general terms, the UBFS separates proximal estuarine environments from overlying distal estuarine environments. The juxtaposition of facies across the upper-bay flooding surface can be pronounced, for example, where flood-tidal facies overlie upper-bay facies.

Ravinement Surface.—

The most widespread flooding surface is the marine ravinement surface (Nummedal and Swift, 1987), which is formed by erosional shoreface retreat during rising sea level. The depth of shoreface erosion on the Texas shelf is about 8 m and is a function of wave, storm, and tidal power (Nummedal and Swift, 1987). The ravinement surface is regionally continuous. Over the incised valley it separates estuarine and marine deposits. On the interfluves, where it amalgamates with SB_2, it separates offlapping sequences 5e and 5c from transgressive marine deposits of stage 1 (Fig. 4). The ravinement is characterized by truncation of reflectors below and subtle onlap above (Figs. 5, 9).

Fluvial Facies.—

As previously noted, stage 1 fluvial deposits are not well imaged on seismic profiles. The data wipe-out zone beneath the incised valleys can be an aid in their identification as the valley edge often coincides with the masking of deep reflectors (Fig. 9). Geotechnical borings indicate that fluvial facies vary from 6 to 16 m thick (average about 9 m) and locally fine upwards from fine gravel to fine sand (Fig.

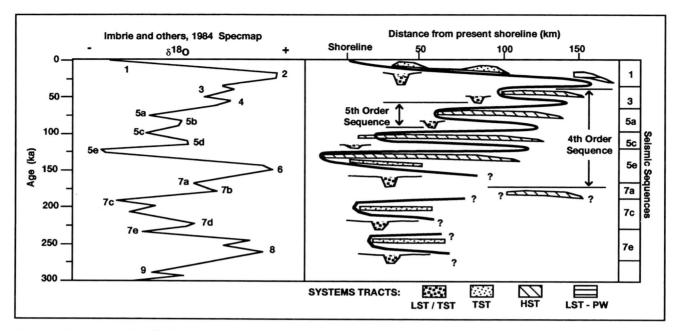

Fig. 8.—Comparison of the distribution of fifth-order sequences to the δ¹⁸O curve of Imbrie and others (1984). Each fifth-order sequence has a lowstand component (incised fluvial complex) and a highstand component (prograding, offlapping sequence) separated by a transgressive surface. Taken together the fifth-order sequences form the highstand systems tract of the fourth-order sequence (δ¹⁸O stages 6 to 2). LST-PW—lowstand prograding wedge.

7). Where sampled (CEI cores, Pearson and others, 1986), the stage 1 fluvial sands are quartzose, fine grained (2.5 phi), poorly sorted, and significantly more rounded (rounded to subrounded) than other sediments examined.

Upper-bay/Bayhead-delta Facies.—

The upper-bay facies is distinctive in seismic character, but as yet there are only core descriptions (from Nelson and Bray, 1970 and geotechnical borings) which tie to the seismic data. Internally, the upper-bay facies contains horizontal, subparallel reflectors. This facies reaches a maximum thickness of 8 m and thins up valley where it pinches out against the bayline so that the upper-bay/bayhead-delta complex forms a flat-topped wedge bounded at the base by the sloping bayline and at the top by a UBFS. A diagnostic feature is that the upper contact shows minor erosion and relief of three meters or less (Fig. 9). Geotechnical borings show a marked increase in sediment stiffness and decrease in water content at this contact (Fig. 11). These characteristics likely result from subaerial exposure, perhaps in a tidal marsh or a bayhead delta-plain setting that is periodically wet and dry. Tidal or distributary channeling may also account for the erosional relief observed (Frey and Basan, 1985).

Very low-angle clinoforms (dips ≈0.15°) that prograde down the valley axis characterize the delta front of the bayhead delta. Strike-oriented profiles show the bayhead delta lobes to be lenticular and fill former bathymetric lows. Typical faunas of the Trinity Delta include species of the foraminifera *Ammonia, Elphidium* and *Ammotium,* and the pelecypods *Rangia* and *Crassostrea* (McEwen, 1969). In borings which penetrate upper-bay and bayhead-delta fa-

cies, the lithologies are described as predominantly brown-green muds with minor fine sands. Significant amounts of plant debris are present.

Figures 12, 13, and 14 show the distribution of upper-bay and bayhead-delta deposits. The upper surfaces of upper-bay/bayhead-delta complexes occur at discrete elevations of −29 m, −20 m, and −14 m.

Middle to Lower Bay Facies.—

Middle and lower-bay facies show continuous horizontal internal reflectors that onlap at the lower contact (Fig. 9). Geotechnical borings describe these sediments as soft, olive-green muds that have characteristically high water contents (> 75%) (Fig. 11). Shell beds (3–5 cm thick) of *Mulinia* hash and silty sand occur within the laminated muds. Oyster reefs would be expected to occur in this facies although none were noted in core or seismic profiles. Preserved middle-bay facies range from 3 to 5 m in thickness.

Tidal Facies.—

Two tidal facies, flood-tidal delta and tidal inlet, are recognized in the seismic data. Long, low-angle clinoforms (dips ≈0.25°) characterize the flood-tidal delta. The clinoforms indicate a transport direction landward and oblique to the valley axis. The flood-tidal delta in Figures 5 and 15 downlap onto the bayline surface and upper-bay facies. The clinoform reflectors generally toplap at the upper surface of the flood-tidal delta. Locally the marine ravinement surface truncates the upper surface. The maximum thickness of flood-tidal deposits is 15 m. On seismic line *J*, the flood-tidal facies have a pattern of toplapping landward progradation followed by an aggradational phase and then resumed

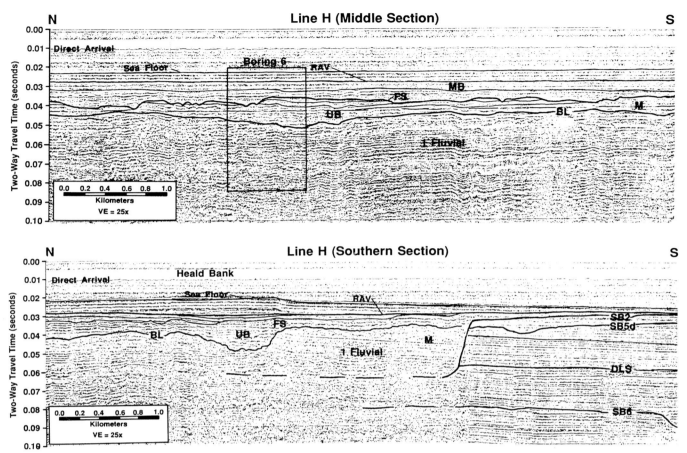

FIG. 9.—Line H, from the southern edge of the Sabine incised valley, shows the low erosional relief associated with the flooding surface (FS) above the upper-bay facies (UB). Note how deeper Pleistocene reflectors are wiped-out beneath the valley margin. DLS—Stage 5e downlap surface, M—sea-floor multiple, BL—bayline, MB—middle bay, RAV—ravinement surface, SB—sequence boundary. Box indicates position of geotechnical boring 6, see Figure 12 for location.

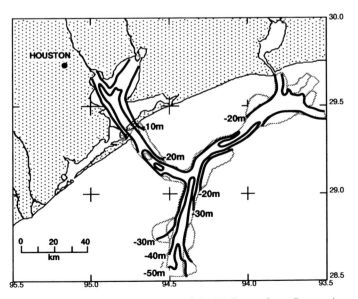

FIG. 10.—Structural contour map of the bayline surface. Contour interval = 10 m, sediment velocity = 1550 m/s.

progradation (Fig. 15). At least four aggradation-progradation cycles were observed, with each aggradational phase stepping up 1 to 2 m. Geotechnical borings which penetrated interpreted flood-tidal delta facies describe the interval as soft to firm, green-gray clays with silty to sandy interbeds.

The tidal-inlet channel is characterized by sigmoidal clinoform reflectors (maximum dips range from 0.35 to 0.45°) which accrete laterally across the valley (Fig. 16). The basal contact is erosive with preserved relief of about 9 m from the margin to the center of the inlet. The ravinement surface forms the upper boundary of the inlet sequence. Figure 17 demonstrates the cut and fill seismic character of shallow tidal-channel or spit-platform deposits. Geotechnical boring #7 (Fig. 18) ties to Figure 17 and describes the tidal facies as soft clay with sand and shells. Figure 18 also demonstrates that the shallow channeled interval is well above the fluvial deposits. Tidal-inlet fills are distributed as discrete pods (Figs. 12, 14). The erosive base of the tidal-inlet facies is only locally preserved. Where the tidal pods do not occur, the tidal-channel base erosional surface is either absent or has been modified by ravinement.

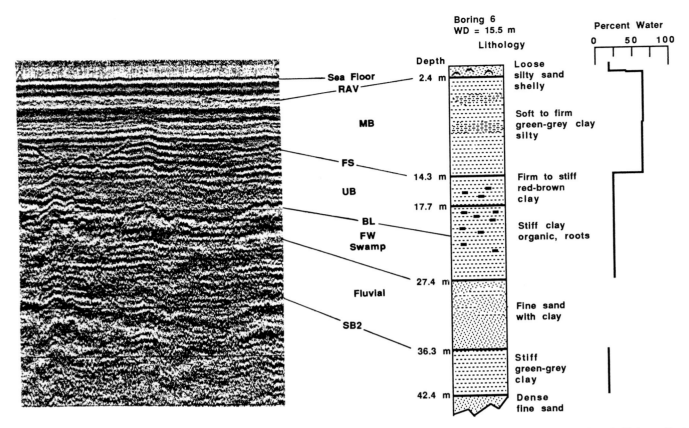

FIG. 11.—Comparison of seismic profile H to geotechnical boring 6. Reflector quality within fluvial deposits, below the broad, high-amplitude bayline reflector, is poor. The fluvial facies is 15 m thick. The eroded surface of the upper-bay facies ties to a change from soft, high water content estuarine muds to stiffer clays. UB—upper bay, BL—bayline, FS—flooding surface, MB—middle bay, RAV—ravinement surface, SB—sequence boundary. See Figures 9 and 12 for locations.

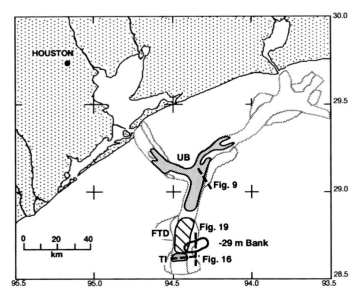

FIG. 12.—Depositional environments for the −29 meter stillstand parasequence (PS₁). UB—upper bay/bayhead delta, FTD—flood-tidal delta, TI—tidal inlet, −29 m bank—marine shelf sand body.

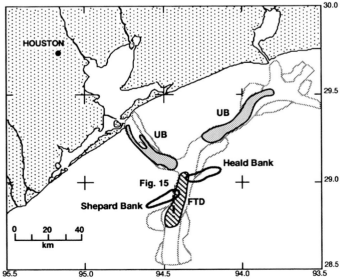

FIG. 13.—Depositional environments for the −20 meter stillstand parasequence (PS₂). UB—upper bay/bayhead delta, FTD—flood-tidal delta, Shepard and Heald Banks—marine shelf sand bodies.

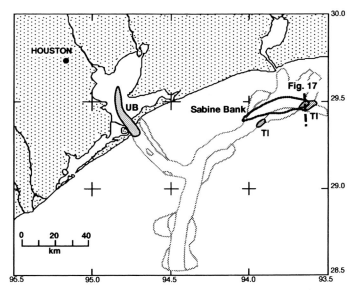

FIG. 14.—Depositional environments for the −14 meter stillstand parasequence (PS₃). UB—upper bay/bayhead delta, TI—tidal inlet, Sabine Bank—marine shelf sand body.

Marine Mud and Shelf Sand Facies.—

Reflectors within the marine facies are horizontal and parallel, but where this facies is thin (<1 m), real reflectors are difficult to distinguish from the sea floor pulse. Numerous piston cores penetrate the marine-mud facies inasmuch as it forms the present sea-floor surface. These sediments are bioturbated, sandy, green-gray muds. Thickness of marine facies is greatest (1.5 m to 2.5 m) over the incised valley, owing to increased accommodation caused by compaction of valley-fill sediments.

The shelf sand banks are prominent bathymetric features; for example, the crest of Sabine Bank is 7.5 m above the surrounding sea floor. Internal structure of the banks is obscured by ringing of the sea-floor pulse (Figs. 9, 17) due presumably to their uniform lithology. Because internal ve-

locity contrasts are minimal, no internal reflections are produced. The shelf sand bodies contain 80 to 95% sand to coarse silt, and mean-grain size for this fraction is 2.2 to 2.6 phi. Shells and shell fragments coarser than −1 phi constitute from 2 to 10% of the sediments. Sand banks in interfluve areas lie on the ravinement surface (which coincides with SB₂) so that the sand bodies are relatively flat based. Where shelf sands overlie portions of the incised valley, they are juxtaposed with diverse depositional environments beneath the ravinement, including estuarine muds, flood-tidal delta, and tidal inlets. The flood-tidal deltas and tidal inlets are truncated by the ravinement surface (Figs. 15, 17) so they are likely sand sources for the marine sand banks. Locally, there are thin deposits preserved between the ravinement surface and SB₂ outside the valley (Fig. 19). No cores penetrate these areas, but we suspect these are preserved barrier island/lagoon or strandplain facies as they lie along strike near the tidal inlets (Fig. 12).

Transgressive Valley-fill Model

An idealized valley-fill succession resulting from a steady sea-level rise and a continuous sediment supply will consist of fluvial, bayline surface, upper bay, bayhead delta, middle bay, tidal delta, tidal inlet, ravinement surface, and offshore marine facies. A core taken anywhere along the valley axis would encounter all these facies because the facies contacts would parallel the bayline surface slope. In contrast, valley-fill facies, and particularly the upper-bay/bayhead-delta and tidal-inlet/delta facies, within the Trinity/Sabine system are distributed discontinuously (Figs. 12, 13, 14). We present a model to explain the discontinuous facies architecture that incorporates Frazier's (1974) proposal that sea level rose in a step-like manner.

In the model, sea-level change is assumed to be the primary control on valley-fill facies architecture. Essentially, three variables control the stratal patterns which result from changes in accommodation and relative sea level: eustasy, subsidence, and sediment supply. Rates of sea-level rise average 0.7 cm/a for the early Holocene period and 0.3 cm/a for the late Holocene period. In contrast, Winker (1979)

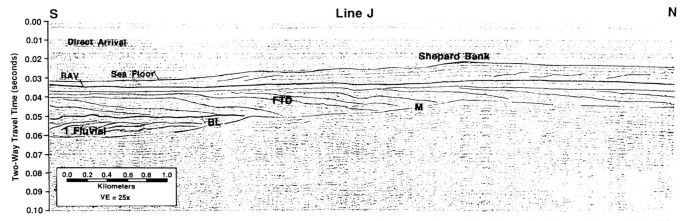

FIG. 15.—Line J, a dip-oriented seismic profile showing toplap and aggradation within flood tidal delta facies. M—sea-floor multiple, BL—bayline, FS—flooding surface, RAV—ravinement surface, SB—sequence boundary. See Figure 13 for location.

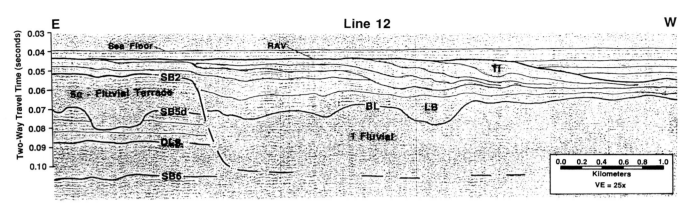

Fig. 16.—Line 12, a strike-oriented seismic profile through tidal-inlet facies, which shows sigmoidal lateral accretion. BL—bayline, LB—lower bay, RAV—ravinement surface, SB—sequence boundary, DLS—stage 5e downlap surface. See Figure 12 for location.

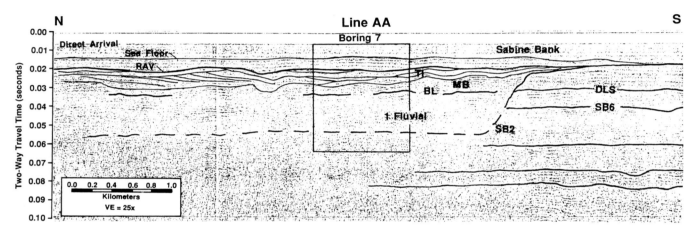

Fig. 17.—Line AA, seismic profile through tidal-inlet facies and the seaward side of Sabine Bank. Numerous shallow cut and fills with reactivation surfaces represent spit platform deposits. BL—bayline, MB—middle bay, TI—tidal inlet, RAV—ravinement surface, SB—sequence boundary, DLS—stage 5e downlap surface. Box indicates position of geotechnical boring 7 (Fig. 18). See Figure 14 for location.

estimated an average subsidence rate of 0.01 cm/a for the Texas coast and inner shelf during the late Wisconsinan-Holocene period. This order of magnitude difference in rate suggests subsidence plays a minor role in controlling stratigraphy on the inner to middle shelf. To better understand the role of sediment supply, in future research we will compare the Trinity/Sabine valley to other incised valleys along the Texas shelf. If the valley fills all show similar and coeval stratal patterns, then eustasy is most likely the primary control.

The upper-bay flooding surface represents transgression across a surface that was equal to sea level (i.e., base level) during periods of relative stillstand (Fig. 20). Seismic reflections of these surfaces approximate time lines. Within the estuarine realm, flooding surfaces (and time lines) are horizontal and vertically separated.

Updip, flooding surfaces (and time lines) onlap the bayline surface (Fig. 20). In theory, time lines would cross the bayline surface and project into the fluvial environment. However, for practical dating purposes (i.e., radiocarbon methods), time lines become amalgamated at the surface of the fluvial deposits because that is where datable organic material is concentrated. Freshwater swamps and peats, which will underlie the bayline surface and have often been used to date sea-level position (e.g., Nelson and Bray, 1970; Pearson and others, 1986), are currently found over 35 km inland from the head of Trinity Bay. This suggests freshwater swamp and peat deposits are not always the best materials for dating the position of former shorelines.

Downdip, flooding surfaces (and time lines) are truncated at the ravinement surface (Fig. 20). If sea-level rise is discontinuous, the ravinement surface should have segments with distinct ages. These distinct segments may be smeared by later storm reworking. Nevertheless, the ravinement surface will be diachronous in a regional sense, becoming younger toward the basin margin (Nummedal and Swift, 1987).

Ideally, during a sea-level stillstand (time − T_1), the complete spectra of valley-fill environments coexist (Fig. 20). Sediments fill a wedge-shaped space resulting from a prior rise in sea level. Upper-bay and bayhead-delta facies fill the upper portion of the estuary. Progradation of the bayhead delta can produce aggradation of the river. Meanwhile, flood-tidal delta and tidal-inlet deposits retrograde

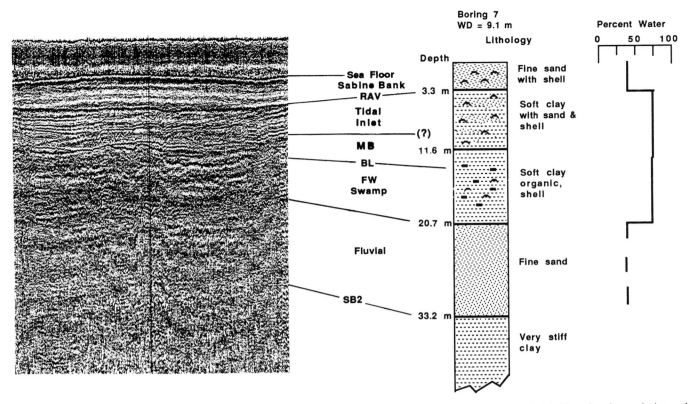

FIG. 18.—Comparison of line AA with geotechnical boring 7. Tidal-inlet facies contain clays with sand and shells. Note that the sandy interval associated with the tidal inlet is well above the sandy fluvial facies. BL—bayline, FW—freshwater swamp?, MB—middle bay, RAV—ravinement surface, SB—sequence boundary.

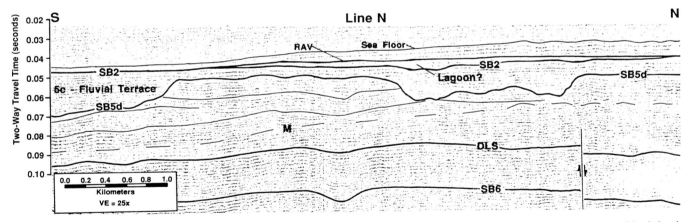

FIG. 19.—Line N, dip-oriented seismic profile through the −29 m Bank. Deposits between SB_2 and ravinement may be preserved back barrier lagoon. RAV—ravinement surface, SB—sequence boundary, DLS—stage 5e downlap surface.

from the estuary mouth. Given time, estuarine sediments will aggrade to the equilibrium depths imposed by wind-driven and tidal currents and base-level. Coeval strandplain or barrier island/lagoon deposits occur along strike from the estuary mouth at approximately the same elevation as upper-bay deposits.

Next follows a period of rapid sea-level rise. Estuarine sedimentation is inferred to be at a minimum during rapid

rise, so this phase is preserved as landward shifts of the bayline and ravinement surfaces. Moreover, the previous base level to which estuarine sediments have aggraded becomes the UBFS (note the UBFS will not be a perfectly flat surface as illustrated, but rather it will reflect the topography/bathymetry of the stillstand estuarine system). In this model, the UBFS is unique in that it alone, at least in principle, is able to preserve the time and elevation (be-

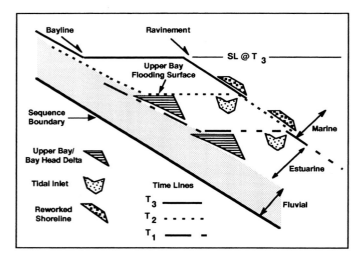

FIG. 20.—Incised-valley fill model, longitudinal profile. Note upper-bay flooding surfaces ($\approx$ time lines) are horizontal and vertically separated within the estuarine succession. See text for explanation. No scale intended.

cause the surface of the upper-bay/bayhead-delta facies approximates base level) of the onset of the rapid sea-level rise phase. Barrier island, strandplain, and tidal deposits, which formed during stillstand, are reworked by the ravinement process. Finally, the model repeats as sediments aggrade to fill the newly created space (times T_2, T_3).

Sea-level History

The paired upper-bay and tidal facies, bounded by flooding surfaces, define three parasequences (PS_1, PS_2, and PS_3) which step landward within the Trinity/Sabine incised valley (Fig. 21). These parasequences formed during sea-level stillstands. Former sea level is estimated from the elevation of the relatively flat upper surface of upper-bay deposits. Principle evidence for sea-level control is the similar elevation of the paired upper-bay/tidal-inlet facies. The age

of stillstands is estimated by integrating the relatively sparse radiocarbon dates with the seismic stratigraphy (i.e., by determining the relationship of dates to the bayline, upper-bay flooding, and ravinement surfaces). For example, Figure 22 illustrates how the radiocarbon-dated cores relate to these surfaces for PS_2. The peats dated in core TGB-C (≈ 10.2 ka, Rehkemper, 1969) lie below the bayline flooding surface and, therefore, have little relation to the age of the overlying parasequence. *Rangia* from core TGB-D date the upper bay-facies of PS_2 at 7.9 ka (Rehkemper, 1969). The ravinement surface that truncates the PS_2 UBFS is dated at approximately 7.0 ka from *Mulinia* in core NB-13 (Nelson and Bray, 1970) and at approximately 7.5 ka from *Mulinia* in core G-142 (Thomas, 1990). Heald Bank, the former PS_2 shoreline deposit, dates younger than its corresponding PS_2 estuarine parasequence, owing to the incorporation of younger shell material by ravinement and marine reworking (Fig. 22). The ravinement surface of the previous parasequence (PS_1) is dated at 8.7 ka (*Mulinia* sample, core G-151, Thomas, 1990). We conclude that PS_2 deposition began after 8.7 ka and ended approximately 7.0 ka (Figs. 22, 23). Using similar analyses we have estimated the ages of PS_1 and PS_3 (Fig. 23) (Thomas, 1990). This method yields good age estimates of the terminal flooding phase for each parasequence but not for the onset of stillstand.

Sea-level history for the Trinity/Sabine area corresponds well to the chronostratigraphy proposed for the Mississippi Delta region by Penland and others (1988) (Fig. 23). PS_3 correlates to the Teche delta-plain (late Holocene, 3.3 to 6.7 ka) progradation (Penland and others, 1988). Ravinement of the Teche delta plain (2.5–3.3 ka, Penland and others, 1988) produced a series of transgressive shelf sand bodies, Ship Shoal and Trinity Shoal, which should be time equivalent to Sabine Bank. Transgression of the early Holocene delta plain (≈ 7.0 ka, Penland and others, 1988) also produced a shelf sand body, Outer Bank, which would correlate to Shepard and Heald banks (PS_2). These correlations support sea-level control of parasequence stratigraphy inasmuch as the Trinity/Sabine valley and the Mississippi Delta have quite different subsidence and sedimentation rates.

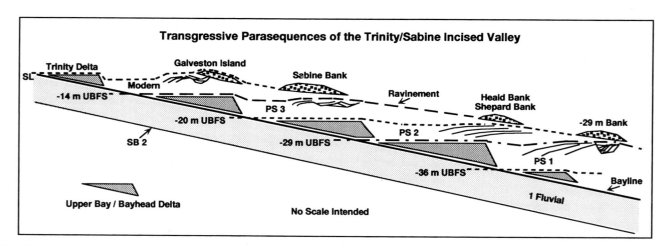

FIG. 21.—Composite longitudinal profile of the Trinity/Sabine incised-valley system. For each stillstand position there are paired upper-bay and flood-tidal delta/tidal-inlet facies. The upper-bay flooding surfaces (UBFS) bound each landward-stepping parasequence (PS).

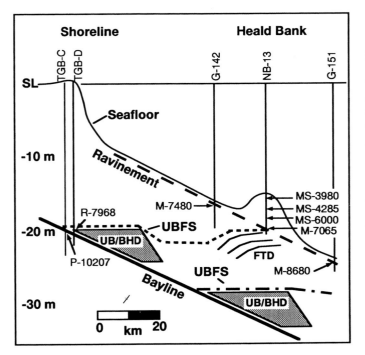

FIG. 22.—Dip section of the Trinity incised valley that demonstrates the relationship of radiocarbon dates to the flooding surfaces (bayline, upper bay, and ravinement) for PS₂. TGB cores from Rehkemper (1969), NB core from Nelson and Bray (1970), and G cores from Thomas (1990). See Figure 13 for core locations. Ages in radiocarbon years, no corrections are applied. MS—mixed marine shells, M—*Mulinia*, R—*Rangia*, P—peat, UB/BHD—upper bay/bayhead delta, UBFS—upper-bay flooding surface, and FTD—flood-tidal delta.

Incised-valley Fill Facies Architecture

Sea level appears to be the dominant control of valley-fill facies distribution in the low sediment supply, low subsidence rate setting of the Trinity/Sabine valley system. Considerable variability among the parasequences exists, especially regarding the presence/preservation of flood-tidal delta and tidal-inlet deposits. This variability in facies architecture is examined in the light of changing rates of sea-level rise.

Fluvial Realm.—

Hypothetically, the flooding surfaces formed by periods of rapid rise can be projected through the bayline surface into the fluvial deposits. Within the fluvial environment, periods of rapid rise and stillstand may be manifested as surfaces of minimal sedimentation followed by aggradational deposits. Core control and seismic resolution within the stage 1 fluvial deposits are limited, and so the internal geometry can not be resolved. However, the bayline-surface structure map, which approximates the river gradient, reveals the geometry of the top of the fluvial deposits (Figs. 10, 24). Although the gradient appears uniform regionally, there are interesting local "steps" in or steepenings of the bayline surface.

The most prominent step in the bayline is just landward of the modern Trinity delta. Cores described by Rehkemper (1969) show stacked channel facies that occur at two elevation ranges (−1 to −2.5 m and −9 to −14 m). The lower channel surface matches the trend of the bayline structure

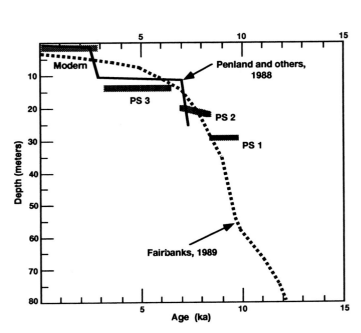

FIG. 23.—Comparison of the age and elevation of stillstand parasequences PS₁, PS₂, and PS₃ to sea-level curves for the Holocene.

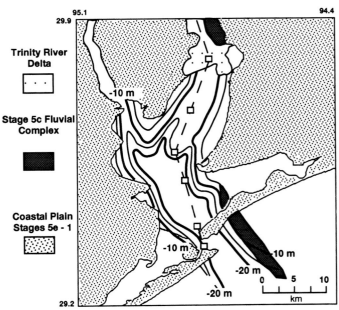

FIG. 24.—Detailed structural-contour map of the bayline surface in Galveston Bay. Adapted from Smyth (1991). One bayline step is in lower Trinity Bay (from >−20 m to <−15 m), and the other in upper Trinity Bay (from >−10 m to 0 m, the height of modern delta-distributary channels). Contour interval = 5 m, depth conversion velocity = 1550 m/s. Boxes and dashed line indicate position of cores and cross-section in Figure 25.

map and represents its up-valley extension (Fig. 25). The upper channel is the modern river channel and floodplain that formed as the Trinity Delta prograded into the bay. Projecting the regional bayline gradient updip from the lower channel in core WAL-211 enables an estimation of the highstand turnaround point (or furthest inland extent of the bayline) (Fig. 25). This method predicts that the former head of Trinity Bay was 32 km inland from the present bayline. The present stream gradient of the Trinity River begins to flatten (from 0.00028 to 0.00020) about 40 km inland. The projected bayline and current floodplain/delta-plain surfaces define a wedge of sediment deposited since sea-level highstand about 3,000 years ago. Progradation of the Trinity Delta into the bay has produced the apparent step in the bayline (apparent in that on seismic profiles only the top of the shallowest fluvial channel is imaged).

Another bayline step occurs in lower Trinity Bay, where boring descriptions suggest a major change in bayline elevation from −21 to −14 m (Figs. 24, 25). Throughout the rest of the Trinity/Sabine valley, no other unequivocal steps in the bayline were detected on seismic profiles. Locating these steps without detailed core control is difficult, and care must be taken to discriminate steps in the stage 1 fluvial surface from elevation differences associated with the older fluvial terraces.

The bayline step at −21 to −14 m correlates in elevation to PS_3, while the step from −11 to −1 m corresponds to the modern sea-level stillstand (Figs. 21, 25). The duration of both of these stillstands is about three thousand years (Fig. 23). This implies that in the low sediment supply regime of the Trinity River significant bayhead-delta progradation (basinward shift of the bayline) requires extended periods of sea-level stillstand. Flattening of the Trinity River gradient may reflect the phenomenon of subaerial accommodation, as suggested by Posamentier and Vail's (1988) models of equilibrium profile shifts and as observed in Leopold and Bull's (1979) results from erosion check-dam studies.

Estuarine Realm.—

Facies preservation is a function of how deep (stratigraphically) within the valley fill the deposit occurs. Stage

1 fluvial deposits are the best preserved because they are, without exception, at the base of the SB_2 valley. For the estuarine portion of each parasequence to maintain the same preservation potential, it can not overlap with the previous parasequence. In essence, the preservation potential increases if deposits fill an empty hole (valley). Rapid and large sea-level rises increase accommodation space and the probability of complete parasequence preservation. Within the study area, the size of the empty hole is relatively constant as the depth of SB_2 incision and thickness of stage 1 fluvial facies are fairly uniform (Fig. 7).

Conversely, slow and small sea-level rises decrease preservation potential. In this case, estuarine parasequences will overlap and deposit into already partially filled space. The result is that stratigraphically higher deposits (typically lower bay, flood-tidal delta, and tidal inlet) are susceptible to ravinement. Siringan (1993) estimated the depth of ravinement offshore of Galveston Island to be −8 m.

The evolution and preservation of Trinity/Sabine valley-fill deposits reflect changing rates of sea-level rise. PS_1 apparently followed a period of rapid rise in sea level and filled an empty valley (excluding fluvial deposits). A consequence of the preceding rapid sea-level rise is that the estuary was elongate and deep. Such an estuary shape can amplify tidal range, which likely caused the extensive flood-oriented tidal deposits of PS_1; volumetrically, PS_1 (Figs. 12, 21) is composed of 50% flood-tidal delta, 42% upper-bay/bayhead-delta, and 8% tidal-inlet facies.

PS_2, which represents a period of small sea-level rises, overlaps with PS_1; thus, accommodation for estuarine deposition was already partially filled. The small amplitude sea-level rises are inferred from the alternating aggradational and progradational geometry of the flood-tidal delta (Fig. 15). The combination of previously filled accommodation space and small, sea-level rises caused tidal-inlet facies (if ever deposited) not to be preserved. PS_2 is composed of 68% upper-bay/bayhead-delta, 21% flood-tidal delta, and 11% middle-bay facies (Figs. 13, 21).

PS_3 represents a long, sea-level stillstand (about three thousand years), and differs from previous parasequences in that it occurs upstream of the confluence of the Trinity

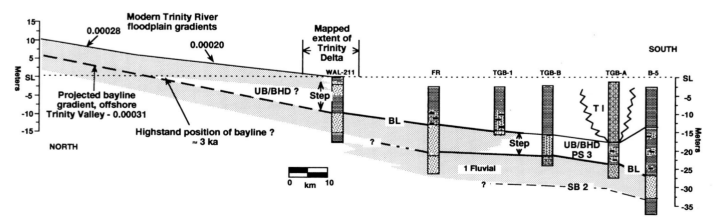

FIG. 25.—Core transect within Galveston Bay that demonstrates the occurrence of bayline surface steps. See Figure 24 for location and text for explanation. SB—sequence boundary, BL—bayline surface, UB/BHD—upper bay/bayhead delta

and Sabine rivers (Fig. 14). Volume estimates for PS 3 were not attempted because the upper-bay/bayhead-delta facies of the Sabine valley is overlain by the chenier plain east of Sabine Lake (Fig. 14). Within the Trinity valley, no flood-tidal delta or tidal-inlet facies are recognized. This appears anomalous given the time available to develop an inlet (the modern inlet complex at Bolivar Roads formed within the last three thousand years, Siringan, 1993). Considering the degree of overlap with and duration of PS$_2$, it appears that little accommodation space remained and the lower-bay facies of PS$_3$ were truncated by ravinement.

By comparison, within the Sabine valley, PS$_3$ tidal facies are preserved (Fig. 14). On one hand, this supports the contention that time was sufficient to form inlets during PS$_3$ and that those tidal facies within the Trinity valley segment were later truncated. On the other hand, it raises the question of what caused differences in preservation between adjacent valleys which surely experienced the same eustatic influence. One factor may be shelf gradient, which is lower offshore of Sabine Pass (0.00028) than Galveston Bay (0.00045). Therefore, for a given amplitude of sea-level rise the shoreface translates farther landward on a lower gradient shelf and decreases the effects of ravinement offshore. On the relatively steeper shelf offshore of Galveston Bay, the tidal inlet of PS$_3$ may have remained within the lower shoreface zone and was completely reworked. Siringan (1993) demonstrated that depth of ravinement is less on lower-gradient shelves of the Texas coast.

The estuarine valley-fill parasequences of the Trinity/Sabine system show a progressive change in preservation; through time, tidal-inlet, and flood-tidal delta facies are less well preserved (Fig. 21). The decrease in preservation of lower-bay facies reflects the overall slowing in the rate of sea-level rise about 6 ka (Fig. 23). The slowing of sea-level rise extended the duration of stillstands (allowing more time to fill available space) and caused more overlap of parasequences.

Marine Realm.—

The original interpretations of Curray (1960) and Frazier (1974) that large shelf sand bodies on the Texas continental shelf formed during sea-level stillstands continue to have merit. This study indicates that though the formation of sand bodies was initiated during stillstands, they were subsequently reworked and transported landward by shoreface ravinement as sea level rose. Periods of rapid sea-level rise, responsible for shelf sand body reworking and isolation, are manifested as discontinuities (upper-bay flooding surfaces) within the valley-fill deposits.

In most cases, there are large shelf sand bodies associated with the distal portion of each parasequence. As alluded to earlier, locally, portions of the original shoreline complex can be identified. The −29 m sand bank associated with PS$_1$ is proposed to be a reworked barrier island because there are deposits (lagoonal?) preserved between the ravinement and SB$_2$ (Fig. 19). Figure 12 shows that the −29 m bank lies 5 km landward of the PS$_1$ tidal inlet, which indicates the original shoreline position. In another case, tidal facies of the PS$_3$ shoreline have been truncated and reworked to contribute to formation of Sabine Bank (Fig.

17). The absence of abundant shoreline facies suggests these lithosomes were poorly preserved and also suggests they are probable sediment sources for the marine shelf sand banks.

Neither the shoreline facies nor the shelf sand body is preserved for PS$_3$ within the Trinity incised valley (Fig. 14). In this case, not only has the original shoreline/inlet complex been reworked but the shelf sand body as well. We propose that the shelf sand derived from shoreline deposits of the PS$_3$ Trinity valley was continually reworked and became the nucleus of Galveston Island. Radiocarbon dates on shells from Galveston Island (age of oldest shells ≈7.2 ka) indicate a large amount of reworked material within the older portions of the barrier (Bernard and others, 1970). Again, we attribute the more efficient shoreface ravinement above the Trinity valley (relative to the Sabine valley) to the steeper shelf gradient.

CONCLUSIONS

Both long-term (50 m, 20 ka) and short-term (5–10 m, <1 ka) sea-level changes have influenced the evolution of the Trinity/Sabine incised-valley system. The generalized facies architecture of the valley fill is summarized in a block diagram of the study area and schematic cross sections (Fig. 26).

Long-term sea-level changes, caused by the cyclic growth of Wisconsinan ice sheets, produced cycles of valley incision and aggradation. Within the Trinity/Sabine incised valley, these cycles are preserved as terraced fluvial complexes (Fig. 26). We estimate that fluvial aggradation occurred up to 150 km inland of the coeval shoreline. The fluvial complexes and their contemporaneous offlapping sequences are fifth-order sequences, which together form the highstand systems tract of a fourth-order sequence.

Landward-stepping parasequences comprise the stage 1 transgressive valley fill of the Trinity/Sabine incised valley. Upper-bay flooding surfaces, which separate proximal from distal estuarine facies, bound three parasequences. The wedge-shaped space defined by upper-bay flooding surfaces filled with seaward-prograding, upper-bay and bayhead-delta deposits and landward-prograding, flood-tidal delta and tidal-inlet deposits. The three parasequences defined represent sea-level stillstands during transgression. Sea-level control (as opposed to subsidence or sedimentation rate) is implied by: (1) the occurrence of paired, upper-bay and tidal facies at the same elevation, (2) the discontinuous distribution of upper-bay facies and pod-like distribution of tidal inlets, and (3) the similarity in chronostratigraphy to the Mississippi Delta region.

Changing rates of sea-level rise affected the architecture of fluvial, estuarine, and marine facies. During extended stillstands, fluvial channels aggrade and stack in response to bayhead-delta progradation. Large sea-level rises enhance preservation of flood-tidal and tidal-inlet facies by minimizing parasequence overlap and maximizing accommodation. Barrier islands and strandplains form during stillstand but are substantially reworked by subsequent sea-level rise. Periods of rapid rise are manifested as upper-bay flooding surfaces within the estuarine succession.

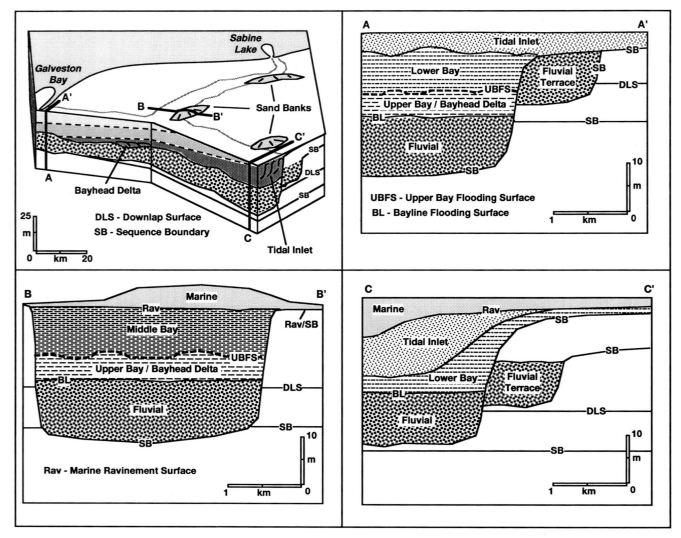

FIG. 26.—Summary diagram of the Trinity/Sabine incised-valley system. Block diagram illustrates the landward-stepping pattern of the three estuarine parasequences (gray tones). The three cross-sections (based on seismic profiles) demonstrate the variability of vertical facies successions. At locations *A* and *C*, there are facies obviously missing, which indicate the presence of a discontinuity. At location *B*, the facies succession from upper bay/bayhead delta to middle bay appears conformable, but actually there is a parasequence-bounding flooding surface that separates them.

ACKNOWLEDGMENTS

This research is funded by grants from the National Science Foundation grant (#OCE 8908320), the Petroleum Research Fund (#23494-AC8), and the Continental Shelf Division of the Marine Minerals Technology Center. The following oil companies participate in the Rice University Marine Geology and Geophysics Industrial Associates Group: Amoco, Arco, British Petroleum, Conoco, Exxon, Marathon, Shell, Unocal, and Union Pacific Resources. We thank Bruce Levell and Dag Nummedal for their helpful reviews and suggestions and Shell Development Company and Shell Western Exploration and Production for reproduction services.

REFERENCES

ABDULAH, K. C., AND ANDERSON, J. B., 1991, Eustatic controls on the evolution of the Pleistocene Brazos-Colorado deltas, Texas, *in* Coastal Depositional Systems in the Gulf of Mexico, Quaternary Framework and Environmental Issues: Austin, Twelfth Annual Research Conference, Gulf Coast Section, Society of Economic Paleontologists and Mineralogists Foundation, p. 1–7.

ALLEN, G. P., AND POSAMENTIER, H. W., 1993, Sequence stratigraphy and facies models of an incised valley fill: the Gironde Estuary, France: Journal of Sedimentary Petrology, v. 63, p. 378–391.

ANDERSON, J. B., AND THOMAS, M. A., 1991, Marine ice-sheet decoupling as a mechanism for rapid, episodic sea-level change: the record of such events and their influence on sedimentation: Sedimentary Geology, v. 70, p. 87–104.

BARTEK, L. R., ANDERSON, J. B., AND ABDULAH, K., C., 1991, A case study of the preservation potential of the coastal lithosomes of small deltaic systems: examples from the Holocene of the Texas continental shelf, *in* Coastal Depositional Systems in the Gulf of Mexico, Quaternary Framework and Environmental Issues: Austin, Twelfth Annual Research Conference, Gulf Coast Section, Society of Economic Paleontologists and Mineralogists Foundation, p. 15–25.

BERNARD, H. A., 1950, Quaternary geology of southeast Texas: Unpublished Ph. D. Dissertation, Louisiana State University, Baton Rouge, 164 p.

BERNARD, H. A., MAJOR, C. F., PARROTT, B. S., AND LEBLANC, R. J., 1970, Recent Sediments of Southeast Texas: a Field Guide to the Brazos Alluvial and Deltaic Plains and the Galveston Barrier Island Complex: Austin, University of Texas at Austin, Bureau of Economic Geology, Guidebook no. 11, 132 p.

BERRYHILL, H., L., JR., SUTER, J., R., AND HARDIN, N., S., 1986, Late Quaternary Facies and Structure, Northern Gulf of Mexico: Interpretations from Seismic Data: Tulsa, American Association of Petroleum Geologists Studies in Geology, no. 23, 289 p.

COLEMAN, J. M. AND ROBERTS, H. H., 1988, Sedimentary development of the Louisiana continental shelf related to sea level cycles: Geomarine Letters, v. 8, p. 63—119.

COLMAN, S. M., AND MIXON, R. B., 1988, The record of major Quaternary sea-level changes in a large coastal plain estuary, Chesapeake Bay, eastern United States: Palaoegeography, Palaeoclimatology, Palaeoecology, v. 68, p. 99—116.

CURRAY, J. P., 1960, Sediments and history of the Holocene transgression, continental shelf, Northwest Gulf of Mexico, in Shepard, F. P., Phleger, F. B., and Van Andel, T. H., eds., Recent Sediments, Northwest Gulf of Mexico: Tulsa, American Association of Petroleum Geologists, p. 221–266.

EMILIANI, C., 1958, Paleotemperature analysis of core 280 and Pleistocene correlations: Journal of Geology, v. 66, p. 264–275.

FAIRBANKS, R. G., 1989, A 17,000-year glacio-eustatic sea level record: influence of glacial melting rates on the Younger Dryas event and deepocean circulation: Nature, v. 342, p. 637–642.

FISK, H. N., 1944, Geological investigation of the alluvial valley of the lower Mississippi River: Vicksburg, United States Army Corps of Engineers, Mississippi River Commission, 227 p.

FLETCHER, C. H., KNEBEL, H. J., AND KRAFT, J. C., 1990, Holocene evolution of an estuarine coast and tidal wetlands: Geological Society of America Bulletin, v. 102, p. 283–297.

FRAZIER, D. E., 1974, Depositional episodes: their relationship to the Quaternary stratigraphic framework in the Northwest portion of the Gulf Basin: Austin, Texas Bureau of Economic Geology Geologic Circular 74–1, 28 p.

FREY, R. W., AND BASAN, P. B., 1985, Coastal salt marshes, in Davis, R. A., Jr., ed., Coastal Sedimentary Environments: New York, Springer-Verlag, p. 225–302.

GAGLIANO, S. M., AND TOM, B. G., 1967, Deweyville Terrace, Gulf and Atlantic coasts: Baton Rouge, Louisiana State University, Coastal Studies Bulletin 1, p. 23–41.

HAYS, J. D., IMBRIE, J., AND SHACKLETON, N. J., 1976, Variations in the Earth's orbit: Pacemaker of the ice ages: Science, v. 194, p. 1121–132.

IMBRIE, J., HAYS, J. D., MARTINSON, D. G., MCINTYRE, A., MIA, A. C., MORELY, J. J., PISIAS, N. G., PRELL, W. L., AND SHACKLETON, N. J., 1984, The orbital theory of Pleistocene climate: support for a revised chronology of the marine $\delta^{18}O$ record, in Berger, A. J., Imbrie, J., Hays, J., Kukla, G., and Saltzman, B., eds., Milankovitch and Climate, Part 1: Dordrecht, Reidel, p. 269–305.

LEOPOLD, L. B., AND BULL, W. B., 1979, Base level, aggradation, and grade: Proceedings of the American Philosophical Society, v. 123, p. 168–202.

MCEWEN, M. C., 1969, Sedimentary facies of the Trinity delta, in Lankford, R. R., and Rodgers, J. J. W., eds., Holocene Geology of the Galveston Bay Area: Houston, Houston Geological Society, p. 53–77.

MCFARLAN, E. JR., AND LEROY, D. O., 1988, Subsurface geology of the Late Tertiary and Quaternary deposits, coastal Louisiana and the adjacent continental shelf: Transactions of the Gulf Coast Association of Geologic Societies, v. 38, p. 421—433.

NELSON, H. F., AND BRAY, E. E., 1970, Stratigraphy and history of the Holocene sediments in the Sabine-High Island area, Gulf of Mexico, in Morgan, J. P., ed., Deltaic Sedimentation Modern and Ancient: Tulsa, Society of Economic Paleontologists and Mineralogists Special Publication 15, p. 48–77.

NUMMEDAL, D., AND SWIFT, D. J. P., 1987, Transgressive stratigraphy at sequence-bounding unconformities: some principles derived from Holocene and Cretaceous examples, in Nummedal, D., Pilkey, O. H., and Howard, J. D., eds., Sea-Level Fluctuation and Coastal Evolution: Tulsa, Society of Economic Paleontologists and Mineralogists Special Publication 41, p. 241–260.

PEARSON, C. E., KELLEY, D. B., WEINSTEIN, R. A., AND GAGLIANO, S. M., 1986, Archaeological investigations on the outer continental shelf: a study within the Sabine River valley, offshore Louisiana and Texas: Baton Rouge, Coastal Environments Incorporated, a report for Minerals Management Service, United States Department of the Interior, 314 p.

PENLAND, S., RAMSEY, K. E., MCBRIDE, R. A., MESTAYER, J. T., AND WESTPHAL, K. A., 1988, Relative sea-level rise and delta-plain development in the Terrebonne Parish region: Baton Rouge, Louisiana Geological Survey, Coastal Geology Technical Report, no. 4, 121 p.

POSAMENTIER, H. W., AND VAIL, P. R., 1988, Eustatic controls on clastic deposition II—Sequence and systems tract models, in Wilgus, C. K., Hastings, B. S., Kendall. C. G. St. C., Posamentier, H. W., Ross, C. A., and VanWagoner, J. C., eds., Sea-level Changes: an Integrated Approach: Tulsa, Society of Economic Paleontologists and Mineralogists Special Publication 42, p. 125–154.

REHKEMPER, L. J., 1969, Sedimentology of Holocene estuarine deposits, Galveston Bay, Texas: Unpublished Ph. D. Dissertation, Rice University, Houston, 67 p.

SARZALEJO, S., ANDERSON, J. B., COTERILL, K., AND VAIL, P. R., 1993, High frequency cyclicity in East Texas outer shelf and upper slope sequences revealed by high resolution seismic data and platform borings (abs.): American Association of Petroleum Geologists Convention, Program with Abstracts, New Orleans, Louisiana, p. 176–177.

SHACKLETON, N. J., 1967, Oxygen isotope analysis and Pleistocene temperatures re-assessed: Nature, v. 215, p. 15–17.

SHIDLER, G. L., 1986, Seismic and physical stratigraphy of Late Quaternary deposits, south Texas coastal complex, in Shidler, G. L., ed., Stratigraphic Studies of a Late Quaternary Barrier-Type Coastal Complex, Mustang Island-Corpus Christi Bay Area, South Texas Gulf Coast: Washington, D. C., United States Geological Survey Professional Paper 1328, p. 9–31.

SIRINGAN, F. P., 1993, Coastal lithosome evolution and preservation during an overall rising sea level: East Texas gulf coast and continental shelf: Unpublished Ph. D. Dissertation, Rice University, Houston, 226 p.

SMYTH, W. C., 1991, Seismic facies analysis and depositional history of an incised valley system, Galveston Bay area, Texas: Unpublished. M. S. Thesis, Rice University, Houston, 170 p.

SUTER, J. R., 1986, Ancient fluvial systems and Holocene deposits, southwestern Louisiana continental shelf, in Berryhill, H. L., Suter, J. R., and Hardin, N. S., Late Quaternary Facies and Structure of the Northern Gulf of Mexico: Interpretation from Seismic Data: Tulsa, American Association of Petroleum Geologists Studies in Geology 23, p. 81–130.

SUTER, J. R., BERRYHILL, H. L., AND PENLAND, S., 1987, Late Quaternary sea-Level fluctuations and depositional sequences, southwest Louisiana continental shelf, in Nummedal, D., Pilkey, O. H., and Howard, J. D., eds., Sea-level Fluctuation and Coastal Evolution: Tulsa, Society of Economic Paleontologists and Mineralogists Special Publication 41, p. 199–219.

THOMAS, M. A., 1990, The impact of long-term and short-term sea-level changes on the evolution of the Wisconsinan-Holocene Trinity/Sabine incised valley system, Texas continental shelf: Unpublished Ph. D. Dissertation, Rice University, Houston, 314 p.

THOMAS, M. A., AND ANDERSON, J. B., 1991, Late Pleistocene sequence stratigraphy of the Texas continental shelf: relationship to $\delta^{18}O$ curves: in Coastal Depositional Systems in the Gulf of Mexico, Quaternary Framework and Environmental Issues: Austin, Twelfth Annual Research Conference, Gulf Coast Section, Society of Economic Paleontologists and Mineralogists Foundation, p. 265–270.

THOMAS, M. A., ANDERSON, J., B., AND SIRINGAN, F., P., 1991, The response of low to moderate sediment supply incised valley systems to episodic sea-level rises (abs.): American Association of Petroleum Geologists, v. 75, p. 681.

VAIL, P. R., MITCHUM, R. M., AND THOMPSON, S., 1977, Seismic stratigraphy and global changes of sea level, part 4, global cycles and relative changes of sea level, in Peyton, C. E., ed., Seismic Stratigraphy—Applications to Hydrocarbon Exploration: Tulsa, American Association of Petroleum Geologists Memoir 26, p. 83–97.

WILKINSON, B. H., AND BYRNE, J. R., 1977, Lavaca Bay—transgressive deltaic sedimentation in a central Texas estuary: American Association of Petroleum Geologists Bulletin, v. 61, p. 427–443.

WILLIAMS, S. J., PRINS, D. A., AND MEISBURGER, E. P., 1979, Sediment distribution, sand resources, and geologic character of the inner continental shelf off Galveston County, Texas: Fort Belvoir, United States Army Corps of Engineers, Miscellaneous Report No. 79–4, 159 p.

WINKER, C. D., 1979, Late Pleistocene fluvial-deltaic deposition: Texas coastal plain and shelf: Unpublished M. S. Thesis, University of Texas, Austin, 187 p.

STRATIGRAPHY OF THE MISSISSIPPI-ALABAMA SHELF AND THE MOBILE RIVER INCISED-VALLEY SYSTEM

JACK L. KINDINGER
United States Geological Survey, Center for Coastal Geology, 600 4th St. S., St. Petersburg, FL 33701
PETER S. BALSON
British Geological Survey, Coastal Geology Group, Keyworth, Nottingham, UK NG125GG
AND
JAMES G. FLOCKS
United States Geological Survey, Center for Coastal Geology, 600 4th St. S., St. Petersburg, FL 33701

ABSTRACT: The Mobile River incised-valley system located in the northern Gulf of Mexico occupies an area from southern Alabama through Mobile Bay to the outer Mississippi-Alabama continental shelf. During the Wisconsinan regression, this incised-valley system was fluvially eroded and extended across the exposed shelf to a shelf-margin delta complex. The last postglacial transgression drowned the entrenched alluvial valleys and reworked the alluvial fill and estuarine deposits to form shoals on the middle shelf. As the postglacial transgression slowed, Mobile Bay was formed. Mobile Bay is a large estuarine system protected by barrier islands. This paper documents the late Quaternary history of the Mobile River incised valley and fill.

Mobile Bay is a large (>1000 km²) microtidal estuary in southern Alabama that receives drainage through the Mobile River system. The Mobile River catchment is the fourth largest in the United States and terminates at the bayhead delta of Mobile Bay. The bay is a classic example of a wave-dominated, drowned, fluvial incised valley. During the middle-late Wisconsinan, glacial maximum, relative sea level was approximately 120 m lower than present. The Mobile River incised valley was a conduit for drainage from the catchment to the shelf margin. The sediment carried by the fluvial system during this lowstand passed through the Mobile River incised valley, across the exposed shelf and was deposited on the shelf margin as deltaic lobes.

Rapid sea-level rise forced coastal-plain shorelines landward across the present mid-continental shelf. Transgression of the estuary mouth left a series of estuary-mouth-bar deposits that were reworked and overlie alluvial fill. These sand-rich deposits were submerged by the continuing transgression and reworked to form shoals. As the Holocene sea-level rise slowed, the Mobile River incised valley became an estuarine depocenter. In the present alluvial valley, lowstand deposits are overlain by estuarine sediments deposited during the initial flooding of the valley and subsequent formation of Mobile Bay.

During the present highstand, longshore sediment transport formed a spit across much of the bay mouth, creating a restricted estuary into which a bayhead delta has prograded. Late Holocene deposits in Mobile Bay consists predominantly of lagoonal sediments with bayhead-delta deposits encroaching into the northern end of the bay.

The Holocene incised-valley fill (estuarine facies) underlying Mobile Bay fit well into the conceptual facies model of a microtidal wave-dominated estuary. The model does not fit as well, however, with the rapidly transgressed shelf portion of the incised valley. The down dip section does not contain a clearly identifiable (from seismic profiles) estuarine facies; the valley fill is primarily fluvial and is overlain by marine shoals. In the Mobile River incised valley, the distal portion of the valley was rapidly drowned, allowing the thin estuarine facies to be reworked. The proximal portion was drowned more slowly, leaving the estuarine facies intact. Thus, the single incised valley contains two very different types of fill.

INTRODUCTION

Recent industrial and academic concerns have ignited interest in the evolution and history of incised valleys. Incised valleys commonly result from fluvial down cutting in response to sea-level fall. Sediments that fill incised valleys form regionally elongated belts of channelized sandstones and are potential reservoirs for hydrocarbons (Weimer, 1984; Krystinik and Blakeney-DeJarnett, 1990; Blakeney-DeJarnett and Krystinik, 1992) and hard mineral resources (McBride and others, 1991). The geologic imprint of fluvial incisions across the modern continental shelf provides evidence of sea-level change and records the pathways for sediment transport from the river catchment to the shelf break. This sedimentary pathway can serve as an analog to ancient incised valleys that represent conduits for shelfward transport.

There have been many examples of Pleistocene incised fluvial valleys documented from around the world, including the Gulf of Mexico (e.g., Bouma and others, 1982; Suter and Berryhill, 1985; Berryhill, 1986; Suter and others, 1987; Thomas and Anderson, 1989, 1991; Anderson and others, 1990, 1991, 1993; Bartek and others, 1990, 1991; Nichol and others, 1993), the Atlantic shelf of the United States (e.g., Uchupi, 1970; Harris, 1983; Matteucci, 1984; Knebel and Circé, 1988), the southwestern

French coast (e.g., Allen and Posamentier, 1993), and the French Mediterranean coast (e.g., Allen and Posamentier, 1993). Ancient examples include those from the Upper Carboniferous section in Namurian Clare basin, Ireland (Elliott and Pulham, 1991), the Viking Formation in Alberta, Canada (Allen and Posamentier, 1991; Boreen and Walker, 1991), and the Pennsylvanian and Cretaceous of the United States (Baum and Vail, 1988; Weimer and Sonnenberg, 1989; Krystinik and Blakeney-DeJarnett, 1990; Van Wagoner and others, 1990; Dolson and others, 1991; Jennette and others, 1991).

The deposits which fill incised fluvial valleys range from non-marine through estuarine to open marine (Allen and Posamentier, 1991; Boyd and Honig, 1992; Dalrymple and others, 1992; Allen and Posamentier, 1993). Elliott and Pulham (1991) give an example of incised valleys completely filled with fluvial sediments. An example of highly complex mixed fills of fluvial, estuarine, and/or marine sands that onlap and fill incised valleys of the J Sandstone (Horsetooth Member) in the Denver Basin has been described by Baum and Vail (1988).

Mobile Bay and estuaries along the Gulf of Mexico margin typically originated as incised fluvial valleys that formed during the most recent eustatic sea-level fall and were drowned by the ensuing postglacial sea-level rise. Most of these estuaries have been filling with sediment both from landward fluvial sources and from seaward flood-tidal delta and tidal-inlet sources. The purpose of this paper is to describe the late Quaternary evolution of the Mississippi-Alabama shelf, Mobile River incised valley, and Mobile Bay.

Physiography

The Mississippi-Alabama shelf province is located in the northern Gulf of Mexico. The Gulf is categorized as a small ocean basin (Menard, 1967) with predominantly microtidal systems with tidal ranges from 0.0 to 0.8 m. This province encompasses the eastern Louisiana barrier islands and shelf, the Mississippi-Alabama barrier islands and shelf, Mississippi Sound, and Mobile Bay (Fig. 1; Martin and Bouma, 1978). The stratigraphy and morphology of the eastern Louisiana barrier islands and adjacent shelf are dominated by the multiple, stacked, delta complexes of the Mississippi River. Mississippi Sound and Mobile Bay are estuarine systems that have evolved differently. Mississippi Sound, initially a shallow open-marine coast, was created by westward-migrating barrier islands. Mobile Bay is a wave-dominated estuary (as defined by Dalrymple and others, 1992) formed from a drowned river valley. During the most recent lowstand, the Mobile River incised into Pleistocene deposits. Since the lowstand, the valley has been progressively flooded and partially closed off by a westward-prograding Holocene spit. The spit has restricted the circulation of marine waters and allowed the valley to fill primarily with lagoonal deposits.

The Tombigbee and Alabama Rivers that flow into Mobile Bay drain an area of the eastern United States that is second in discharge only to the Mississippi River system and is the fourth largest of the entire country (Fig. 1A). The primary sources of sediment for the Mississippi-Alabama shelf are the Mobile, Pascagoula, Pearl, and Mississippi Rivers.

Mississippi-Alabama shelf bathymetry is characterized in general as a smooth, gently sloping sea floor, broadest to the west (~125 km) and narrowing to the east (~60 km; Fig. 2A). A more complex bathymetry is found near midshelf (−30 m) and is identified as ridge-and-trough topography of marine shoals (Fig. 3). The shelf break ranges in depth from −60 m in the west to −100 m in the east.

The topography and shallow subsurface characteristics of the Mississippi-Alabama shelf were formed by the late Wisconsinan sea-level cycle. These characteristics are the result of offlapping deltaic deposition over onlapped sediments with intervening periods of erosion during lowstand. Typically, the progradational sediments overlie transgressive marine deposits with little evidence of structural deformation such as faulting or diapirism. The main topographic features on the shelf are sand ridges, that may be the remains of drowned barrier islands (Frazier, 1974) or inner-shelf shoals (Penland and others, 1989) and a belt of limestone pinnacles near the shelf break (Laswell and others, 1990). Mazzullo and Bates (1985) divided the present shelf into distinct regions on the basis of surficial grain morphology and age. They reported that the Mississippi-Alabama outer shelf was covered by a thin layer of relict,

well-sorted, fine to medium quartzose sand of late Pleistocene and early Holocene age. These sands were deposited by rivers of the southeastern United States. The westernmost part of the shelf, which includes the St. Bernard and modern birdsfoot lobes of the Mississippi Delta, is covered by Holocene sand, silt, and clay deposited in association with the Mississippi Delta (Ludwick, 1964; Mazzullo and Bates, 1985; Kindinger and others, 1991b).

Data Base and Previous Studies

The incised, Mobile River valley has been a conduit for sediment transport throughout late Quaternary time. Numerous studies have been conducted within the Mississippi-Alabama shelf province, but few have been of regional scope. This study is based on new data, reinterpretation of old seismic data, and on unpublished data collected in previous studies. During 1991 and 1992, 130 line-km of high-resolution, single-channel, seismic-reflection profiles and vibracores were collected by the U. S. Geological Survey (USGS) in cooperation with the Geological Survey of Alabama (GSA), Mississippi Office of Geology (MOG), Louisiana Geological Survey (LGS), and Marine Minerals Technology Center (MMTC) in Mississippi (Fig. 1).

Low-power (200–400 Joule) boomer systems were used in Mobile Bay during 1990 and 1991 to collect 385 line-km of high-resolution seismic data. As part of the cooperative study of Mobile Bay, 26 vibracores were collected by the GSA and described by Mars and others (1992). Older data were reinterpreted, including 380 line-km of 400 Joule, minisparker seismic profiles, and 21 vibracores from Mobile Bay were collected as part of a 1982 USGS and Mississippi-Alabama Sea Grant cooperative (Brande and others, 1982a).

The Holocene history of the Mobile Bay basin has been the focus of several modern stratigraphic and sedimentological studies (Parker and Hummell, 1991; Mars and others, 1992; Otvos and Howat, 1992), but none have directly focused on the pre-Holocene history or geologic connection between bay and shelf. Previous geological investigations in Mobile Bay were concerned with the detection and mapping of oyster reefs, both living and buried, assessment of historical changes in sedimentation rate, topography of the bay bottom (Ryan, 1969; Ryan and Goodel, 1972; May, 1976), recognition of the underlying Miocene sediments (Otvos, 1973, 1985; Isphording, 1976, 1977), and formation and development of the barrier islands (Otvos, 1973, 1985). May (1976) provided a limited chronology for the north part of the bay including the bayhead delta. These studies primarily used probes, cores, and core cuttings to characterize Mobile Bay and surrounding landforms.

May (1976), Brande and others (1982b), and Parker and Hummell (1991) described the Holocene stratigraphy of Mobile Bay using high-resolution, single-channel seismic data and vibracores. Their studies were hindered by shallow biogenic gas masking the seismic signal in the midsection of the bay. Otvos (1985) described several pre-Holocene formations based primarily on drill-hole samples and vibracores and showed that these formations extend from onshore Alabama-Mississippi to the subsurface of Mobile

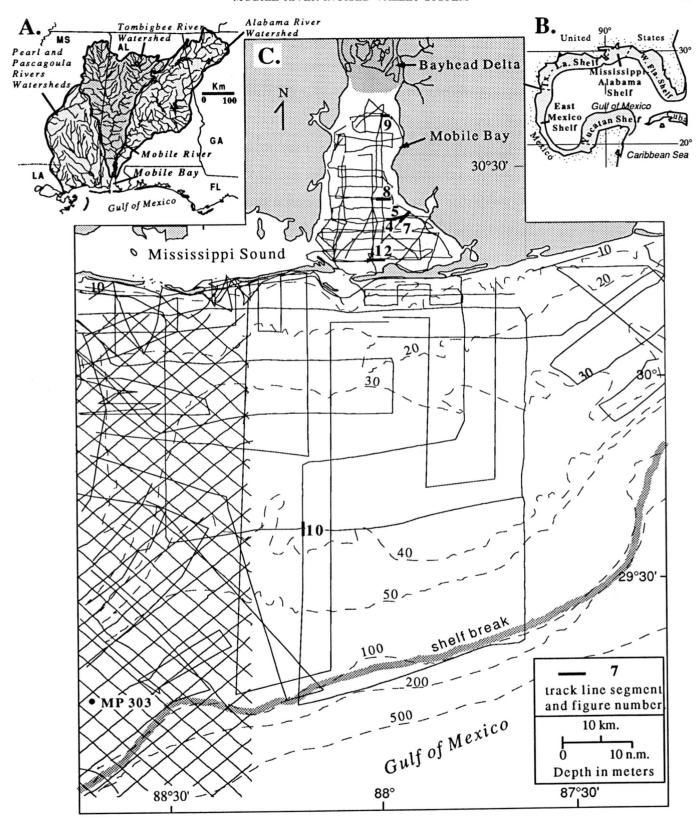

FIG. 1.—Location of seismic profiles collected from the Mississippi-Alabama shelf and Mobile Bay: (A) catchments of the Pearl and Pascagoula, Tombigbee and Alabama Rivers, the primary sediment sources for the Mississippi-Alabama shelf and Mobile Bay; (B) location of the Mississippi-Alabama shelf within the continental shelf system of the Gulf of Mexico; (C) location of high-resolution, single-channel, seismic-reflection profiles collected from Mobile Bay and Mississippi-Alabama shelf.

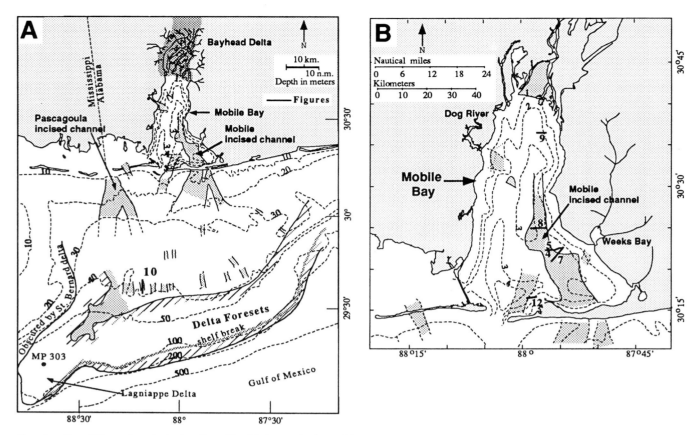

FIG. 2.—Late Wisconsinan incised valleys identified on seismic profiles from Mississippi-Alabama shelf and Mobile Bay. (A) Distribution of incised valleys from Mississippi-Alabama shelf including delta foresets of associated shelf-margin delta. (B) Primary incision of the Mobile River system along the eastern margin of Mobile Bay during the Wisconsinan lowstand. Location of seismic-profile examples in following figures are shown as numbered bold lines.

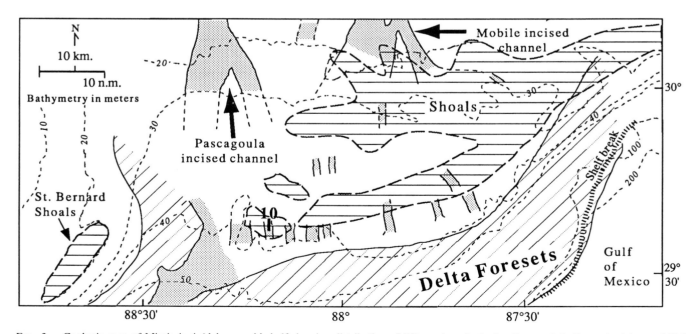

FIG. 3.—Geologic map of Mississippi-Alabama mid-shelf showing distribution of Wisconsinan incised valleys and shelf-margin delta, and Holocene transgressive shoals and irregular bathymetry seaward of the Mobile incised channel.

Bay. These included the Prairie and Biloxi Formations of the late Pleistocene.

From 1990 to 1992, the USGS and MMTC used the Huntec Sea Otter boomer and Delph-1 digital acquisition systems to collect 1750 line-km of high-resolution seismic data from the Alabama-Mississippi shelf (Fig. 1). Additional Alabama-Mississippi shelf high-resolution, single-channel-seismic data sets were also used: 2500 line-km of 800 Joule minisparker and 3.5 kHz profiles (Kindinger and others, 1982; Kindinger, 1988b, 1989a, b) and 1150 line-km of Geopulse boomer profiles (Kindinger, 1989b).

Previous studies of the western portion of the Alabama-Mississippi shelf, to which Mobile Bay is related, have shown the shelf to be underlain by multiple, stacked deltas (Coleman, 1976; Coleman and Roberts, 1988; Kindinger, 1988b). Results from high-resolution, seismic-stratigraphic analysis have shown the presence of a late-Pleistocene, progradational, deltaic clinoform wedge, previously mapped as the Lagniappe delta (Kindinger, 1988a, 1989a, b). Roberts and others (1991) sampled this clinoform wedge by a continuous borehole. Core samples from the borehole contained faunal and sedimentary structure assemblages indicative of the deltaic environment described from seismic profiles by Kindinger (1989b). Sydow and others (1992) used the combined results of these studies and new data to refine the late-Pleistocene deltaic history of the western Alabama-Mississippi shelf.

STRATIGRAPHIC NOMENCLATURE

The modern seismic-sequence stratigraphic approach has been developed primarily by research for the petroleum industry (Payton, 1977; Berg and Woolverton, 1985). This approach was initially designed for use with low-frequency, multichannel, digital seismic data and relatively large geologic sections. Whereas the industrial seismic-stratigraphic approach is valid, it has not always been adequate for a relatively shallow, high-resolution study without some modification. Recent workers have provided documentation from studies of outcrop, well-log, and high-resolution, shallow-penetration seismic data, demonstrating that the stratigraphic principles developed for industry are also applicable to smaller-scale stratal geometries (see references in Tables 1 and 2 of Posamentier and Weimer, 1993). The high-resolution, single-channel seismics used in this study have greater resolution and less penetration than low frequency, multichannel systems. This equipment allows the delineation of high-frequency, sixth-order (0.01–0.03 Ma; Posamentier and Weimer, 1993) depositional sequences. Thus, terminology for megasequence or sequence boundary is not as applicable. Mitchum and Van Wagoner (1990) recognized that high-frequency sequences and parasequences may represent fourth- and fifth-order cyclicity. Posamentier and others (1992) describe the sequence stratigraphy of a small fan delta built in a roadside drainage ditch to demonstrate that sequence-stratigraphic concepts are scale independent, both spatially and temporally. Consequently depositional sequences can be recognized not only at third-order scale (0.5–3.0 Ma) but also at fourth-order (0.08–0.5 Ma), fifth-order (0.03–0.08 Ma), or even sixth-order (0.01–0.03 Ma) (Posamentier and Weimer, 1993).

Whereas the term depositional subsequence as used by Hubbard and others (1985) represents third-order cycles of 1 to 10 Ma, the definition is applicable to this paper with slight modification. They divided sequences into subsequences and individual gross depositional environments. A subsequence is defined as the smallest chronostratigraphic unit that is mapped to follow specific environments within a prospective depositional sequence.

The depositional environment for each subsequence depositional unit can be inferred by its internal reflection pattern or seismic character (seismic facies; Mitchum and others, 1977). By identifying the internal reflection pattern and reflection terminations (downlap, onlap, parallel, transparent, chaotic), it is possible to reconstruct the depositional environment.

STRATIGRAPHIC FRAMEWORK OF MOBILE BAY AND THE MISSISSIPPI-ALABAMA SHELF

There have been several seismic-stratigraphic descriptions of Mobile Bay (Brande and others, 1982a, b; Kindinger and others, 1991a; Mars and others, 1992). Lithologic and stratigraphic units within the late Quaternary Mobile Bay alluvial valley can be delineated into Pleistocene and Holocene age. The lowest mappable unit identified on seismic profiles relates to the transgression before the late Wisconsinan sea-level fall. There are older, deeper alluvial deposits identifiable on some seismic profiles that indicate that the Mobile Bay valley had been a conduit for older fluvial systems during the Pleistocene (Fig. 4).

Seismic Subsequences and Characteristics

Depositional subsequence boundaries (SsB) appear on seismic-reflection data from Mobile Bay and the Missis-

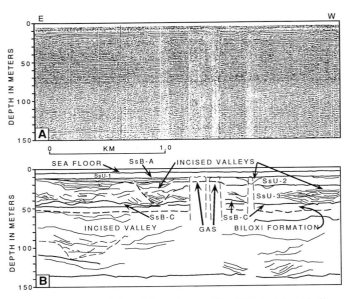

FIG. 4.—Characteristic mini-sparker profile (400 Joule) with line-drawing interpretation, south Mobile Bay. Line drawing shows placement of sea floor, SsU-1, SsB-A, SsU-2 with incised valleys, SsB-B, SsU-3 (alluvial deposits of the paleo-Mobile River system), SsB-C, and pre-Holocene incised valley. Location of profile is shown on Figure 2B.

sippi-Alabama shelf as local to regional seismic reflections representing unconformity or disconformity surfaces. These reflections have been correlated to available lithologic data. Rates of sedimentation and sea-level change affected the number and distribution of subsequence units and boundaries identifiable during the geologic time frame investigated. From Wisconsinan to Holocene time, sedimentation rates within Mobile Bay were relatively higher than on the shelf. In the subsurface of Mobile Bay, three subsequence boundaries and subsequence units (SsU) are readily mapped, with two other subsequences recognized and discussed (examples of these and deeper units are shown in Fig. 4). Each subsequence unit thickens toward the center of the bay.

The uppermost horizon in Figure 4 is the modern bay floor, a relatively smooth bottom. Water depth in the bay averages from 2 to 4 m. The shallowest subsequence unit (SsU-1) is bounded by the modern bay floor and SsB-A. It is acoustically transparent with local, weak, parallel internal reflections that onlap SsB-A along the previous shore margins (Fig. 5). SsB-A has been identified as a transgressive surface which is defined as the first significant marine-flooding surface within the subsequence. SsB-A is the reflection marking the last, small, valley incisions before the flooding of the bay. In vibracores, onlapping deposits of SsU-1 have been identified as Holocene marine lagoonal deposits. The unit is 3 to 7 m thick toward the center of the bay (Fig. 6).

Subsequence boundary A is the basal boundary of the lagoonal unit (SsU-1) and upper surface of SsU-2 (Figs. 5, 7). The subsequence unit (SsU-2) below SsB-A is acoustically semi-transparent with common evidence of filled incisions within the subsequence (Figs. 5, 7). Typically, the internal reflections within these channels are high-angle clinoform to parallel, implying lateral accretion and abandonment fill (Fig. 7). The valleys are 200 to 500 m in width and have an average thalweg depth of 4 to 6 m. Another character common to many channels in all units is the presence of presumed biogenic gas migrating upward from the thalweg of the incisions (Fig. 5). Low-amplitude parallel

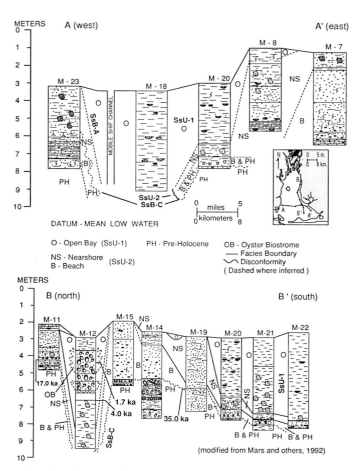

FIG. 6.—Vibracore lithologic cross sections A-A' and B-B' from Mobile Bay. Cross section A-A' illustrates (1) relatively thick open-bay/estuarine facies (SsU-1; M-18) that thins to bay margins, (2) beach/nearshore facies (SsU-2) with an upper contact (SsB-A) that is a fining-upward transition, and (3) basal contact (SsB-C; PH) that is the Pleistocene boundary. Cross section B-B' along east margin of Mobile Bay shows vibracores M-11, M-12 and M-19 contained datable material with dates of 1.7 and 4.0 ka from within the estuarine facies (SsU-1), and 17.0 and 35.0 ka from below the Pleistocene contact. Location of cross sections shown in inset map of Mobile Bay.

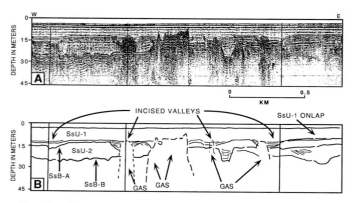

FIG. 5.—Boomer (100 Joule) seismic profile (A) with line-drawing interpretation (B), central Mobile Bay. Erosion horizon SsB-B is overlain by the onlapping reflections of SsU-2, SsB-A, and SsU-1. Example of incised valleys of SsU-2. Common example of migration of biogenic(?) gas from thalweg of incisions. Location of profile is shown on Figure 2B.

reflections that onlap the margins of the embayment are also present in SsU-2 (Fig. 8). The maximum, central-bay thickness of SsU-2 is 5 to 10 m.

The basal subsequence boundary (SsB-B) of SsU-2 is a nonconformity that consists of a high-amplitude reflection identified as an erosional horizon that was formed by the fluvial erosion of Pleistocene deposits. Along the subsurface margins of Mobile Bay, SsB-B is an erosional contact (Figs. 5, 8); whereas, in the mid-bay area the horizon is the upper boundary of the alluvial fill of the Mobile River deposited during the late Wisconsinan lowstand (Fig. 9). Offshore on the Mississippi-Alabama shelf, this horizon is very near the sea floor with a veneer of sediment over much of the area. In some areas this horizon crops out.

Subsequence boundary B is the upper surface of subsequence unit 3 (SsU-3), the channel fill of the paleo-Mobile River (Fig. 9) which is located near the central axis of Mo-

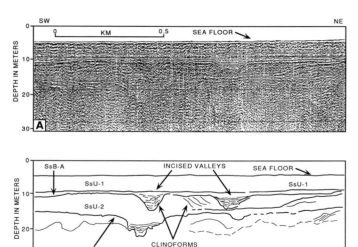

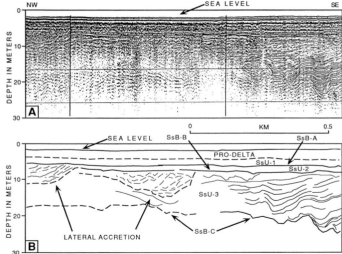

FIG. 7.—Boomer (100 Joule) seismic profile (A) with line drawing interpretation (B), central Mobile Bay. Profile shows high-angle, clinoform alluvial fill within incisions of unit SsU-2. Location of profile is shown on Figure 2B.

FIG. 9.—Boomer (100 Joule) seismic profile (A) with line-drawing interpretation (B), north-central Mobile Bay. Profile shows paleo-Mobile River, incised valley fill (SsU-3) with clinoform reflections interpreted as lateral accretion deposits. The prodelta deposits of the bayhead delta overlie the open bay/estuarine facies (SsU-1) at this location, but interfinger with the unit elsewhere. Location of profile is shown on Figure 2B.

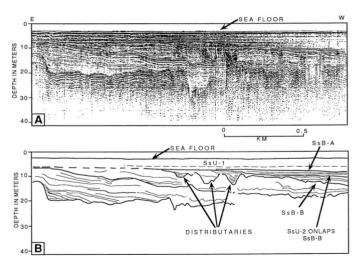

FIG. 8.—Boomer (100 Joule) seismic profile (A) with line drawing interpretation (B), Mobile Bay east margin. Erosional surface SsB-B is overlain by onlapping reflections of SsU-2, SsB-A, and SsU-1. Distributaries were incised during lower sea level. Location of profile is shown on Figure 2B.

part of the bay has a width of about 7 km and a depth of 45 m. The incised channel lies along the east margin of the present bay and exits the bay beneath the Holocene beach-ridge complex of Morgan Peninsula (Fig. 2B). Offshore, the channel bifurcates and is difficult to trace across the shelf. However, evidence of channel incision extends to the outer shelf (Fig. 10) updip of a shelf-margin delta that was deposited by the river system during the late Wisconsinan lowstand (Fig. 2A).

Each of the three subsequence units (SsU-1, -2, -3) is defined by a specific depositional environment and the

bile Bay. SsU-3 is bounded below by subsequence boundary C (SsB-C). Near the south end of Mobile Bay, the alluvial fill of the paleo-Mobile River is greater than 30 m thick. The internal reflection patterns of the valley fill (SsU-3) are characterized by chaotic to high-angle clinoform reflections, interpreted as lateral-accretion deposits (Figs. 7, 9). The incised valley (SsB-C) dimensions within Mobile Bay vary from north to south. In the northern part of the bay, the channel width is about 3 km with an erosional depth of 25 m. Along the eastern mid-bay, the channel is 2 to 4 km in width and 30 m deep. The channel in the south

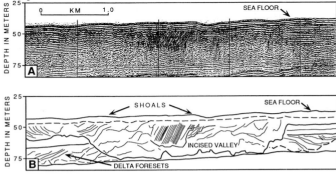

FIG. 10.—Boomer (400 joule) seismic profile (A) with line-drawing interpretation (B), from Mississippi-Alabama outer shelf, showing paleo-Mobile River incised-valley fill with clinoform reflections interpreted as lateral accretion deposits and delta foresets of the shelf-margin delta lobe. Incised-valley fill is overlain by sand ridges (shoals) reworked from estuarine-mouth-barrier complex or presumably drowned barrier islands. Location of profile is shown on Figure 2A.

depositional environment of each subsequence unit in the study area was controlled by changes in sea level. Subsequence unit 1 consists of fine-grained muds characteristic of an estuarine/lagoonal environment. Subsequence unit 2 is composed of the sandy sediments of alluvial plain crossed by streams, grading seaward to a tide-influenced fluvial environment. Subsequence unit 3 is composed of fluvial sands, deposited by the Mobile River during the most recent lowstand.

LATE PLEISTOCENE TO HOLOCENE HISTORY

The Mississippi-Alabama shelf is covered by relatively thin Upper Pleistocene and Holocene deposits. On the western shelf, Kindinger (1988b) identified five stages of shelf evolution from early Wisconsinan time to present. These stages were controlled by relative sea-level changes and are defined by the stratigraphic position of depositional units and erosional horizons. Stage 1 was an early Wisconsinan lowstand that exposed the shelf to subaerial erosion followed by a transgression (stage 2). Stage 3 occurred during the late Wisconsinan regression, with fluvial incision (SsB-C) across the shelf and deposition of a shelf-margin delta. Stages 4 and 5 represent the Holocene transgression and deposition of the St. Bernard delta, respectively. Stages 3 and 4 are typical of shelf evolution for the majority of the Mississippi-Alabama shelf, including the Mobile incised valley and estuarine system. Stage 3 correlates with the incision of the Mobile River system across the shelf (SsB-C); whereas, Stages 4 and 5 are correlative to the transgression (SsB-B) and subsequent estuarine infill (SsU-1) of Mobile Bay.

Kindinger (1989b) and Sydow and others (1992) have developed a depositional history for the shelf-margin delta (Lagniappe) originally reported by Kindinger (1988b). Roberts and others (1991) and Sydow and others (1992) have shown that this delta is part of a larger delta that forms the Mississippi-Alabama shelf. Roberts and others (1991) present a detailed description of a borehole (MP 303) drilled in the western outer shelf, which penetrates the delta (Fig. 1). Their interpretations produced a chronology (Fig. 11) of a pre-Wisconsinan (approximately 140 ka) lowstand, pre- to early Wisconsinan highstand with fluctuating sea level (125 to 70 ka), middle to late Wisconsinan regression to lowstand (70 to 18–13 ka), and late Wisconsinan to Holocene transgression (18 ka to present). The chronostratigraphy of this borehole provides an excellent calibration for the shelf seismic stratigraphy described by Kindinger (1988a, b) and Sydow and others (1992). The middle to late Wisconsinan lowstand reported by Roberts and others (1991) correlates with the shelf incision of the Mobile River system (SsB-C).

Wisconsinan Regression and Lowstand

Relative sea level prior to the middle Wisconsinan regression fluctuated and approached present levels (Williams, 1984). As sea level fell, the Mobile River system incised the emergent shelf surface, forming the basal boundary of the incised valley, SsB-C. Shoreline regression and coastal-plain development continued across the shelf to

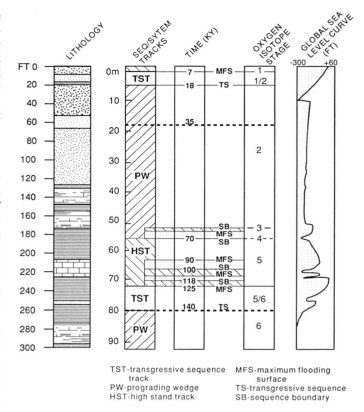

TST-transgressive sequence track
PW-prograding wedge
HST-high stand track

MFS-maximum flooding surface
TS-transgressive sequence
SB-sequence boundary

(modified from Robert and others, 1991)

FIG. 11.—Borehole MP 303, lithology and interpretations. The borehole penetrated the late Wisconsinan shelf-margin delta of the Mississippi-Alabama shelf. Interpretations by Roberts and others (1991) show a pre-Wisconsinan (~140 ka) lowstand, pre- to early Wisconsinan highstand with fluctuating sea level (125 to 70 ka), middle to late Wisconsinan regression to lowstand (70 to 18–13 ka), and late Wisconsinan to Holocene transgression (18 ka to present). Location of borehole shown on Figure 1.

approximately the middle shelf. At this point, the Mobile River system was possibly joined by the Pascagoula River system that was down-cutting across the shelf. Progradation of a large shelf-margin delta complex began seaward of this area.

The shelf-margin delta extends eastwards from near the modern Mississippi River delta (Kindinger, 1989b; Sydow and others, 1992) to a point due south of Perdido Bay (Fig. 2A). The delta complex is a lowstand wedge in the late Wisconsinan, lowstand systems tract and is characterized on the shelf by incised-valley fill (SsU-3) and on the slope by a progradational wedge geometry. The seismic character of this delta complex resembles descriptions reported by Kindinger (1989b) and Sydow and others (1992) for the Lagniappe delta (Fig. 2A), which is the western lobe of the Mississippi-Alabama shelf-margin delta complex. The lowest level of late Wisconsinan, relative sea level found in this study was −120 m, as indicated by the maximum depth of stream erosion on the shelf margin (−118 m; Sydow and others, 1992).

Mobile Bay was the conduit for sediment transport from the Mobile River catchment to the shelf margin throughout the regression and lowstand. Interpretation of seismic profiles shows that the late Wisconsinan fluvial channel (SsB-C) beneath Mobile Bay was incised to a maximum depth of 45 m below present sea level in the southern parts of the bay.

Holocene Transgression

Transgression of the Continental Shelf.—

The early Holocene rapid transgression began around 18 ka (Roberts and others, 1991) but sea level did not rise continuously. The main topographic features on the middle shelf are sand ridges that may be the remains of drowned barrier islands (Frazier, 1974) or inner-shelf shoals (Penland and others, 1989). Shoals such as the St. Bernard Shoals, located on the western part of the Mississippi-Alabama shelf (Fig. 3), presumably mark a position slightly landward of reworked ancient shorelines. The St. Bernard Shoals were one of several shoals formed as the Mississippi River deposited a series of shelf-phase delta plains on the mid-continental shelf during the transgression (Penland and others, 1989).

According to the Barbados sea-level curve of Fairbanks (1989), sea level rose rapidly from 18 to 6 ka with a much slower rise after 6 ka. In agreement with Fairbanks (1989), are the interpretations of Mars and others (1992), who report rapid inundation of Mobile Bay between 7.5 to 6.0 ka and slower rates of rise after 6.0 ka.

The Mississippi-Alabama mid-shelf bathymetry to −30 m has a complex ridge-and-trough topography (Fig. 3) that was formed by a combination of sediments delivered by the paleo-Mobile River drainage system and was reworked from a landward-migrating estuary-mouth barrier complex during the Holocene transgression. The estuary-mouth barrier complex presumably passed through a shoreface environment and then was reworked as marine shoals. Holocene deposition on the Mississippi-Alabama middle to inner shelf has been restricted to incised-valley fill and shoals, SsU-3 and SsB-C (Fig. 10). The valley fill is visible as high-angle clinoform reflections within the incised channel.

Transgression of Mobile River Incised Valley.—

As the Holocene transgression flooded the shelf, the basinward portion of the Mobile River incised valley was drowned (10 to 7.5 ka), forming a wave-dominated estuary. This paleovalley (delimited by SsB-C) was filled with fluvial deposits (SsU-3) that are overlain by reworked marine shoals or barrier sands. The distal end of the incised valley has a relatively thin, incomplete transgressive succession. Lagoonal/estuarine deposits were not identifiable in seismic profiles. Rapid sea-level rise may have outpaced the deposition of estuarine sediment, or the estuarine sediment may have been removed by transgressive reworking.

The original entrance of the Mobile River valley lies beneath Morgan Peninsula on the east side of the valley (Fig. 2B). Initial inundation of the entrenched river valley occurred through this entrance. Coastal shorelines were established to the east and west of the bay mouth. The entrance was constrained by antecedent topography, namely the Gulfport barrier complex (Sangamonan) to the east and a topographic high formed by a relic Pleistocene ridge (Otvos, 1985) to the west (underneath the western Morgan Peninsula ridge complex). Early in the transition from a fluvial to a marine environment, the main channel bifurcated and a new distributary flowed westward around the Pleistocene topography (Fig. 2B). Strandplain or beach-ridge progradation from the east shore began near the end of the transgression. The strandplain prograded across the eastern bay entrance, restricting offshore-to-bay tidal flow, thus leaving the western channel to become the present entrance to the bay. Deposition from the strandplain-beach-ridge complex has extended into the south end of the bay and is seen as high-angle clinoforms (Fig. 12).

May (1976) and Mars and others (1992) have provided a detailed reconstruction of the Holocene inundation of Mobile Bay. Their data have been combined here with new data and modified interpretations to produce a cross-sectional schematic of Mobile Bay (Fig. 13A). As the Holocene transgression progressed, the river valley became a wide flood plain, crossed by streams (anastomosed) draining from the north that were at times virtually unconfined channels (SsB-A and SsU-2). Distributaries such as Dog River and Weeks Bay entered the Mobile Bay basin along the margins. Sea level rose and alluvial deposition ceased in the area of the present bay. This non-marine facies is included here as part of SsU-1. Mars and others (1992) described this facies along the basin margin as nearshore facies with sedimentary structures that included localized mud drapes, muddy sand pockets, and burrows.

Fine-grained, open-bay or lagoonal, fining-upward deposits (SsU-1) accumulated following inundation (Fig. 6). May (1976) and Mars and others (1992) demonstrated that the initial bay extended farther north and was slightly deeper than today. It was postulated, but not documented, by Smith (1981) that the bay extended more than 65 km further north before infilling by bayhead delta sediments (SsU-1). Near the bayhead delta, the late Wisconsinan fluvial incision is overlain by transgressive-phase and regressive delta-front deposits.

DISCUSSION OF ESTUARINE FACIES MODELS AND INCISED VALLEYS

The conceptual facies model presented by Dalrymple and others (1992) states that, ideally, all estuaries possess a three-

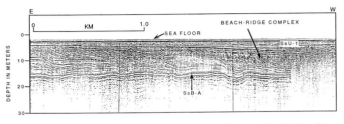

FIG. 12.—Boomer (100 Joule) seismic profile, south Mobile Bay. Morgan Peninsula, late Holocene beach-ridge complex showing high-angle clinoform reflections. The beach-ridge complex overlies SsB-A. Lagoonal deposits of SsU-1 overlie the beach-ridge complex. Location of profile is shown on Figure 2B.

A.

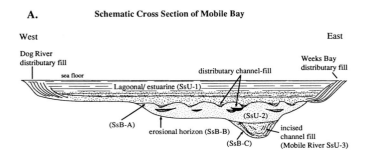

B.

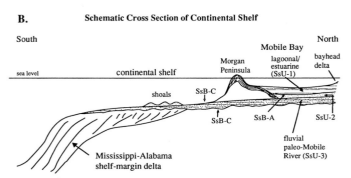

FIG. 13.—Schematic cross sections of Mobile Bay (A) and shelf break to Mobile Bay (B) (not to scale). (A) illustrates the geometry and facies relation within the bay. (B) illustrates the relative position of the Mobile Bay estuarine fill to the shelf depositional facies.

fold (tripartite) structure: an outer marine-dominated zone, central mixed zone, and an inner river-dominated zone. They also recognized that these zones are not equally developed in all estuaries. The late Holocene to modern Mobile Bay estuary has well-defined facies of the three zones; whereas, estuarine facies are poorly developed or absent from the distal, transgressed portion of the estuary on the shelf. Dalrymple and others (1992) divide estuaries into two types, wave- and tide-dominated, based on the dominant marine process. Mobile Bay is a wave-dominated estuary with well-defined tripartite zonation. The transgressed portion of the incised valley possesses a less well-defined zonation that may be similar to the sand-rich facies of the tide-dominated estuary of the conceptual model. The history of the Mobile River estuary recorded in the incised-valley fill may represent a change in dominant marine process from tide-dominated to wave-dominated due to changes in the rate of sea-level rise.

Lake Calcasieu is similar in structure and stratigraphy to the late Holocene Mobile Bay. Lake Calcasieu is located on the Louisiana coast of the Gulf of Mexico. Nichol and others (1993) recognized three major facies in the Calcasieu valley: (1) a tide-influenced fluvial facies including subfacies of floodplain, interdistributary basin, fluvial channel and bayhead delta, (2) a central basin with fringing intertidal marshes, and (3) a low-relief prograded barrier that separates the estuary from the Gulf of Mexico. These facies are comparable to those found in Mobile Bay: (a) the tide-influenced fluvial subfacies are represented by SsU-2 and

SsU-3, (b) the central basin is represented by SsU-1, and (c) low-relief prograded barrier is represented by Morgan Peninsula across Mobile Bay.

During the last lowstand, other incised river valleys comparable to the Mobile River incised valley were cut across the continental shelf of the Gulf of Mexico. The Trinity/Sabine incised valley of the east Texas shelf has been intensely studied by Thomas and Anderson (1989, 1991) and Anderson and others (1990, 1991, 1993). Anderson and others (1993) describe the transgressive valley fill of the Trinity and Sabine valleys to be dominated by estuarine muds, while the Brazos and Colorado valleys are dominated by fluvial sands. Anderson and others (1991) have described multiple, backstepping parasequences of paired bayhead delta and associated flood-tidal delta tidal-inlet facies within the Trinity/Sabine incised valley; whereas Bartek and others (1991) have reported overstepped deltas (Holocene transgressed deltas) associated with the Brazos incised valley of the central Texas coast. The formation of these parasequences and deltas is evidence of the intermittent sea-level rise during the Holocene transgression. Whereas the presence of reworked marine shoals on the central Mississippi-Alabama shelf are strong evidence of stillstands during the Holocene transgression, no clear evidence of multiple, backstepping parasequences or shelf-phase deltas has been observed within the Mobile River incised valley system. Formation of these Mississippi-Alabama shelf shoals during the Holocene transgression may coincide with the development of backstepping parasequences and associated overstepped deltas of the Texas shelf incised valleys. Absence of backstepping parasequences and shelf-phase deltas in the Mobile River incised valley may be attributed to a lower mud content and less sediment supply than in the incised valleys of the Texas shelf.

CONCLUSIONS

This paper documents the late Quaternary history of the Mobile River incised valley and its fill. The Mobile River incised valley is a drowned, low-energy, wave-dominated microtidal estuary located on the Mississippi-Alabama shelf. The shelf is a relatively stable platform unaffected by the regional subsidence associated with the adjacent Mississippi Delta. Sea level, prior to middle Wisconsinan deposition, stood near present level. The Mobile River incised-valley system was entrenched across the shelf during the middle to late Wisconsinan regression and was a conduit for sediment transport by the Mobile River from its catchment to a lowstand shelf-margin delta. This delta complex extends from the Lagniappe delta in the west to the eastern edge of the Mississippi-Alabama shelf. Maximum sea-level withdrawal was measured from incised channels to be −120 m below present.

Rapid, early Holocene transgression drowned the fluvial valley, forming an estuary. This early transgression may have outpaced estuarine deposition or the estuarine deposits may have been removed by transgressive reworking. The Mississippi-Alabama shelf bathymetry to −30 m has a complex ridge-and-trough topography. The ridge-and-trough topography may have been formed by the reworking of the fluvial valley fill to form shoals. As the late Holocene transgression continued to inundate the incised Mobile River valley, the modern Mobile Bay was formed and became a depocenter for the sediment load of the Mobile River system. The bay has subsequently partially filled with a relatively thick, lagoonal/estuarine deposit (SsU-1). There has been limited late Holocene to Recent sedimentation on the shelf.

Morgan Peninsula was formed near the end of the Holocene transgression. Longshore sediment transport formed a sand plug (strandplain or beach ridge) across much of the southern bay mouth. Deposition in Mobile Bay has been dominated by estuarine/lagoonal sediments with delta-front deposits encroaching into the northern end of the bay, where the Mobile and Tombigbee Rivers have produced a bay-head delta.

In the subsurface of Mobile Bay, three subsequences and three boundaries were identified. Each subsequence was deposited in a specific depositional environment: SsU-1 (the youngest subsequence) is an estuarine/lagoonal deposit; SsU-2 is an alluvial plain that grades seaward to a tide-influenced fluvial environment; and SsU-3 is fluvial fill deposited by the Mobile River. Evidence of early Holocene sediment transport through the Mobile River incised system is provided by the alluvium deposited as the initial fill (SsU-3) in the incised valleys (defined by SsB-C), a shelf-margin delta complex, and sand shoals formed by transgressive reworking of valley fill sediments. Subsequence boundary B separates the alluvial fill (SsU-3) from an overlaying acoustically semitransparent, transgressive unit (SsU-2). This tide-influenced fluvial deposit is bounded above by a transgressive surface (SsB-A). The youngest Holocene subsequence unit (SsU-1) identified in the Mobile Bay subsurface is composed of acoustically transparent, onlapping lagoonal deposits.

The late Holocene incised-valley fill (estuarine facies) underlying Mobile Bay fits well into a previously developed, conceptual facies model of a microtidal, wave-dominated estuary. Shallow subsurface estuarine facies of Mobile Bay contain a tripartite structure: an outer marine-dominated zone, a central mixed zone, and an inner river-dominated zone. The model does not fit as well with the rapidly transgressed shelf portion of the incised valley, however. The down-dip section does not contain a clearly identifiable (from seismic profiles) estuarine facies; the valley fill is primarily fluvial overlain by marine shoals. The microtidal, wave-dominated, estuarine facies model accounts for many variations but inherently cannot account for facies that are not preserved. In the example of the Mobile River incised valley, the distal portion of the valley was rapidly drowned, leaving the thin estuarine facies to be reworked, while the proximal portion was drowned more slowly, preserving the facies. Thus, the single incised valley contains two very different types of fill.

ACKNOWLEDGMENTS

This paper is an outgrowth of a general synthesis of what has been learned about the Mississippi-Alabama province over the last 15 years. Collection and interpretation of data and cores could not have been accomplished without the cooperation and research assistance of the Louisiana Geological Survey, Geological Survey of Alabama, Mississippi Office of Geology, and Mississippi Marine Minerals Technology Center. Field assistance was provided by the crews of the Research Vessels KIT JONES and GYRE. Assistance on the ERDA-1 was provided by Conrad Tome. The authors thank the British Geological Survey (NERC) for allowing the participation of Dr. Balson in this project, and he publishes with the permission of the Director. Over this period we have benefited from discussions with a large number of people, especially R. L. Hummell, R. A. McBride, R. J. Miller, S. J. Parker, S. Penland, E. A. Shinn, and J. R. Suter. Helpful comments regarding the manuscript were provided by R. Boyd, R. W. Dalrymple, J. Hopkins, B. H. Lidz, and M. Nichols.

The contents of this publication do not necessarily reflect the views and policies of the U. S. Department of Interior nor does the mention of trade names or commercial products constitute their endorsement by the United States Government.

REFERENCES

ALLEN, G. P., AND POSAMENTIER, H. W., 1991, Facies and stratal patterns in incised valley complexes: examples from the recent Gironde estuary (France) and the Cretaceous Viking Formation (abs.): American Association of Petroleum Geologists Bulletin, v. 73, p. 534.

ALLEN, G. P., AND POSAMENTIER, H. W., 1993, Sequence stratigraphy and facies model of an incised valley fill: the Gironde estuary, France: Journal of Sedimentary Petrology, v. 63, p. 378–391.

ANDERSON, J. B., ABDULAH, K. C., SARZALEJO, S., SIRINGAN, F. P., AND THOMAS, M., 1993, Distribution of sandy facies within late Quaternary systems tracts of the east Texas continental shelf and slope (abs.): American Association of Petroleum Geologists, Program with Abstracts, p. 67.

ANDERSON, J. B., SIRINGAN, F. P., SMYTH, W. C., AND THOMAS, M. A., 1991, Episodic nature of Holocene sea level rise and the evolution of Galveston Bay (abs.): Houston, Gulf Coast Section, Society of Economic Paleontologists and Mineralogists 12th Annual Research Conference, Coastal Depositional Systems in the Gulf of Mexico, Program with Extended and Illustrated Abstracts, p. 8–14.

ANDERSON, J. B., SIRINGAN, F. P., AND THOMAS, M. A., 1990, Sequence stratigraphy of the Late-Pleistocene-Holocene Trinity/Sabine Valley system: relationship to the distribution of sand bodies within the transgressive systems tract (abs.): Houston, Gulf Coast Section, Society of Economic Paleontologists and Mineralogists 11th Annual Research Conference, Sequence Stratigraphy as an Exploration Tool, Program with Abstracts, p. 15–20.

BARTEK, L. R., ANDERSON, J. B., AND ABDULAH, K. C., 1990, The importance of overstepped deltas and "Interfluvial" sedimentation in the transgressive systems tract of high sediment yield depositional systems Brazos-Colorado Deltas, Texas (abs.): Houston, Society of Economic Paleontologists and Mineralogists Gulf Coast Section Eleventh Annual Research Conference, Sequence Stratigraphy as an Exploration Tool, Program with Abstracts, p. 52–70.

BARTEK, L. R., ANDERSON, J. B., AND ABDULAH, K. C., 1991, A case history of the preservation potential of the coastal lithosomes of small deltaic systems: examples from the Holocene of the Texas continental shelf (abs.): Houston, Society of Economic Paleontologists and Mineralogists Gulf Coast Section Twelfth Annual Research Conference, Coastal Depositional Systems in the Gulf of Mexico, Program with Abstracts, p. 15–25.

BAUM, G. R., AND VAIL, P. R., 1988, Sequence stratigraphic concepts applied to Paleogene outcrops, Gulf and Atlantic basins, in Wilgus, C. K., Hastings, B. S., Kendall, C. G. St. C., Posamentier, H. W., Ross, C. A., and Van Wagoner, J. C., eds., Sea-level Change: An Integrated Approach: Tulsa, Society of Economic Paleontologists and Mineralogists Special Publication 42, p. 309–327.

BERG, O. R., AND WOOLVERTON, D. G., eds., 1985, Seismic Stratigraphy II: An Integrated Approach to Hydrocarbon Exploration: Tulsa, American Association of Petroleum Geologists Memoir 39, 276 p.

BERRYHILL, H. L., JR., ed., 1986, Late Quaternary Facies and Structure, Northern Gulf of Mexico: Tulsa, American Association of Petroleum Geologists, Studies in Geology 23, 289 p.

BLAKENEY-DEJARNETT, B. A., AND KRYSTINIK, L. F., 1992, Sequence analysis of the Pennsylvanian Morrow Formation, eastern Colorado and western Kansas (abs.): American Association of Petroleum Geologists, Program with Abstracts, p. 9.

BOREEN, T. D., AND WALKER, R. G., 1991, Definition of allomembers and their facies assemblages in the Viking Formation, Willesden Green area, Alberta: Bulletin of Canadian Petroleum Geology, v. 39, p. 123–144.

BOUMA, A. H., BERRYHILL, H. L., KNEBEL, H. J., AND BRENNER, R. L., 1982, Continental shelf and epicontinental seaways, in Scholle, P.A., and Spearing, D., eds., Sandstone Depositional Environments: Tulsa, American Association of Petroleum Geologists Memoir 31, p. 281–327.

BOYD, R., AND HONIG, C., 1992, Estuarine sedimentation on the eastern shore of Nova Scotia: Journal of Sedimentary Petrology, v. 62, p. 569–583.

BRANDE, S., DINGER, J. S., MCANNALLY, C. W., MILLER, R., AND KINDINGER, J. L., 1982a, Seismic survey of Mississippi Sound, Mississippi and Mobile Bay, Alabama (abs.), in Kelly, J. R., ed., Mississippi Sound Symposium: Mobile, Mississippi-Alabama Sea Grant Consortium, MASGP-81-007, p. 105–115.

BRANDE, S., DINGER, J. S., MILLER, R. J., AND KINDINGER, J. L., 1982b, Seismic survey of Mississippi Sound, Mississippi (abs.), in Kelly, J. R., ed., Mississippi Sound Symposium: Mobile, Mississippi-Alabama Sea Grant Consortium, MASGP-81-007, p. 99–104.

COLEMAN, J. M., 1976, Deltas: Processes of Deposition and Models for Exploration: Champaign, Continuing Education Publication Company, Incorporated, 102 p.

COLEMAN, J. M., AND ROBERTS, H. H., 1988, Sedimentary development of the Louisiana continental shelf related to sea level cycles: Geo-Marine Letters, v. 8, p. 1–119.

DALRYMPLE, R. W., ZAITLIN, B. A., AND BOYD, R., 1992, Estuarine facies models: conceptual basis and stratigraphic implications: Journal of Sedimentary Petrology, v. 62, p. 1130–1146.

DOLSON, J. C., MULLER, D. S., EVETTS, M. J., AND STEIN, J., 1991, Regional paleotopographic trends and production, Muddy Sandstone (Lower Cretaceous), central and northern Rocky Mountains: American Association of Petroleum Geologists Bulletin, v. 75, p. 409–435.

ELLIOTT, T., AND PULHAM, A. J., 1991, The sequence stratigraphy of Upper Carboniferous deltas, western Ireland (abs.): American Association of Petroleum Geologists Bulletin, v. 75, p. 568.

FAIRBANKS, R. G., 1989, A 17,000-year glacio-eustatic sea level record: influence of glacial melting rates on the younger Dryas event and deep-ocean circulation: Nature, v. 342, p. 637–642.

FRAZIER, D. E., 1974, Depositional episodes: their relationship to the Quaternary stratigraphic framework in the northwestern portion of the Gulf basin: Austin, Texas Bureau of Economic Geology, Geological Circular 74-1, 28 p.

HARRIS, J. D., 1983, Pleistocene events from the shallow structure of the middle and outer continental shelf of New Jersey: Unpublished M.S. Thesis, University of Rhode Island, Providence, 112 p.

HUBBARD, R. J., PAPE, J., AND ROBERTS, D. G., 1985, Depositional sequence mapping as a technique to establish tectonic and stratigraphic framework and evaluate hydrocarbon potential on a passive continental margin, in Berg, O. R., and Woolverton, D. G., eds., Seismic Stratigraphy II: An Integrated Approach to Hydrocarbon Exploration: Tulsa, American Association of Petroleum Geologists Memoir 39, p. 79–91.

ISPHORDING, W., 1976, Multivariate mineral analysis of Miocene-Pliocene coastal plain sediments: Transactions, Gulf Coast Association of Geological Societies, v. 26, p. 326–331.

ISPHORDING, W., 1977, Petrology and stratigraphy of the Alabama Miocene: Transactions, Gulf Coast Association of Geological Societies, v. 27, p. 304–313.

JENNETTE, D. C., JONES, C. R., VAN WAGONER, J. C., AND LARSEN, J. E., 1991, High-resolution sequence stratigraphy of the Upper Cretaceous Tocito Sandstone: the relationship between incised valleys and hydrocarbon accumulation, San Juan, basin, New Mexico, in Van Wa-

goner, J. C., Jones, C. R., Taylor, D. R., Nummedal, D., Jennette, D. C., and Riley, G. W., eds., Sequence Stratigraphy Applications to Shelf Sandstone Reservoirs, Outcrop to Subsurface Examples: Tulsa, American Association of Petroleum Geologists Field Conference Guidebook, unpaginated.

KINDINGER, J. L., 1988a, Delta deposition influenced by diapiric uplifts (abs.): American Association of Petroleum Geologists Bulletin, v. 72, p. 206.

KINDINGER, J. L., 1988b, Seismic stratigraphy of the Mississippi-Alabama shelf and upper continental slope: Marine Geology, v. 83, p. 74–94.

KINDINGER, J. L., 1989a, Upper Pleistocene to Recent shelf and upper-slope deposits of offshore Mississippi-Alabama, in Morton, R.A., and Nummedal, D., eds., Shelf Sedimentation, Shelf Sequences, and Related Hydrocarbon Accumulation: Proceedings, 7th Annual Research Conference, Gulf Coast Section, Society of Economic Paleontologists and Mineralogists Foundation, p. 163–174.

KINDINGER, J. L., 1989b, Depositional history of the Lagniappe delta, northern Gulf of Mexico: Geo-Marine Letters, v. 9, p. 59–66.

KINDINGER, J. L., HUMMEL, R., PARKER, S., AND MINK, R., 1991a, Holocene development of a drown river valley, Mobile Bay, Alabama (abs.): Mobile, Society of Economic Paleontologists and Mineralogists/International Geological Correlation Programme Project 274 Research Conference on Quaternary Coastal Evolution, Programs and Extended Abstracts, unpaginated.

KINDINGER, J. L., MILLER, R. J., STELTING, C. E., AND BOUMA, A. H., 1982, Depositional history of Louisiana-Mississippi outer continental shelf: United States Geological Survey Open-File Report 82-1077, 55 p.

KINDINGER, J. L., PENLAND, S., WILLIAMS, S. J., BROOKS, G. R., AND SUTER, J. R., AND MCBRIDE, R. A., 1991b, Late Quaternary geologic framework, north-central Gulf of Mexico: Seattle, Coastal Sediments 1991 Proceedings Specialty Conference, p. 1096–1110.

KNEBEL, H. J., AND CIRCE, R. C., 1988, Late Pleistocene drainage systems beneath Delaware Bay: Marine Geology, v. 78, p. 285–302.

KRYSTINIK, L. F., AND BLAKENEY-DEJARNETT, B. A., 1990, Sedimentology of the upper Morrow Formation in eastern Colorado and western Kansas, in Sonnenberg, S. A., Shannon, L. T., Rader, K., von Drehle, W. F., Martin, G. W., eds., Morrow Sandstones of Southeast Colorado and Adjacent Areas: Denver, Rocky Mountain Association of Geologists, p. 37–50.

LASWELL, J. S., SAGER, W. W., SCHROEDER, W. W., REZAK, R., DAVIS, K. S., AND GARRISON, G. S., 1990, Atlas of high-resolution geophysical data, Mississippi-Alabama marine ecosystems study: New Orleans, U. S. Department of the Interior, Minerals Management Service, Gulf of Mexico OCS Regional Office, 40 p.

LUDWICK, J. C., 1964, Sediments in northwestern Gulf of Mexico, in Miller, R. L., ed., Papers in Marine Geology, Shepard Commemorative Volume: New York, Macmillan Company, p. 204–238.

MARS, J. C., SHULTZ, A. W., AND SCHRODER, W. W., 1992, Stratigraphy and Holocene evolution of Mobile Bay in southwestern Alabama: Transactions, Gulf Coast Association of Geologucal Societies, v. 42, p. 529–542.

MARTIN, R. G., AND BOUMA, A. H., 1978, Physiography of Gulf of Mexico, in Bouma, A. H., Moore, G. T., and Coleman, J. M., eds., Framework, Facies, and Oil-Trapping Characteristics of the Upper Continental Margin: Tulsa, American Association of Petroleum Geologists, Studies in Geology No. 7, p. 3–19.

MATTEUCCI, T. D., 1984, High-resolution seismic stratigraphy of the North Carolina continental margin-Cape Fear region: sea level cyclicity, paleobathymetry, and Gulf Stream dynamics: Unpublished M. S. Thesis, University of South Florida, Tampa, 151 p.

MAY, E. B., 1976, Holocene sediments of Mobile Bay, Alabama: Alabama Marine Resources Bulletin, v. 11, 25 p.

MAZZULLO, J., AND BATES, C., 1985, Sources of Pleistocene silt and sand for the northeast Gulf of Mexico shelf and Mississippi fan: Transactions, Gulf Coast Association of Geological Societies, v. 35, p. 457–466.

MCBRIDE, R. A., BYRNES, M. R., PENLAND, S., POPE, D. L., AND KINDINGER, J. L., 1991, Geomorphic history, geologic framework and hard mineral resources of the Petit Bois Pass area Mississippi-Alabama (abs.): Houston, Gulf Coast Section, Society of Economic Paleontologists and Mineralogists 12th Annual Research Conference, Coastal Depositional

Systems in the Gulf of Mexico, Program with Extended and Illustrated Abstracts, p. 116–127.

MENARD, H. W., 1967, Transitional types of crust under small ocean basins: Journal of Geophysical Research, v. 72, p. 3061–3073.

MITCHUM, R. M., JR., VAIL, P. R., AND SANGREE, J. B., 1977, Seismic stratigraphy and global changes of sea level, part 6: stratigraphic interpretation of seismic reflection patterns in depositional sequences, *in* Payton, C. E., ed., Seismic Stratigraphy-Applications to Hydrocarbon Exploration: Tulsa, American Association of Petroleum Geologists Memoir 26, p. 117–133.

MITCHUM, R. M., JR., AND VAN WAGONER, J. C., 1990, High-frequency sequences and eustatic cycles in the Gulf of Mexico Basin (abs.): Houston, Gulf Coast Section Society of Economic Paleontologists and Mineralogists 12th Annual Research Conference, Coastal Depositional Systems in the Gulf of Mexico, Program with Extended and Illustrated Abstracts, p. 257–267.

NICHOL, S. L., BOYD, R., AND PENLAND, S., 1993, Stratigraphy of a wave-dominated estuary: Lake Calcasieu, Louisiana (abs.): American Association of Petroleum Geologists, Program with Abstracts, p. 157.

OTVOS, E. G., JR., 1973, Geology of the Mississippi-Alabama coastal area and nearshore zone: New Orleans, New Orleans Geological Society, 1973 Spring Field Trip Guidebook, 67 p.

OTVOS, E. G., JR., 1985, Coastal Evolution, Louisiana to Northwest Florida: New Orleans, New Orleans Geological Society, 1985 Spring Field Trip Guidebook, 91 p.

OTVOS, E. G., AND HOWAT, W. E., 1992, Late Quaternary units and marine cycles: correlations between northern Gulf sectors: Transactions, Gulf Coast Association of Geological Societies, v. 42, p. 571–585.

PARKER, S. J., AND HUMMELL, R. L., 1991, Holocene Stratigraphy of Mobile Bay, Alabama (abs.): Houston, Gulf Coast Section, Society of Economic Paleontologists and Mineralogists 12th Annual Research Conference, Coastal Depositional Systems in the Gulf of Mexico, Program with Extended and Illustrated Abstracts, p. 256.

PAYTON, C. E., ed., 1977, Seismic Stratigraphy-Applications to Hydrocarbon Exploration: Tulsa, American Association of Petroleum Geologists Memoir 26, 516 p.

PENLAND, S., SUTER, J. R., MCBRIDE, R. A., WILLIAMS, S. J., KINDINGER, J. L., AND BOYD, R., 1989, Holocene sand shoals offshore of the Mississippi River delta plain: Transactions, Gulf Coast Association of Geological Societies, v. 39, p. 471–480.

POSAMENTIER, H. W., ALLEN, G. P., AND JAMES, D. P., 1992, High resolution sequence stratigraphy- the East Coulee delta, Alberta: Journal of Sedimentary Petrology, v. 62, p. 310–317.

POSAMENTIER, H. W., AND WEIMER, P., 1993, Siliciclastic sequence stratigraphy and petroleum geology- Where to from here?: American Association of Petroleum Geologists Bulletin, v. 77, p. 731–742.

ROBERTS, H. H., FILLON, R. F., KOHL, B., BOUMA, A. H., AND SYDOW, J. C., 1991, Lithostratigraphy, biostratigraphy, and isotopic investigations of a borehole in Main Pass area, Block 303: a calibration of high resolution seismic stratigraphy (abs.): Houston, Gulf Coast Section, Society of Economic Paleontologists and Mineralogists 12th Annual Research Conference, Coastal Depositional Systems in the Gulf of Mexico, Program with Extended and Illustrated Abstracts, p. 217–222.

RYAN, J. J., 1969, A Sedimentologic Study of Mobile Bay, Alabama: Tallahassee, Sedimentological Research Laboratory, Department of Geology, Florida State University, 109 p.

RYAN, J. J., AND GOODEL, H. G., 1972, Marine geology and Estuarine history of Mobile Bay, Alabama, part 1. Contemporary sediments, *in* Nelson, B. W., ed., Environmental Framework of Coastal Plain Estuaries: Boulder, Geological Society of America Memoir 133, p. 517–554.

SMITH, W. E., 1981, Geologic features and erosion control in Alabama Gulf coastal area: Tuscaloosa, Geological Survey of Alabama, Information Series 57, University of Alabama, 57 p.

SUTER, J. R. AND BERRYHILL, H. L., JR., 1985, Late Quaternary shelf-margin deltas, northwest Gulf of Mexico: American Association of Petroleum Geologists Bulletin, v. 69, p. 77–91.

SUTER, J. R., BERRYHILL, A. H., JR., AND PENLAND, S., 1987, Late Quaternary sea-level fluctuations and depositional sequences, southwest Louisiana continental shelf, *in* Nummedal, D., Pilkey, O. H., and Howard, J. D., eds., Sea-level Fluctuation and Coastal Evolution: Tulsa, Society of Economic Paleontologists and Mineralogists Special Publication 41, p. 199–219.

SYDOW, J. C., ROBERTS, H. H., BOUMA, A. H., AND WINN, R., 1992, Constructional subcomponents of a shelf-edge delta, northeast Gulf of Mexico: Transactions, Gulf Coast Association of Geological Societies, v. 42, p. 717–726.

THOMAS, M. A., AND ANDERSON, J. B., 1989, Glacial eustatic controls on seismic sequences and parasequences of the Trinity/Sabine incised valley, Texas continental shelf: Transactions Gulf Coast Association of Geological Societies, v. 39, p. 563–569.

THOMAS, M. A., AND ANDERSON, J. B., 1991, Late Pleistocene stratigraphy of the Texas continental shelf: relationship to δ^{18} O curves (abs.): Houston, Society of Economic Paleontologists and Mineralogists Gulf Coast Section Twelfth Annual Research Conference, Coastal Depositional Systems in the Gulf of Mexico, Program with Abstracts, p. 265–270.

UCHUPI, E., 1970, Atlantic Continental Shelf and Slope of the United States-Shallow Structure: Washington, D. C., United States Geological Survey Professional Paper 529-I, 44 p.

VAN WAGONER, J. C., MITCHUM, R. M., JR., CAMPION, K. M., AND RAHMANIAN, V. D., 1990, Siliciclastic Sequence Stratigraphy in Well Logs, Cores, and Outcrops for High-Resolution Correlation of Time and Facies: Tulsa, American Association of Petroleum Geologists, Methods in Exploration Series 7, 55 p.

WEIMER, R. J., 1984, Relation of unconformities, tectonics, and sea level changes, Cretaceous of Western Interior, U.S.A., *in* Schlee, J. S., ed., Interregional Unconformities and Hydrocarbon Accumulation: Tulsa, American Association of Petroleum Geologists Memoir 36, p. 7–35.

WEIMER, R. J., AND SONNENBERG, S. A., 1989, Sequence stratigraphic analysis, Muddy (J) Sandstone reservoir, Wattenberg Field, Denver Basin, Colorado, *in* Coalson, E., Kaplan, S. J., Keighen, C. W., Oglesby, C. A., and Robinson, J. W., eds., Sandstone Reservoirs: Rocky Mountain Association of Geologists, p. 197–220.

WILLIAMS, D. F., 1984, Correlation of the Pleistocene marine sediments of the Gulf of Mexico and other basins using oxygen isotope stratigraphy, *in* Healy-Williams, N., ed., Principles of Pleistocene Stratigraphy Applied to Gulf of Mexico: Boston, Human Resources Development Corporation Publication, p. 65–118.

INCISED VALLEYS AND BACKSTEPPING DELTAIC DEPOSITS IN A FORELAND-BASIN SETTING, TORRES STRAIT AND GULF OF PAPUA, AUSTRALIA

PETER T. HARRIS*

Ocean Sciences Institute, University of Sydney, Sydney NSW 2006, Australia

ABSTRACT: The Fly River of Papua New Guinea presently discharges approximately 6,500 m^3/s and carries an estimated sediment load of 85 million tonnes/yr to the continental shelf of southern Papua New Guinea at the northern end of Australia's Great Barrier Reef; the area is thus a major carbonate/siliciclastic transition zone. The River has constructed a tidally dominated, "funnel-shaped" estuary together with an offshore prograding delta in which prodelta sediments are accreting at rates of up to 0.1 m/yr. During the last glacial lowering of sea level, base level for the fluvial system was lowered and numerous channels were cut into the Pleistocene flood-plain deposits of the continental shelf. The valleys thus formed are seen in bathymetric and seismic sections incised up to 60 m below the level of the surrounding seabed. They are found concentrated within a 20–25 km wide zone which divides siliciclastic and carbonate deposits and which extends along part of the present-day Papua New Guinea coastline and eastwards into the Gulf of Papua; they do not extend across the adjacent Torres Strait area located further southwest.

During the subsequent Holocene transgression, many of these valleys were back-filled by the landward-retreating fluvial system. High-resolution boomer seismic profiles show valleys infilled with fluvial cut-and-fill deposits and overlain by prograding deltaic sediments which overfill the valleys. Some valleys, however, are only partially infilled with sediment and are presently scoured and maintained by strong tidal currents. In such "tidally-scoured" cases, the relict deltaic units are truncated and overlain by a thin veneer of Holocene sediment as determined from core samples.

INTRODUCTION

Of the processes effecting the formation and infilling of incised valleys, the changes caused by a rise or fall of relative sea level are of fundamental importance. A lowering of sea level results in fluvial erosion, entrenchment and the formation of a valley (a sequence boundary; e.g., Vail and others 1977; Van Wagoner and others, 1990). The generalized stratigraphic succession produced by an estuary in relation to a subsequent rise and stabilization of relative sea level consists of an erosional unconformity overlain by alluvial channel deposits followed by estuarine/marine units, which vary in character depending upon sediment supply and the relative influence of tides and waves (Dalrymple and others, 1992).

Previous studies of incised valleys and valley-fill successions have focussed mainly on systems located on passive continental margins with a relatively low sediment influx. In the present study, high-resolution seismic and core data, obtained from an epicontinental seaway in the Papua New Guinea foreland basin, are examined. Prevalence of a humid tropical climate and active orogenic uplift has resulted in high terrigenous sediment input rates throughout the Quaternary and progradation over adjacent carbonate platform deposits. During the last glacial lowering of sea level approximately 20,000 years ago, the Papuan rivers flowed out across what is now the submerged continental shelf, cutting valleys in relation to the lower base level. Landward retreat of the fluvial systems during the Holocene transgression might be expected to have resulted in the infilling of any valleys found along the retreat path. The question arises: "What is the spatial distribution of relict fluvial valleys and estuarine-deltaic deposits on the southern Papua New Guinea continental shelf?" The present study will examine the available bathymetric, high-resolution seismic and core data in order to answer this question.

*Present Address: Australian Geological Survey Organisation, Antarctic CRC, GPO Box 252C, University of Tasmania, Hobart Tasmania 7001, Australia

GEOLOGICAL SETTING

Regional Tectonic Setting

The island of Papua New Guinea-Irian Jaya is the northern extension of the Australian continental plate, forming a continent-island arc collision boundary (Jaques and Robinson, 1977; Fig. 1). Following the break-up of Gondwanaland, Australia moved northward passing from temperate into tropical climatic zones (Davies and others, 1989). From Eocene to early Miocene time, the margin remained passive with up to 500 m of temperate, shallow-water carbonate shelf sediments accumulating (Pigram and others, 1989). Mid-Oligocene collision along the northern margin initiated uplift and foreland basin development. Tropical (carbonate) platform reefs proliferated in a 500–600 km wide epicontinental seaway (the proto-Torres Strait) located south of the emergent Papuan landmass.

Throughout Neogene and into Quaternary deposition, terrigenous sediments derived from the emergent collisional highlands have prograded southward across much of this shallow seaway, burying shelf carbonate and platform reef deposits. These are presently exposed as relict reefal limestones in southern Papua New Guinea and on adjacent islands (e.g., Saibai Island; Fig. 2), which exhibit doline karst features (Fig. 1) and which are partially buried by terrigenous sediments. Middle Miocene, shallow-water carbonates have been drilled at −3,000 m in the foreland basin south of the orogen, whereas shallow water carbonates of the same age are found at 1,000 m elevation in the northern Papuan Highlands, illustrating the extent of basin subsidence and highlands orogeny, respectively (Veevers, 1984). Interestingly, the tectonic setting of present-day Papua New Guinea has been suggested as a modern analogue for the Cretaceous of western North America and the Appalachian mountain system of eastern North America (Dott and Batten, 1976; Baldwin and Butler, 1982).

The Fly River

The Fly River of southern Papua New Guinea is the region's major fluvial system. The river discharges approx-

Incised-valley Systems: Origin and Sedimentary Sequences, SEPM Special Publication No. 51
Copyright © 1994, SEPM (Society for Sedimentary Geology), ISBN 1-56576-015-8

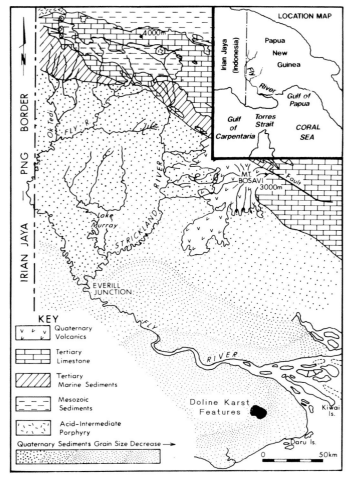

FIG. 1.—Geological map of the Fly River catchment in Papua New Guinea (after Harris and Baker, 1991).

imately 6500 m³/s and carries an estimated sediment load of 85 million tonnes/yr to the Gulf of Papua at the northern end of Australia's Great Barrier Reef. The head-waters of the Fly are within the central cordillera of Papua New Guinea, characterised by elevations of 4,000 m and rainfall as high as 10 m/yr (Fig. 1). The extreme topography and rainfall decrease rapidly towards the coast where rainfall averages about 2 m/yr over a low relief floodplain (the Fly Platform) with a mean elevation of around 20 m (Fig. 2).

The course of the Fly is thought to have switched from west to east, to either side of a north-south trending basement ridge which extends northward from Cape York on the Australian mainland (Fig. 2). Tectonism causing the "Oriomo uplift" is speculated to have diverted the Fly to its present eastward course about 36,000 years BP (Blake and Ollier, 1969). Prior to this time, it has been suggested that the Fly River flowed southwestward into what was then "Lake Carpentaria" (Jones and Torgersen, 1988). However, the exact timing of any changes in the river course and the actual positions of paleo-river courses are unclear from the available data (Loffler, 1977).

The Present-day Shelf Environment

The shelf area comprising Torres Strait and the Gulf of Papua forms a shallow, low-gradient platform, typically 10 to 15 m in depth, distally steepened towards the east (Fig. 2). The sill depth for Torres Strait is about 12 m (Harris, 1988). Slopes are extremely gentle, with the 10 to 15 m and 15 to 20 m isobaths spaced up to 50 km apart (i.e., < 0.006°). However, the bathymetry does become more complex in proximity to steep-sided coral reefs which may have vertical sides, locally. A notable bathymetric feature is the deep channel forming Missionary Passage, located at the northern end of the Warrior Reefs, which is up to 60 m in depth locally. Other deep channels are located to the north of Saibai Island and among the complex of patch reefs located in the east between the Warrior Reefs and the shelf edge (Fig. 2). Water depths increase rapidly to the east of the Great Barrier Reef, which is located on the shelf margin of the Coral Sea basin (Fig. 2), but the Gulf of Carpentaria seabed (to the west) is flat and featureless due to the absence of coral reefs and reaches a maximum depth of only about 65 m (Jones and Torgersen, 1988).

In the Gulf of Papua, an extensive, shallow deltaic system occurs in 5 to 30 m water depth, bordered by a steep gradient prodelta in 20 to 50 m of water, which extends along the coast between the Fly and Purari River mouths. The available bathymetry indicate a more complex, off-shore-onshore trending seafloor topography on the middle to outer shelf between 50 and 100 m depth (Fig. 2). The shelf edge occurs at about 120 to 14 0 m depth.

Oceanographic features of the Torres Strait region are the large tidal range (3.8 m on springs at Daru; Fig. 2), with associated strong tidal currents. Currents are accelerated in all of the constricted inter-reef channels (i.e., passes of the Warrior Reefs), and local spring tidal current speeds of up to 5 knots (2.5 m/s) are recorded on nautical charts. One current meter, located in 20 m water depth 10 km to the northeast of Cape York, recorded near-bed (1 m above the bed) peak speeds of 1.3 m/s (Harris, 1989). These strong tidal flows dominate in the transport and dispersal of sediments within the Fly Delta/Torres Strait system. The seabed exhibits local zones (i.e., reef passes) scoured clear of any unconsolidated sediment, leaving a lag gravel or limestone pavement (Harris, 1988). With increasing distance from the scoured zones, sediment of decreasing grain size is deposited, grading from lag gravel and bedrock exposures to sand/gravel ribbons to subtidal dunes. At a distance from the reef passes, current strengths are diminished enough to allow fine silt- and clay-sized particles to settle out from suspension (Harris and Baker, 1991). Such a pattern is similar to that found in the west European shelf seas and is characteristic of a tidally dominated shelf environment (Harris, 1988; Harris and Baker, 1991). Cyclone-induced waves and currents may cause the upper 4 to 6 cm of sediment to be eroded and redistributed over the shelf (Gagan and others, 1990) and wind-driven currents may cause seasonal reversals in the direction of subtidal dune migration (Harris, 1989; 1991). However, the distribution and morphology of Holocene deposits in Torres Strait are primarily a product of strong tidal currents.

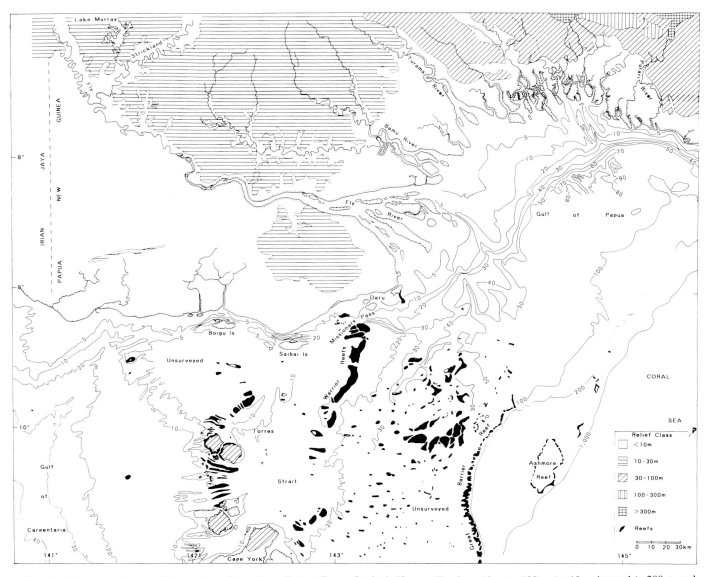

Fig. 2.—Bathymetric map of the southern Papua New Guinea-Torres Strait shelf area. The 5 m, 10 m to 100 m (at 10 m intervals), 200 m and 1000 m isobaths are shown based on data abstracted from Royal Australian Navy charts and unpublished Ocean Sciences Institute data.

Wind-driven currents of up to 0.2 m/s flow generally towards the east through Torres Strait during the northwest Monsoon (November-April) and towards the west during the southeast trade wind season (May-October; Wolanski and others, 1988). Complex gyres are established in the Gulf of Papua by wind-driven currents which dominate in the long-term mixing of estuarine/deltaic and open marine water masses. The general pattern is one of weak southward flows during the northwest Monsoon (November-April) with stronger northeastward-flowing coastal currents along the delta front during the southeast trade wind season (Wolanski and Eagle, 1991).

Surface waves are limited in their height and period by fetch and water depth in Torres Strait. Open water expanses between reefs and the coastline are generally less than 50 km. The Strait is protected by the Great Barrier Reef from

long-period swell waves originating in the Coral Sea. However, Coral Sea surface waves are able to propagate northwestwards into the Gulf of Papua since there is no shelf edge barrier reef in this area (Fig. 2); for about 70% of the time these waves have significant heights of between 1.6 m (September-November) and 1.9 m (December-August; Thom and Wright, 1983).

The junction of the Fly River Delta and the Great Barrier Reef (GBR) is a major terrigenous-clastic/carbonate transition; over a wide area, calcareous sediment is diluted with terrigenous mud. Analyses of surficial sediments suggest deposition of present day Fly River sediments is largely restricted to within 25 km of the delta and to within 10 km of the southern Papua New Guinea coastline. Carbonate content increases to >80% at a distance of 20 km to the south of the Fly Delta. At >60 km distance, calcareous mud, produced by the erosion of bioclasts in zones of high tidal energy, constitutes more than 50% of the mud-size fraction (Harris and Baker, 1991). Inter-reef (shelf) sediments are derived primarily from benthonic foraminifers, supplemented with bryozoans, molluscs, the blue-green alga *Halimeda*, and small amounts of corals (Maxwell, 1968; Harris, 1988; Bryce, 1988; Kracik, 1990).

Late Quaternary Sea-level Changes:

In Australia, it has been shown that sea level fell to at least −120 m during the last glacial episode (Veeh and Veevers, 1970; Thom and Chappell, 1975; Chappell and Shackleton, 1986). Over much of the last 100,000 years, sea level has remained in the range of 40–70 m below its present position (Fig. 3). The available data (e.g., Thom and Roy, 1983; Chappell and others, 1983; Pillans, 1987) indicates that the most recent sea level rise began about 19,000 years ago, reaching a maximum rate of about 20 m per 1,000 years between about 11,000–12,000 years ago. This rise was followed by lesser rates of transgression until the present sea level was reached by about 6,500 years ago (Fig. 3).

Studies of isostatic changes in relative sea level on the Australian continental shelf have been summarised by Nakada and Lambeck (1989). In general, isostatic adjustments along the Australian shoreline resulted in a relative, sea-level highstand of ~1–2 m between 5,000 to 6,000 years ago. The analysis of Nakada and Lambeck (1989) does not take into account deformation of the shelf by sediment loading. Such could be significant in the Gulf of Papua/Torres Strait coastal area which is supplied with large amounts of sediment by the Papuan rivers (e.g., Torgersen and others, 1983; Veevers, 1984, p. 210–221).

Changes in sea-level due to tectonic affects are thought to be limited in the case of the Australian continent which is considered to be relatively stable. The collision boundary in Papua New Guinea forms a northern, tectonically active zone, but the effect of this zone (in terms of late Pleistocene to Holocene sea level change) does not appear to extend southwards into the Australian (Cape York) region (see also Bryant and others, 1988, and Aubrey and Emery, 1988). The rate of basin subsidence in the Torres Strait area (~2 cm per 1,000 years) is negligible in comparison to eustatic sea-level fluctuations.

METHODS

Cruises have been carried out to the Torres Strait and Fly Delta area by Sydney University's Ocean Sciences Institute (OSI) using HMAS *Cook* in 1988 and 1990 and RV *Sunbird* in 1991 (Harris and others, 1990, 1991). Seismic profiles were obtained during the *Cook* and *Sunbird* cruises using a Ferranti ORE Geopulse boomer system operated at 150 to 350 joules. This system was connected to an EPC 3600 graphic recorder and operated at a sweep speed of 0.25 to 0.5 seconds. Sidescan sonar data were obtained using a Klein model 590 dual frequency (100 and 500 kHz) fish and analogue recorder during the *Cook* (1990) cruise. Navigation for the surveys was by Global Positioning System.

Seismic data were used to identify sedimentary units with emphasis on the interpretation of deposits associated with infilled valleys. Unfilled (bathymetric) valleys were located using available bathymetric data provided by nautical charts, air photographs, unpublished OSI echo-sounding records, and "fair sheets" examined at the Royal Australian Navy Hydrographic Office, North Sydney. Bathymetric data are not available for some "unsurveyed" parts of the study area (Fig. 2).

Cores were obtained using an electrically powered vibrocorer with a 6 m long × 7.5 cm diameter aluminum barrel. In the laboratory, vibrocores were photographed and subsampled at not more than 30 cm intervals. Surface sediments and core subsamples were analysed for gravel-sand-mud content using 2.0 and 0.063 mm sieves. Carbonate content was determined using an acid bomb (Muller and Gastner, 1977). Minerals were identified by standard methods (Grim, 1968) using a Phillips X-ray diffractometer (XRD). Thin sections allowed examination of petrographic characteristics (grain composition, matrix, and cement) and for any diagenetic alterations.

Carbon-14 dates were determined for shell and peat samples by the Macintosh Centre for Quaternary Dating, University of Sydney (Table 1). For shell samples, the ages were corrected for the oceanic reservoir effect (−450 ±35 years in eastern Australia; Bowman, 1985) and using the calibration curve of Stuiver and others (1986). Cores which intersected rapidly accreting deltaic muds were analysed for

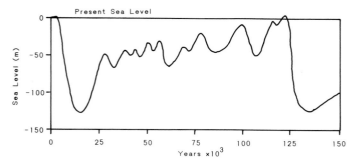

FIG. 3.—Eustatic sea-level curve for the past 150,000 years (after Chappell and Shackleton, 1986).

TABLE 1.—RADIOCARBON DATES OBTAINED. CORES ARE NUMBERED BY CRUISE (C-88 = COOK CRUISE OF 1988, C-90 = COOK CRUISE OF 1990 AND SB-91 = SUNBIRD CRUISE OF 1991). AGES GIVEN ARE CORRECTED FOR OCEANIC RESERVOIR EFFECT AND USING A CALIBRATION CURVE (SEE TEXT FOR DETAILS).

Core No.	Depth in Core	Age ± Years BP	Lab Number	Water Depth (m)
C-88.13VC8	165–166 cm	9,280 ± 90	SUA2837	40 m
C-88.13VC8	322–325 cm	9,280 ± 100	SUA2838	40 m
C-88.14VC9	338–340 cm	26,900 ± 1,500	SUA2839	33 m
C-88.20VC15	38–40 cm	2,840 ± 210	SUA2842	29 m
C-88.20VC15	100–102 cm	8,500 ± 300	SUA2843	29 m
C-90.22VC3	410–412 cm	4,970 ± 140	SUA2950	17 m
C-88.17VC12	60–65 cm	2,520 ± 160	SUA2840	20 m
C-88.18VC13	50–55 cm	2,850 ± 110	SUA2841	21 m
C-88.24VC14	96–100 cm	4,620 ± 100	SUA2844	24 m
C-90.31VC5	265–267 cm	530 ± 180	SUA2951	21 m
C-90.88VC14	274–276 cm	6,060 ± 290	SUA2952	44 m
SB-91.121PC11	248–250 cm	modern	SUA3032	10 m

sedimentation rate by lead-210 analysis (see Harris and others, 1993, for details of the method used).

Sediment Core Data

A total of 35 cores have been obtained at locations in Torres Strait, the Great North East Channel and on the Fly Delta (Fig. 4). Harris and others (1991, 1993) have recognized four sedimentary facies on the bases of grain size, lithology, carbonate content, visual appearance, and the results of radiocarbon (Table 1) and lead-210 dating: (1) shelf facies, (2) deltaic facies, (3) transgressive estuarine-mud facies, and (4) Pleistocene clay-soil facies (Fig. 5). The facies evolved in conjunction with sea-level transgression during the late Quaternary (<30,000 years BP).

The shelf facies comprises unconsolidated, calcareous, gravelly muddy sands grading into well sorted, terrigenous,

deltaic, sandy muds towards the Fly Delta. The calcareous sands (unit S in Fig. 5) comprise the upper 50 to 150 cm of cores obtained south of the Fly Delta. Radiocarbon dates obtained from the base of this unit range from 4,620 to 2,520 years BP, demonstrating that deposition occurred after sea level reached its stillstand position 6,500 years BP. Cores show signs of intense bioturbation. Variation in composition is also related to the proximity of reefs; reef-proximal cores penetrated pebble- to cobble-sized limestone debris, part of a talus-slope deposit.

Deltaic sedimentation associated with the Fly River has been described by Harris and others (1993). Fly prodelta deposits are laminated to massively bedded terrigenous muds, containing generally less than 10% fine quartz sand. The bedding is typically 2 to 5 cm in thickness, equivalent to the annual sedimentation rate as determined by lead-210 dating. The beds are therefore annual deposits (varves) and are interpreted as forming in relation to seasonal variation

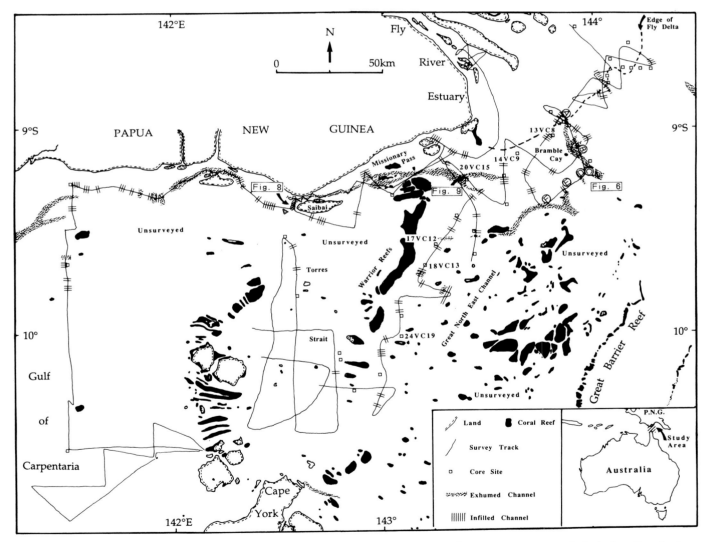

Fig. 4.—Location and distribution of infilled and unfilled valleys observed in seismic and bathymetric data, respectively (only valleys having a relief >10 m below the surrounding level are shown). The location of geophysical survey track lines with sections shown in Figures 6, 8 and 9, together with cores sites are indicated.

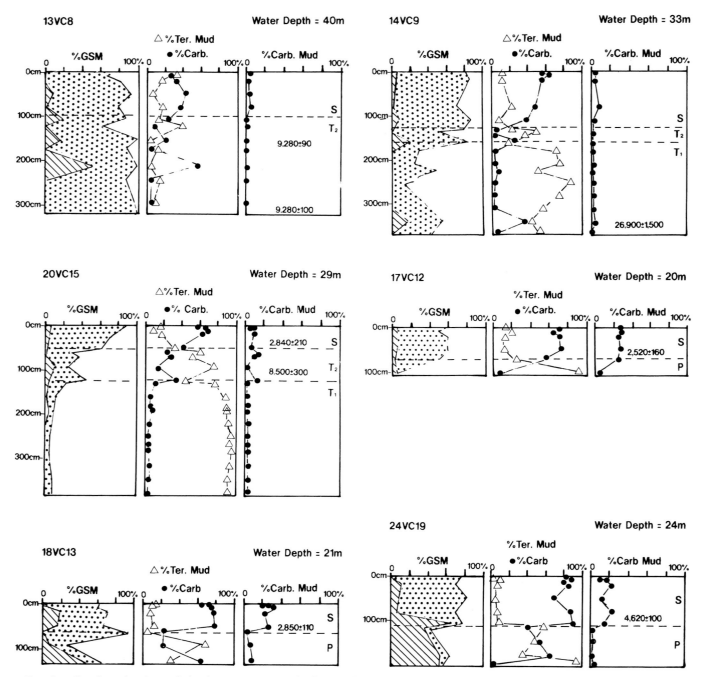

Fig. 5.—Core logs showing variation in percentage gravel (diagonal line shading), sand (dotted shading), mud (no shading), carbonate content, terrigenous mud, and carbonate mud (from Harris and others, 1991; see Fig. 4 for core locations). Symbols S, T_1, T_2, and P refer to facies as described in the text. The age of radio-carbon dated samples is shown with error limits (see Table 1 for data on radiometric dates).

in surface wave energy; large waves produced by the south-easterly trade winds cause reworking and winnowing of sediments leaving a sandy layer which is draped by mud during the lower-energy monsoon season (Harris and others, 1993). The deltaic system lies generally in the 8 to 30 m depth range (distal deltaic sediments are deposited in water depths of up to 50 m in the northern Gulf of Papua) and is prograding offshore at a rate of about 6 m/yr, burying the

more slowly accreting (0.02 cm/yr), calcareous, inter-reef shelf deposits.

The transgressive estuarine-mud facies was encountered in cores obtained in 29 to 40 m water depth on the shelf offshore of the Fly Delta and not in cores obtained from Torres Strait or the Great North East Channel. The facies occurs as two distinct units; a well-sorted, grey terrigenous clay (T_1 in Fig. 5) and interbedded, gravelly-muddy quartz sands and mangrove peats (T_2 in Fig. 5). Individual sand and peat beds are 1 to 30 cm in thickness and are commonly bioturbated. Radiocarbon dates indicate the peat was deposited after 8,500 to 9,300 years BP, which coincides with a sea level 10 to 15 m below its present position, during the period of post-glacial, sea-level transgression and flooding of the shelf (Fig. 3). Deposition of the unit appears to have been rapid (of the order of 1 meter per 100 years) in some areas since identical radiocarbon dates were obtained 150 cm apart from core 13VC8 (Fig. 5).

The well-sorted, grey, terrigenous sandy clay forming Unit T_1 is found beneath Unit T_2. One radiocarbon date from a bivalve shell gave an age of 26,900 ±1,500 years BP (core 14VC9; Table 1, Fig. 5). This shell was extracted from a shell layer, and it is unknown whether it is allochthonous or (lived and died) *in situ*. However, the sea level at 27,000 years BP was about 50 m below that at present (Fig. 3) which is well *below* the present water depth of the core site (33 m). Thus the shell was probably eroded from an older marine deposit and redeposited landward of its original position during the Holocene transgression; if this interpretation is correct, then Unit T_1 is early Holocene (>~10,000 years?) in age (Fig. 5).

The Pleistocene clay-soil facies (unit P in Fig. 5) consists of a cohesive, reddish-brown to bluish-grey montmorillonite clay (Harris and Baker, 1991) containing pedogenic limestone concretions (caliche). The clay was encountered in cores collected at water depths of 20 to 37 m. The caliche nodules were probably formed as early diagenetic products of groundwater-related subaerial processes. Thus, this clay is interpreted as a Pleistocene soil formed during a period when the present-day Torres Strait was subaerially exposed at a lower relative sea-level.

Seismic Data

About 2,500 km of geophysical data have been obtained, providing a reconnaissance data base of sidescan sonar and high-resolution, boomer-seismic profiles from the study area (Fig. 4). Seismic data show a persistent sub-bottom reflector which has been termed reflector "A" by previous GBR workers (e.g., Searle and others, 1981; Johnson and others 1982; see Figs. 6, 7, 8, 9). Reflector "A" has been shown elsewhere to represent the Holocene/Pleistocene unconformity (Harvey and others, 1979). It was formed by erosional processes during the last glacial lowering of sea level (a Type 1 boundary in the terminology of Van Wagoner and others 1987).

Although reflector "A" is easily identified south of 9°, where only a thin Holocene veneer overlies this surface (e.g., Fig. 9), northwards from the Bramble Cay region (Fig. 4) numerous superimposed and laterally discontinuous cut-and-fill units occur in the seismic records, and reflector "A" becomes difficult to distinguish. Core data (see above) indicate that thick (>5 m) sediment units, deposited during the post-glacial transgression, occur in this area. These constitute a Holocene transgressive systems tract (TST), using the terminology of Van Wagoner and others (1987).

Incised valleys depicted by reflector "A" have a relief locally of 60 milliseconds and occur both as unfilled (sub-marine) valleys and in the subsurface as infilled features containing thick sediment deposits (20–60 milliseconds 2-way time) which mask the relict morphology (Figs. 6, 7, 8, 9). Sediments infilling the incised valleys exhibit at least two seismic facies: facies "a"- cut-and-fill structures located in the lower sections of valleys (e.g., at 1150 hrs in Fig. 7 and at 1536 hrs in Fig. 8) and facies "b"- horizontal and foreset beds, 1 to 5m in thickness which drape facies "a." The total thickness of facies "b" reaches 10–20 m and, in locations offshore of the present Fly Delta, the valleys have been over-filled such that positive seabed relief occurs directly above the infilled valley (e.g., at time 1150 hrs on Figs. 6 and 7). In the Torres Strait area and along the southern Papua New Guinea coastline (Fig. 4), reflectors indicate that valley incision and infilling have been followed by an erosional event (e.g., Fig. 8). In such cases, the mainly horizontal to shallow-dipping beds are truncated on the valley sides (note the truncation of beds at core site 121PC11; Fig. 8).

Elsewhere, in the southern part of the study area, erosional processes have resulted in outcrops of reflector "A" on the seafloor (Fig. 9) where it is only thinly covered by Holocene carbonate, as determined from cores obtained in the Great North East Channel (i.e., unit S in Fig. 5). Seabed erosion is indicated by the truncation of bedded units (Fig. 9), and reworking is shown by the widespread occurrence of subtidal dunes (Fig. 9; see also Harris, 1988). Strong tidal currents, reaching a maximum near-bed speed of 0.8 m/s, were measured at site CM3 (Harris and others, 1991; see Fig. 8) indicating the erosive nature of local currents.

Unfilled valleys form extensive bathymetric features (Fig. 4) reaching 20 to 60 m below the level of the surrounding seabed. These are found to occur mainly within 25 km of the southern coast of Papua New Guinea (Fig. 4). One valley appears to extend continuously for over 100 km through Missionary Passage and to the north of Saibai Island (Fig. 4). Although such valleys are partially infilled with sediments locally (Figs. 8, 9; see above), the valleys appear to be scoured free of any unconsolidated sediments at other locations where tidal currents are accelerated through the narrow passes between reefs and islands.

Finally, an acoustically turbid to opaque unit has been identified, occurring laterally over distances of up to 1.3 km in seismic sections (Fig. 6). The occurrence of this unit is restricted to the area north of 9° 20' and was not evident in the data obtained south of this latitude (i.e., the unit occurs in the Gulf of Papua but not in the Great North East Channel or Torres Strait). These units may be interpreted either as carbonate reefs or as sediments containing biogenic gas (or both). The close proximity of Holocene reefs growing at the present sea surface (e.g., Bramble Cay is located 5 km away from the unit in one area; Fig. 6) to some of these buried features is suggestive of a reefal origin. However, no cores have been obtained which can confirm this hypothesis.

DISCUSSION
Infilled Valleys

The material infilling many of the valleys appears to have been deposited during the post-glacial transgression. Core

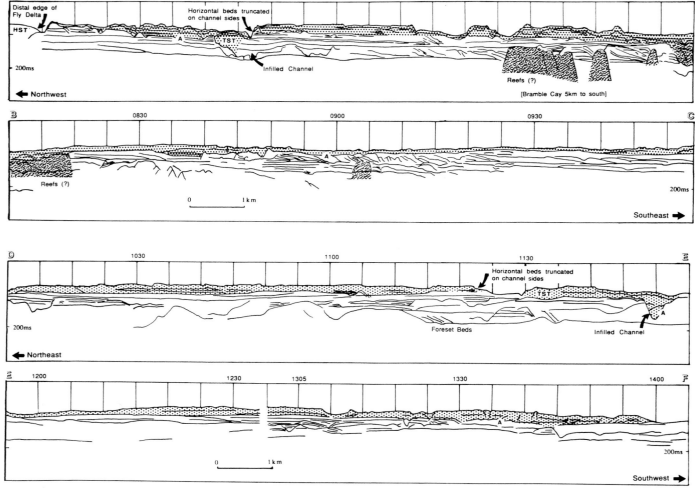

FIG. 6.—Line drawings of seismic profiles extending offshore from the Fly Delta showing what are interpreted as infilled valleys (associated with prograding fluvial-deltaic deposits, foreset beds, etc.) and buried coral-reef deposits (and/or biogenic gas?). The position of reflector "A" is indicated. The shaded area (dotted) above reflector A, representing "transgressive systems tract" (TST) deposits, pinches out towards the southwest. Fly Delta deposits constitute highstand systems tract (HST) deposits. See Figure 4 for location of section.

20VC15 (Figs. 5, 9) penetrated 3.5 m into transgressive sediments infilling one valley. Similarly, cores 13VC8 and 14VC9 (Figs. 4, 5) intersected a facies with an age and lithology indicative of deposition during the transgression; these deposits correlate with what has been labelled a transgressive systems tract (TST) in Figure 6. The units identified within the transgressive systems tract in seismic sections (e.g., Fig. 7) may be similar in origin to the deltaic lobes associated with the Mississippi Delta which are thought to reflect changes in the rate of transgression or short-lived still stands (e.g., Boyd, 1989).

For example, the section shown in Figure 7, located directly offshore of the present-day Fly pro-delta, shows an incised surface at a depth of about 60 m below present sea level (interpreted as a sequence boundary; reflector "A") which exhibits a valley incised to a depth a further 60 m below the level of the surrounding surface defined by reflector "A" (i.e., to a depth of around 120 m below present

sea level; Fig. 7). The valley is infilled with sediments, interpreted as fluvial, cut-and-fill channel deposits (seismic facies "a"; see above), draped by horizontally bedded sediments 10–20 m in thickness, interpreted as relict pro-delta deposits (facies "b"). Hence, the valley was cut during the last sea-level lowstand (~18,000 years ago) and was infilled during the transgression with fluvial and possibly estuarine sediments, although the gradation from fluvial into deltaic sediments appears abrupt (Fig. 7). The fluvial sediments comprising facies "a" would comprise a part of the lowstand systems tract (LST), using the terminology of Van Wagoner and others (1987). An apparent pause in the rise of relative sea level resulted in a period of progradation which overfilled the valley forming the observed deltaic deposits (TST). Subsequent transgression submerged the delta in its present water depth of 50–60 m, and a thin (1–2 m thick) drape of Holocene, muddy carbonate sediment overlies this unit. Such a pattern of positive relief over an in-

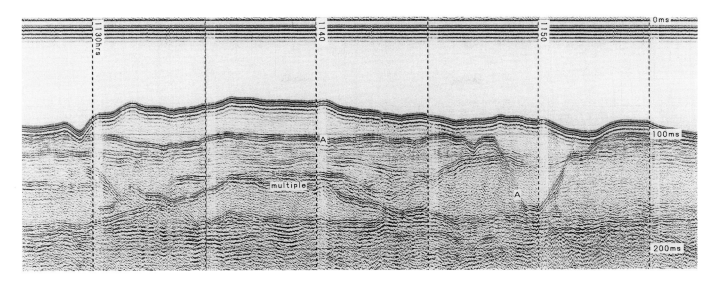

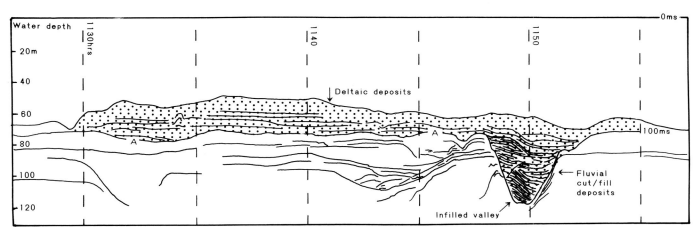

FIG. 7.—Example of (A) unprocessed boomer seismic section and (B) interpretation corresponding to 1130–1150 hrs shown in Figure 6. The section shows a valley infilled with what are interpreted as fluvial cut-and-fill deposits. The valley fill sediments are capped by what are interpreted as deltaic deposits which "overfill" the valley (see text for discussion). The positions of the first multiple and reflector "A" are indicated.

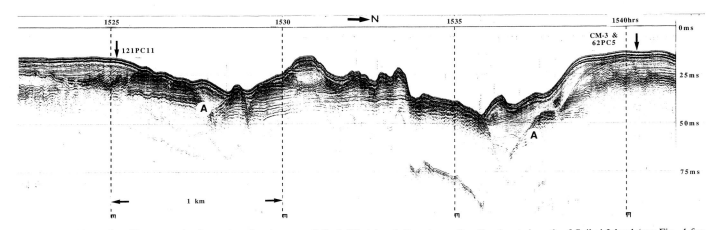

FIG. 8.—Example of boomer-seismic section showing a partially infilled (partially exhumed) valley located north of Saibai Island (see Fig. 4 for location of section). What is interpreted as reflector "A" extends through the section outcropping on the seabed around the location of 1535 hrs. The present seabed represents another episode of incision of the bedded deposits (note truncation of foreset beds near core 121PC11) which are overlain by a >2-m thick veneer of Holocene sediment. Piston core (PC) and self-recording current meter (CM) sites are indicated.

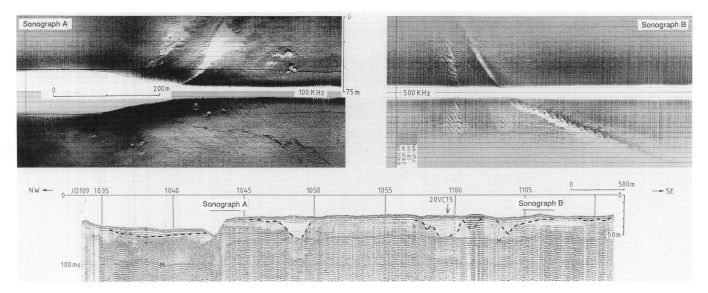

Fig. 9.—Example of sidescan sonagraphs and seismic section showing erosional seafloor with dunes and outcrops of older material on the seabed. Dashed lines mark the position of what is interpreted as reflector "A." Note the infilled valley associated with core 20VC15 (see Fig. 5 for core log). M = multiple. See Figure 4 for location of section.

filled channel has been attributed elsewhere in the Great Barrier Reef to the deposition of fluvial deltaic deposits under the influence of a rising sea level (Johnson and others, 1982).

The apparent "pause" in sea-level rise invoked above may have been related to a number of factors, including an increase in the fluvial sediment supply of the river (and apparent regression) or an actual pause in the rate of eustatic sea-level rise (e.g., Carter and Johnson, 1986). It is not possible to specify the controlling process from the available data. Nevertheless, this situation of deltaic deposits overfilling a relict paleovalley in the absence of any significant estuarine deposits does not appear to have been described in previous studies of Quaternary estuarine depositional successions (e.g., see review by Dalrymple and others, 1992). The present case of an incised valley infilled with fluvial-deltaic, depositional units has developed within the framework of a fluvial system having a relatively high rate of sediment input; in contrast, most modern incised-valley (estuarine) studies have been carried out where the fluvial sediment supply is relatively small.

Unfilled Valleys

Elsewhere on the shelf, valleys were exhumed or left unfilled during and/or after the Holocene transgression. On first inspection, the occurrence of unfilled valleys on the shelf directly offshore from the Fly Delta appears to be a paradox as the immense sediment load of the Fly should be expected to have infilled any incised valleys as the shoreline retreated landwards during the post-glacial transgression. However, several factors may explain the occurrence of such valleys: (i) they were not infilled during the transgression due to strong currents and/or because of an episode of low sediment supply; (ii) they were abandoned

by the fluvial system prior to the transgression and thus were not infilled; and/or (iii) they were infilled but then exhumed by strong currents.

Certain segments of a valley may have been left unfilled during the transgression as current activity restricted sediment deposition. Alternatively, the river system may have undergone a period of lower sediment delivery to a particular section of the coastal zone. If such valleys were rapidly transgressed, it is possible that their relief was preserved.

If valley formation was followed by stream avulsion, the valley might have been left unfilled during transgression. For example, if a valley was incised at some time around or prior to 18,000 years BP (in relation to a lower position of sea level) and was then abandoned by the fluvial system which formed it, there would be no significant fluvial source of sediment to the valley, and its depth could be maintained during the Holocene transgression provided that estuarine sedimentation sourced from the sea was insufficient to infill the valley.

Tidal currents at the present time are known to be strong within restricted areas of the shelf (see above). It is conceivable that unconsolidated deposits infilling a valley could have been eroded under the present hydrodynamic regime (e.g., the valley at 1125–1130 hrs in Fig. 6). Similarly, it is likely that at various times during the post-glacial transgression, tidal currents would have been strong, locally. As discussed above, the channel located to the north of Saibai Island may have been re-incised in this way. The erosional episode, which resulted in the truncation of the transgressive deltaic sediments (seismic facies "b") and the partial exhumation of the valley north of Saibai Island, formed a tidal ravinement surface (Fig. 8). Given that the above interpretation of the deposits is correct, then erosion must have occurred towards the end of the post-glacial transgression and may have been caused by strong tidal currents established when Torres Strait was first opened. This deep bathymetric valley, along the southern Papua New Guinea coastline, lies well below the level of the seabed in all of the surrounding areas of Torres Strait (Fig. 2) which forms a low-relief plateau. Consequently, it was the site of the first opening of Torres Strait as the rising sea-level first flooded this relatively deep incised valley during the Holocene transgression around 9,000 years ago, thus joining the Coral Sea and Gulf of Carpentaria.

CONCLUSIONS

Seismic profiling and bathymetric data document the occurrence of incised valleys on the continental shelf adjacent to the Fly River Delta. Some valleys were infilled with sediment during the early part of the Holocene transgression, 8,000–9,000 years BP, based on dated core samples and were "over-filled" such that fluvial deposits exhibiting cut-and-fill structures are overlain by horizontal and foreset-bedded deltaic sediments deposited during an apparent pause in the Holocene sea-level rise. Other valleys were never infilled or were exhumed in the Holocene. One extensive, unfilled valley system extends for over 100 km along the southern coastline of Papua New Guinea. Valleys (both infilled and unfilled) are absent in the part of the study area located south of latitude 10°S.

ACKNOWLEDGMENTS

The author is grateful for the financial support of the Australian Defence Science and Technology Organisation and of the Australian Research Council (Ref. No. A39131170). The Royal Australian Navy provided ship time on HMAS *Cook* for this project. Vibrocoring and boomer-seismic equipment was purchased by a grant awarded by the University of Sydney. Thanks to Dr. Bob Dalrymple (Queens University, Ontario) for valuable discussions and for providing a critical review of an earlier version of this paper. The paper benefited from critical reviews provided by Dr. Donald Forbes (Geological Survey of Canada, Bedford Institute of Oceanography, Nova Scotia) and by an anonymous reviewer.

REFERENCES

AUBREY, D. G., AND EMERY, K. O., 1988, Australia—an unstable platform for tide-gauge measurements of changing sea levels: a reply: Journal of Geology, 96, p. 640–643.
BALDWIN, B., AND BUTLER, J. R., 1982, Hamilton's Indonesia map and the Appalachian mountain system: Journal of Geological Education, v. 30, p. 93–96.
BOWMAN, G. M., 1985, Revised radiocarbon oceanic reservoir correction for southern Australia: Search, v. 16, p. 164–165.
BLAKE, D. H., AND OLLIER, C. D., 1969, Geomorphological evidence of Quaternary tectonics in south western Papua: Review of Geomorphological Dynamics, v. 19, p. 28–32.
BOYD, R., 1989, Relation of sequence stratigraphy to modern sedimentary environments: Geology, v. 17, p. 926–929.
BRYANT, E. A., ROY, P. S., AND THOM, B. G., 1988, Australia—an unstable platform for tide-gauge measurements of changing sea levels: a discussion: Journal of Geology, v. 96, p. 635–640.
BRYCE, S. M., 1988, Composition and Distribution of Surficial Sediments in Torres Strait and the Northern Great Barrier Reef: Unpublished B. Sc. (Hons.) Thesis, University of Sydney, Sydney, 118 p.

CARTER, R. M., AND JOHNSON, D. P., 1986, Sea-level controls on the post-glacial development of the Great Barrier Reef, Queensland: Marine Geology, v. 71, p. 137–164.
CHAPPELL, J., CHIVAS, A., WALLENSKY, E., POLOCH, H. A., AND AHARON, P., 1983, Holocene palaeo-environmental changes, central to north Great Barrier Reef inner zone: Bureau of Mineral Resources Journal of Australian Geology and Geophysics, v. 8, p. 223–236.
CHAPPELL, J., AND SHACKLETON, N. J., 1986, Oxygen isotopes and sea level: Nature, v. 324, p. 137–140.
DALRYMPLE, R. W., ZAITLIN, B. A., AND BOYD, R., 1992, Estuarine facies models: conceptual basis and stratigraphic implications: Journal of Sedimentary Petrology, v. 62, p. 1130–1146.
DAVIES, P. J., SYMONDS, P. A., FEARY, D. A., AND PIGRAM, C. J., 1989, The evolution of the carbonate platforms of northeast Australia , *in* Crevella, P. D., Wilson, J. L., Sarg, J. F., and Read, J. F., eds., Controls on Carbonate Platform and Basin Development: Society of Economic Paleontologists and Mineralogists Special Publication 44, Tulsa, p. 233–258.
DOTT, R. H., AND BATTEN, R. L., 1976, Evolution of the Earth: New York, McGraw-Hill, 506 p.
GAGAN, M. K., CHIVAS, A. R., AND HERCZEG, A. L., 1990, Shelf wide erosion, deposition and suspended sediment transport during cyclone Winifred, central Great Barrier Reef, Australia: Journal of Sedimentary Petrology, v. 60, p. 456–470.
GRIM, R. E., 1968, Clay Mineralogy: New York, McGraw Hill, 438 p.
HARRIS, P. T., 1988, Sediments, bedforms and bedload transport pathways on the continental shelf adjacent to Torres Strait, Australia-Papua New Guinea: Continental Shelf Research, v. 8, p. 979–1003.
HARRIS, P. T., 1989, Sandwave movement under tidal and wind-driven currents in a shallow marine environment: Adolphus Channel, northeastern Australia: Continental Shelf Research, v. 9, p. 981–1002.
HARRIS, P. T., 1991, Reversal of subtidal dune asymmetries caused by seasonally reversing wind-driven currents in Torres Strait, northeastern Australia: Continental Shelf Research, v. 11, p. 655–662.
HARRIS, P. T., AND BAKER, E. K., 1991, The nature of sediments forming the Torres Strait turbidity maximum: Australian Journal of Earth Sciences, v. 38, p. 65–78.
HARRIS, P. T., BAKER, E. K., AND COLE, A. R., 1990, Sandwave movement, currents and sedimentation in Torres Strait: Results obtained during a cruise of HMAS Cook in April 1990: Sydney, University of Sydney Ocean Sciences Institute Report No. 43, 225 p.
HARRIS, P. T., BAKER, E. K., AND COLE, A. R., 1991, Final Report: sandwave movement, currents and sedimentation in Torres Strait including results obtained during a cruise of R. V. Sunbird in September 1991: Sydney, University of Sydney Ocean Sciences Institute Report No. 47, 113 p.
HARRIS, P. T., BAKER, E. K., COLE, A. R., AND SHORT, S. A., 1993, Preliminary study of sedimentation in the tidally dominated Fly River Delta, Gulf of Papua: Continental Shelf Research, v. 13, p. 441–472.
HARVEY, N., DAVIES, P. J., AND MARSHALL, J. F., 1979, Seismic refraction: a tool for studying coral reef growth: Bureau of Mineral Resources Journal of Australian Geology and Geophysics, v. 4, p. 141–147.
JAQUES, A. L., AND ROBINSON, G. P., 1977, The continent island/arc collision in northern Papua New Guinea: Bureau of Mineral Resources Journal of Australian Geology and Geophysics, v. 2, p. 289–303.
JOHNSON, D. P., SEARLE, D. E., AND HOPLEY, D., 1982, Positive relief over buried post-glacial channels, Great Barrier Reef: Marine Geology, v. 46, p. 149–159.
JONES, M. R., AND TORGERSEN, T., 1988, Late Quaternary evolution of Lake Carpentaria on the Australia-New Guinea continental shelf: Australian Journal of Earth Science, v. 35, p. 313–324.
KRACIK, M. E. P., 1990, Holocene Sea Level Transgression on Carbonate-Fluvio-Deltaic Sediments, Torres Strait: Unpublished B. Sc. (Hons.) Thesis, University of Sydney, Sydney, 86 p.
LOFFLER, E., 1977, Geomorphology of Papua New Guinea: Canberra, Australian National University Press, 258 p.
MAXWELL, W. G. H., 1968, Atlas of the Great Barrier Reef: Amsterdam, Elsevier, 258 p.
MULLER, G., AND GASTNER, M., 1971, The "karbonate bombe" a simple device for the determination of the carbonate content in sediments, soils and other materials: Neus Fahrbuch fur Mineralogie (Monatshefte), v. 10, p. 466–469.

NAKADA, M., AND LAMBECK, K., 1989, Late Pleistocene and Holocene sea-level change in the Australian region and mantle rheology: Geophysical Journal, v. 96, p. 497–517.

PIGRAM, C. J., DAVIES, P. J., FEARY, D. A., AND SYMONDS, P. A., 1989, Tectonic controls on carbonate platform evolution in southern Papua New Guinea: passive margin to foreland basin: Geology, v. 17, p. 199–202.

PILLANS, B. J., 1987, Quaternary sea-level changes: southern hemisphere data, *in* Devoy, R. J. N., ed., Sea Surface Studies: A Global View: Kent, Croom Helm, p. 264–293.

SEARLE, D. E., HARVEY, N., HOPLEY, D., AND JOHNSON, D. P., 1981, Significance of results of shallow seismic research in the Great Barrier Reef province between 16° 10′S and 20° 05′S: Manila, Fourth International Coral Reef Symposium, v. 1, p. 531–539.

STUIVER, M., PEARSON, G. W., AND BRAZIUNAS, T., 1986, Radiocarbon age calibration of marine samples back to 9000 cal yr B. P.: Radiocarbon, v. 28, p. 980–1021.

THOM, B. G., AND CHAPPELL, J., 1975, Holocene sea levels relative to Australia: Search, v. 6, p. 90–93.

THOM, B. G., AND ROY, P. S., 1983, Sea level change in New South Wales over the past 15,000 years, *in* Hopley, D., ed., Australian Sea Levels in the Past 15,000 Years: A Review: Townsville, James Cook University, Department of Geography, p. 64–84.

THOM, B. G., AND WRIGHT, L. D., 1983, Geomorphology of the Purari Delta, *in* Petr, T., ed., The Purari- Tropical Environment of a High Rainfall River Basin: The Hague, Dr W Junk, p. 47–65.

TORGERSEN, T., HUTCHINSON, M. F., SEARLE, D. E., AND NIX, H. A., 1983, General bathymetry of the Gulf of Carpentaria and the Quaternary physiography of Lake Carpentaria: Palaeogeography, Palaeoclimatology, Palaeoecology, v. 41, p. 207–225.

VAIL, P. R., MITCHUM, R. M., AND THOMPSON, S. I., 1977, Seismic stratigraphy and global changes of sea level from coastal onlap, *in* Payton, C. E., ed., Seismic Stratigraphy- Applications to Hydrocarbon Exploration: Tulsa, American Association of Petroleum Geologists Memoir 26, p. 63–81.

VAN WAGONER, J. C., MITCHUM, R. M., JR., POSAMENTIER, H. W., AND VAIL, P. R., 1987, Key definitions of sequence stratigraphy, *in* Bally, A. W., ed., Atlas of Seismic Stratigraphy: Tulsa, American Association of Petroleum Geologists Studies in Geology, p. 11–14.

VAN WAGONER, J. C., MITCHUM, R. M., CAMPION, K. M., AND RAHMANIAN, V. D., 1990, Siliciclastic sequence stratigraphy in well logs, cores and outcrops: concepts for high resolution correlation of time and facies: Tulsa, American Association of Petroleum Geologists Methods in Explorati on Series, No. 7, 55 p.

VEEH, H. H., AND VEEVERS, J. J., 1970, Sea level at −175 m off the Great Barrier Reef 13,600 to 17,000 years ago, Nature, v. 226, p. 536–537.

VEEVERS, J. J., Ed., 1984, Phanerozoic Earth History of Australia: Oxford, Clarendon Press, 418 p.

WOLANSKI, E., RIDD, P., AND INOUE, M., 1988, Currents through Torres Strait, Journal of Physical Oceanography, v. 18, p. 1535–1545.

WOLANSKI, E., AND EAGLE, A. M., 1991, Oceanography and sediment transport, Fly River Estuary and Gulf of Papua: Aukland, Proceedings 10th Australasian Conference on Coastal and Ocean Engineering, p. 453–457.

EVOLUTION OF AN INCISED-VALLEY FILL, THE PINE RIDGE SANDSTONE OF SOUTHEASTERN WYOMING, U.S.A.: SYSTEMATIC SEDIMENTARY RESPONSE TO RELATIVE SEA-LEVEL CHANGE

OLE J. MARTINSEN*

Geologisk Institutt Avd. A, Universitetet i Bergen, 5007 Bergen, Norway

ABSTRACT: The Campanian (Upper Cretaceous) Pine Ridge Sandstone of southeastern Wyoming, U.S.A., represents the fill of an incised valley formed as a response to Laramide uplift and relative sea-level fall in the Rocky Mountain foreland.

Two distinct phases of incised-valley fill, and a subsequent phase of wave-influenced deltaic deposition, can be distinguished in the Pine Ridge Sandstone, reflecting a systematic change of the dominant controls on deposition in response to relative sea-level change: (1) An *early lowstand* succession of fluvial, soft-sediment deformed deposits laid down during relative fall of sea level. This facies may have been a response to valley-wall and/or valley-profile oversteepening caused by relative sea-level fall and river incision; (2) A *late lowstand* succession, dominated by fluvial, tidally-influenced, meandering-channel sandstones, deposited during the early stages of relative sea-level rise when the incised valley still retained a constrained, estuarine morphology. A *transgressive* succession, dominated by wave-influenced shallow-water deltas, was deposited subsequently as the valley was overflooded, caused by an increasing rate of relative sea-level rise. This morphological expansion caused an increase in wave energy at the expense of a decrease in the tidal influence.

This systematic change of deposition from fluvial, deformed deposits, through tidally-influenced fluvial deposition, to wave-dominated deltaic deposition may be a predictable succession of facies expected to occur during the incision and filling of valley systems related to drops and rises of relative sea level.

INTRODUCTION

Sequence stratigraphy has lately received increasing attention, particularly due to the interest in applying the sequence concepts to outcrops (e.g., Leckie and Singh, 1991; Pomar, 1991; Van Wagoner and others, 1990, 1991). An important development is that more emphasis is put on understanding the depositional history of the sediments through classic facies analysis within a sequence-stratigraphic framework. Only through such an approach at outcrop or in modern environments (e.g., Boyd and others, 1989) can one acquire full understanding of the significance of suspected key surfaces and other sequence components. Outcrop studies are a vital part of sequence stratigraphy, particularly since studies in sequence stratigraphy move toward high-resolution applications (e.g., Leckie and others, 1991; Posamentier and others, 1992).

Incised valleys are an integral part of the Exxon depositional sequence model (e.g., Posamentier and others, 1988) because they manifest relative sea-level fall and have the sequence boundary at their base. Incised valleys are also important economically since they frequently contain high-quality reservoir rocks encased in marine mudstones (Posamentier, 1991; Van Wagoner, 1991). Until recently, relatively few examples of incised valleys were published (see Harms, 1966; Weimer, 1984), but lately more examples have been presented (Pattison, 1988, 1991; Wood and Hopkins, 1989; Anderson and others, 1990; Krystinik and Blakeney, 1990; Van Wagoner and others, 1990, 1991; Allen, 1991; Allen and Tesson, 1991; Berman and others, 1991; Elliott, 1991; Leckie and Singh, 1991). Galloway (1989) doubted the significance of incised valleys due to the proposed difficulty in recognizing sequence boundaries (cf. Martinsen, 1991), particularly in well-logs, and because shelfal canyon systems, which may be the final manifestation of incision during sea-level lowstand as, for example, along the U.S. Atlantic Seaboard (e.g., McMaster and

Ashraf, 1973; Farre and others, 1983), are also thought to form readily during periods of sea-level rise due to sediment instabilities and mass-flow generation (see also Galloway and others, 1991).

The purpose of the present study is to describe and interpret facies successions and sequence-stratigraphic development of an incised valley which is interpreted to have formed as a response to uplift of a local mountain range in the deformed, late Cretaceous Laramide foreland of Wyoming, U.S.A. (Fig. 1). Particularly, an attempt will be made to illustrate that the sedimentary fill has a systematic organization as a response to changes of relative sea level.

REGIONAL GEOLOGICAL FRAMEWORK

Overview

In Cretaceous time, southeastern Wyoming was part of the foreland flexure east of the Sevier thrust belt (e.g., Jordan, 1981; Cross, 1986) on the western margin of the Cretaceous Interior Seaway. At around 90Ma, the foreland started disintegrating into smaller basins, caused by uplift of local mountain ranges (e.g., Lowell, 1983; Steidtmann and Middleton, 1991). This deformed foreland situation is rather unusual and may have been caused by very shallow underplating of the Pacific plate underneath the American plate during subduction (Cross, 1986).

The regional geology of the Sevier foreland was, for the remainder of the Cretaceous and into Tertiary time, strongly influenced by interaction between thrust activity in the Sevier belt and uplift of Laramide ranges to the east (cf. Schmidt and Perry, 1988 and references therein; Devlin and others, 1990). These tectonic movements had important impact on the development of the regional sedimentary framework and local basin-fill patterns (e.g., Weimer, 1984; W. J. Devlin, pers. commun., 1993).

In southeastern Wyoming, the present-day tectonic picture is that of several sedimentary basins surrounded by Laramide uplifts (Fig. 1). Two of these basins are the Hanna

---

*Present address: Norsk Hydro Research, Sandsliv. 90, 5049 Sandsli, Norway.

Incised-Valley Systems: Origin and Sedimentary Sequences, SEPM Special Publication No. 51

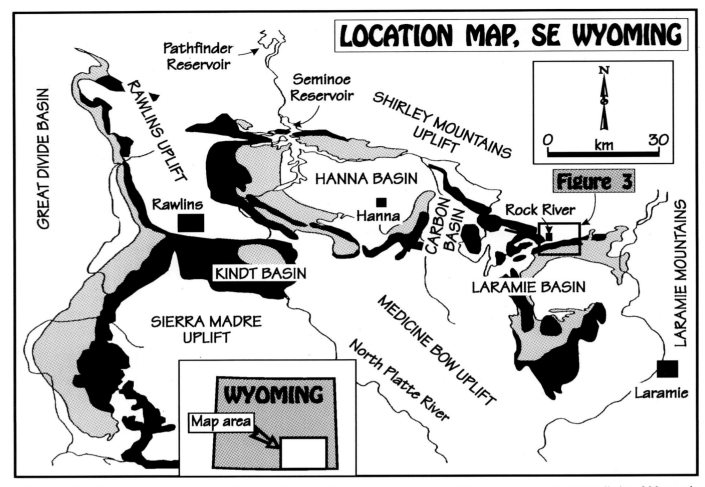

FIG. 1.—Simplified geological map of south-central Wyoming showing main Laramide uplift areas, basins, and outcrop limits of Mesaverde Group (in black) and Maestrichtian and lower Paleocene rocks (in grey). The location of the study area around Rock River is shown (see also Figure 3). Modified from Gill and others (1970).

Basin and the Laramie Basin, both of which are presently much smaller than their late Cretaceous size due to truncation by the local uplifts (cf. Kaplan and Skeen, 1985; LeFebre, 1988; Martinsen and others, 1993).

Mesaverde Group

During Campanian time, the Hanna and Laramie Basins were filled by Mesaverde Group sediments (Fig. 2A; cf. Gill and others, 1970). Following deposition of the extensive, marine Steele Shale, the shoreline prograded from the west leading to deposition of shallow-marine and shoreface sandstones of the Haystack Mountains Formation (Martinsen and Tillman, 1989). This was succeeded by continued shoreline progradation toward the east and deposition of the fluvio-deltaic Allen Ridge Formation in the Hanna Basin, which is transitional into shallow-marine sediments of the Rock River Formation in the Laramie Basin. The uppermost part of the Allen Ridge becomes increasingly marine

towards its top, suggesting shoreline retreat toward the west (Gill and others, 1970; Martinsen and others, 1993).

A major paleogeographic change then seems to have occurred. The dominantly fluvial Pine Ridge Sandstone overlies the Allen Ridge/Rock River Formations with a major unconformity at the base (Gill and others, 1970; Figs. 2A, B). This unconformity can only be recognized in the easternmost parts of the Hanna Basin and in the Laramie Basin, where the Pine Ridge Sandstone has been interpreted as an incised-valley fill sandstone (Martinsen and others, 1993). In the westernmost parts of the Hanna Basin, an apparently continuous sedimentary succession occurs, but Gill and others (1970) argued that at least three ammonite zones were missing there (see Fig. 2A, middle column). Martinsen and others (1993) could not verify the existence of a sedimentological break or major stratigraphic boundary within this part of the succession but suggested that this area was influenced by higher subsidence, or acted as an interfluve to the incised-valley system in the east. The Pine Ridge incised-valley system in the east has been interpreted to have

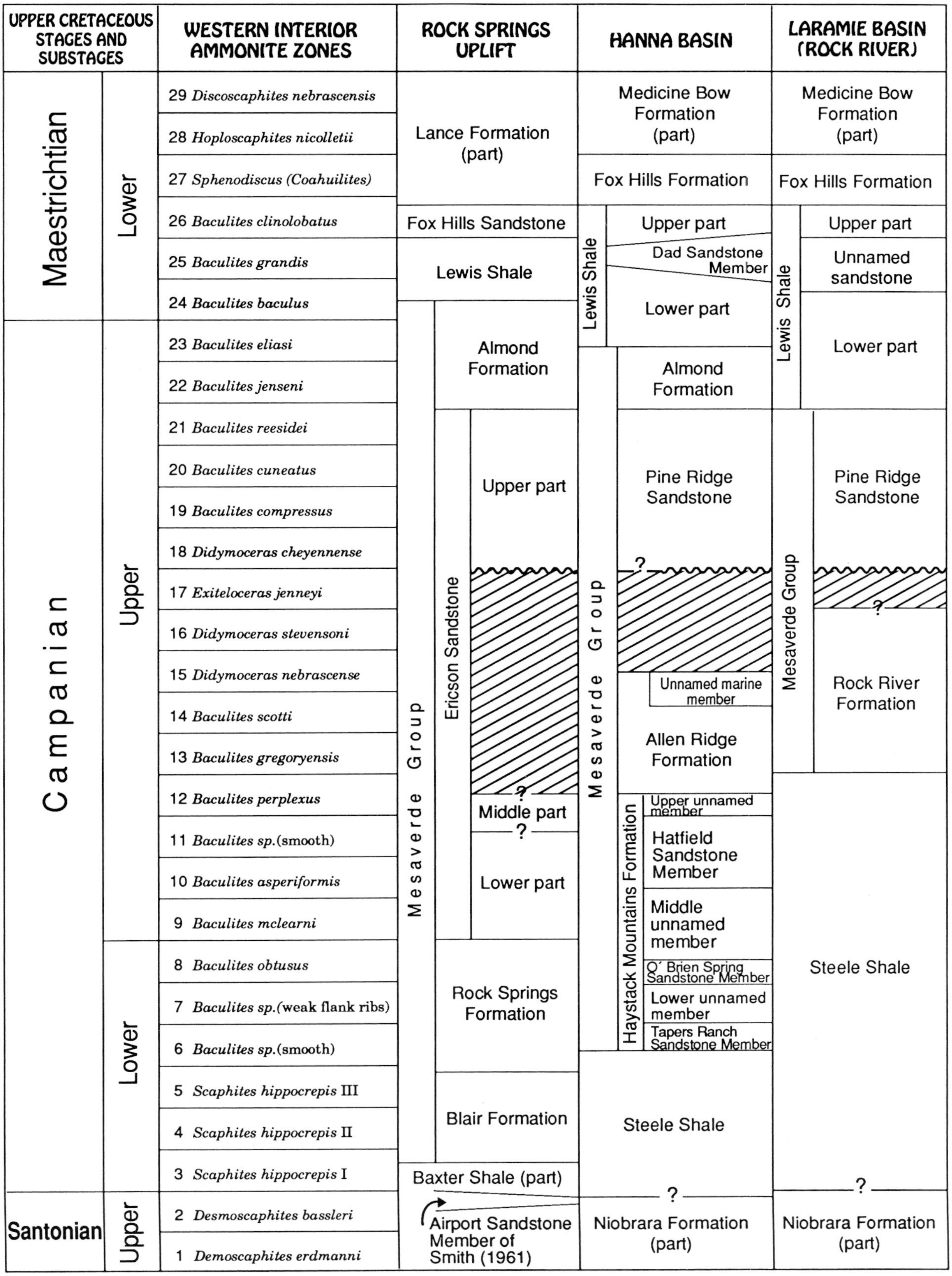

UPPER CRETACEOUS STAGES AND SUBSTAGES		WESTERN INTERIOR AMMONITE ZONES	ROCK SPRINGS UPLIFT	HANNA BASIN	LARAMIE BASIN (ROCK RIVER)
Maestrichtian	Lower	29 *Discoscaphites nebrascensis*	Lance Formation (part)	Medicine Bow Formation (part)	Medicine Bow Formation (part)
		28 *Hoploscaphites nicolletii*			
		27 *Sphenodiscus (Coahuilites)*		Fox Hills Formation	Fox Hills Formation
		26 *Baculites clinolobatus*	Fox Hills Sandstone	Upper part	Upper part
		25 *Baculites grandis*	Lewis Shale	Lewis Shale — Dad Sandstone Member	Unnamed sandstone
		24 *Baculites baculus*		Lower part	Lewis Shale
Campanian	Upper	23 *Baculites eliasi*	Almond Formation	Almond Formation	Lower part
		22 *Baculites jenseni*			
		21 *Baculites reesidei*	Upper part (Ericson Sandstone)	Pine Ridge Sandstone	Pine Ridge Sandstone
		20 *Baculites cuneatus*			
		19 *Baculites compressus*			
		18 *Didymoceras cheyennense*		?	?
		17 *Exiteloceras jenneyi*			
		16 *Didymoceras stevensoni*			
		15 *Didymoceras nebrascense*		Unnamed marine member	Rock River Formation
		14 *Baculites scotti*			
		13 *Baculites gregoryensis*		Allen Ridge Formation	
		12 *Baculites perplexus*	? Middle part	Upper unnamed member	
		11 *Baculites sp.(smooth)*	? Lower part	Hatfield Sandstone Member	
		10 *Baculites asperiformis*		Middle unnamed member	Steele Shale
		9 *Baculites mclearni*			
	Lower	8 *Baculites obtusus*	Rock Springs Formation	O'Brien Spring Sandstone Member	
		7 *Baculites sp.(weak flank ribs)*		Lower unnamed member	
		6 *Baculites sp.(smooth)*		Tapers Ranch Sandstone Member	
		5 *Scaphites hippocrepis III*	Blair Formation	Steele Shale	
		4 *Scaphites hippocrepis II*			
		3 *Scaphites hippocrepis I*	Baxter Shale (part)	?	?
Santonian	Upper	2 *Desmoscaphites bassleri*	Airport Sandstone Member of Smith (1961)	Niobrara Formation (part)	Niobrara Formation (part)
		1 *Demoscaphites erdmanni*			

FIG. 2.—(A) Regional lithostratigraphy and ammonite zonation across south-central Wyoming. Modified from Gill and others (1970).

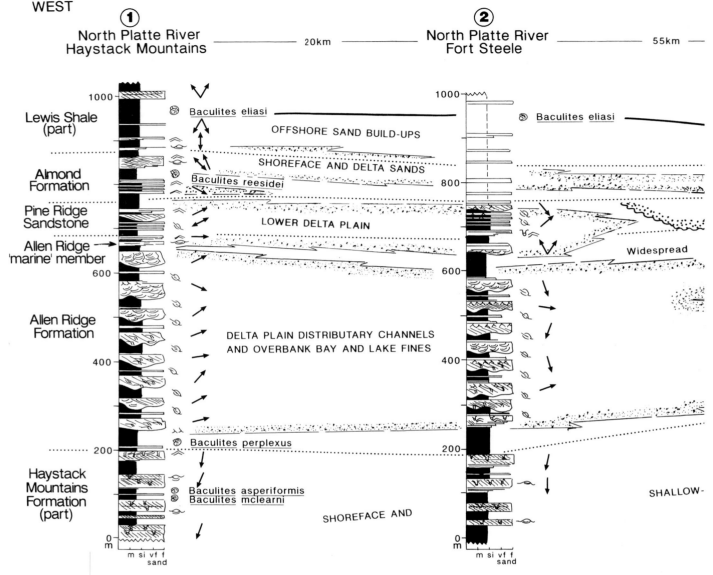

FIG. 2.—(B) Cross-section from west to east across the Hanna and Laramie Basins to show regional overview of the middle and upper parts of
and incision during this time interval, not the extent of the specific valley discussed here.

been supplied from the north, from the paleo-Sweetwater Arch, while in the west, sediment supply was from the west (Martinsen and others, 1993). These differences in sedimentary style indicate there is no sedimentological or chronological correlation of the Pine Ridge between the western Hanna Basin and areas to the east.

In addition, in a regional analysis, Weimer (1984) described local uplifts in Wyoming (and also elsewhere in the Rockies) and correlated them to several uplift phases. The unconformity below the Pine Ridge Sandstone has been correlated with the unconformities below the basal Ericson Sandstone of the Rock Springs Uplift and the Teapot Sandstone of the Powder River Basin (all mid-Campanian or

approximately 73Ma), both well-known valley-fill sandstones (cf. Weimer, 1984). This correlation suggests that although these uplifts clearly were local in effect and style, an uplift event was marked across the Wyoming foreland at this time.

The Almond Formation overlies the Pine Ridge Sandstone (Figs. 2A, B), and represents deposition in shoreface and deltaic systems gradually retreating towards the northwest (Gill and others, 1970; Martinsen and others, 1993). This overall northerly retreat culminated during deposition of the lowermost parts of the overlying Lewis Shale and was succeeded by renewed progradation from the north (Perman, 1990). The base of the Lewis Shale is time-trans-

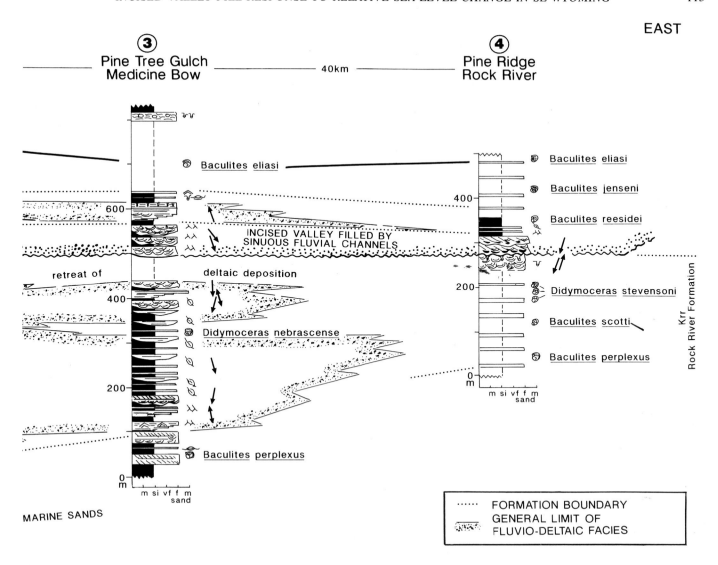

the Mesaverde Group. The extent of the incised-valley in the Pine Ridge Sandstone is schematic and only shows the interpreted areal effect of uplift

gressive, so that toward the east, it overlies progressively older strata. This is because of the general retrogradational character of the underlying Almond Formation, which backsteps towards the west and shales out in the western part of the Laramie Basin. There, the Lewis Shale lies more or less directly on top of the Pine Ridge Sandstone (Gill and others, 1970).

An extensive discussion of the sequence-stratigraphic architecture on a basinal scale has been presented by Martinsen and others (1993). The present paper concentrates on the development of the Pine Ridge Sandstone in the western part of the Laramie Basin, where its environmental interpretation is substantiated by detailed facies analysis and a

detailed documentation of the temporal development of the unit in response to relative sea-level changes.

FACIES AND FACIES ASSOCIATIONS

Introduction

Two outcrops, located a few kilometers south of Rock River, Albany County, illustrate best the temporal evolution of the Pine Ridge system. These two outcrops are located at Lower and Upper Pine Ridge (Figs. 1, 3; outcrops located at, respectively, SE1/4, section 9 to SW1/4, section 11, and SE1/4, section 18 to NW1/4, section 16, both in T 20 N, R 76 W).

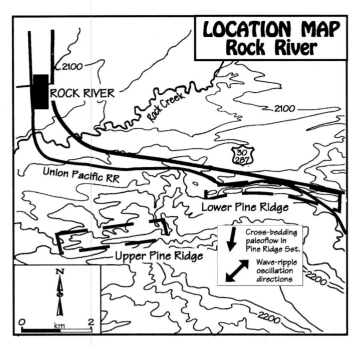

FIG. 3.—Locality map of the Rock River area. See Figure 1 for location. The general paleocurrent directions for cross-bedding and wave-formed ripples in the Pine Ridge Sandstone are shown for comparison with outcrop locations. Detailed rose plots of the paleocurrents are shown in Figure 7.

The focus of this study is on the detailed, temporal and vertical development of the Pine Ridge incised-valley system. The sections at Lower and Upper Pine Ridge, although only 3 km apart, illustrate different developments but with some overlap. Therefore, the facies of the two associations are described together below, while later on, the facies associations are described separately.

Main Depositional Facies

Three facies are discussed from the Pine Ridge Sandstone. Only two of these, which are exposed at Lower Pine Ridge, actually occur within what is interpreted as an incised valley. However, for stratigraphic and sedimentological context, the topmost facies of the underlying Rock River Formation and the top facies of the Pine Ridge Sandstone are also described.

Upper Shoreface Sandstones (Rock River Formation).—

The topmost 15 m of the Rock River Formation are composed of white, fine- to medium-grained sandstones which dominantly are trough cross-stratified. The trough cross-bedding occurs in sets generally less than 1 m thick, and the paleocurrents show an asymmetric bidirectional character, with the dominant flow being directed toward the SW.

Locally, the sandstone is hummocky and/or swaley cross-stratified (Fig. 4). The lateral relationship to the cross-stratified sandstone is not always clear because of lack of outcrop, but these two structures seem to occur at approximately the same stratigraphic level. The uniform color and grain size of the sandstone also contribute to making identification of the contact between these two parts difficult.

Bioturbation is quite common in patches, but the upper parts of the sandstone are generally devoid of traces. *Ophiomorpha* dominates (Fig. 4), but large escape traces are observed also.

This facies is interpreted to represent shallow-marine sand deposition. This is suggested by the bidirectional trough cross-stratification in combination with the hummocky and swaley cross-strata and the *Ophiomorpha* burrows (cf. Pollard and Goldring, 1993). The entirely sandy nature of the facies suggests continuous reworking in a relatively high-energy (<15–20 m water depth) setting above storm-wave base. The dominance and thickness of trough cross-bedding suggests sustained flow. It is probable that the sandstone could have been deposited on the upper shoreface and continuously reworked by longshore currents. McCubbin (1982) described an example from the Gallup Sandstone of New Mexico where the entire upper shoreface succession was trough cross-stratified due to reworking in longshore-drift channels. A similar setting can be envisaged for the uppermost part of the Rock River Formation. The hummocky/swaley cross-strata may have been formed during periods of intense storm reworking of the upper shoreface.

Martinsen and others (1993) interpreted the coastline to have been oriented generally N-S during deposition of the Rock River Formation. Thus, the NE-SW paleocurrents observed in this facies are broadly coherent with a longshore-drift origin of the trough cross-stratified sandstone.

Regional Erosion Surface and Chaotic, Deformed Sandstones.—

These sandstones are much greyer and visually distinct from the Rock River Formation sandstones. They are al-

FIG. 4.—*Ophiomorpha* burrows in hummocky cross-stratified sandstone, Rock River Formation, Lower Pine Ridge. Markings on Jacob's staff are 10 cm long.

ways separated from the underlying shallow-marine sandstones by a prominent boundary which can be traced for more than 2 km along Lower Pine Ridge, and can also be seen at Upper Pine Ridge, 3 km away (Fig. 5A). The boundary occurs on a regional scale at least one magnitude larger than channel-base surfaces within the overlying facies (see below), which can only be followed with certainty for only a few hundred meters. The regional boundary is locally rooted (Fig. 5B), and pedogenic modification extends up to 1.5 m into the underlying sandstones. However, rooting does not occur below the deformed sandstone lenses described below. On the scale of the outcrop (about 2 km long), the contact is relatively flat, but locally has a relief of up to 5 m, where there is clear truncation of underlying strata. Such truncations are seen everywhere along the extent of the surface.

The mainly massive, chaotic, convex-up sandstones occur as lenses up to 5 m thick and several hundred meters wide above the regional boundary (Fig. 5C). These lenses are truncated by the overlying facies. The sandstone is medium-grained, dominantly, but can locally be coarse-grained where load balls of coarser sand apparently have sunk into finer sand. There is no evidence for a systematic internal organization or primary structures, and no systematic grain-size trends are observed. The sandstones are characteristically penetrated by a conjugate set of joints, which only very rarely is seen in adjacent lithologies.

Locally, the sandstone has a very chaotic appearance, and this is most prominent where it contains large volumes of mudflakes. The mudflakes vary in size from less than 1 cm long, up to 30 m long and 1 m thick. The flakes are dominantly flat-lying, but in several cases they are disordered and apparently float in the sandy matrix (Fig. 5D). Most commonly, the mudflakes occur in the lower parts of the sandstone, but may be present through the entire thickness. The mudflakes are bioturbated by small endogenic burrows, which resemble fodinichnial *Planolites*. The burrows are entirely restricted to the mudflakes.

The marked boundary between the Rock River Formation and the Pine Ridge Sandstone is interpreted to be a regional erosion surface, based on its regional extent (at least 5 km) and the documentation of truncation of underlying strata along its extent. In addition, the clear evidence for pedogenic modification and rooting suggests subaerial exposure of the erosion surface and not merely cut and fill and relatively rapid burial in channels of the overlying facies. These factors suggest that the surface has a wider significance than a channel-base erosion surface.

The chaotic sandstones are interpreted to have been emplaced by mass-movement processes or been thoroughly deformed by post-depositional processes. This interpretation is based on their chaotic character, the largely unorganized mudflakes and their size (up to 30 m long), and the entire lack of primary, current-generated structures such as cross-bedding or parallel lamination. It is difficult to decide on the precise mode of deposition. Gravitational gliding from a nearby steeper slope and/or a hyperconcentrated flow are possible transport agents. The lack of well-defined bedding may suggest local mounding and accumulation of sand following only short transport. Longer transport, for

instance by quasi-turbulent, high-concentration flows, probably would have caused better organization and bedding, although their internal characteristics may have been massive. Since no clear bedding is observed, it is suggested that mass gliding and/or post-depositional modification/ liquefaction were responsible for deposition and the final character of these sandstones. This is also supported by the mudflakes or rafts up to 30 m long which most likely were transported and moved by downslope gliding. The complete lack of primary structures may suggest that post-depositional modification was not the primary cause for the chaotic appearance. Most likely, there would have been some hint of primary structures if this was the case.

Only very low slopes are needed to generate sediment gliding. Prior and Coleman (1978) showed how only 0.5° slopes were needed to cause slumping in the Mississippi delta-front area. In the present case, the slopes were probably significantly higher (possibly 10–15°). Excessive sediment supply or undercutting are common causes for slope oversteepening on both subaerial and subaqueous slopes (cf. Brunsden and Prior, 1984, and references therein). In the present case, erosional undercutting is considered to be the most likely mechanism. It is not entirely clear whether this facies was deposited subaerially or subaqueously. Nonetheless, the stratigraphic position above the rooted, regionally important surface between the Rock River Formation and the Pine Ridge Sandstone suggests deposition very near to, if not dominantly in subaerial conditions.

The mudflakes are erosional remnants of mudstone eroded by mass movements. The burrows suggest that this mudstone was brackish or marine, and this accords with the marine interpretation of the Rock River Formation below. This mudstone is likely to have been positioned stratigraphically above the shoreface sandstones of the underlying Rock River Formation, since nowhere along the extent of the outcrops can it be documented that mudstone flakes were eroded from below the shoreface sandstones.

Fluvial and Distributary Channel Sandstones.—

These are of two types:
*Heterolithic, Tidally-Influenced, Channel-Belt Sandstones.—*These sandstones form a belt which is continuous along the entire outcrop (2 km) at Lower Pine Ridge. The channels are up to 400 m wide and 8 m thick and are bounded below by sharp surfaces along which there is clear evidence for erosion of underlying strata. Some of the sandstones and their lower boundaries are correlative for several hundred meters. In one case, the lower surface cuts down to the level of the regional boundary between the Rock River Formation and the Pine Ridge Sandstone (approximately 8 m of downcutting), and modifies this surface. Where the underlying, deformed sandstones are not present, the channel-base surfaces merge with the regional erosion surface between the Rock River Formation and the Pine Ridge Sandstone.

Internally, the channelized sandstones are characterized by large-scale (up to 8 m vertical extent, which equals the depth of the channels), low-angle (up to 10° dip) accretion surfaces (Figs. 5A, 6A) which dominantly dip towards the

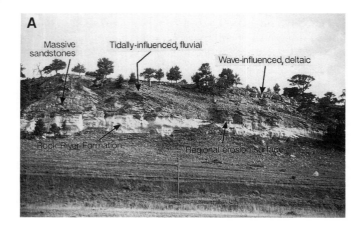

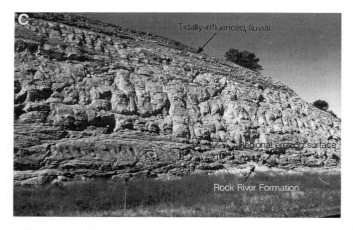

FIG. 5.—(A) The central portion of Lower Pine Ridge, with the white sandstones of the shallow-marine Rock River Formation at the base, erosively overlain by the Pine Ridge Sandstone. The erosion surface can be traced for several kilometers. Note the low-angle accretion surfaces in the tidally-influenced fluvial sandstones dipping to the right above a lens of massive, deformed sandstone. At the top, laterally continuous, wave-influenced deltaic sandstones are exposed. The height of the exposure is approximately 10 m. (B) Pedogenic modification and rootlets at the erosive, regional boundary between the Rock River Formation and the Pine Ridge Sandstone, Upper Pine Ridge. Markings on Jacob's staff are 10 cm long. (C) Massive, deformed sandstone facies at Lower Pine Ridge. Note the internal distortion, and the small-scale relief on the regional erosion surface. Coal-bearing, tidally-influenced fluvial sediments are exposed at the top of the cliff, which is 10 m high. (D) Close-up of the deformed sandstone facies showing chaotic arrangement of mudstone clasts. Markings on Jacob's staff are 10 cm long.

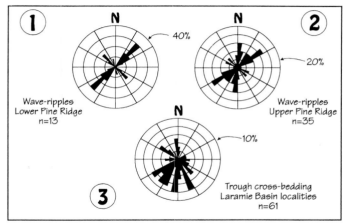

FIG. 7.—Paleocurrent rose diagrams from the Pine Ridge Sandstone. Diagram 3 is a composite diagram from various localities in the Rock River area.

FIG. 6.—(A) Inclined heterolithic stratification and lateral-accretion surfaces of the tidally-influenced, fluvial-channel facies at Lower Pine Ridge. Note the several channel-base and internal erosion surfaces and the truncated coal seam (upper left-hand corner). The accretion surfaces in the lower left hand channel dip towards view. The exposure is approximately 4 m high. (B) Rhythmic bedding and double clay drapes in the tidally-influenced fluvial-channel facies at Lower Pine Ridge. The markings on the Jacob's staff are 10 cm long.

west. The surfaces separate 5 to 30 cm thick sandstone units and interbedded mudstones (Fig. 6A), and define sets of inclined heterolithic stratification. The sandstones contain isolated sets of trough cross-strata, with paleocurrent directions that are oblique or normal to the orientation of the dip of the accretion surfaces. On isolated surfaces, current ripples are seen which suggest paleoflow **along** the strike of the accretion surfaces.

Paleocurrent measurements from the two Pine Ridge localities described here and from laterally correlative outcrops in the Laramie and eastern Hanna Basins show a dominant paleoflow toward the SSW with a subordinate northerly trend (Fig. 7).

Commonly, drapes of mudstone occur along the foresets of the cross-bedding. In a few cases, it is quite obvious that the drapes occur in a rhythmic fashion (Fig. 6B), where drapes alternately envelope thinner and thicker sandstone wedges. The sandstone is locally mottled and slightly disturbed on a very fine scale, suggesting bioturbation. In ad-

dition, *Planolites* burrows occur in the interbedded mudstones.

In several cases, the channelized sandstones fine upwards from medium-grained sand to silt (cf. Fig. 8A), and a lateral fining can be observed locally where the sandstones fine from medium-grained sand to silt within a few hundred meters, **always** in the direction of dip of the low-angle accretion surfaces. Autochtonous coals, rooted zones, or very organic-rich mudstones (high abundance of transported plant debris) cap the fining-upward successions.

The channelized sandstones are interpreted as fluvial/distributary channels. The low-angle accretion surfaces are interpreted to be lateral-accretion surfaces, based on their low angle (thus not slip faces) and the oblique or perpendicular direction of sediment transport in relation to the dip of the surfaces that is observed from smaller structures. The inclined heterolithic stratification, rhythmic occurrence of mud drapes and the bioturbation suggest tidal influence.

Homogenous, distributary-channel sandstones.—These sandstones occur at the top of the succession at Lower Pine Ridge, and throughout the succession at Upper Pine Ridge (Figs. 8A, 9A). They are entirely sandy, up to 12 m thick and 500 m wide, and form lenticular complexes which clearly truncate underlying strata (Fig. 9A). Internally they appear to be massive, but at several places there are hints of trough cross-stratification. Locally, there are accumulations of mudflakes, which generally seem to be aligned along bedding. Deformed and convoluted strata also occur locally. At least one internal truncation surface can be documented (Fig. 9A, section 4). Rootlets are common on the tops of these sandstones.

The mappable, overall lenticular form and erosive base (Fig. 9A), the internal structures and rooted tops, and the size, suggest that these sandstones are major fluvial/distributary channel sandstones. The internal deformation structures suggests post-depositional disturbance, perhaps induced by water-escape.

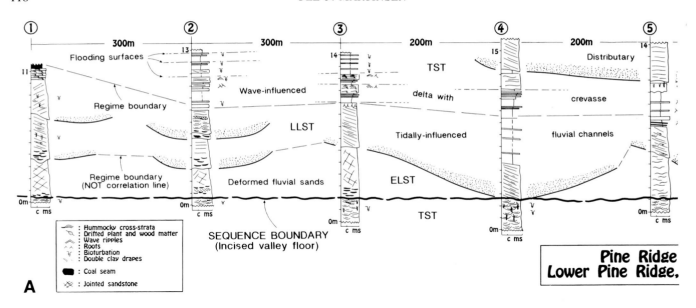

FIG. 8.—(A) Cross-section from Lower Pine Ridge illustrating sedimentologic and stratigraphic development. The regime boundaries are inserted gressive systems tract. See text for explanation and further details. (B) Close-up mosaic of area between Section 7 and Section 8 in (A), showing (interpreted sequence boundary), the massive, deformed sandstones (early lowstand) with a 30 m-long mudstone raft, and an overlying tidally-

Wave-influenced Bay-fill Sediments.—

These units are cyclic, generally 0.5–4 m thick, have a lateral extent of from less than 100 m up to 1200 m, and typically coarsen upward from siltstone to medium-grained sandstone (Figs. 9A, 10A). They occur on top of the succession at Lower Pine Ridge, while at Upper Pine Ridge, they occur throughout the section including immediately above the regional boundary between the Rock River Formation and the Pine Ridge Sandstone (Figs. 9B, 10B).

The contacts between the lower fine-grained material and the upper sandstones vary from being entirely gradational to erosional with solemarks and guttercasts. Although most

of the units are tabular, at Lower Pine Ridge some of the upper sandstones are also channelized, but the channels are never more than 20–30 m wide and 5–6 m thick. At Upper Pine Ridge in the west, the coarsening-upward units are interbedded with major channel sandstones up to 12 m thick and 500 m wide (see description above and further discussion below).

Internally, a diverse suite of primary structures is observed. The siltstones are often faintly laminated, sometimes showing evidence of either asymmetric or symmetric cross-laminae. The sandstones are either cross-laminated, in places quite evidently symmetric (Fig. 10A), or horizontally-laminated, but locally, small-scale cross-bedding

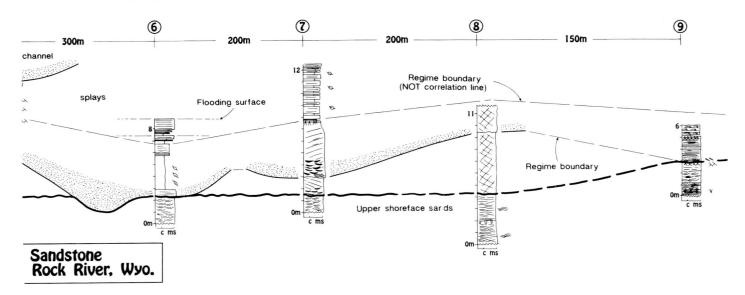

Sandstone
Rock River, Wyo.

to illustrate the tripartite division of the Pine Ridge Sandstone. ELST: early lowstand systems tract; LLST: late lowstand systems tract; TST: trans-
the white shallow-marine sandstones of the Rock River Formation (transgressive sediments of underlying sequence), the regional erosion surface
influenced, fluvial-channel sandstone (late lowstand).

up to 20–30 cm thick is seen. While the units at Upper Pine Ridge may show symmetric cross-lamination throughout (Fig. 10A), at Lower Pine Ridge it is more common to observe symmetric ripples only at the top of the coarsening-up units. In both localities, the ripples indicate bidirectional or oscillatory paleoflow in a NE-SW direction (Figs. 1, 2, 7).

The interbedded siltstones are always very organic rich, almost lignitic in places. The tops of the coarsening-up units are almost invariably rooted, in places extensively, except for those near the top of the western part of the association at Upper Pine Ridge where no roots occur. The rooted zones

are immediately overlain by dark mudstones with little evidence for current influence.

The coarsening-upward units were probably deposited in very shallow water where sediment influx filled the available accommodation space, as suggested by the thin character and rooted tops. Furthermore, the plant-rich siltstones and symmetric ripples suggest deposition in a wave-influenced bay setting. The units with sharp-based sandstones suggest very rapid incursion of coarser sediments, and probably represent crevasse splays (the tabular units) and crevasse channels (the channelized units). The gradationally-based units probably represent small bay deltas or mi-

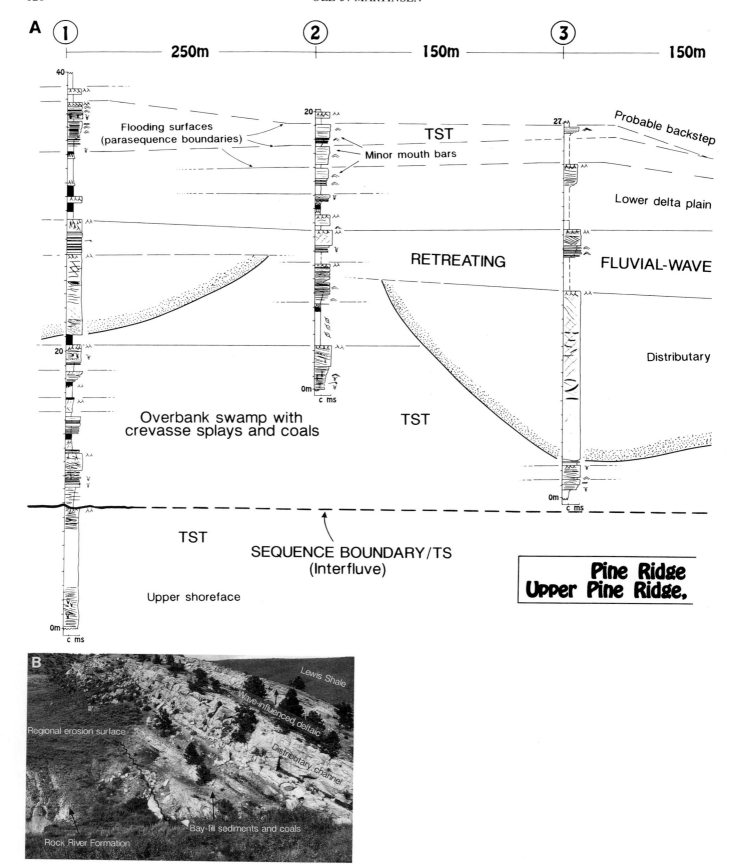

A

Flooding surfaces
(parasequence boundaries)

TST

Minor mouth bars

Probable backstep

Lower delta plain

RETREATING

FLUVIAL-WAVE

Overbank swamp with
crevasse splays and coals

TST

Distributary

TST

SEQUENCE BOUNDARY/TS
(Interfluve)

Pine Ridge
Upper Pine Ridge,

Upper shoreface

B

Lewis Shale

Wave-influenced deltaic

Regional erosion surface

Distributary channel

Rock River Formation

Bay-fill sediments and coals

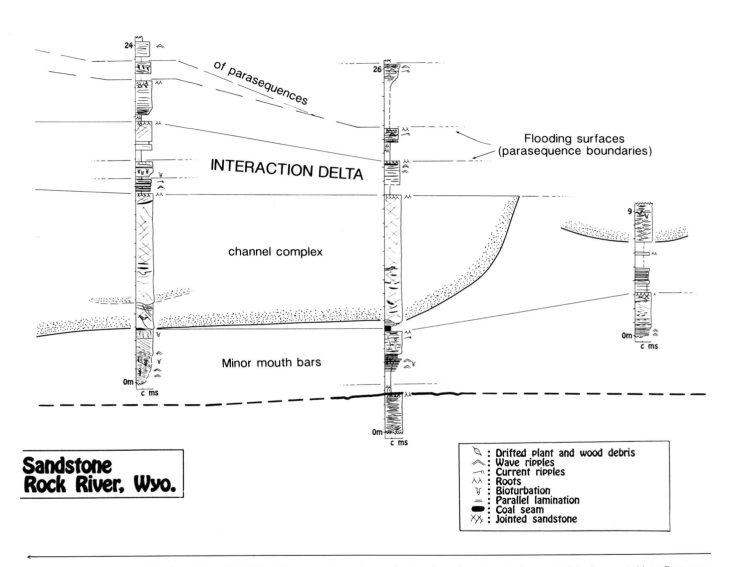

FIG. 9.—(A) Cross-section from Upper Pine Ridge illustrating the sedimentologic and stratigraphic development of the interpreted interfluve area. Further explanation is given in text. (B) Overview photograph of the eastern part of Upper Pine Ridge. Note the downcut of the regional erosion surface (interpreted sequence boundary) towards viewer. Compare with (A). The thickness of the section in view is approximately 35 m.

nor mouth bars at the mouth of crevasse channels or minor distributaries.

The repetitive occurrence of these coarsening-upward cycles shows repeated filling of the bay within which they were deposited. Consequently, the boundaries between the coarsening-up successions reflect deepening and flooding.

Thus, in effect, the top surface of each cycle is a flooding surface.

It is arguable whether the western and uppermost coarsening-up units at Upper Pine Ridge actually were deposited within a bay setting. The lack of roots on the tops and the higher wave influence suggest a more open and deeper-water

FIG. 10.—(A) Coarsening-upward succession of the wave-influenced deltaic facies at Upper Pine Ridge. Note the symmetric wave-ripples on the top of several beds throughout the succession. Backpack for scale. (B) Overbank mudstones, sandstones, and coals directly above the regional erosion surface in the eastern part of Upper Pine Ridge (Section 1, Fig. 9). Note the lenticular minor mouth bar which apparently fills in relief on top of the regional erosion surface. Jacob's staff, 1.5 m long, for scale.

environment. These may have been nearer the mouth of an unprotected bay.

Lower Pine Ridge Facies Association

The exposed thickness of the Pine Ridge Sandstone is a maximum of 13 m at Lower Pine Ridge (Figs. 3, 8A). Including the exposed thickness of the underlying Rock River Formation (Fig. 8A), the total thickness is 16 m. The association is characterized by five main components (in vertical stratigraphic order; see also Figs. 5A, 8B): (1) upper shoreface sandstones of the Rock River Formation; (2) regional, subaerial erosion surface between the Rock River Formation and the Pine Ridge Sandstone (traceable over the entire length of the outcrop); (3) deformed fluvial sandstones; (4) sinuous, fluvial-channel deposits with tidal influence; and (5) wave-influenced, bay-fill sediments. Since

the divisions between (3), (4) and (5) are distinct, regime[1] boundaries have been drawn between them in Figure 8A to illustrate better the vertical development. However, it is stressed that these regime boundaries are not correlation lines, nor of chronostratigraphic significance, since the overall change between the facies (e.g., from tidal to wave-influence) could not be expected to occur simultaneously over the entire area.

As seen in Figures 8A and B, the vertical and temporal evolution of the Lower Pine Ridge facies association shows prominent environmental changes within only a limited thickness of strata. The burrowed mudstone clasts of the deformed sandstone suggests that marine mudstones were deposited after deposition of the shoreface sandstones of the Rock River Formation. These mudstones must then have been eroded, and a regionally extensive erosion surface developed which partly truncated the upper shoreface sandstones. This is thought to record a relative fall of sea level for the following reasons: (1) the regional extent of more than 5 km, which exceeds the observed extent of overlying channel sandstones by at least one order of magnitude (channel widths less than 500 m); (2) the rooting and pedogenic modification of the surface; (3) the erosion of marine mudstones and superposition of fluvial strata on underlying shoreface sandstones showing that the succession did not result from "normal" progradation where channels cut a sandy shoreface, and that a basinward shift of facies took place; and (4) the regional erosion surface extends below *both* the deformed sandstones *and* the later channel sandstones (where the surface is rooted), suggesting that the process responsible for formation of the erosion surface had more to do with emplacement of the deformed sandstones and pedogenesis than with erosion and deposition within the fluvial channels. None of these four points is diagnostic of relative sea-level fall, but together they strongly suggest that such a process took place. The separation in scale and time between formation of the rooted, regional erosion surface and overlying channel-base erosion surfaces indicates a much more regional truncation event which was probably subaerial in nature.

The fact that roots are only developed where the deformed sandstones are absent suggests that the processes responsible for these two products took place contemporaneously, or that emplacement of the deformed sandstones eroded roots formed earlier. However, since the deformed sandstones do not seem to be erosive into the underlying marine sandstones (they rather seem to sit as pods on the regional surface), it is suggested that the roots and the deformed sandstones formed more or less contemporaneously. Perhaps the deformed sandstones were supplied from local steeper slopes (less than 1° slopes needed; cf. Prior and Coleman, 1978; but probably substantially higher

---

[1]Regime is merely intended to describe a package of sediments deposited under specific environmental conditions, as for example 'fluvial/tidal channel regime' or 'wave-influenced bay regime'. This is considered useful in the present example since there are clearly laterally extensive units deposited within the same general environmental setting, but which do not have chronostratigraphic significance and have a broader connotation than facies.

in the present case) into lower areas, while plants grew in slightly higher or terraced areas (Figs. 11, 12).

The overall change from deformed sandstones to sinuous, fluvial channels with tidal influence shows that the depositional environment changed substantially. The multilateral character indicates that the channels were part of a larger channel belt although a well-developed multistorey trend did not develop. The upward change from the tidally-influenced, channel-belt sandstones to wave-influenced, bay-fill sediments with no tidal influence suggests a thorough change of the depositional environment to more open conditions.

This change from formation of a regional, pedogenically-modified erosion surface to wave-influenced, bay-fill sediments and then to the marine Lewis Shale above can best be considered as a response to rising relative sea level following a relative sea-level lowstand. This is discussed further below.

Upper Pine Ridge Facies Association

The facies association at Upper Pine Ridge, 3 km west of Lower Pine Ridge (Fig. 3) is different from that at Lower Pine Ridge in that the basal deformed sandstones are absent, and there is no well-developed, overlying, single-storey, multi-lateral channel belt (Fig. 9A, B). From base to top, the facies association consists of: (1) upper shoreface sandstones of the Rock River Formation; (2) the rooted, regional erosion surface; and (3) coals, overbank and bay-fill fines, coarsening upward bay-fill cycles, and two major distributary-channel sandstones.

Several important changes can be observed within the Upper Pine Ridge outcrop. The bay-fill cycles at the top thin upwards and become progressively more wave-influenced, particularly in the western part of the section. Coal seams are preferentially developed in the easternmost section, where there also seems to be the least wave influence (Fig. 9A).

This facies association represents a depositional setting where fluvial and wave processes interacted. It is likely that a relative sea-level fall occurred after deposition of the Rock River Formation to account for the rooted, regional erosion surface (Fig. 10B; see discussion above for the regional erosion surface in the Lower Pine Ridge facies association). Subsequently, a rise of relative sea level must have oc-

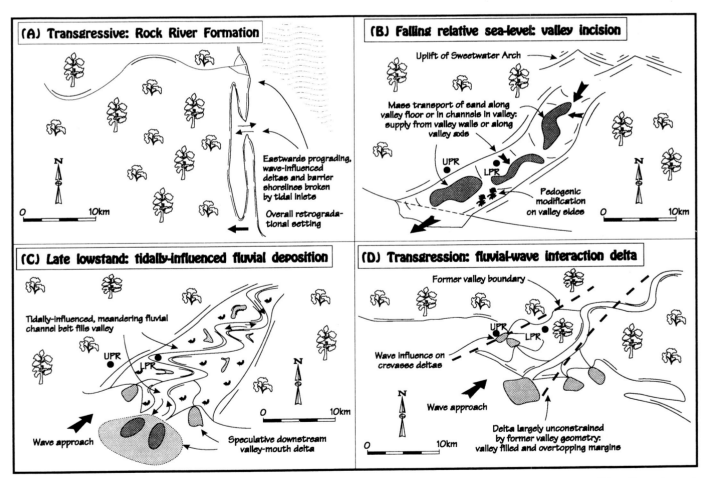

FIG. 11.—Sketch summing up the four main depositional phases for the development of the uppermost parts of the Rock River Formation and the Pine Ridge Sandstone. A full explanation is given in the text. LPR and UPR indicate the interpreted positions of, respectively, Lower and Upper Pine Ridge with respect to the incised valley, LPR being within the incised valley and near its margin, while UPR represents an interfluve position.

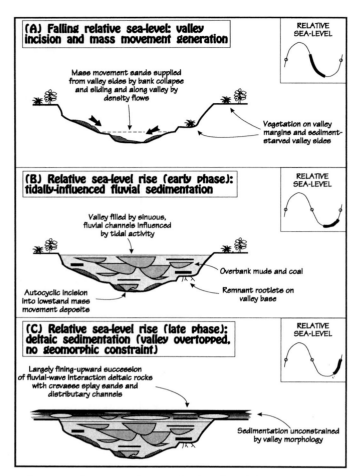

(A) Falling relative sea-level: valley incision and mass movement generation

Mass movement sands supplied from valley sides by bank collapse and sliding and along valley by density flows

Vegetation on valley margins and sediment-starved valley sides

RELATIVE SEA-LEVEL

(B) Relative sea-level rise (early phase): tidally-influenced fluvial sedimentation

Valley filled by sinuous, fluvial channels influenced by tidal activity

Overbank muds and coal

Autocyclic incision into lowstand mass movement deposits

Remnant rootlets on valley base

RELATIVE SEA-LEVEL

(C) Relative sea-level rise (late phase): deltaic sedimentation (valley overtopped, no geomorphic constraint)

Largely fining-upward succession of fluvial-wave interaction deltaic rocks with crevasse splay sands and distributary channels

Sedimentation unconstrained by valley morphology

RELATIVE SEA-LEVEL

FIG. 12.—Conceptual diagram showing the relationship between the three main depositional phases of the Pine Ridge Sandstone and relative sea level. Further explanation is given in the text.

curred, since wave-influenced, bay-fill sediments directly overlie the rooted erosion surface. Thus, it is likely that the boundary between the Rock River Formation and the Pine Ridge Sandstone has a double significance, both as a lowstand erosion surface and as a subsequent flooding surface.

Upper Pine Ridge deposition took place in a setting dominated by single distributary-channels, overbank deposits and peat growth. These characteristics seem to suggest a lower delta-plain environment. Gradations within this setting can also be shown. The coal-dominated eastern part probably remained close to emergence, allowing plant growth and peat accumulation only interrupted by periods of clastic influx from crevasse splays. The western part, however, was either too influenced by clastics, or perhaps more likely remained submerged for critical periods of time, preventing vegetation growth.

The thinning-upward of the bay-fill cycles may suggest retrogradation and incipient abandonment of the depositional system. This is supported by the accompanied increase in wave-influence upward, showing an increasing exposure to open-marine processes.

OUTCROP CORRELATION, DEPOSITIONAL ENVIRONMENT
AND RELATION TO RELATIVE SEA LEVEL

Based on the sedimentological data and the paleocurrent information (Figs. 3, 7; see also Fig. 11), a significant paleo-environmental change must have occurred between deposition of the Rock River Formation and the Pine Ridge Sandstone. The Rock River Formation correlates with the Allen Ridge Formation in the western part of the Hanna Basin (Gill and others, 1970; Martinsen and others, 1993). The Rock River/Allen Ridge system prograded to the east, while, as shown earlier, the Pine Ridge system was supplied from the northeast.

Through classic mapping, the regional erosion surface or boundary between the Rock River Formation and Pine Ridge Sandstone can be mapped confidently from Lower to Upper Pine Ridge (cf. Hyden, 1965; Gill and others, 1970). This, however, is the only means for detailed and exact correlation. Correlation based on facies interpretations are less accurate, but the following correlation scheme is suggested. Below the formation boundary/regional erosion surface, the Rock River Formation in both localities consists of upper shoreface sandstones, and a correlation of these over 3 km seems unproblematic. Above the boundary, there is no clear correlation between the lower deformed sandstones of Lower Pine Ridge, and the deltaic deposits at Upper Pine Ridge. Rather, these deltaic deposits seem to correspond more closely in nature to the uppermost deltaic rocks of Lower Pine Ridge. Thus, it is suggested that the two lowermost facies at Lower Pine Ridge, the deformed sandstones and the tidally-influenced fluvial sandstones thin out and are not represented at Upper Pine Ridge.

The uppermost deltaic sediments show a gradation from Lower to Upper Pine Ridge which supports this correlation. At Lower Pine Ridge, there is little wave-influence and numerous coals, suggesting a more landward setting than at Upper Pine Ridge, where there is a more seaward succession with greater wave influence and fewer coal seams, at least in the westernmost parts (see Figs. 8A, 9A). This is supported by the paleocurrent data (Figs. 3, 7), which show paleoflow toward the SSW. The two localities are positioned on a line oriented ENE-WSW with respect to one another, indicating that they represent a laterally-oblique transition relative to the paleovalley axis.

Consequently, it is suggested that the lower parts of the Pine Ridge Sandstone at Lower Pine Ridge were deposited within an incised valley. The reasons for this interpretation are (Figs. 11A, B): (1) the transition from a sandy shoreface and marine mudstone succession to fluvial sandstones deformed by slumping across a locally rooted, but regionally important erosion surface most likely resulted from a relative sea-level lowstand (see discussion above); (2) the slumped and deformed sandstones directly above the erosion surface; (3) the tidally-influenced channel sandstones above the deformed sandstones; and (4) the lateral correlation scheme presented above. Although none of these points by themselves are conclusive of an incised-valley setting, on a combined basis they point towards such an interpretation. Relative sea-level fall will tend to result in incision of streams (observable at any scale; cf. Posamentier and others, 1992) and basinward shifts of facies (e.g., Van Wagoner and others, 1988). Only in an unusual case would relative sea-level lowering produce perfect peneplanation without any sign of stream/valley incision.

The deformed, fluvial sandstones above the regional erosion surface, which may have been deposited by slumping from a nearby slope, also indirectly suggest the presence of an incised valley. Such deposits form next to or on a local slope and, combined with the other observations, are best explained within an incised-valley setting. The tidal character of the overlying fluvial channel-belt sandstones are best explained as having formed within a laterally constrained setting, and again, combined with the other interpretations and observations, an incised-valley setting is suggested.

The fill of the valley probably started to accumulate during the incision by the formation and deposition of the deformed sandstones. These were probably formed during falling relative sea level (Fig. 11B) because this was also the time when the valley sides were oversteepened and undercut, and slope gradients the highest. Unloading by the incision may therefore have caused retrogressive slumping and mass movement.

The next phase of valley fill was that of the tidally-influenced fluvial channels (Fig. 11C). These clearly meandering channels occur at Lower Pine Ridge but have no equivalents at Upper Pine Ridge. The tidal influence was probably enhanced by the constrained, valley morphology developed during the incision. However, it is likely that a rise of relative sea level occurred between deposition of the deformed sandstones and the tidally-influenced fluvial sandstones to explain the introduction of a tidal influence. Furthermore, the superposition of tidally-influenced fluvial sandstones above the subaerially formed rooted horizon on the regional erosion surface points to a relative sea-level rise. Finally, the lack of significant deformation in the tidally-influenced sandstones suggests an overall reduction of depositional slope and this may also relate to a rise of relative sea level.

The latest phase of deposition of the Pine Ridge Sandstone was dominated by wave-influenced deltaic deposition with no evidence for tidal processes (Fig. 11D), indicating another overall change in the main controls on deposition. It is arguable whether this facies was deposited within an incised valley. More likely, these deposits reflect sedimentation outside the valley or, at a time when the valley had been filled and the interfluves flooded, during a further rise of relative sea level. The complete change from a tidally-influenced setting to a wave-influenced setting, as seen at Lower Pine Ridge, supports this, suggesting a morphological expansion probably caused by the filling of the incised valley (Fig. 11). This is further supported by the relatively rapid change upward to the marine Lewis Shale (cf. Gill and others, 1970), which was deposited when marine waters flooded across the Pine Ridge Sandstone.

Limitation of interpreted valley-fill facies to Lower Pine Ridge suggests that the facies and regional erosion surface at Upper Pine Ridge formed on an interfluve of the incised valley. Thus, this locality could be a lateral correlative to Lower Pine Ridge or perhaps an obliquely downstream correlative since the uppermost deltaic facies seem to have more of an open-bay character or lower delta-plain character than at Lower Pine Ridge. This is substantiated and discussed above and supported by the paleocurrent data (Fig. 7).

The vertical succession at Lower Pine Ridge, consisting of shoreface sandstones bounded above by a regional, subaerial erosion surface, mass movement-deformed sandstones, tidally-influenced fluvial sandstones, and wave-influenced deltaic deposits which are further overlain by marine shales, indicates a relative sea-level control on deposition. Particularly the fact that the transitions between these regimes are largely sharp, and that within a particular regime there is no evidence of the processes operating within subjacent or superjacent regimes, supports a relative sea-level control.

SEQUENCE STRATIGRAPHY AND LITHOLOGICAL PREDICTION

The Allen Ridge Formation in the western part of the Hanna Basin, the correlative of the Rock River Formation, shows a clearly developed, westward backstepping pattern, probably caused by renewed Absaroka thrusting in the Sevier belt to the west (Jordan, 1981; Martinsen and others, 1993). This transgressive systems tract is anomalous since it occurs immediately below the lowstand erosion surface below the Pine Ridge Sandstone. Martinsen and others (1993) ascribed this relationship to an intricate interplay between Sevier thrusting and Laramide uplifts, which caused subsidence patterns to be out-of-phase (Devlin and others, 1990). Thus, the uplift which caused the unconformity below the Pine Ridge Sandstone probably occurred independently of but simultaneously with the increased subsidence responsible for the retrogradation at the top of the Allen Ridge and Rock River Formations. These relationships are discussed in full in Martinsen and others (1993) and will not be commented on further here.

The regional boundary between the Rock River Formation and Pine Ridge Sandstone shows evidence for regional extent beyond that expected of normal fluvial or distributary channels, subaerial exposure and a basinward shift of facies. It thus seems legitimate to interpret this boundary as a sequence boundary in Exxon terms (Figs. 8A, 9A; see discussion above; Van Wagoner and others, 1988).

The facies transition from shoreface sandstones to deformed, mass-movement sandstones, the eroded burrowed mudstones, and the superposition of the deformed sandstones on top of the rooted, regional erosion surface suggest that the deformed sandstones are lowstand deposits and probably were deposited during fall of relative sea level. They are thus relatively early lowstand deposits (although they must post-date all lowstand incision). There is no information on stacking patterns to support this interpretation, but the facies and the facies transitions suggest such a conclusion.

The transition from deformed, mass-movement sandstones to tidally-influenced meandering-channel deposits indicates that a relative sea-level rise occurred. Therefore, merged with the channel-base erosion surfaces, a flooding surface probably occurs at the base of the channel deposits. Whether these channel deposits should be termed part of the lowstand or part of the transgressive phase largely depends on the stacking patterns of the sediments. Due to outcrop limitations, the stacking pattern cannot be determined conclusively. Some authors (e.g., Van Wagoner and others, 1990) have associated tidally-influenced, fluvial deposits deposited during a stillstand or slow rise of relative sea level with the latest part of the lowstand phase. It is possible that such a situation could also apply in the present case, but the interpretation remains unresolved until the stacking pattern of the rocks has been documented.

The bay-fill deltaic rocks at the top of the succession at Lower Pine Ridge and the entire deltaic succession at Upper Pine Ridge probably represent a transgressive systems tract for the following reasons: (1) a rise of relative sea level must have occurred between deposition of the tidally-influenced fluvial sandstones and the wave-influenced deltaic rocks at Lower Pine Ridge, and between the formation of the subaerial, regional erosion surface and the deltaic sediments at Upper Pine Ridge (Figs. 8A, 9A); (2) there is a clear, thinning-upward character of the bay-fill cycles, particularly at Upper Pine Ridge, with an increase of sedimentary structures suggesting wave-influence; and (3) these deltaic sediments are directly overlain by the marine Lewis Shale. These three points collectively suggest that retrogradation took place.

The evidence for a rise of relative sea level at the base of the wave-influenced deltaic sediments is quite evident on the interpreted valley interfluve at Upper Pine Ridge, where there is a direct transition from the rooted sequence boundary to bay-fill successions. Thus, the sequence boundary here must be merged with a transgressive surface (Fig. 9A). At Lower Pine Ridge, this transition seems more gradual, and no one flooding/transgressive surface can confidently be correlated across the outcrop (Fig. 8A). This is perhaps also to be expected, since it is likely that the wave-influenced deltaic setting evolved gradually (but still relatively rapidly) from the tidally-influenced, fluvial setting. It is unlikely that the transition took place instantaneously everywhere. More probably, some tidally-influenced channels remained active while the interchannel areas were converted from floodplain areas to more open bays during gradual flooding.

Lowstand deposits within incised valleys commonly consist of braided or meandering channel deposits (Van Wagoner and others, 1990; Allen, 1991), but in most instances, these deposits tend to form during the late lowstand when sea level has started to rise. During the early lowstand, when relative sea level falls and incised valleys are cut, sedimentation more commonly occurs in deltaic or shoreline wedges beyond the valleys, for instance as products of forced regressions (Plint, 1988; Posamentier and Chamberlain, 1991; Posamentier and others, 1992). Therefore, mass-movement sandstones formed during the relative fall of sea level or early lowstand are rather unusual and have not been documented in great detail. Mass-movement deposits may help identify lowstand erosion surfaces where other evidence such as subaerial erosion and pedogenesis is lacking.

Although facies zonations are common in incised-valley fill sandstones and estuarine successions, even at a process

level (Zaitlin and Schultz, 1984, 1990; Dalrymple and others, 1992), the observations in the Pine Ridge Sandstone suggest a variation to the theme. The mass-movement to tidally-influenced fluvial channel to wave-influenced deltaic succession indicates a systematic response not only to rising relative sea level, but also to changing valley slope and morphology. During falling relative sea level, at the time of highest valley slope and hydraulic gradient, mass-movement processes operated. During the late lowstand stage, when relative sea level had started to rise, the constrained morphology of the valley was retained and enhanced tidal influence, while the valley gradient was reduced sufficiently to allow for development of meandering channels. During the transgressive stage, the valley margins were overtopped, leading to a morphological expansion and a change from tidal to wave influence.

An overall fluvial-tide-wave vertical evolutionary pattern is observed in many incised-valley fill successions and estuaries (Anderson and others, 1990; Nichol, 1991; Pattison, 1991) and reflects increasing marine influence related to a relative rise of sea level. This three-fold subdivision produces a high degree of predictability in such successions, although the detailed, process-scale predictability is highly dependent on the specific structural and environmental setting. Sediment type, calibre, sediment stability, and slope gradients are particularly important factors to consider in this respect.

CONCLUSIONS

1. The Campanian Pine Ridge Sandstone of the Hanna and Laramie Basins, southeastern Wyoming, is an incised-valley fill deposit formed as a response to Laramide tectonic uplift and subsequent relative sea-level fall and rise.
2. Following deposition of upper shoreface sandstones of the underlying Rock River Formation, a marked drop of relative sea level occurred causing subaerial exposure, fluvial incision, regional truncation and valley formation.
3. During the relative fall of sea level, deformed, mass-movement sandstones were deposited within the valley. Because of a relative rise of sea level, these were overlain by tidally-influenced, fluvial-channel sandstones which filled the valley. Together, these two facies form, respectively, the early and late lowstand deposits.
4. A major phase of flooding occurred across the filled valley and interfluve areas, causing a wave-influenced deltaic system to develop. Due to continued, relative sea-level rise and insufficient sediment supply, the delta system retrograded. This backstepping delta system represents a transgressive systems tract, which was subsequently flooded by the extensive, overlying Lewis Shale.

ACKNOWLEDGMENTS

The author wishes to thank Norsk Hydro for financial support during the study. Field work was carried out during the Fall of 1990 and 1991 while serving as a visiting assistant professor at the University of Wyoming. Thanks are extended to Jim Steidtmann and Randi Martinsen for great help, guidance, and hospitality while in Laramie. Early versions of this manuscript were read by William Helland-Hansen and Ron Steel. Constructively critical reviews by Rod Tillman and Bob Dalrymple are also acknowledged.

REFERENCES

ALLEN, G. P., 1991, Sedimentary processes and facies in the Gironde estuary: a recent model for macrotidal estuarine systems, *in* Smith, D. G., Reinson, G. E., Zaitlin, B. A., and Rahmani, R., eds., Clastic Tidal Sedimentology: Calgary, Canadian Society of Petroleum Geologists Memoir 16, p. 29–40.

ALLEN, G. P., AND TESSON, M., 1991, High-frequency parasequences and sequences in a Pleistocene lowstand prograding wedge complex on the Rhone shelf (France): eustatic, isostatic and tectonic controls, *in* Leckie, D. A., Posamentier, H. W., and Lovell, R. W. W., eds., Proceedings 1991 NUNA Conference on High-Resolution Sequence Stratigraphy: Banff, Geological Association of Canada, p. 1a–1b.

ANDERSON, J. B., SIRINGAN, F. P., AND THOMAS, F. P., 1990, Sequence stratigraphy of the late Pleistocene-Holocene Trinity-Sabine valley system: relationship to the distribution of sand bodies within the transgressive systems tract: Houston, Proceedings 11th Annual Research Conference, Gulf Coast Section SEPM, p. 15–20.

BERMAN, A. E., DOLSON, J., MULLER, D., EVETTS, M. J., AND STEIN, J. A., 1991, Paleogeography of an emergent marine shelf: Muddy sandstone (Lower Cretaceous), Rocky Mountain region, USA, *in* Leckie, D. A., Posamentier, H. W., and Lovell, R. W. W., eds., Proceedings 1991 NUNA Conference on High-Resolution Sequence Stratigraphy: Banff, Geological Association of Canada, p. 2–6.

BOYD, R., SUTER, J., AND PENLAND, S., 1989, Relation of sequence stratigraphy to modern sedimentary environments: Geology, v. 17, p. 926–929.

BRUNSDEN, D., AND PRIOR, D. B., eds., 1984, Slope Instability: Chichester, John Wiley & Sons, 620 p.

CROSS, T. A., 1986, Tectonic controls on foreland basin subsidence and Laramide style deformation, western United States, *in* Allen, P. A., and Homewood, P., eds., Foreland Basins: Oxford, International Association of Sedimentologists Special Publication 8, p. 15–39.

DALRYMPLE, R. W., ZAITLIN, B. A., AND BOYD, R., 1992, Estuarine facies models: conceptual basis and stratigraphic implications: Journal of Sedimentary Petrology, v. 62, p. 1130–1146.

DEVLIN, W. J., RUDOLPH, K. W., EHMAN, K. D., AND SHAW, C. A, 1990, The effect of tectonic and eustatic cycles on accomodation and sequence stratigraphic framework in the southwestern Wyoming foreland basin (abs.): Nottingham, 11th International Sedimentological Congress, International Association of Sedimentologists, p. 131.

ELLIOTT, T., 1991, High-resolution sequence stratigraphy of Upper Carboniferous deltaic systems in the West Clare Basin, Ireland, *in* Leckie, D. A., Posamentier, H. W., and Lovell, R. W. W., eds., Proceedings 1991 NUNA Conference on High-Resolution Sequence Stratigraphy: Banff, Geological Association of Canada, p. 11–12.

FARRE, J. A., MCGREGOR, B. A., RYAN, W. B. F., AND ROBB, J. M., 1983, Breaching the shelfbreak: passage from youthful to mature phase in submarine canyon evolution, *in* Stanley, D. J., and Moore, G. T., eds., The Shelfbreak: Critical Interface on Continental Margins: Tulsa, Society of Economic Paleontologists and Mineralogists Special Publication 33, p. 25–39.

GALLOWAY, W. E., 1989, Genetic stratigraphic sequences in basin analysis I: Architecture and genesis of flooding-surface bounded depositional units: American Association of Petroleum Geologists Bulletin, v. 73, p. 125–142.

GALLOWAY, W. E., DINGUS, W. F., AND PAIGE, R. E., 1991, Seismic and depositional facies of Paleocene-Eocene Wilcox Group submarine canyon fills, northwest Gulf Coast, USA, *in* Weimer, P., and Link, M. H., eds., Seismic Facies and Sedimentary Processes of Submarine Fans and Turbidite Systems: New York, Springer-Verlag, p. 247–271.

GILL, J. R., MEREWETHER, E. A., AND COBBAN, W. A., 1970, Stratigraphy and nomenclature of some Upper Cretaceous and Lower Tertiary rocks in south-central Wyoming: Washington, D. C., United States Geological Survey Professional Paper, v. 667, p. 1–53.

HARMS, J. C., 1966, Stratigraphic traps in a valley-fill, western Nebraska: American Association of Petroleum Geologists Bulletin, v. 50, p. 2119–2149.

HYDEN, H. J., 1965, Geologic map of the Rock River Quadrangle, Albany County, Wyoming, United States Geological Survey Geologic Quadrangle Map GQ-472: Washington, D.C., United States Geological Survey.

JORDAN, T. E., 1981, Thrust loads and foreland basin evolution, western United States: American Association of Petroleum Geologists Bulletin, v. 65, p. 2506–2520.

KAPLAN, S. S., AND SKEEN, R. C., 1985, North-south regional seismic profile of the Hanna Basin, Wyoming, *in* Gries, R. R., and Dryer, R. C., eds., Seismic Exploration of the Rocky Mountain Region: Denver, Rocky Mountain Association of Geologists and Denver Geophysical Society, p. 219–224.

KRYSTINIK, L. F., AND BLAKENEY, B. A., 1990, Sedimentology of the upper Morrow Formation in eastern Colorado and western Kansas, *in* Sonnenberg, S. A., Shannon, L. T., Rader, K., von Drehle, W. F., and Martin, G. W., eds., Morrow Sandstones in Southeast Colorado and Adjacent Areas: Denver, Rocky Mountain Association of Geologists, p. 37–50.

LECKIE, D. A., POSAMENTIER, H. W., AND LOVELL, R. W. W., eds., 1991, Proceedings 1991 NUNA Conference on High-Resolution Sequence Stratigraphy: Banff, Geological Association of Canada, 186 p.

LECKIE, D. A., AND SINGH, C., 1991, Estuarine deposits of the Albian Paddy Member (Peace River Formation) and lowermost Shaftesbury Formation, Alberta, Canada: Journal of Sedimentary Petrology, v. 61, p. 825–849.

LeFEBRE, G. B., 1988, Tectonic Evolution of Hanna Basin, Wyoming: Laramide Block Rotation in the Rocky Mountain Foreland: Unpublished Ph. D. Dissertation, University of Wyoming, Laramie, 240 p.

LOWELL, J. D., ed., 1983, Foreland Basins and Uplifts: Denver, Rocky Mountain Association of Geologists, 392 p.

MARTINSEN, O. J., 1991, Unconformities or flooding surfaces—the perpetual problem of recognizing and using key chronostratigraphic surfaces: examples from the Upper Cretaceous of the Western Interior and the Upper Carboniferous of northern England, *in* Leckie, D. A., Posamentier, H. W., and Lovell, R. W. W., eds., Proceedings 1991 NUNA Conference on High-Resolution Sequence Stratigraphy: Banff, Geological Association of Canada, p. 36–38.

MARTINSEN, O. J., MARTINSEN, R. S., AND STEIDTMANN, J. R., 1993, Mesaverde Group (Upper Cretaceous), southeastern Wyoming, USA: allostratigraphy vs. sequence stratigraphy in a tectonically active area: American Association of Petroleum Geologists Bulletin, v. 77, p. 1351–1373.

MARTINSEN, R. S., AND TILLMAN, R. W., 1989, Haystack Mountains Formation: Casper, Wyoming Geological Association Guidebook, Fortieth Field Conference, p. 263–268.

McCUBBIN, D. G., 1982, Barrier island and strand plain facies, *in* Scholle, P. A., and Spearing, D., eds., Sandstone Depositional Environments: Tulsa, American Association of Petroleum Geologists Memoir 32, p. 247–279.

McMASTER, R. L., AND ASHRAF, A., 1973, Extent and formation of deeply buried channels on the continental shelf off southern New England: Journal of Geology, v. 81, 374–379.

NICHOL, S. L., 1991, Zonation and sedimentology of estuarine facies in an incised valley, wave-dominated, microtidal setting, New South Wales, Australia, *in* Smith, D. G., Reinson, G. E., Zaitlin, B. A., and Rahmani, R., eds., Clastic Tidal Sedimentology: Calgary, Canadian Society of Petroleum Geologists Memoir 16, p. 41–58.

PATTISON, S. A. J., 1988, Transgressive, incised shoreface deposits of the Burnstick Member (Cardium 'B' sand) at Caroline, Crossfield, Garrington and Lochend; Cretaceous Interior Seaway, Alberta, Canada, *in* James, D. P., and Leckie, D. A., eds., Sequences, Stratigraphy, Sedimentology: Surface and Subsurface: Calgary, Canadian Society of Petroleum Geologists Memoir 15, p. 155–166.

PATTISON, S. A. J., 1991, Crystal, Sundance and Edson valley-fill deposits, *in* Leckie, D. A., Posamentier, H. W., and Lovell, R. W. W., eds., Proceedings 1991 NUNA Conference on High-Resolution Sequence Stratigraphy, Banff, Alberta: Geological Association of Canada, p. 44–47.

PERMAN, R. C., 1990, Depositional history of the Maastrichtian Lewis Shale in south-central Wyoming: deltaic and interdeltaic, marginal marine through deep-water marine, environments: American Association of Petroleum Geologists Bulletin, v. 74, p. 1695–1717.

PLINT, A. G., 1988, Sharp-based shoreface sequences and 'offshore bars' in the Cardium Formation of Alberta: their relationship to relative changes in sea-level, *in* Wilgus, C. K., Hastings, B. S., Kendall, C. G. ST. C, Posamentier, H. W., Ross, C. A., and Van Wagoner, J. C., eds., Sea-level Changes: An Integrated Approach: Tulsa, Society of Economic Paleontologists and Mineralogists Special Publication 42, p. 357–370.

POLLARD, J. E. AND GOLDRING, R., 1993, Ichnofabrics containing *Ophiomorpha*: significance in shallow-water facies interpretation: Journal of the Geological Society, London, v. 150, p. 149–164.

POMAR, L., 1991, Reef geometries, erosion surfaces and high-frequency sea-level changes, upper Miocene Reef Complex, Mallorca, Spain: Sedimentology, v. 38, p. 243–269.

POSAMENTIER, H. W., 1991, An overview of sequence-stratigraphic concepts, *in* Leckie, D. A., Posamentier, H. W., and Lovell, R. W. W., eds., Proceedings 1991 NUNA Conference on High-Resolution Sequence Stratigraphy: Banff, Geological Association of Canada, p. 62–74.

POSAMENTIER, H. W., ALLEN, G. P., AND JAMES, D. P., 1992, High-resolution sequence stratigraphy- the East Coulee delta, Alberta: Journal of Sedimentary Petrology, v. 62, p. 310–317.

POSAMENTIER, H. W., AND CHAMBERLAIN, C. J., 1991, High-resolution sequence stratigraphic analysis of a lowstand shoreline; Viking Formation, Joarcam Field, Alberta, *in* Leckie, D. A., Posamentier, H. W., and Lovell, R. W. W., eds., Proceedings 1991 NUNA Conference on High-Resolution Sequence Stratigraphy: Banff, Geological Association of Canada, p. 47–49.

POSAMENTIER, H. W., JERVEY, M. T., AND VAIL, P. R., 1988, Eustatic controls on clastic deposition I: conceptual framework, *in* Wilgus, C. K., Hastings, B. S., Kendall, C. G. ST. C, Posamentier, H. W., Ross, C. A., and Van Wagoner, J. C., eds., Sea-level Changes: An Integrated Approach: Tulsa, Society of Economic Paleontologists and Mineralogists Special Publication 42, p. 109–124.

PRIOR, D. B., AND COLEMAN, J. M., 1978, Disintegrating retrogressive landslides on very low angle subaqueous slopes, Mississippi Delta: Marine Geotechnology, v. 3, p. 37–60.

SCHMIDT, C. J., AND PERRY, W. J., eds., 1988, Interaction of the Rocky MountainForeland and the Cordilleran Thrust Belt: Boulder, Geological Society of America Memoir 171, 597 p.

SMITH, J. H., 1961, A summary of stratigraphy and paleontology, Upper Colorado and Montanan Groups, southcentral Wyoming, northeastern Utah, and northwestern Colorado, *in* Symposium on Late Cretaceous Rocks, Wyoming and Adjacent Areas: Casper, Wyoming Geological Association 16th Annual Field Conference, p. 101–112.

STEIDTMANN, J. R., AND MIDDLETON, L. T., 1991, Fault chronology and uplift history of the southern Wind River Range, Wyoming: implications for Laramide and post-Laramide deformation in the Rocky Mountain foreland: Geological Society of America Bulletin, v. 103, p. 472–485.

VAN WAGONER, J. C., 1991, The stratigraphic expression and significance of sequence and parasequence boundaries, *in* Leckie, D. A., Posamentier, H. W., and Lovell, R. W. W., eds., Proceedings 1991 NUNA Conference on High-Resolution Sequence Stratigraphy: Banff, Geological Association of Canada, p. 56–57.

VAN WAGONER, J. C, MITCHUM, R. M., CAMPION, K. M., AND RAHMANIAN, V. D., 1990, Siliciclastic sequence stratigraphy in well logs, cores and outcrops: concepts for high-resolution correlation of time and facies: American Association of Petroleum Geologists Methods in Exploration Series 7, 55 p.

VAN WAGONER, J. C., NUMMEDAL, D., JONES, C. R., TAYLOR, D. R., JENNETTE, D.C., AND RILEY, G.W., eds., 1991, Sequence Stratigraphy Applications to Shelf Sandstone Reservoirs: Tulsa, American Association of Petroleum Geologists, Field Conference Guidebook, Book Cliffs, Utah, and San Juan Basin, New Mexico.

VAN WAGONER, J. C., POSAMENTIER, H. W., MITCHUM, R. M., VAIL, P. R., SARG, J. F., LOUTIT, T. F., AND HARDENBOL, J., 1988, An overview of the fundamentals of sequence stratigraphy and key definitions, *in* Wilgus, C. K., Hastings, B. S., Kendall, C. G. ST. C, Posamentier, H. W., Ross, C. A., and Van Wagoner, J. C., eds., Sea-level Changes: An Integrated Approach: Tulsa, Society of Economic Paleontologists and Mineralogists Special Publication 42, p. 39–45.

WEIMER, R. J., 1984, Relation of unconformities, tectonics, and sea-level changes, Cretaceous of Western Interior, USA, *in* Schlee, J. S., ed., Interregional Unconformities and Hydrocarbon Accumulation: Tulsa, American Association of Petroleum Geologists Memoir 36, p. 7–35.

WOOD, J. M., AND HOPKINS, J. C., 1989, Reservoir sandstones in estuarine valley fill: Lower Cretaceous Glauconitic member, Little Bow Field, Alberta, Canada: American Association of Petroleum Geologists Bulletin, v. 73, p. 1361–1382.

ZAITLIN, B. A., AND SHULTZ, B. C., 1984, An estuarine embayment fill model from the Lower Cretaceous Mannville Group, west-central Saskatchewan, *in* Stott, D. F., and Glass, D. J., eds., Mesozoic of Middle North America: Calgary, Canadian Society of Petroleum Geologists Memoir 9, p. 455–469.

ZAITLIN, B. A., AND SHULTZ, B. C., 1990, Wave-influenced estuarine sand body, Senlac heavy oil pool, Saskatchewan, Canada, *in* Barwis, J. H., McPherson, J. G., and Strudlick, J. R., eds., Sandstone Petroleum Reservoirs: New York, Springer-Verlag, p. 363–387.

ICHNOLOGICAL ASPECTS OF INCISED-VALLEY FILL SYSTEMS FROM THE VIKING FORMATION OF THE WESTERN CANADA SEDIMENTARY BASIN, ALBERTA, CANADA

JAMES A. MacEACHERN AND S. GEORGE PEMBERTON
Ichnology Research Group, Department of Geology, University of Alberta, Edmonton, Alberta, Canada, T6G 2E3

ABSTRACT: The Upper Albian Viking Formation produces hydrocarbons from anomalous deposits in the Crystal, Willesden Green, Cyn-Pem, Sundance, and Edson fields of west-central Alberta. These anomalous deposits are interpreted to represent lowstand incised-valley systems, and are erosionally juxtaposed against regionally extensive offshore to lower shoreface parasequences. These parasequences are stacked into a progradational parasequence set of the preceding highstand systems tract. The stratigraphically underlying parasequences possess trace fossil assemblages characterized by abundant, uniform burrowing with a high diversity of elements from the *Cruziana* ichnofacies. These characteristics, coupled with abundant specialized and complex feeding and grazing structures, attest to an equilibrium community under fully marine conditions.

The underlying parasequences contrast markedly with the anomalous incised-valley deposits. The valley fill deposits overlie an erosional discontinuity typically corresponding to a co-planar surface of lowstand erosion and transgressive erosion or marine flooding (FS/SB), that is locally demarcated by the substrate-controlled *Glossifungites* ichnofacies. The incised-valley deposits best fit a wave-dominated estuarine model. The succession displays a tripartite zonation of facies associations corresponding to the main depositional zones of the estuary: the sandy Bay Head Delta, the muddy Central Basin, and the sandy Estuary Mouth. A fourth depositional complex corresponds to Channel-fill and reflects probable stages of re-incision into previous estuarine deposits during renewed sea-level fall, although locally, distributary channels, tidal channels, and tidal inlets may be indicated. The trace fossil suite of the estuarine system is characterized by a variable and sporadic distribution of burrowing, variability in ichnogenera distribution, and dominance by simple structures of trophic generalists. The suite is dominated by opportunistic suites characteristic of stressed environments, particularly those subjected to fluctuations in salinity, episodic deposition, variable aggradation rates, and variability in substrate consistency. Specialized feeding and grazing structures are of secondary importance in the trace fossil suite, but record periods of fully marine, unstressed conditions. The estuarine system appears to have ranged repeatedly from brackish to fully marine. Although the character of the ichnological record in valley fills is complex, this complexity is, itself, distinctive and differentiates it from the underlying highstand parasequences of the regional succession.

INTRODUCTION

The Viking Formation has been an intensively explored petroleum target in Alberta since the early 1930's and is generally regarded as a series of elongate NW-SE trending sand bodies, reflecting shoreface successions. Interest in the Viking Formation waned until the discovery of the Crystal Field in 1978 (Fig. 1). Not only was the new field a prolific oil producer, but it was anomalous in its roughly N-S orientation, virtually normal to the inferred paleoshoreline trends. Reinson (1985) and Reinson and others (1988) were among the first to recognize these Viking Formation deposits as the products of an incised-valley system. Other Viking Formation fields such as Willesden Green, Sundance, Edson, and Cyn-Pem, discovered in 1955, 1971, 1973, and 1986, respectively, also demonstrated a roughly N-S orientation but were not interpreted as incised valley fill deposits until considerably later. Boreen (1989) and Boreen and Walker (1991) were the first to characterize the Willesden Green Field as an incised-valley system. Pattison (1991a, b) was the first to interpret the Sundance, Edson, and Cyn-Pem deposits as incised-valley systems and confirmed Reinson's original interpretation of the Crystal field.

Study of the facies successions and their distribution within the fields demonstrates both the complex history of sedimentation and the variable nature of the processes operating within the valley systems. Stratigraphic analysis highlights the fact that valleys routinely become the locus of re-incision during successive periods of relative sea-level lowstand, producing a lateral and vertical juxtaposition of non-contemporaneous valley-fill deposits and the localized preservation of erosional remnants of earlier estuarine successions. As a result, detailed reconstructions of depositional histories within incised valleys are exceedingly difficult, commonly surpassing the capacity of the existing database to discern (Zaitlin, pers. commun., 1992).

With the exception of Pemberton and others (1992c), detailed ichnological analysis has been an under-utilized tool in the interpretation of the subenvironments present within incised-valley systems and in the recognition of the stratigraphic discontinuities associated with their fills. Ichnology is ideally suited to impart valuable data about the depositional environment not readily obtainable from lithofacies analysis alone. This paper seeks to demonstrate the effectiveness of integrating ichnological analysis with sedimentology, both in the delineation of the valley margins and in the enhancement of paleoenvironmental interpretations of facies within estuarine, incised-valley complexes of the Viking Formation. Enhanced recognition, coupled with more reliable and precise interpretations of the individual facies, provides a superior understanding of the conditions responsible for the observed facies associations within the valley systems and the depositional histories of the particular valley deposits.

GENERAL ESTUARINE MODELS

Dalrymple and others (1992) have recently provided a good summary of the various definitions and proposed models of estuaries. They suggested a general, unified facies model, primarily based on the relative importance of the marine processes (wave and tidal energy) operating on the complex. Fluvial processes, although an important factor in the nature of sediment accumulation and facies distribution within the valley, appear to constitute a minor element in the overall character of the estuary. Implicit in their definition of an estuary is that it fills in response to a relative rise in sea level.

Incised-Valley Systems: Origin and Sedimentary Sequences, SEPM Special Publication No. 51

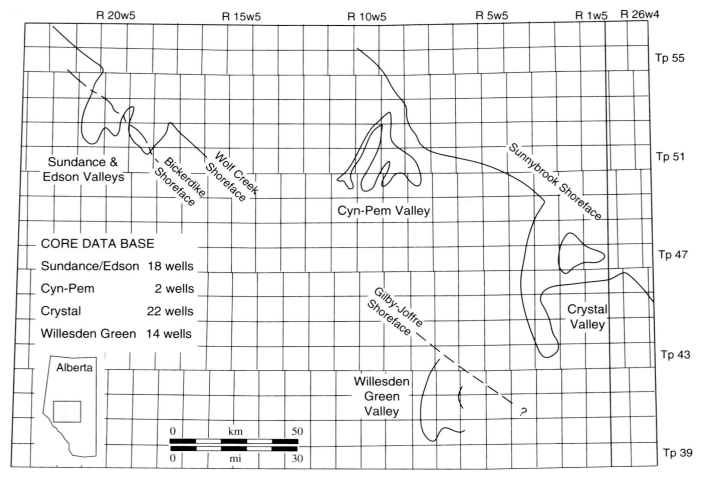

FIG. 1.—Study area. The map shows the proposed valley outlines for 5 Viking Formation incised valley systems. Modified after Pattison (1991a). The database employed consists of 56 cored intervals.

In modern estuaries, a tripartite zonation of facies or facies associations, reflecting the interaction of marine and fluvial processes, is readily observed. Van Veen (1936) was one of the earliest to recognize this overall textural zonation in his study of the Haringvliet Estuary of The Netherlands. He pointed out that three zones could be distinguished within the tidally-modified portions of the Rhine and Maas rivers and their estuary (the Haringvliet): a fluviatile-sand zone, a central zone where sand was essentially absent, and a marine-sand zone. Unfortunately, this doctoral work was largely ignored or overlooked due to its publication in Dutch. Oomkens and Terwindt (1960) referred to this work in their study of inshore, estuarine sediments of the Haringvliet, but the significance of the observed zonation appears to have eluded researchers of the time. Allen (1971), working on the Gironde estuary, and Dörjes and Howard (1975), working on the Ogeechee River-Ossabaw Sound estuary of Georgia, observed similar textural variations, which they attributed to the same interactions of marine processes and fluvial energy.

The establishment of a wave-dominated estuary model (Fig. 2) resulted mainly from the work of Roy and others (1980) on Holocene intervals along the embayed New South

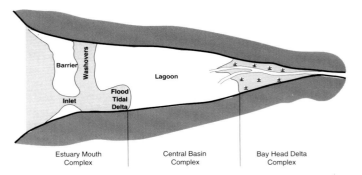

FIG. 2.—Wave-dominated, embayed estuary model. Tripartite zonation of facies reflects the Bay Head Delta, Central Basin, and Estuary Mouth complexes. Tidal inlet and distributary channels constitute elements of Channel-fill complex. Modified after Dalrymple and others (1992).

Wales coast of Australia. This model appears to explain the facies distributions in many modern estuaries as well as the facies associations for a large number of ancient deposits, including the Viking Formation examples in the Western Canada Sedimentary Basin. Dalrymple and others (1992) regard this facies model as an end member in a continuum from wave-dominated to tide-dominated estuarine settings. The wave-dominated estuary system can be separated into three main depositional complexes: the Bay Head Delta, the Central Basin, and the Estuary Mouth, heading from a landward to seaward direction (Fig. 2).

Pattison (1991a, b) recognized the appropriateness of this wave-dominated estuarine model to explain the observed facies types and their distributions within the Crystal, Sundance-Edson and Cyn-Pem valley systems. Boreen (1989) and Boreen and Walker (1991) recognized the Willesden Green example as an estuarine, incised-valley deposit, but did not place it into this conceptual framework. Observations of the facies and their paleogeographic distributions indicate that the same depositional model effectively explains the accumulation of sediment within the Willesden Green valley system as well. Although detailed sedimentologic and stratigraphic studies have been conducted on these deposits (e.g., Reinson and others, 1988; Boreen, 1989; Boreen and Walker, 1991, Pattison, 1991a, 1992), virtually no detailed ichnology has been undertaken, with the exception of Pemberton and others (1992c) who concentrated on the Crystal incised valley alone. This paper builds on the excellent sedimentologic and stratigraphic studies of others through the integration of detailed ichnological analysis. A total of 56 cored wells were logged for this study, 22 from Crystal, 14 from Willesden Green, 18 from Sundance/Edson, and both cores from Cyn-Pem (Fig. 1). The integration of ichnology serves to enhance the recognition of incised-valley deposits in the ancient record and to refine the interpretation of the various depositional subenvironments present within estuarine incised valleys.

REGIONAL SETTING AND STRATIGRAPHY OF THE VIKING FORMATION

The Lower Cretaceous (Upper Albian) Viking Formation occurs as a regionally extensive interval of sandstones, shales and rare conglomerates throughout the subsurface of Alberta and Saskatchewan (Fig. 3). The Viking Formation grades out of marine shales of the Joli Fou Formation, which represent a major (2nd-order?) transgression over a sequence boundary developed on the Mannville Group. The Viking Formation corresponds to a regressive period and comprises a complex series of 3rd-, 4th- and possibly 5th-order cycles of progradational, transgressive and lowstand events. The Viking Formation is abruptly overlain by the unnamed marine shales of the Colorado Group, reflecting a return to major (2nd-order?) marine transgression. The complexity of the Viking Formation is reflected in the proposed allostratigraphic paradigms for the interval (cf. Boreen and Walker, 1991; Pattison, 1991a, 1992) and the continuing controversy regarding its sequence-stratigraphic history. The Viking Formation is roughly equivalent in age and stratigraphic position to the Paddy Member of the Peace River Formation in northwest Alberta (Stelck and Koke, 1987), the Bow Island Formation in southwest Alberta (Glaister, 1959), and the Muddy Sandstone of Montana (McGookey and others, 1972).

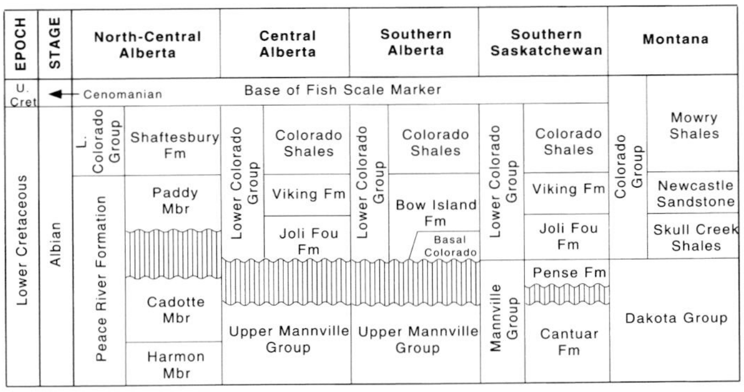

The lowstand event responsible for the development of some of the Viking incised-valley systems has been suggested to correspond to the 98 ma eustatic fall of sea level of Vail and others (1977), Haq and others (1987), and Reinson and others (1988) and may also correspond, in part, to the unconformity separating the Cadotte Member and Paddy Member of the Peace River Formation in north-central Alberta (Leckie and Reinson, pers. commun., 1991).

APPLICATIONS OF ICHNOLOGY TO VIKING FORMATION INCISED-VALLEY SYSTEMS

Ichnology can be effectively applied to Viking Formation incised-valley complexes in two main ways. The first is through the use of substrate-controlled ichnofacies in recognizing and delineating stratigraphic discontinuities, such as the incised-valley base and margins and the overlying transgressive surfaces of erosion. The second is through the study of ichnological successions and the recognition of marked differences between the trace fossil assemblages of underlying, fully marine suites and those within the estuarine valley deposits. Variations in the trace fossil suites associated with the different estuarine depositional complexes highlight a number of environmental stresses imposed upon the infaunal trace-makers.

SUBSTRATE-CONTROLLED ICHNOFACIES AND VALLEY-MARGIN RECOGNITION

Traditionally, it was thought that there were only three ways in which trace fossils could be utilized in chronostratigraphy: (1) as a means of tracing the evolution of behavior, (2) as morphologically-defined entities (with no assumptions concerning their genesis), and (3) as substitutes for the tracemaking organisms (Magwood and Pemberton, 1990). More recently, however, trace fossils and in particular substrate-controlled trace fossils are proving to be one of the most important groups of fossils in delineating stratigraphically important boundaries related to sequence stratigraphy (MacEachern and others 1990, 1991a, b, 1992a, b; Savrda, 1991a, b; Pemberton, and others, 1992a).

Three substrate-controlled ichnofacies have been established (Bromley and others, 1984): *Trypanites* (hardground suites), *Teredolites* (woodground suites), and *Glossifungites* (firmground suites). Although all three suites may in-

EPOCH	STAGE	North-Central Alberta		Central Alberta		Southern Alberta		Southern Saskatchewan		Montana
U. Cret	Cenomanian			Base of Fish Scale Marker						
Lower Cretaceous	Albian	L. Colorado Group	Shaftesbury Fm	Lower Colorado Group	Colorado Shales	Lower Colorado Group	Colorado Shales	Colorado Group	Colorado Shales	Colorado Group	Mowry Shales
		Peace River Formation	Paddy Mbr		Viking Fm		Bow Island Fm		Viking Fm		Newcastle Sandstone
					Joli Fou Fm		Basal Colorado		Joli Fou Fm		Skull Creek Shales
			Cadotte Mbr		Upper Mannville Group		Upper Mannville Group	Mannville Group	Pense Fm		Dakota Group
			Harmon Mbr						Cantuar Fm		

FIG. 3.—Stratigraphic chart, showing the position of the Viking Formation and its equivalents.

dicate the presence of a regional stratigraphic discontinuity, the *Glossifungites* ichnofacies is by far the most commonly encountered in Viking intervals. The *Glossifungites* ichnofacies (redefined by Frey and Seilacher, 1980) encompasses trace fossils associated with semilithified or firm substrates. Such substrates typically consist of dewatered, cohesive muds, due to subaerial exposure or burial with subsequent erosional exhumation (Fig. 4). Less commonly, *Glossifungites* suites may be developed within incipiently-cemented sandstone substrates, although no unequivocal examples have been recognized in the Viking Formation.

Recognition of the Glossifungites Ichnofacies

Firmground traces are dominated by vertical to subvertical dwelling structures of suspension-feeding organisms (Figs. 4 and 5). The most common structures correspond to the ichnogenera *Diplocraterion, Skolithos, Psilonichnus, Arenicolites,* and firmground *Gastrochaenolites.* Dwelling structures of deposit-feeding organisms are also constituents of the ichnofacies, and include firmground *Thalassinoides/Spongeliomorpha* and *Rhizocorallium.* The presence of such unlined vertical shafts within shaly intervals is anomalous, as such structures cannot be maintained in soft muddy substrates. *Glossifungites* ichnofacies traces are typically robust, commonly penetrating 20–100 cm below the bed junction. Many shafts tend to be 0.5–1.0 cm in diameter, particularly *Diplocraterion habichi* and *Arenicolites.* This scale of burrowing is in sharp contrast to the predominantly horizontal, diminutive trace fossils common to shaly intervals. The firmground traces are very sharp-walled and unlined, reflecting the stable, cohesive nature of the substrate at the time of colonization and burrow excavation (e.g., Fig. 5E). Many structures, particularly in outcrop, show preserved sculptings or scratch marks on the burrow wall, confirming that construction of the dwelling burrow occurred in a firm substrate. Further evidence of substrate stability, which is atypical of soft muddy beds, is the passive nature of burrow filling. This demonstrates that the structure remained open after the tracemaker vacated the burrow, thus allowing material from the succeeding depositional event to passively fill the open structure. If such an unlined burrow had been excavated in soft mud, the

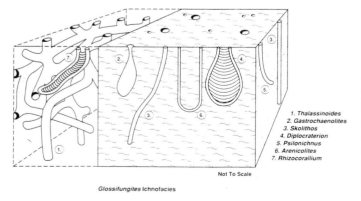

1. Thalassinoides
2. Gastrochaenolites
3. Skolithos
4. Diplocraterion
5. Psilonichnus
6. Arenicolites
7. Rhizocorallium

Not To Scale

Glossifungites Ichnofacies

FIG. 4.—Trace-fossil association characteristic of the *Glossifungites* ichnofacies (modified after Frey and Pemberton, 1984).

domicile would have collapsed upon burrow vacation. The post-depositional origin of the *Glossifungites* suite, in relation to the original softground assemblage, is clearly demonstrated by the ubiquitous cross-cutting relationships observed in the rock record. The final characteristic of the *Glossifungites* suite is the tendency to demonstrate colonization in large numbers. In several examples, seven to fifteen firmground traces, commonly *Diplocraterion habichi,* have been observed on the bedding plane of a 9-cm (3.5-inch) diameter core, corresponding to a density of between 1100 and 2300 shafts per square meter. Similar populations were observed from *Glossifungites* suites present on the modern coast of Georgia (Pemberton and Frey, 1985). Dense populations are typical of many opportunistic assemblages (Levinton, 1970; Pemberton and Frey, 1984).

Stratigraphic Implications of the Glossifungites Ichnofacies

In siliciclastic settings, most firmground assemblages are associated with erosionally exhumed (dewatered and compacted) substrates and, hence, correspond to erosional discontinuities. Although certain insect and animal burrows in the terrestrial realm may be properly regarded as firmground (e.g., Fürsich and Mayr, 1981) or, more rarely, hardground suites, they have a low preservation potential and constitute a relatively minor element in the preserved record of these associations. The overwhelming majority of these assemblages originate in marine or marginal-marine settings, particularly in pre-Tertiary intervals. As such, a discontinuity may be generated in either subaerial or submarine settings, but colonization of the surface is associated with marine conditions. The marine nature of substrate colonization has important implications regarding the genetic interpretation of the discontinuity in question. Finally, the substrate-controlled ichnocoenose, which cross-cuts the pre-existing softground suite, reflects conditions *post-dating* both initial deposition of the underlying unit and its erosional exhumation following burial. The *Glossifungites* suite, therefore, corresponds to a depositional hiatus between the erosional event and sedimentation of the overlying unit; significant depositional cover precludes firmground colonization. These three aspects of the *Glossifungites* suite make it useful both in the recognition of the discontinuity and in its genetic interpretation.

Ichnology of Viking Formation Incised-Valley Surfaces

In many incised-valley fills, determining whether the fill is associated with lowstand conditions or with the ensuing transgression may, in part, be resolved by trace fossil analysis. In the Viking Formation of the Crystal, Willesden Green, Sundance-Edson, and Cyn-Pem fields, the margins of the incised valleys are commonly demarcated by a *Glossifungites* assemblage, indicating that the initial preserved deposits are marine or marginal marine in nature. This suggests that the valleys did not fill until the onset of the ensuing transgression. Either the valleys served as a zone of sediment bypass and possessed little or no fluvial deposits, or these lowstand deposits were subsequently eroded and reworked during the transgression. The bulk of the surfaces

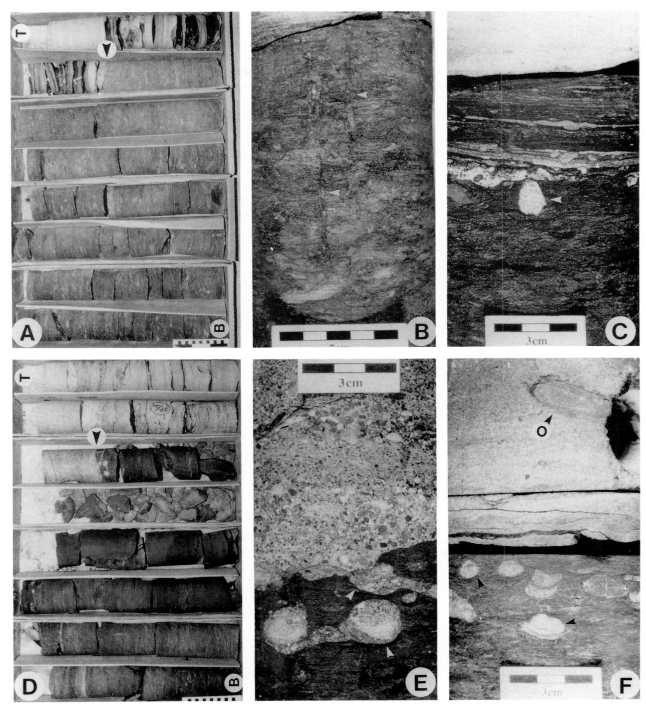

FIG. 5.—Co-planar surfaces of lowstand erosion and transgressive erosion (FS/SB) associated with incised valleys. (A and B) Crystal Field, 08-26-45-4W5. (A) Core photograph (1831.2–1835.8 m) showing thoroughly burrowed, lower offshore silty shales coarsening upward into upper offshore sandy shales of a regional Viking Formation parasequence, erosionally truncated and overlain by interbedded sandstones and shales of the Central Basin complex (arrow). A 15 cm scale is present in the lower left of the photo. Core base at lower left (B); top at upper right (T). (B) The contact (1832 m) shows a *Cruziana* (softground) assemblage, cross-cut by muddy, sand-filled *Diplocraterion* (arrows) of the *Glossifungites* ichnofacies. (C) The Crystal valley margin is also marked by firmground *Gastrochaenolites* (arrow) in the 04-01-46-4W5 well, at a depth of 1804.7 m. (D and E) Willesden Green Field, 10-35-40-7W5. (D) Core photograph (2326.2–2329.8 m) showing a coarsening-upward cycle near the base, capped by a marine flooding surface, passing into shelfal to lower offshore silty shales. These are erosionally truncated by pebbly sandstones and conglomerates of the Estuary Mouth complex (arrow). A 15 cm scale is present in the lower left of the photo. Core base at lower left (B); top at upper right (T). (E) The contact (2327 m) is marked by robust *Rhizocorallium saxicava* (arrows) of the *Glossifungites* assemblage. (F) The Willesden Green valley margin is marked by *Diplocraterion* and *Thalassinoides* (arrows) of the *Glossifungites* ichnofacies in the 11-31-40-6W5 well, at a depth of 2285.8 m. Note the *Ophiomorpha* (O) in the sandstone of the overlying Channel-fill complex, attesting to a marine influence on valley filling.

within the valley correspond to co-planar (amalgamated) lowstand surfaces of erosion and transgressive surfaces of erosion (i.e., FS/SB). The base of the valley, therefore, typically serves both as a sequence boundary and as the base of the transgressive systems tract.

More recently, Allen and Posamentier (1993) and Zaitlin and others (this volume) have designated a number of transgressive surface types within valley fill successions. They discriminate between the transgressive surface (corresponding to the initial flooding surface), the wave ravinement surface, the tidal scour ravinement surface, and the maximum flooding surface (Fig. 6). All surfaces may be demarcated by a *Glossifungites* assemblage, although the zones of colonization are clearly restricted to the limits of marine influence within the valley.

Widespread *Glossifungites* suites may be developed within the valley where the initial flooding surface is directly amalgamated with the sequence boundary (FS/SB). Where initial fluvial lowstand deposits separate the two surfaces, a substrate-controlled suite is absent. In situations where the initial flooding surface is highly erosive, lowstand fluvial deposits may be completely reworked, and the sequence boundary colonized. Such *Glossifungites* assemblages may be overlain by relatively thick, transgressively reworked lags.

During continued transgressive fill of the valley, erosive shoreface retreat of the barrier complex generates a relatively widespread wave ravinement surface, which may become amalgamated with the initial flooding surface and/or the sequence boundary. This type of FS/SB is largely restricted to the mouth of the estuary complex and, with continued transgressive fill, rises stratigraphically as the wave ravinement surface incises into previously deposited estuarine valley fill. Consequently, the wave ravinement surface may facilitate firmground colonization along its entire extent but correspond to an FS/SB only near the valley mouth, passing landward into an inter-valley transgressive surface of erosion (TSE).

The development and migration of tidal inlets also favors the generation of firmgrounds, which may become colonized by the *Glossifungites* ichnofacies. These tidal scour ravinement surfaces may locally erode through all previous valley fill deposits and incise into the sequence boundary, generating a relatively localized FS/SB. With continued erosive shoreface retreat during transgressive fill of the valley system, these tidal scour ravinement surfaces may rise stratigraphically and incise into previously deposited estuarine deposits, producing areally restricted *Glossifungites*-demarcated TSE. Fluvial channel diastems, which may appear sedimentologically similar, are not colonised because the surfaces are generated landward of the marine limit in the valley.

If the valley is ultimately filled during transgression, the potential exists to generate a widespread *Glossifungites*-demarcated TSE corresponding to the maximum flooding surface. A high energy (erosive) maximum flooding surface favors truncation of the upper portion of the valley and generation of widespread firmgrounds across both the valley fill and the adjacent valley margins and interfluves, which may become colonized by a substrate-controlled, trace fossil suite. In contrast, low energy (non-erosive) maximum flooding surfaces may not permit firmground colonization except along the valley margins and interfluves where sub-

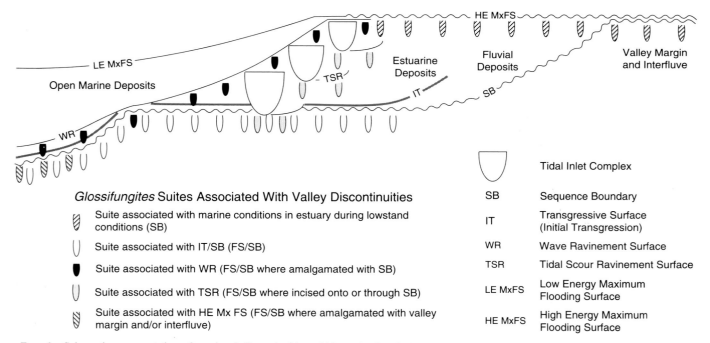

FIG. 6—Schematic representation of erosional discontinuities within a simple (single stage) incised-valley system. The diagram also shows the zones which may contain *Glossifungites* assemblages. The surfaces locally amalgamate with one another, affording the possibility of *Glossifungites* suites of differing stage of valley infill overprinting one another. The diagram is adapted from Zaitlin and others(this volume).

aerial exposure has caused the substrates to dewater and become firm.

In situations where the valley is subjected to re-incision events during subsequent periods of sea-level fall, new sets of FS/SB and inter-estuarine TSE may be cut and colonized. The compound fills of such valley systems typically display numerous dissected and locally amalgamated segments of *Glossifungites*-demarcated surfaces and require careful stratigraphic analysis in order to discriminate one from another, delineate their extents in the valley, and place them into a sequence stratigraphic framework.

In all Viking Formation examples, the FS/SB is excavated into coarsening upward, regional, Viking Formation silty shales, sandy shales, and shaly sandstones of the underlying highstand parasequences (discussed below). These intervals contain fully marine, high diversity, and abundant distal to proximal *Cruziana* softground suites (Fig. 7). In the Crystal Field, the erosional truncation is marked by a *Glossifungites* assemblage consisting of numerous sharp-walled, unlined *Diplocraterion* shafts (Figs. 5A, B), firmground *Thalassinoides*, *Diplocraterion habichi*, and firmground *Gastrochaenolites* (Fig. 5C). At Willesden Green, the valley base is locally marked by a *Glossifungites* assemblage consisting of spectacular *Rhizocorallium saxicava* (Figs. 5D, E), *Thalassinoides* (Fig. 5F), *Arenicolites*, *Skolithos*, and *Diplocraterion habichi*. The Sundance/Edson valley surface is only rarely demarcated by firmground *Thalassinoides/Spongeliomorpha*, while the Cyn-Pem valley is marked by abundant firmground *Arenicolites* and *Skolithos* in one of only two cored intervals in the valley system. The presence of this substrate-controlled trace fossil assemblage greatly enhances the recognition and genetic interpretation of the incised valley discontinuity surface (MacEachern and others, 1992b; Pemberton and others, 1992a). Recognition of ichnologically-demarcated discontinuities, integrated with the distinctive ichnological successions characterizing the estuarine deposits, has proven to be a powerful tool in the paleoenvironmental resolution of these complex Viking Formation intervals.

ICHNOLOGICAL SUCCESSIONS OF REGIONAL VIKING FORMATION PARASEQUENCES

Laterally adjacent to and underlying the incised-valley deposits of the Viking Formation are a number of coarsening-upward parasequences of regional extent, informally referred to as the regional Viking cycles. These grade out of the marine shales of the underlying Joli Fou Formation, which transgressively overlie a sequence boundary developed on the Mannville Group (i.e., FS/SB; Fig. 3). Five, main coarsening-upward successions (fourth-order parasequences), the lower two of which contain numerous minor cycles (fifth-order parasequences), are interpreted to reflect changes in relative sea level (Pattison, 1991a). The parasequences occur as a regionally extensive, progradational parasequence set, indicating accumulation within a highstand systems tract, which downlaps onto the Joli Fou Formation marine shales of the underlying transgressive systems tract.

Three facies make up a complete coarsening cycle, although the minor cycles rarely comprise a complete cycle.

The basal facies (Facies 1) consists of thoroughly burrowed silty shales (Figs. 7A, B). Silt is dispersed biogenically throughout the facies and may locally be present as discontinuous stringers. Very rare, lower very fine-grained to upper very fine-grained sand interbeds (<2 cm thick) containing low-angle, wavy parallel lamination or combined-flow ripple lamination are locally intercalated.

The trace fossils of Facies 1 are uniformly distributed and present in most intervals studied, with the exception of the accessory traces (Figs. 8 and 9A). *Helminthopsis*, *Chondrites*, *Planolites*, and *Terebellina* comprise the dominant elements of the suite, while *Zoophycos* and *Thalassinoides* constitute the secondary elements. *Asterosoma*, *Teichichnus*, *Rhizocorallium*, *Palaeophycus*, and *Rosselia* are uncommon and comprise the accessory elements.

Grading from the silty shale facies is the sandy shale facies (Facies 2; Figs. 7C, D). Sand is typically lower very fine- to upper fine-grained and is present both as biogenically dispersed grains and as remnant wavy parallel laminated, oscillation rippled, or combined-flow ripple laminated beds. Burrowing is typically both uniform and intense.

The trace fossil suite of Facies 2 is more diverse than that of the silty shales underlying it (Figs. 7C, D), and is dominated by *Helminthopsis*, *Chondrites*, *Planolites*, *Terebellina*, *Teichichnus*, and *Asterosoma* (Fig. 9B). Secondary elements are *Zoophycos*, *Palaeophycus*, *Thalassinoides*, *Skolithos*, and *Diplocraterion*. Accessory elements are represented by *Rosselia*, *Arenicolites*, *Cylindrichnus*, *Rhizocorallium*, *Ophiomorpha*, *Siphonichnus*, *Lockeia*, and fugichnia (escape traces).

Grading upward from the sandy shale facies is the shaly sandstone facies (Facies 3; Figs. 7E, F). The sand grain size ranges from lower very fine to upper fine, though is typically lower fine. Mud is generally dispersed throughout the facies and is present as partings and discontinuous stringers. Discrete sandstone beds are rare but show wavy parallel lamination where present. The general absence of discrete sandstone beds reflects the high degree of bioturbation and the penetrative action of infauna more robust than in the previously described facies (cf. Wheatcroft, 1990).

The dominant trace fossil elements of Facies 3 are *Planolites*, *Terebellina*, *Chondrites*, *Helminthopsis*, *Asterosoma*, *Palaeophycus*, *Skolithos*, *Teichichnus*, *Rosselia*, and *Diplocraterion*, though individual ichnogenera are less abundant and occur with less consistency than in the underlying facies (Fig. 9C). Secondary elements include *Ophiomorpha*, *Arenicolites*, *Zoophycos*, and *Cylindrichnus*, while *Thalassinoides*, *Rhizocorallium*, *Schaubcylindrichnus*, *Lockeia*, *Siphonichnus*, and fugichnia constitute the accessory elements.

The cycles reflect both coarsening upward of facies and an increase in diversity of ichnogenera under fully marine conditions. Each complete cycle is interpreted as lower offshore to lower shoreface progradation (Fig. 10). The silty shale facies (Facies 1) reflects a dominance of grazing and deposit-feeding structures of the distal *Cruziana* ichnofacies and is interpreted as lower offshore deposition. Rare, thin sand beds correspond to the distal deposits of exceptionally strong storms. The sandy shale facies (Facies 2) shows a more diverse suite of trace fossils and a dominance

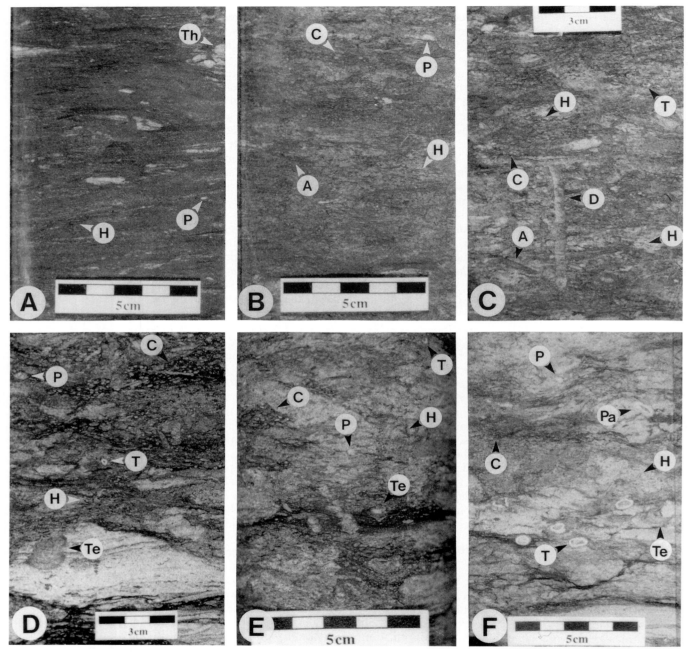

FIG. 7.—Depositional facies comprising parasequences of the regional Viking Formation. (A) Silty shale with a moderate degree of burrowing, and containing thin, biogenically mottled sandstone stringers. *Planolites* (P), *Helminthopsis* (H), *Thalassinoides* (Th), and *Chondrites* (C) are present. The facies is interpreted to reflect lower offshore deposition. Sundance Field, 12-12-54-20W5, depth 2633.7 m. (B) Thoroughly burrowed, silty shale, with a high proportion of interstitial silt and sand, interpreted to as lower offshore deposits. *Helminthopsis* (H), *Planolites* (P), *Chondrites* (C), and small *Asterosoma* (A) are present. Sundance Field, 12-12-54-20W5, depth 2630.4 m. (C) Thoroughly burrowed sandy shale, interpreted to reflect upper offshore deposition. *Helminthopsis* (H), *Chondrites* (C), *Terebellina* (T), *Planolites* (P), *Asterosoma* (A), and *Diplocraterion* (D) are present. Sundance Field, 10-34-54-20W5, depth 2578.6 m. (D) Thoroughly burrowed, sandy shale facies with a remnant, distal storm bed near the base. Trace fossils include *Chondrites* (C), *Planolites* (P), *Terebellina* (T), *Helminthopsis* (H), and *Teichichnus* (Te). The facies is interpreted to reflect upper offshore deposition. Sundance Field, 07-36-54-20W5, depth 2484.4 m. (E) Intensely burrowed, shaly sandstone facies interpreted as a distal lower shoreface deposit. *Helminthopsis* (H), *Chondrites* (C), *Planolites* (P), and *Teichichnus* (Te) are visible. Edson Field, 10-04-53-18W5, depth 2410.6 m. (F) Thoroughly burrowed, shaly sandstone facies with *Terebellina* (T), *Teichichnus* (Te), *Palaeophycus* (Pa), *Planolites* (P), small *Chondrites* (C), and *Helminthopsis* (H). The facies is interpreted to reflect distal lower shoreface deposition. Crystal Field, 13-05-46-3W5, depth 1754.0 m.

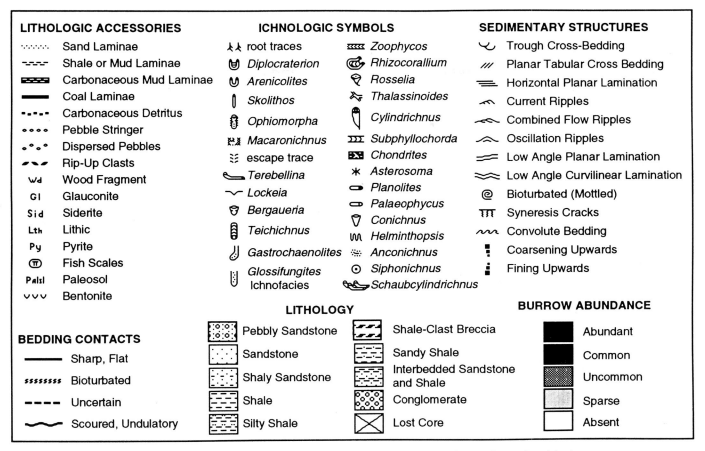

FIG. 8.—Legend of symbols employed in lithologs and trace fossil distribution graphs employed in the paper.

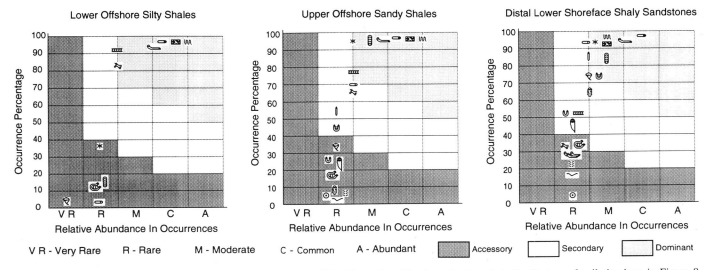

FIG. 9.—Trace fossil distributions in facies of the regional Viking Formation. The legend of symbols for the trace fossils is given in Figure 8. The vertical axis records the percentage of intervals encountered containing a particular trace fossil. The horizontal axis records the relative abundance of the trace fossil when it **does** occur in the interval. The graphs are based on observations in core and are not rigorously statistical. Dominant, secondary and accessory fields are subjectively determined.

ICHNOLOGICAL-SEDIMENTOLOGICAL SHOREFACE MODEL

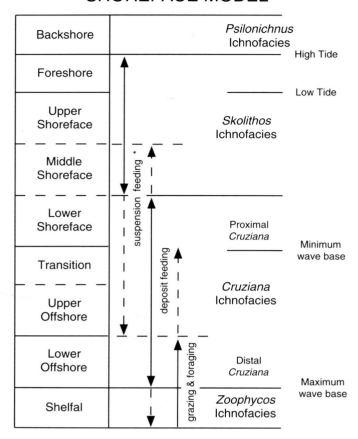

* Many tube dwellers are passive carnivores rather than suspension feeders.

FIG. 10.—Conceptual model for shoreface successions based on observations of Cretaceous strata of the Western Interior Seaway of North America. Modified after Pemberton and others (1992a).

Sedimentation is interpreted to have been relatively slow and generally continuous. These suites stand in marked contrast to suites recognized from facies of the incised estuarine valleys.

ICHNOLOGICAL SUCCESSIONS IN VALLEY-FILL SYSTEMS

Within the five, Viking Formation valley-fill systems (Fig. 1), four main depositional complexes were recognized from the facies, defined on the basis of sedimentology and associated softground, trace fossil suites. Three of these complexes correspond to the major depositional zones within a wave-dominated estuary system, namely: the Bay Head Delta, the Central Basin, and the Estuary Mouth (Fig. 2). The fourth depositional complex reflects Channel-fill deposition, commonly demonstrating a marine influence.

Bay Head Delta (BHD) Complex

BHD-1 Facies Association.—

The Bay Head Delta (BHD) complex appears to be characterized by a single facies association (BHD-1 facies association), which consists of an interbedding of four facies. The complex is well represented in the Sundance/Edson and Crystal valley deposits. Neither core from Cyn-Pem system nor any from the Willesden Green valley penetrated this complex. Deposits in this zone are overwhelmingly sandy, with mud beds rare and less than 1 cm thick. Mud also occurs as thin, biogenically disturbed or mottled interlaminae within the sandstone beds. The BHD-1 facies association roughly corresponds to FA4 of Pattison (1991a).

The most common facies in the BHD-1 facies association comprises 10–25 cm thick, well sorted, wavy parallel laminated, lower to upper fine-grained sandstone beds (Figs. 11A–D). These are generally erosionally amalgamated into bedsets greater than 1 m thick, although they may locally grade upwards into combined-flow, ripple and oscillation ripple laminated sandstones. Muddy interlaminae are moderately abundant and typically occur towards the tops of some beds. Locally, thin (<1 cm) mud layers mantle the rippled tops of beds.

Trace fossils are rare overall, although they may reach moderate abundances near the tops of beds. Fugichnia occur in low numbers in virtually every interval encountered. Near the upper contacts of individual beds, *Ophiomorpha* (Fig. 11D), *Skolithos, Teichichnus, Palaeophycus, Arenicolites, Conichnus, Cylindrichnus, Diplocraterion,* or exceedingly rare *Macaronichnus simplicatus* may be present. Individual beds rarely possess more than a few ichnogenera.

This first facies is interpreted to reflect episodic, storm-bed deposition, presumably near the bay head delta front. The thinness of the beds and preservation of waning-stage storm deposits near the tops of many beds illustrates the comparatively low-energy nature of tempestite emplacement in this zone, particularly when compared with those generated along open coast shorefaces (cf. MacEachern and Pemberton, 1992; Pemberton and others, 1992b). The tempestites observed in this facies reflect deposition by storm waves which were generated on and propagated across the central basin of the estuary itself. The trace fossil suite present

of deposit feeding over grazing behavior. The introduction of suspension feeding and passive carnivore structures is also distinctive. This facies is interpreted as upper offshore deposition at and above storm-weather wave base. Thin sandstones record preservation of storm beds whose thicknesses exceeded the infauna's ability to completely obliterate it. The shaly sandstone facies (Facies 3) shows an increase in diversity of behavior but less of a dominance by individual ichnogenera. Deposit-feeding structures dominate, with diminishing influence of grazing behavior and enhanced influence of suspension feeding, reflecting a proximal *Cruziana* suite. This facies is interpreted to represent distal lower shoreface deposits. The trace fossil suites show abundant burrowing, characterized by a high diversity of forms, a lack of dominance by a few forms, presence of significant numbers of specialized feeding/grazing structures, and uniform distribution of individual elements supportive of an equilibrium (K-selected), unstressed community (cf. Pianka, 1970) within fully marine environments.

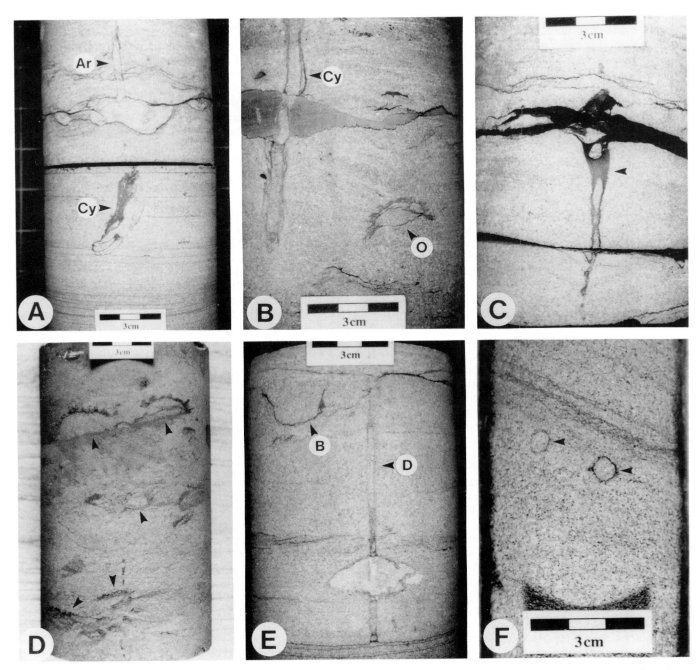

Fig. 11.—Depositional facies of the Bay Head Delta complex. (A) Wavy, parallel-laminated fine sandstone passing into burrowed sandstone, reflecting storm bed deposition on the delta front. *Cylindrichnus* (Cy) and *Arenicolites* (Ar) correspond to opportunistic colonization of the storm bed. The mottled top of the bed reflects the replacement of this suite by the resident fairweather community. Crystal Field, 16-24-45-04W5, depth 1807.1 m. (B) Wavy, parallel-laminated fine sandstone corresponding to storm-bed deposition on the delta front. Siderite-cemented mudstone interbed is present, penetrated by *Cylindrichnus* (Cy). *Ophiomorpha* (O) is also present. Crystal Field, 11-12-46-04W5, depth 1704.9 m. (C) Tempestite bed with wavy, parallel laminae near base, passing into combined-flow ripple lamination. *Rosselia* (arrow) occurs near top. Crystal Field, 16-24-45-04W5, depth 1791.4 m. (D) Burrowed top of delta-front storm bed, with robust *Ophiomorpha* (arrows). Edson Field, 03-22-52-19W5, depth 2613.4 m. (E) Stacked, low-angle to horizontal parallel laminated sandstone passing into current ripple lamination. Facies is interpreted as delta-slope sediment gravity flow deposits. Note the mud-lined *Diplocraterion* shaft (D) and the *Bergaueria* (B) near the top. Crystal Field, 16-24-45-04W5, depth 1801.3 m. (F) Moderately-sorted, medium-grained, trough cross-stratified sandstone facies, interpreted as distal portions of distributary channels. *Palaeophycus* (arrows) demonstrates a marine influence on sandstone accumulation. Sundance Field, 06-27-52-21W5, depth 2871.9 m.

in this facies reflects the episodic nature of deposition. Fug-ichnia record the escape of buried or sediment-entrained organisms, while initial opportunistic colonization of the top of the storm beds is manifest by a low diversity suite (at any one locality) of vertical dwelling and suspension-feeding structures (e.g., *Skolithos, Arenicolites, Diplocraterion, Ophiomorpha,* or *Conichnus*). This assemblage is ultimately replaced by the resident fairweather community of the setting, consisting mainly of deposit-feeding structures (e.g., *Teichichnus, Palaeophycus, Macaronichnus, Cylindrichnus,* and *Planolites*). The degree of preservation of the trace fossil suite may reflect the duration of fairweather conditions, the intensity of the succeeding storm event (i.e., the degree of erosional amalgamation), or a combination of the two. More thoroughly burrowed, muddy sandstone beds probably correspond to longer periods of fairweather conditions or to deposition of thin (<15 cm) storm beds. Thin beds favor more thorough biogenic homogenization because many organism's structures exceed this thickness (Wheatcroft, 1990). This first facies comprises the most intensely burrowed zone of the BHD-1 facies association.

The second facies is commonly interstratified with these tempestites and manifest by 5–20 cm thick, upper very fine- to upper fine-grained, horizontal planar-laminated sandstones, passing upward into current rippled, climbing (aggradational) rippled and rarer, combined-flow rippled sandstones (Fig. 11E). Sorting is good, although organic detritus is locally abundant. Clay interlaminae are rare. These beds have been termed "PR" beds by Pattison (1991a). Trace fossils are quite rare; fugichnia are the most common, although a few isolated intervals possess rare *Ophiomorpha, Diplocraterion, Cylindrichnus, Skolithos,* or *Bergaueria. Planolites* may also be present, associated with mud interlaminae.

This facies is also interpreted to reflect episodic deposition, but in this case, related to rapid emplacement of sand under high current speeds and/or very shallow water (upper flow regime) conditions. The rippled tops record waning stage of flow, locally with associated rapid deposition (i.e., aggradational ripples). Possible depositional scenarios include seasonal, flood-stage deposition from the river/distributary channel, overbank sheet flow, or delta front-style sediment-gravity flow deposition. The latter mechanism is favored for these deposits, given the close association with the delta-front tempestites. The largely unburrowed nature of this facies, coupled with the local presence of syneresis cracks in thin mud layers capping some beds, supports a possible fluvial influence on the event deposition. Failure of organisms to colonize the tops of such beds may reflect generally higher sedimentation rates associated with the bay head delta and/or periodic "freshening" of the central basin during periods of enhanced fluvial discharge through the BHD during seasonal floods.

The third facies of the BHD-1 facies association is less common and comprises sharp-based, 10–25 cm thick bed sets of upper fine- to lower medium-grained, trough cross-stratified sandstone, amalgamated into intervals 0.5–2.5 m thick (Fig. 11F). Mudstone rip-up clasts, locally siderite-cemented, organic detritus and rare coalified wood fragments are generally common; lithic pebbles, including chert, may also be present. These beds are generally unburrowed, although locally, *Ophiomorpha, Palaeophycus,* and *Planolites* occur in low numbers, typically associated with muddy interlaminae or thin interbeds.

The thinness of bed sets and the presence of high-angle, foreset cross-stratification with thin toesets indicates that the bedforms responsible for this facies were small subaqueous dunes. These beds of trough cross-stratification may correspond to distal portions of distributary channels near the delta front. Some beds, particularly the unburrowed ones, may have been deposited under mainly fluvial conditions, although the local presence of burrowing demonstrates that some intervals were clearly marine-influenced. No obvious tidal structures (e.g., tidal bundles) were recognized.

The final facies in the BHD-1 facies association is the least common and consists of massive (apparently structureless) to convolute bedded fL-fU sandstones with rip-up clasts and locally abundant carbonaceous detritus. Sorting is generally good. Upper and lower contacts are poorly preserved. The facies occurs in beds up to 2 m in thickness. No trace fossils were noted.

This facies is interpreted to reflect rapid sediment deposition during river floods, with associated dewatering and corresponding failure commonly achieving liquefaction. Alternatively, these sands may also reflect storm wave-induced liquefaction of sand at the delta front.

The preserved record of the BHD complex (Fig. 12) consists mainly of delta front sandstones, delta slope sandstones, distal portions of distributary channels, and possibly interdistributary bay deposits. Interdistributary bay deposits are indistinguishable from the sandy facies association of the Central Basin complex, discussed below. Distributary mouth bar deposits probably have a high preservation potential but have not yet been documented. The lack of delta plain, levee, or other shallow subtidal, intertidal, and supratidal deposits within the Viking examples at Sundance/Edson and Crystal is the result of transgressive erosion (ravinement) across the system or locally, due to multiple-stage channel re-incision in the valley.

The ichnological record of the BHD shows overall low degrees of burrowing, which is typically localized and sporadic. The trace fossil suite appears to lack any clearly dominant elements (Fig. 13). Only *Planolites* occurs in all studied intervals and is present in rare to moderate numbers. *Palaeophycus, Skolithos, Ophiomorpha,* and fugichnia constitute the secondary elements, along with *Teichichnus, Arenicolites, Cylindrichnus,* and *Rosselia. Diplocraterion, Terebellina, Lockeia, Conichnus, Bergaueria, Macaronichnus, Asterosoma, Thalassinoides,* and *Siphonichnus* comprise the accessory elements of the suite.

It is interesting that, overall, the trace fossil diversity is high (16 ichnogenera were noted), although any one interval may possess as few as 3 or 4 ichnogenera. The stresses imposed on the organisms and their resulting behavior appear to be due largely to the episodic nature of deposition and associated variable sedimentation rates rather than to strongly reduced salinity, although brackish-water conditions may have been important as well.

The most common biogenic structures in the facies association record escape by buried or entrained organisms

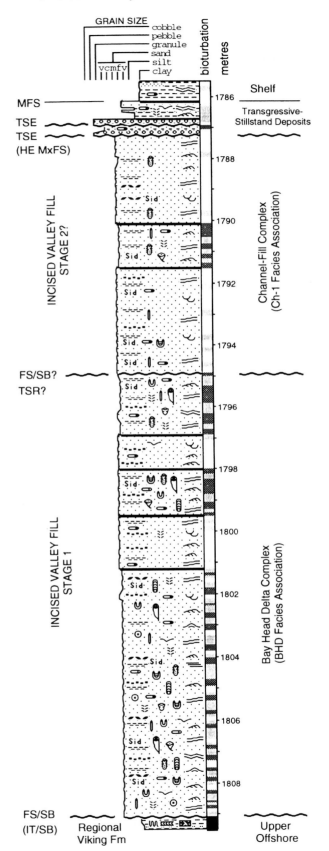

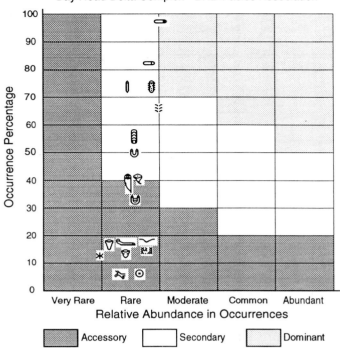

FIG. 13.—Trace fossil distribution in facies of the Bay Head Delta complex. The legend of symbols for trace fossils are given in Figure 8.

within an event bed, followed by opportunistic colonization of the sandy substrate after the disturbance, reflected by *Skolithos*, *Ophiomorpha*, and *Arenicolites*. Replacement of this initial community by the resident fairweather community is manifested by the overprinting of the opportunistic suite by deposit-feeding structures such as *Planolites*, *Palaeophycus*, *Teichichnus*, *Cylindri chnus*, and *Rosselia*. The remaining ichnogenera record relatively uncommon organism behaviors or overall poor preservation of complete fairweather suites due to the erosional amalgamation of the event beds. Given preservation of shallower water and delta plain deposits of the BHD complex, biogenic structures may reflect a greater indication of brackish-water conditions, as observed in estuarine deposits of the McMurray Formation and the Grand Rapids Formation (e.g., Wightman and others, 1987; Beynon and others, 1988; Beynon and Pemberton, 1992; Ranger and Pemberton, 1992).

FIG. 12.—Litholog of a sandy valley-fill interval, erosionally truncating regionally extensive Viking Formation parasequences (FS/SB). The lower portion of the valley fill consists of storm beds, "PR" beds, and rare, thin, trough cross-stratified beds of the Bay Head Delta complex. This complex is erosionally truncated by a possible second stage of valley incision and transgressive fill (FS/SB?), manifest by marine-influenced sandstones of the Ch-1 facies association of the Channel-fill complex. The entire valley system is truncated by ravinement (TSE) during renewed transgression. The interval occurs in the 16-24-45-04W5 well within the Crystal valley system. Legend of the symbols used in the litholog is given in Figure 8.

Central Basin (CB) Complex

The deposits of the Central Basin (CB) complex (Fig. 14) are well represented in the Sundance/Edson and Crystal valley fills and, to a lesser extent, in the Willesden Green valley. Neither cored interval in the Cyn-Pem valley system contains facies of this setting. The facies of the CB form facies associations which correspond to FA2 of Pattison (1991a) and FA3 of Boreen (1989).

The CB complex grades laterally out of the BHD complex in the landward portion of the basin and from the Estuary Mouth (EM) complex in a seaward direction (Fig. 2). Hence, the CB ranges from sand-dominated at either extremity to mud-dominated in the center. Muddy CB deposits (>40% shale) form the CB-1 facies association and are discussed separately from sandy CB intervals (<40% shale; CB-2 facies association).

CB-1 Facies Association.—

The CB-1 facies association consists of the regular interbedding of two basic facies. The most distinctive facies consists of moderately to intensely burrowed, finely interstratified to thickly interbedded sandy mudstones, weakly burrowed, sand- and silt-poor dark mudstones, and thin (millimeter to centimeter scale) sandstone stringers. The overall sand content of the facies varies from 5–50%, although it is typically 20–30%. This facies constitutes greater than 60% of the CB-1 facies association.

The sandy mudstone beds range from 2 cm to 50 cm thick, though they are generally less than 25 cm thick and locally contain dispersed pebbles, organic detritus, coalified wood fragments, and syneresis cracks. Sand is dispersed into the muds principally through biogenic activity.

Dark, sand- and silt-poor mudstones are commonly intercalated as interlaminae or thin interbeds but are typically of subordinate significance in the Sundance/Edson successions. In contrast, this component of the facies is a far more significant element in Willesden Green intervals (Fig. 14B). These units are typically millimeters in thickness but may locally reach 10 cm in some intervals. Syneresis cracks are rare.

Discrete sandstone stringers within the facies range from 0.2–5.0 cm in thickness are vfU-fU, and are regularly interstratified with the sandy mudstone beds. The stringers are typically sharp based and possess combined-flow ripple, oscillation ripple, rare current ripple, and wavy parallel laminae. Where burrowing is moderate to abundant, the stringers are preserved as remnants. Load casts are present locally. Glauconite is present but not abundant.

The facies, as a whole, has the appearance of wavy (rare) to lenticular and pinstriped, interbedded sandstone and shale. Burrowing is variable on a small scale but is relatively uniform throughout the facies interval. Examples from Sundance/Edson and Crystal show a significantly greater degree of burrowing than in Willesden Green. Intervals in the Willesden Green valley system are also somewhat more sporadically burrowed.

The recorded ichnogenera are reasonably diverse but variably distributed (Figs. 14, 15). The facies contains large numbers of *Planolites*, *Teichichnus*, and *Terebellina*, with

less common *Palaeophycus*, *Siphonichnus*, *Lockeia*, *Chondrites*, *Helminthopsis*, *Thalassinoides*, and *Rosselia*, rare *Ophiomorpha*, *Diplocraterion*, and *Cylindrichnus*, with very rare *Rhizocorallium* and *Asterosoma*. The general absence of *Helminthopsis* and *Siphonichnus*, and the greatly diminished abundance of *Terebellina*, *Chondrites*, *Rosselia*, and *Palaeophycus* in the Willesden Green succession compared to Sundance/Edson and Crystal intervals is of some interest.

This facies is interpreted to reflect fairweather deposition of sands and muds within the lagoon or bay environment of the CB complex. Small-scale fluctuations in energy are reflected by the small-scale interbedding of fine-grained beds and sand stringers. Some combined-flow ripple and oscillation ripple laminae may correspond to weak storms tracking across the basin or shallow littoral conditions within the basin. The lenticular to pinstripe-bedded appearance and rare current ripples may also suggest a tidal influence, possibly restricted to monthly or seasonal extremes in tidal energy. Unequivocal tidal structures are lacking. The dark, sand- and silt-poor mudstone interlaminae and thin interbeds may result from river flood discharge through the BHD and rapid suspension fallout of fines into the basin. The largely unburrowed character of such interlaminae and interbeds and the presence of syneresis cracks may support an association of reduced salinity, enhanced environmental stress, and rapid mud deposition, all resulting from increased river discharge into the central basin. As such, there may be a depositional affinity between these units and the "PR" beds of the BHD complex.

Burrowing is uniform on a large scale, but in detail, the distribution of particular ichnogenera is not. Only *Teichichnus*, *Planolites*, and *Terebellina* occur throughout the facies. *Helminthopsis*, though present in many intervals, occurs in bands or zones, and ranges in abundance from rare to relatively common (Fig. 14D). Locally, *Helminthopsis* is absent through fairly thick intervals. *Chondrites* is never abundant, but is sporadically present in rare to moderate amounts. *Rosselia* is locally more common, but is not uniformly distributed through the facies and is present in only about half the studied intervals. This appears to indicate that conditions in the CB routinely varied from nearly fully marine to brackish. Variability in salinity of the basin is most likely related to variations in river discharge through the BHD, periods of high rainfall, tidal exchange through the tidal inlets, and storm-induced washovers at the estuary-mouth barrier bar, any or all of which may reflect seasonal variations.

The other main facies within the CB-1 facies association constitutes less than 40% of the succession and consists of 5–25 cm thick sandstone beds, only rarely erosionally amalgamated into bedsets thicker than 50 cm. The bulk of the sandstones are upper very fine- to upper fine-grained, though very rare lower medium-grained beds are present. Sorting is good to very good with rare interlaminae of mud towards the tops of some beds. Organic detritus is variable in abundance but low overall. Stratification dominantly consists of wavy parallel laminae, locally grading into combined-flow or oscillation ripple laminae. Less commonly, the beds consist exclusively of combined-flow, oscillation, and very rare current ripple lamination. Sandier intervals are dominated by wavy parallel-laminated sandstones and also include thin (<5 cm) "PR" beds. Thin conglomerate beds are very rarely present, ranging from 2–25 cm in thickness in some Crystal CB complexes. These beds have not been observed in Sundance/Edson examples. In contrast, thin conglomerate beds and sandstones containing abundant interstratified and dispersed chert pebbles or granules are typical of this facies in the south arm of the Willesden Green valley system.

The sandstone facies is less thoroughly burrowed than the sandy mudstone facies interstratified with it. Overall, burrow intensities are weak to moderate, with thicker beds generally lacking burrowing except towards their tops. Many of the thin sandstone beds possess only remnant primary structures. Fugichnia are relatively rare elements, though they are present in rare numbers in virtually all studied intervals. The sandstone beds are burrowed with *Palaeophycus*, *Skolithos*, *Arenicolites* (Fig. 14F), rare *Ophiomorpha* (Fig. 14G) and *Diplocraterion*, and very rare *Anconichnus*. *Ophiomorpha*, *Arenicolites*, and fugichnia are more common in Willesden Green intervals than elsewhere, probably owing to the generally sandier nature of these deposits. *Anconichnus* is absent from Willesden Green intervals. Cross-cutting these traces are variable numbers of *Teichichnus*, *Planolites*, *Terebellina*, *Lockeia*, *Thalassinoides*, *Cylindrichnus*, and very rare *Asterosoma*.

This facies is interpreted to reflect storm-bed deposition similar to that described from the BHD complex. The observed suite supports opportunistic colonization of the tempestite with subsequent replacement by the resident fair-weather suite (Pemberton and others, 1992b). The thin-bedded character of the sandstones and abundance of ripple laminae reflects diminished storm influence as a result of deeper-water conditions than those experienced on the delta front of the BHD.

The muddy CB-1 facies association is dominated by *Planolites*, *Teichichnus*, and *Terebellina* (Fig. 15). *Palaeophycus*, *Skolithos*, *Siphonichnus*, *Lockeia*, *Helminthopsis*, *Chondrites*, *Rosselia*, *Arenicolites*, *Thalassinoides*, and fugichnia comprise the secondary elements, while *Asterosoma*, *Ophiomorpha*, *Diplocraterion*, *Cylindrichnus*, *Rhizocorallium*, and *Anconichnus* constitute the accessory elements. Dominant ichnogenera in the fairweather sandy shales largely correspond to structures produced by trophic generalists (i.e., opportunistic organisms; cf. Pianka, 1970; Remane and Schlieper, 1971). These assemblages are characteristic of highly stressed settings, such as those subject to salinity fluctuations. Those dominating the tempestite sandstones reflect rapid colonization of the event bed by opportunistic organisms as well. These assemblages are characteristic of stresses imposed by episodic deposition and variable substrate consistency. The regular alternation between these facies produces an impoverished, mixed *Skolithos-Cruziana* ichnofacies which reflects all three stresses typical of brackish bays and lagoons (cf. Wightman and others, 1987; Beynon and others, 1988; Beynon and Pemberton, 1992; Ranger and Pemberton, 1992).

Many of the secondary and accessory elements of the trace fossil assemblages are not opportunistic but rather record more specialized and elaborate feeding behaviors, which

are less common in stressful environmental settings. Their sporadic distribution and variable abundances in the facies association are interpreted to reflect salinity fluctuations within the CB, which probably ranged repeatedly from brackish to nearly fully marine. Tracemakers of *Helminthopsis*, *Chondrites*, *Asterosoma*, *Conichnus*, *Rhizocorallium*, and *Macaronichnus* probably only occurred in facies of the CB complex when conditions had approached fully marine, and the available substrate was appropriate for that behavior. *Lockeia*, *Rosselia*, *Diplocraterion*, *Cylindrichnus* and *Siphonichnus* appear to possess greater tolerance for the observed stresses in the environment and, consequently, are more commonly present.

Some structures, notably *Asterosoma*, *Rosselia*, and *Cylindrichnus*, are much smaller than their fully marine counterparts. The reduction in size is an evolutionary response by some marine organisms to allow them to inhabit brackish water environments. Reduced salinity affects the size of benthic organisms in a number of ways, such as decreased metabolism, retarded growth and development, and early onset of sexual maturity (Remane and Schlieper, 1971). As well, the rigors of inhabiting brackish settings imposes an increased oxygen requirement on the benthic organisms, and a decreased surface area reduces the total oxygen requirements of the fauna (Remane and Schlieper, 1971). Additionally, organisms inhabiting stressful environments are characterized by a high mortality rate; consequently, more of the biogenic structures observed in core may correspond to juvenile rather than adult tracemakers.

CB-2 Facies Association.—

The CB-2 facies association consists of the same facies as the muddier CB-1 facies association but in different proportions. The fairweather, sandy mudstone deposits constitute less than 40% of the succession with the tempestite sandstones comprising the remainder. The CB-2 facies association is laterally and vertically intergradational with the CB-1 facies association (Fig. 16). As the CB complex grades longitudinally into both the BHD and EM complex as well as laterally towards the valley margins, sand-bed content increases, partly as a function of increased proximity to sediment sources, but also due to decreasing water depths. Amalgamated storm beds may reach thicknesses of 1 m. Thicker storm beds and a progressive decrease in both preserved waning flow deposits and fairweather intervals (i.e., increased erosional amalgamation) argues for increasing proximity to either the BHD or the EM complex. Attempts to differentiate sandy CB successions adjacent to the BHD from those adjacent to the EM complex were unsuccessful. The sedimentology and ichnology appear identical, based on the database available. This similarity may reflect thorough mixing of fresh and marine waters across the basin, widespread influence of river floods and/or enhanced rainfall (either of which can "freshen" the basin), and minimal preservation of fairweather deposits in which evidence of salinity variations are typically recorded.

The trace fossil suite of the CB-2 facies association varies significantly from the CB-1 facies association, as the proportions of "fairweather" sandy mudstones and tempestite sandstones changes. The trace fossil suite of the CB-2

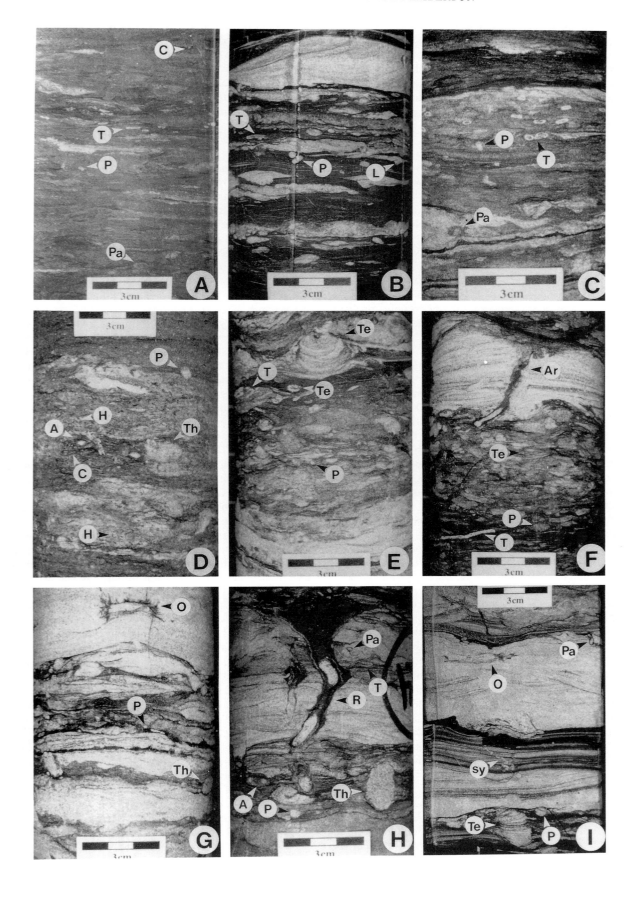

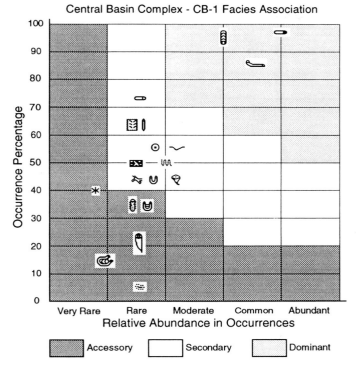

Central Basin Complex - CB-1 Facies Association

FIG. 15.—Trace fossil distribution in facies of the shaly CB-1 facies association of the Central Basin complex. The legend of symbols for trace fossils is given in Figure 8.

facies association is more or less what one might expect from higher energy and increased numbers of episodic depositional events (Fig. 17). The dominant elements consist of fugichnia, *Arenicolites, Palaeophycus, Skolithos,* and *Ophiomorpha,* in addition to *Planolites, Teichichnus,* and thin-walled *Terebellina.* The secondary elements in the CB-2 facies association comprise moderate numbers of *Lockeia, Rosselia, Diplocraterion, Cylindrichnus, Thalassinoides,* and *Siphonichnus.* Accessory elements include *Helmin-*

thopsis, Chondrites, Asterosoma, Conichnus, Anconichnus, Rhizocorallium, and *Bergaueria.*

The increased number of vertical shafts and dwelling structures reflects the increased occurrences of sandy substrates available for opportunistic colonization. All dominant elements remain trophic generalists, employing an r-selected strategy of population dynamics (Pianka, 1970; Remane and Schlieper, 1971). Remnant fairweather deposits contain suites similar to those of the CB-1 facies association and indicate that salinity fluctuations also imparted significant environmental stresses on the tracemaking organisms.

Estuary Mouth (EM) Complex

The Estuary Mouth (EM) complex constitutes the physiographic barrier between the open-marine conditions of the coast from the comparatively more restricted and lower-energy conditions of the estuary *sensu stricto.* Preserved sediments from the estuarine side (Figs. 18A-D) are considerably different from those deposited on the seaward side (Figs. 18E, F) and are, therefore, subdivided into two discrete facies associations. Sediments preserved on the estuarine side of the EM complex (EM-1 facies association) are well represented in cores of the Willesden Green valley system and are comparatively poorly reflected at Crystal and Sundance/Edson. Cores in the Cyn-Pem valley system do not penetrate estuary-mouth deposits. This facies association corresponds to FA3 of Pattison (1991a). Sediments deposited on the seaward side of the estuary mouth constitute the EM-2 facies association and are exclusively represented by cores from the Sundance/Edson and Crystal valley systems.

EM-1 Facies Association.—

The sediments of the EM-1 facies association pass gradationally from the sandy CB-2 facies association of the CB complex and comprise 4 discrete facies. The main facies consists of vfU-fU, wavy to gently undulatory, parallel-laminated sandstones in beds 15–25 cm thick (Figs. 18A,

FIG. 14.—Depositional facies of the Central Basin complex. (A-F) CB-1 facies association: (A) Weakly burrowed, sand-poor shale, reflecting highly stressed conditions and, possibly, the deepest portion of the Central Basin complex. Traces are restricted to small *Terebellina* (T), *Planolites* (P), *Palaeophycus* (Pa), and small *Chondrites* (C). Sundance Field, 15-07-55-20W5, depth 2667.5 m. (B) Weakly burrowed, interbedded combined-flow rippled fine sandstones and shales. Facies reflects minor storm activity and dominant fairweather lagoonal deposition under fairly restricted conditions. Trace fossils consist of *Planolites* (P), *Lockeia* (L), and *Terebellina* (T). Willesden Green Field, 11-15-42-07W5, depth 2263.1 m. (C) Shale-dominated interlaminated sandstone and shale of the Central Basin complex. Burrowing is of moderate intensity with thin-walled *Terebellina* (T), *Planolites* (P), and *Palaeophycus* (Pa) present. Crystal Field, 11-12-46-04W5, depth 1707.7 m. (D) Thoroughly burrowed sand and shale, reflecting nearly fully marine, unstressed conditions in the lagoon. Note the abundant *Helminthopsis* (H), as well as *Chondrites* (C), *Thalassinoides* (Th), *Asterosoma* (A), and *Planolites* (P). Sundance Field, 01-30-54-19W5, depth 2429.7 m. (E) Highly burrowed sandy shales of the Central Basin complex. Remnant storm beds are present, but are largely destroyed by infaunal burrowing. *Teichichnus* (Te), *Terebellina* (T), and *Planolites* (P) dominate. Crystal Field, 08-31-46-03W5, depth 1673.1 m. (F) Thin, storm-generated, wavy parallel-laminated sandstone interbedded with burrowed, fairweather sandy shales. Mud-lined *Arenicolites* (Ar) shafts penetrate the tempestite, while the sandy shales contain abundant *Teichichnus* (Te), *Planolites* (P), and flattened *Terebellina* (T). Crystal Field, 08-31-46-03W5, depth 1666.9 m. (G-I) CB-2 facies association: (G) Sand-dominated, interbedded storm-generated sandstones with subordinate fairweather sandy shales, lying marginal to the Bay Head Delta complex. *Ophiomorpha irregulaire* (O), *Planolites* (P), and *Thalassinoides* (Th) are visible. Crystal Field, 08-31-46-03W5, depth 1674.4 m. (H) Sand-dominated, interbedded sandstones and sandy shales lying proximal to the Estuary Mouth complex. Note the combined-flow, ripple-laminated sandstone penetrated by *Rosselia* (R). *Planolites* (P), *Thalassinoides* (Th), *Asterosoma* (A), *Palaeophycus* (Pa), and *Terebellina* (T) are also present. Willesden Green Field, 06-36-40-07W5, depth 2322.7 m. (I) Sand-dominated, interbedded sandstones and shales deposited adjacent to the Estuary Mouth complex. Combined-flow, ripple lamination and wavy, parallel lamination dominate the sandstones. *Teichichnus* (Te), *Planolites* (P), small *Ophiomorpha* (O), and *Palaeophycus* (Pa) are present. Note the syneresis crack (sy). Willesden Green Field, 04-04-42-07W5, depth 2287.6 m.

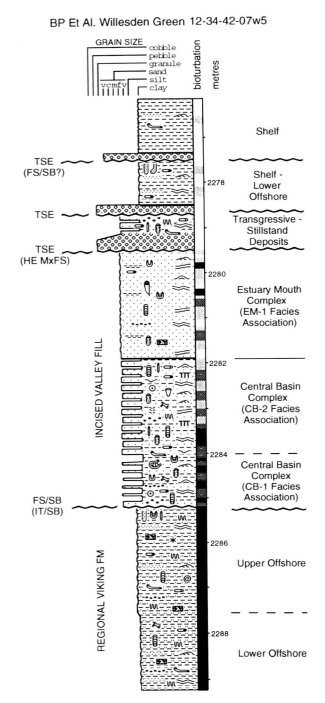

FIG. 16.—Litholog of incised-valley fill consisting of facies of the shaly Central Basin complex (CB-1 facies association) with dispersed pebbles, grading upward into facies of the sandy CB-2 facies association and, finally, into sandstones of the Estuary Mouth complex. The valley fill truncates an underlying, thoroughly burrowed, regionally extensive Viking Formation parasequence. Note the presence of a *Glossifungites* assemblage demarcating the co-planar surface of lowstand erosion and transgressive erosion (FS/SB) at the base of the valley. The valley fill is erosionally truncated by a ravinement surface (TSE) which possibly corresponds to a high energy maximum flooding surface (HE MxFS), and passes into a series of transgressive-stillstand cycles. The interval occurs in the NW arm of the Willesden Green valley, in well 12-34-42-07W5. Legend of the symbols used in the litholog is given in Figure 8.

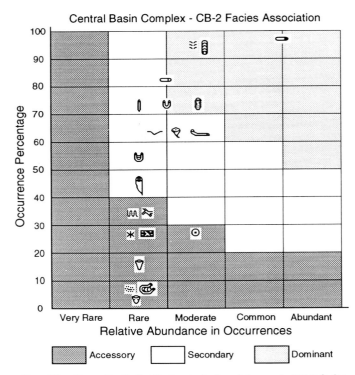

FIG. 17.—Trace fossil distribution in facies of the sandy CB-2 facies association of the Central Basin complex. The legend of symbols for trace fossils is given in Figure 8.

C). These beds are commonly erosionally amalgamated into bedsets up to 1.5 m thick but locally have preserved combined-flow ripple and oscillation ripple laminated tops. In so far as primary sedimentological features are concerned, the depositional mechanism is identical to that of the sandstone facies of the CB-2 facies association; that is, one of episodic tempestite deposition in relatively shallow-water conditions. Burrow intensity is generally uniform and of moderate to high intensity, in marked contrast to equivalent lithofacies in the BHD complex. The observed trace fossils correspond almost exactly to those present in the CB-2 facies association, except that *Helminthopsis*, *Chondrites*, and *Anconichnus* occur in far fewer studied intervals (Fig. 19). This variation probably reflects the overwhelming influence of data from the Willesden Green valley system in which these particular ichnogenera are rare or absent. As in the CB-2 facies association, the suite records opportunistic colonization of the tempestite followed by their subsequent replacement by fairweather communities. In contrast to the CB complex, however, the *Ophiomorpha* trace-maker appears to be the dominant opportunistic colonizer of the storm beds in the EM-1 facies association with *Diplocraterion* almost as common as *Arenicolites* and *Skolithos*, possibly recording less of a salinity-induced stress on organism type and behavior. The rarity of syneresis cracks in this and associated facies may support this observation. In addition, the fairweather communities are less well represented than those in the CB complex, probably due to increased erosive amalgamation of individual beds. *Teichichnus*, *Terebel-*

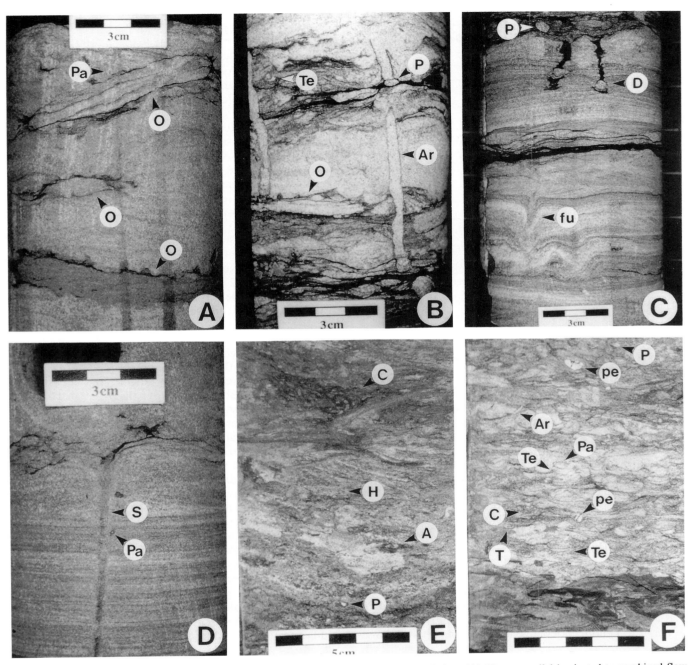

FIG. 18.—Depositional facies of the Estuary Mouth complex. (A-D) EM-1 facies association: (A) Wavy, parallel-laminated to combined-flow, ripple laminated, storm-generated sandstone bed. Note the robust *Ophiomorpha irregulaire* (O), and *Palaeophycus* (Pa). Willesden Green Field, 11-01-41-07W5, depth 2299.3 m. (B) Combined-flow, ripple laminated sandstone with mud interlaminae, reflecting fairweather deposition. Note the *Ophiomorpha* (O), *Arenicolites* (Ar), *Planolites* (P), and *Teichichnus* (Te). Crystal Field, 08-16-48-03W5, depth 1529.1 m. (C) Wavy, parallel-laminated and combined-flow, rippled fine-grained sandstones with *Diplocraterion* (D), fugichnia (fu), and *Planolites* (P). Willesden Green Field, 14-28-42-07W5, depth 2261.3 m. (D) Horizontal to low-angle planar lamination passing into current, ripple laminated fine-grained sandstone, reflecting washover deposition. *Skolithos* (S), and *Palaeophycus* (Pa) penetrate the bed. Willesden Green Field, 11-01-41-07W5, depth 2300.9 m. (E and F) EM-2 facies association: (E) Thoroughly burrowed sandy shale reflecting upper offshore deposition on the barrier bar. *Chondrites* (C), *Helminthopsis* (H), *Planolites* (P), and *Terebellina* are present. Sundance Field, 01-06-55-20W5, depth 2676.5 m. (F) Thoroughly burrowed shaly sandstone reflecting lower shoreface deposition on the barrier bar. *Planolites* (P), *Palaeophycus* (Pa), *Chondrites* (C), *Terebellina* (T), *Teichichnus* (Te), *Arenicolites* (Ar), and dispersed pebbles (pe) are present. Sundance Field, 01-06-55-20W5, depth 2675 m.

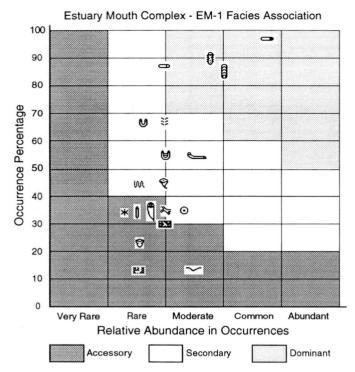

FIG. 19.—Trace fossil distribution in facies of the EM-1 facies association of the Estuary Mouth complex. The legend of symbols for trace fossils is given in Figure 8.

lina, *Planolites*, and *Palaeophycus* remain the most numerous fairweather traces penetrating into the storm beds but are less abundant than their counterparts in the CB complex.

Regularly interstratified with the tempestites are stacked oscillation, combined-flow, and current ripple laminated, lower to upper fine-grained, sandstone beds that are 5–25 cm thick (Fig. 18B). Organic detritus and wood fragments are exceedingly rare. Lithic pebbles, including chert, are locally present but are most common in the south arm of the Willesden Green valley system. Mud interlaminae and thin beds (<5 cm) are abundantly interstratified locally.

Burrow intensity in many of these units is high and physical structures are generally biogenically disturbed or virtually obliterated. Where muddy interlaminae are abundant, high degrees of burrowing imparts a "muddy sandstone" appearance. Dominant ichnogenera are *Ophiomorpha*, *Skolithos*, *Teichichnus*, *Palaeophycus*, *Planolites*, and *Terebellina*, locally with *Rosselia*, fugichnia, *Diplocraterion*, *Arenicolites*, *Lockeia*, and rare *Asterosoma*, *Thalassinoides*, *Siphonichnus*, *Bergaueria*, *Chondrites*, and *Helminthopsis*. The latter ichnogenus is confined to Sundance/Edson and Crystal deposits.

This rippled facies is interpreted to reflect general, fairweather depositional conditions in the shallow-water environments of the EM complex. This facies may also correspond to distal portions of washover lobes or flood-tidal delta deposits, although sediment bodies associated with this latter subenvironment have yet to be documented in Viking Formation EM complexes.

The third facies present within the EM-1 facies association consists of horizontally planar-laminated, lower to upper fine-grained sandstones, grading into current ripple lamination in beds less than 10 cm thick (Fig. 18D). This corresponds to the "PR" beds of Pattison (1991a), and like those observed in the BHD complex, they are generally unburrowed, except for rare fugichnia, *Skolithos*, *Palaeophycus*, *Teichichnus*, and *Planolites* near the tops of beds. As in the BHD complex, this facies is interpreted to reflect high current speed conditions and/or shallow-water transport with waning-flow deposits preserved at the top. Within the EM-1 facies association, the "PR" beds are interpreted to reflect distal washover deposits generated when storm waves breached the barrier system at the mouth and transported sand headward into the estuary.

The final facies encountered from the EM-1 facies association is the least common; it was observed in only one cored interval. The 05-34-42-07W5 well in the north arm of the Willesden Green valley contains a 4 m thick, moderately to poorly sorted, lower fine- to lower medium-grained, low angle, planar stratified, sandstone body, sharply overlying a sandy CB-2 facies association. The sandstone body consists of multiple, erosionally amalgamated beds, most of which are 20–50 cm in thickness. Carbonaceous detritus is abundant and largely dispersed within the sand beds rather than as thin interlaminae. Siderite-cemented rip-up clasts are present although rare. The unit lacks any evidence of ripple lamination. Burrowing is absent.

The interval is interpreted to reflect rapid deposition of sand under relatively high-energy, traction transport, possibly subjected to some storm-wave modification following deposition. The erosive amalgamation of beds supports successive depositional events. The absence of burrowing is curious. It may reflect rapid deposition of the individual beds, as evidenced by the poorly sorted nature of the sand and the abundant dispersed organic detritus. Each successive event may have removed any burrowed zones at the tops of the beds, but more likely, the entire unit as a whole may have been deposited in a very short period of time. This enigmatic facies is tentatively interpreted as part of a major washover lobe deposited when storm waves on the seaward side of the EM complex breached the barrier.

The trace fossil suite for the EM-1 facies association (Fig. 19) is dominated by *Ophiomorpha*, *Teichichnus*, *Palaeophycus*, and *Planolites*. *Arenicolites*, *Diplocraterion*, *Terebellina*, *Helminthopsis*, *Rosselia*, *Siphonichnus*, and fugichnia constitute the secondary elements while *Asterosoma*, *Skolithos*, *Cylindrichnus*, *Thalassinoides*, *Chondrites*, *Bergaueria*, *Rhizocorallium*, *Macaronichnus*, and *Lockeia* comprise the accessory elements. This trace fossil assemblage shows a close genetic affinity with the CB-2 facies association consistent with deposition of the EM-1 facies association on the estuary side of the barrier complex.

As in the CB complex, the trace fossil suite shows a high diversity of forms (19 ichnogenera) over the entire EM-1 facies association, but the distribution of individual elements reflects the presence of various environmental stresses. The higher-energy nature of fairweather deposition is reflected by the general decrease in importance of grazing and deposit-feeding behaviors. Episodic deposition appears to be the main environmental stress indicated by the trace fossil suite in the form of opportunistic colonization of the tempestites by simple, vertical dwelling structures. As in the CB complex, the dominant, fairweather, deposit-feeding structures correspond to those of trophic generalists. The low abundances and sporadic distributions of grazing and specialized feeding/dwelling structures may suggest the presence of salinity fluctuations, although poor preservation of fairweather deposits and the sandier character of the substrates may easily account for this as well.

EM-2 Facies Association.—

The database for the EM-2 facies association is relatively small (7 intervals) and is derived exclusively from the Sundance/Edson and Crystal valley systems. The facies roughly corresponds to FA9 of Pattison (1991a) and comprises two intergradational facies.

The first facies consists of intensely burrowed sandy shale, typically 1.0–1.5 m in thickness (Fig. 18E). Sand size is variable, ranging from lower fine to lower coarse-grained, but generally upper fine- to upper medium-grained and is dispersed throughout the facies, presumably biogenically. The mud is silty, dark, and locally occurs in discontinuous wisps and stringers. Dispersed pebbles, organic detritus, and glauconite are typically present. Remnant, wavy parallel laminae are observed in rare sandstone stringers.

Trace fossils are reasonably diverse and consist of abundant *Planolites*, *Terebellina*, *Helminthopsis*, common *Chondrites* and *Teichichnus*, moderately abundant *Palaeophycus*, *Thalassinoides* and rare *Rosselia*, *Asterosoma*, *Ophiomorpha*, and *Diplocraterion*. This facies is interpreted to reflect upper offshore deposition, similar to the sandy shale facies in the regional Viking parasequences (cf. Fig. 9B).

This facies grades upwards into a thoroughly burrowed, lower to upper fine-grained, muddy sandstone facies, typically 1.0 m in thickness, containing rare, discrete mudstone interlaminae and stringers (Fig. 18F). Pebbles are present though not abundant and are dispersed throughout the facies. Burrowing intensity is typically very high, although rare, wavy parallel laminated beds are locally preserved. The trace fossil suite shows a diverse assemblage, consisting of abundant *Ophiomorpha*, *Planolites*, *Skolithos*, and common *Teichichnus*, *Terebellina*, *Diplocraterion*, *Arenicolites*, and *Palaeophycus*. *Helminthopsis*, *Chondrites*, *Siphonichnus*, *Rosselia*, *Asterosoma*, and *Cylindrichnus* comprise moderate to rare elements of the suite. This facies is interpreted to represent distal lower shoreface deposition, similar to the shaly sandstone facies of the regional Viking parasequences (cf. Fig. 9C).

The EM-2 facies association is sharp-based, resting on an erosion surface locally with a discontinuous granule or pebble lag rarely more than a few clasts thick (Fig. 20). The succession is interpreted to reflect the progradation of upper offshore to distal lower shoreface environments on the seaward side of the EM complex. The high degree of burrowing probably indicates slow accumulation or weakly storm-influenced conditions (MacEachern and Pemberton, 1992), corresponding to the deeper-water conditions on the seaward side of the barrier system as compared to that on

the estuarine side. Despite the small database, the intervals studied show both uniform and abundant burrowing as well as a diverse trace fossil assemblage (14 ichnogenera) throughout the intervals. Individual forms are fairly uniformly distributed with little evidence of dominance by a few ichnogenera in marked contrast to most suites in the estuary proper. The suite is also characterized by a uniform distribution of elaborate and specialized feeding structures. The trace fossil assemblage reflects fully marine, unstressed, K-selected (equilibrium) behavior (cf. Pianka, 1970). The EM-2 facies association is very similar to the regional Viking Formation cycles, though, overall, EM-2 shows a greater proximity to sediment source and lacks the regional distribution of the other.

The sharp base to the succession may locally correspond to an amalgamated FS/SB, reflecting transgressive modification either of the initial valley incision surface or of a subsequent period of re-incision. Alternatively, the surface may correspond to a TSE (ravinement surface) or a low-energy, marine flooding surface, depending on the succession's paleogeographic position and the depositional history of the valley system. The EM-2 facies association is interpreted as the erosional remnant of the barrier-bar system at the estuary mouth (Fig. 20). In the examples studied, the top of the succession is truncated by a TSE that is demarcated by the presence of gritty shales or pebble lags (cf. MacEachern and others, 1992a), reflecting erosive shoreface retreat which stripped off the upper portion of the estuary-mouth barrier complex and left the upper offshore to lower shoreface deposits as an erosional remnant. The evolutionary model of wave-dominated estuary systems proposed by Roy and others (1980) predicts the destruction of the barrier under conditions of extreme or prolonged wave attack.

Channel (Ch) Complex

The Channel (Ch) complex facies associations are well represented in all studied fields. The bulk of the intervals are sandstone-dominated, although pebbly sandstone, and interstratified sandstone and conglomerate intervals are also present particularly in the Willesden Green south field and in the Crystal field. The Crystal field also contains thick conglomerate intervals (FA8 of Pattison, 1991a), as well as thick, structureless sandstone bodies (FA7 of Pattison, 1991a). These latter facies associations are largely unburrowed and, therefore, are not dealt with in detail here.

The Ch complex corresponds to FA6 of Pattison (1991a) but can be subdivided into two discrete facies associations. Both facies associations are identical with respect to physical sedimentology but differ in that one is sporadically burrowed (Ch-1) and the other is entirely unburrowed (Ch-2).

Ch-1 Facies Association.—

The Ch-1 facies association consists of four facies. The dominant facies comprises lower medium- to upper coarse-grained, (typically lower to upper medium-grained), moderately to poorly sorted, trough cross-stratified sandstones (Figs. 21A–D). Beds are generally 10–25 cm in thickness but may reach 50 cm and are commonly erosionally amalgamated into bedsets up to 3.0 m in thickness. Current rip-

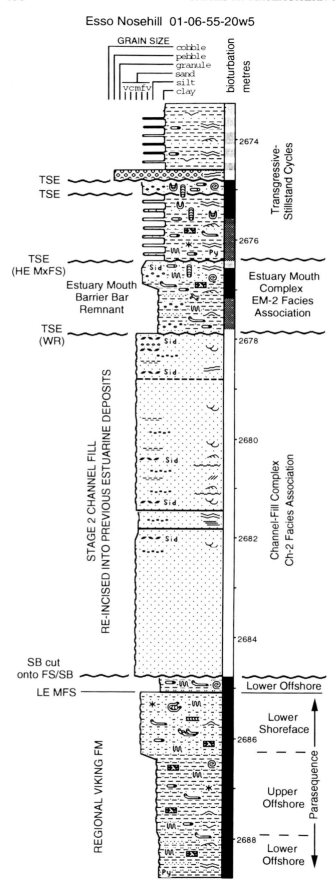

Esso Nosehill 01-06-55-20w5

ple lamination is generally uncommon. The sand is locally quite pebbly and may have intercalated conglomerate beds; clasts consist mainly of intraformationally-derived lithic pebbles and chert pebbles and granules. Siderite-cemented, rip-up clasts are common in all examples. Carbonaceous detritus is present both dispersed and as stringers marking stratification. Glauconite is locally present but rare. Mud interlaminae and thin (<1 cm) beds are locally intercalated. Rare examples from intervals in Crystal and Edson may possess double mud drapes on some foresets, suggesting subtidally-generated tidal bundling of the bedforms. No unequivocal cyclicity could be documented.

Trace fossils in this facies are sporadically distributed and vary from rare to moderate in abundance. *Ophiomorpha* (Figs. 21B, C) and *Skolithos* are the dominant elements of the suite with *Ophiomorpha* burrows reaching 3 cm in diameter. *Diplocraterion*, *Arenicolites*, and fugichnia occur in lesser numbers. *Teichichnus*, *Cylindrichnus* (Fig. 21D), *Palaeophycus*, and *Planolites* are present in most examples and are typically associated with muddy interlaminae and thin beds. *Rosselia* and *Asterosoma* are present but constitute uncommon elements of the suite. Burrow linings are typically thick.

The second facies consists of 10–50 cm thick beds of low angle (<15°) planar and exceedingly rare, wavy parallel laminated, lower fine- to lower medium-grained sandstones (Fig. 21E). These beds are amalgamated into bedsets up to 1.5 m in thickness. Thin, current-ripple laminated sandstone beds are also commonly intercalated. Like the trough cross-stratified sandstones, carbonaceous detritus, lithic pebbles, muddy interlaminae, thin mud beds, and mudstone rip-up clasts are locally intercalated. Locally, granule to pebble, clast-supported conglomerates are interstratified. The conglomerate units are also low-angle, planar cross-stratified.

Burrowing in this facies is typically associated with the muddy interlaminae and thin shale beds. This results in sporadic burrowing, largely confined to relatively thin zones. Burrow intensity is generally moderate to weak. Ichnogenera occur in rare numbers and include *Ophiomorpha*, *Palaeophycus*, *Cylindrichnus*, lesser *Skolithos* and *Planolites*, and rare *Teichichnus* and *Rosselia*. Single occurrences of *Lockeia*, *Conichnus*, and *Chondrites* are present. Fugichnia (Fig. 21E) are relatively common.

FIG. 20.—Litholog of Stage 2 valley fill, reflecting probable deep re-incision through previously deposited estuarine sediments during a subsequent period of relative sea-level lowstand (FS/SB). Note the unburrowed nature of the channel sandstones, indicating the presence of possible fluvially-dominated Ch-2 facies association. At this locality, the second stage of incision has removed all Stage 1 estuarine fill, and Stage 2 sandstones sit directly upon regionally extensive Viking Formation parasequences. Resumed transgression erosionally truncates the Channel-fill complex (TSE) and is overlain by the lower portion of the estuary-mouth barrier bar complex (EM-2 facies association). The barrier complex is erosionally truncated by ravinement during renewed transgression (TSE). The interval occurs in the 01-06-55-20W5 well, within the Sundance arm of the Sundance/Edson valley system. Legend of the symbols used in the litholog is given in Figure 8.

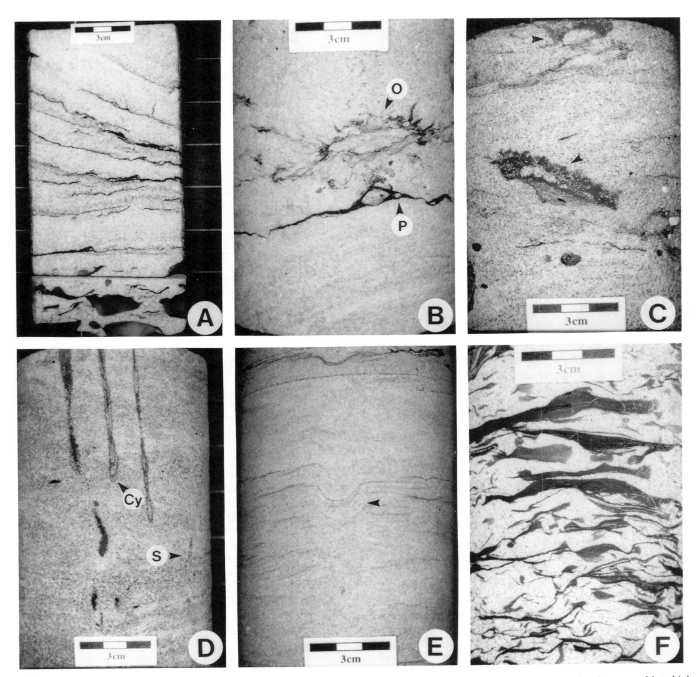

FIG. 21.—Depositional facies of the Channel-Fill complex. (A) Medium-grained sandstone showing low angle toesets, fanning upward into high-angle foresets of a three-dimensional subaqueous dune. Note the siderite-cemented, mudstone, rip-up clasts near the base of the trough cross-stratified bedset. Stratification is marked by carbonaceous detritus. Sundance Field, 12-13-54-21W5, depth 2723.5 m. (B) Moderately well sorted, medium-grained, trough cross-stratified sandstone. The presence of *Ophiomorpha* (O) and *Planolites* (P) attests to a marine influence on the channel fill. Edson Field, 12-34-52-19W5, depth 2586.5 m. (C) Pebbly, trough cross-stratified sandstone with siderite-cemented *Ophiomorpha* (arrows) burrows. Crystal Field, 12-20-46-03W5, depth 1725.7 m. (D) Trough cross-stratified sandstone containing elongate *Cylindrichnus* (Cy) and *Skolithos* (S). Crystal Field, 12-20-46-03W5, depth 1726.4 m. (E) Medium- to upper fine-grained sandstone, containing horizontal to low-angle, planar parallel laminations, passing into current ripple lamination. Note the escape trace (arrow). Crystal Field, 16-24-45-04W5, depth 1790.4 m. (F) Trough cross-stratified sandstone containing abundant mudstone rip-up clasts, forming a shale-clast breccia. Cyn-Pem Field, 06-12-51-11W5, depth 1945.0 m.

The third facies consists of lithic, upper fine- to lower medium-grained, massive (apparently structureless) sandstone, containing organic detritus, muddy stringers, rare mudstone rip-up clasts, and glauconite. Upper and lower contacts are indistinct. Beds range from 50 cm to 2 m in thickness. Burrowing is absent in all examples encountered.

The final facies was only noted from the 06-12-51-11W5 well at Cyn-Pem and consists of lower medium- to lower coarse-grained, moderately-sorted sandstone containing abundant, flat mudstone flakes (?desiccated mudstone chips). This 80 cm thick shale-clast breccia possesses low-angle, planar cross-stratification and is unburrowed (Fig. 21F). Several intervals in the Ch complexes of the Crystal valley contain abundant mud-flake rip-up clasts and may be transitional to this facies.

The Ch-1 facies association reflects a predominance of current-generated sediment transport and deposition. The laterally restricted geographic distribution of the facies association supports channelized flow. The bulk of the association reflects relatively small, migrating subaqueous dunes. The amalgamation of the bedforms into thick intervals supports a reasonably high aggradation rate. The interstratified, low-angle, planar-laminated sandstones with associated current ripple lamination are interpreted as sheet-flow transport of sand with waning-flow conditions locally preserved, possibly reflecting higher flow speeds during flood-stage discharge in the channel or flow near the channel margins. The apparently structureless sandstone beds may reflect rapid deposition, a lack of lithologic contrast to highlight stratification, or penecontemporaneous liquefaction of the bed destroying primary structure. The general rarity of the facies precludes discrimination between these possibilities. The shale-clast breccia suggests current transport of intraformational, possibly desiccated mud flakes from bank settings into the channel environment, presumably under flood conditions.

All ichnogenera in the trace fossil suite of the Ch-1 facies association occur in rare to moderate numbers (Fig. 22). The suite is "dominated" by *Ophiomorpha* and *Skolithos*, while *Planolites*, *Teichichnus*, *Diplocraterion*, *Cylindrichnus*, *Palaeophycus*, and fugichnia comprise the secondary elements. *Asterosoma*, *Rosselia*, *Arenicolites*, *Conichnus*, and *Chondrites* constitute accessory elements.

The suite demonstrates that the Ch-1 facies association accumulated in marine or marginal-marine conditions, although the degree of salinity stress is difficult to determine. The main environmental stress imposed on the suite appears to be related to migration of subaqueous dunes as well as high-energy, sheet-flow conditions with rapid deposition. Migrating dunes pose a severe difficulty to infaunal organisms since progressive avalanching of sand down the slip face of the bedform tends to bury the entrance to the dwelling structures, and the non-cohesive shifting nature of the substrate precludes effective deposit-feeding or grazing behavior. Only elongate shafts and deeply penetrating and branching networks of heavily-lined dwelling structures are ideally suited to these dynamic settings. Fugichnia record the burial of organisms or their entrainment in flows. The remainder of the suite is associated with muddy interlaminae, recording pauses in bedform migration. Most of the

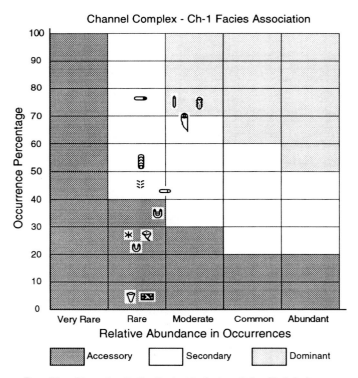

FIG. 22.—Trace fossil distribution in facies of the Ch-1 facies association of the Channel-fill complex. The legend of symbols for trace fossils is given in Figure 8.

feeding structures associated with these pauses are those of trophic generalists, but this may be related more to a paucity of deposited food than to any presumed salinity fluctuations.

The Ch-1 facies association may reflect a number of possible settings, including tidal channels, tidal inlets, or marine-influenced lowstand channels re-incised into previous estuarine deposits. Determining which of these settings are appropriate for a given succession is difficult, particularly with limited well control. Where channels are deeply incised, typically removing all previous estuarine deposits and erosionally overlying regional Viking parasequences, a lowstand-induced, re-incision interpretation is favored. Many such intervals may reach 35 m in thickness.

In contrast, good well control in the south arm of the Willesden Green valley system appears to support a tidal inlet interpretation. The 05-06-41-06W5 well (Fig. 23) intersects a Ch-1 facies association characterized by pebbly, trough cross-stratified and low-angle, planar-stratified sandstones containing a sporadic distribution of *Ophiomorpha*, *Skolithos*, *Diplocraterion*, *Arenicolites*, *Cylindrichnus*, *Palaeophycus*, *Planolites*, and fugichnia. The intervals show a close lateral association with EM-1 facies associations in surrounding wells and are deeply scoured, resting on an FS/SB developed on a regional Viking parasequence. Existing core control is reasonably good and supports a longitudinally restricted geographic extent to this marine-influenced channel succession, features favoring a tidal inlet interpretation. Several intervals in the Sundance/

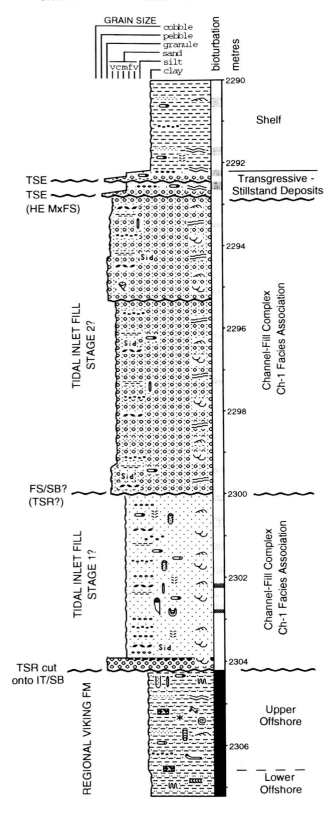

Sicanna Et Al Willesden Green 05-06-41-06w5

Edson valley system are suspected to correspond to tidal inlet deposition, but this cannot yet be substantiated.

The 05-06-41-06W5 well indicates a vertical stacking of tidal inlet fill (Fig. 23). As the entire valley fills, distributary channels typically link up with tidal inlets to drain the valley system. This scenario may produce a channel system which may incise into previous estuarine deposits and locally overlie previous channel sediments. Alternatively, however, stacking of channel deposits may reflect initial channel deposition, followed by partial removal by renewed incision during a succeeding sea-level lowstand. The coarser conglomeratic channel-fill towards the top of the succession may correspond to rejuvenation of the system during a relative lowstand of sea level. It seems reasonable that just as valley systems themselves become the *loci* of successive periods of re-incision, so too, the existing distributary and tidal inlet channels may also serve as the sites of the re-incision during subsequent lowstand conditions. Partial or complete removal of previous channel deposits may occur, particularly if the lowstand is pronounced and the system becomes a zone of sediment bypass. It follows that in many instances, re-incision surfaces (i.e., sequence boundaries) may be picked stratigraphically lower than appropriate, due to the overall similarity between facies in the previous channel and those of the re-incised channel. Without a pronounced grain-size change or compositional change in the nature of the fill, the contact between the two systems may be as indistinguishable as the erosional amalgamation of two, trough cross-stratified, sandstone beds.

Ch-2 Facies Association.—

The Ch-2 facies association was encountered in only in two cored intervals within the Sundance/Edson valley system (cf. Fig. 20). The facies association consists of the same lithofacies as the Ch-1 facies association, barring the shale-clast breccia noted from the Cyn-Pem valley system. Neither interval contained conglomerate beds or pebble stringers. In contrast to the Ch-1 facies associations, this association is entirely unburrowed. Where the facies association rests erosionally on regional Viking parasequences, no *Glossifungites* assemblages were encountered.

The facies association is interpreted to reflect current deposition of sand in a channel setting similar to that of the Ch-1 facies association. It is speculated, however, that the Ch-2 facies association may reflect fluvial- rather than brackish- or marine-influenced channel deposition. As such, these may correspond to fluvial, distributary, or lowstand-

Fig. 23.—Litholog of Channel-fill complexes, interpreted as tidal inlet deposits. Note the *Glossifungites* assemblage at the contact beneath the initial transgressive fill of the valley (FS/SB). The FS/SB has probably been modified by a later tidal scour ravinement surface (TSR) reflecting the base of the tidal inlet. The interval occurs in the 05-06-41-06W5 well, within the southeast arm of the Willesden Green valley system. The coarser-grained channel-fill towards the top may indicate a period of re-incision during a subsequent lowstand. The succession is erosionally truncated at the top (TSE), reflecting resumed transgression. Legend of the symbols used in the litholog is given in Figure 8.

induced, non-marine, re-incised channels rather than to tidal inlets, tidal channels, or transgressively-filled, re-incised channels. Re-incision during a subsequent lowstand of sea level is favored where channels have incised through all previous estuarine facies and have cut into the underlying regional Viking Formation parasequences.

CONCLUSIONS

1. The Viking Formation in the Crystal, Willesden Green, Sundance/Edson and Cyn-Pem fields contain estuarine, incised-valley fill deposits, juxtaposed against regionally extensive, fully marine, highstand progradational cycles.

2. The Viking Formation possesses numerous, coarsening-upward parasequences of regional extent, reflecting offshore to shoreface progradation within fully marine conditions. These successions are informally referred to as the regional Viking cycles. Three thoroughly burrowed and intergradational facies make up a complete coarsening cycle: silty shales, sandy shales, and shaly sandstones, reflecting lower offshore, upper offshore, and distal lower shoreface environments, respectively. The cycles are characterized by an increase in diversity of ichnogenera reflecting a progressive change from mainly grazing and deposit-feeding to mainly deposit-feeding and suspension-feeding behaviors. The trace fossil suites display intense burrowing, and are characterized by a high diversity of forms, a lack of dominance by a few forms, presence of significant numbers of specialized feeding/grazing structures, and a uniform distribution of individual ichnogenera, supportive of an equilibrium (K-selected) community within fully marine environments.

3. In marked contrast to the regional Viking cycles, the ichnological record of the valley-fill systems displays a variable though reduced degree of burrowing, a decrease in uniformity of burrowing, a pronounced variability in the distribution of individual ichnogenera, and a dominance by a few forms. Nonetheless, facies associations within the valley fills show a remarkably high trace fossil diversity. The overall suite is best regarded as a slightly impoverished marine assemblage and is most distinctive in its marked variability. The dominant elements are ubiquitous in distribution and reflect the simple structures of trophic generalists. Such r-selected (opportunistic) behaviors are characteristic of stressed environmental settings, particularly those subjected to salinity fluctuations, episodic deposition, and variability in substrate consistency.

   Many of the secondary and accessory elements of the trace fossil assemblage are not opportunistic and record more specialized and elaborate feeding or grazing behaviors which are uncommon in stressful environmental settings. Their sporadic distribution and variable abundances in the facies associations are interpreted to reflect salinity fluctuations within the estuary which may have repeatedly ranged from brackish to fully marine. In addition, the reduced size of some ichnogenera compared with their fully marine coun-

terparts are also characteristic of brackish-water conditions.

4. Recognition of the valley base or valley margins is facilitated by an integration of stratigraphy, sedimentology, and ichnology. Erosional truncation of underlying regional Viking parasequences may locally be highlighted by the presence of anomalous dispersed pebbles, conglomeratic lags, or anomalous lithofacies. In most of the incised-valley systems, the valley margins are demarcated by a *Glossifungites* assemblage. The presence of this trace fossil suite demonstrates that initial, preserved deposits of the valley fill were marine-influenced, indicating that the valley probably did not fill until the ensuing transgression. The erosional discontinuity demarcating the incised-valley systems, therefore, corresponds to a co-planar (amalgamated) surface of lowstand erosion and transgressive erosion or marine flooding (i.e., FS/SB).

5. The observed facies associations and their distributions within the valley systems indicate that they accumulated in a wave-dominated embayed estuary (barrier estuary) setting. The valley-fill deposits demonstrate a tripartite zonation of facies associations, defining three major depositional zones within the estuary: the Bay Head Delta complex, the Central Basin complex, and the Estuary Mouth complex. A fourth depositional complex reflects channel deposition.

6. The Bay Head Delta complex is characterized by weakly and sporadically burrowed, delta-front storm-bed sandstones with highly subordinate, delta-slope sediment-gravity flows and distal portions of distributary channels. The tempestites are relatively thin, reflecting the low-energy nature of storm events within the estuary compared with those on open coasts. The facies association displays a low degree of burrowing, a sporadic distribution of ichnogenera, and structures predominantly generated by trophic generalists. These characteristics reflect high aggradation rates, episodic deposition and, possibly, reduced salinity as the main controls on the nature of the trace fossil suite.

7. The Central Basin complex consists of two interbedded facies. The most distinctive facies comprises fair-weather deposition of sands and muds within the lagoon or bay environment of the central basin. This facies is dominated by structures reflecting r-selected opportunistic behavior, commonly associated with variable but generally reduced salinity. Reduced size of many structures and presence of synaeresis cracks support brackish-water conditions. The sporadic distribution of secondary and accessory elements, reflecting more elaborate and specialized feeding and grazing behavior, indicates, however, that salinity ranged repeatedly from brackish to fully marine. Salinity fluctuations may have been seasonal, related to variations in river discharge, rainfall, and/or storm washovers of the barrier complex at the estuary mouth.

   The other main facies consists of thin, storm-generated, wavy parallel to combined-flow and oscillation ripple laminated sandstone beds. In this facies, the dominant ichnological elements reflect rapid colonization of the event bed by opportunistic organisms in response to episodic deposition. The alternation between fairweather and storm deposits produces a mixed *Skolithos-Cruziana* ichnofacies. Detailed inspection of the suite demonstrates, however, that the assemblage is quite complicated and records highly variable depositional conditions. Salinity fluctuations, episodic deposition, and variable substrate consistency appear to be the dominant stresses imparted on the tracemaking organisms.

8. The Estuary Mouth complex consists of two facies associations. The dominant facies association (EM-1) reflects deposition on the estuary side of the mouth, and consists of moderately to abundantly burrowed, fairweather, ripple laminated sandstones, interbedded with storm-generated sandstones, washover sandstones, and possible tidal inlet sandstones. The trace fossil suite shows a high diversity of forms over the entire facies association, but the distribution of individual elements reflects opportunistic behavior related to episodic deposition. Salinity stresses may have also occurred but are difficult to resolve.

   The facies association deposited on the seaward side of the estuary mouth (EM-2) is erosionally-bounded and interpreted as the basal portion of the estuary-mouth barrier bar complex itself. Resting on a co-planar FS/SB or, locally, a marine flooding surface and erosionally truncated by an overlying TSE, the facies association coarsens upward from intensely burrowed sandy shales to shaly sandstones. These facies are interpreted to reflect the upper offshore to distal lower shoreface erosional remnant of the barrier complex. The trace fossil suite shows a uniform distribution of individual forms, a high degree of burrowing, a reasonable diversity of elements, a lack of dominance by a few ichnogenera, and the presence of moderate numbers of elaborate and specialized grazing and feeding/dwelling structures. The overall assemblage is consistent with fully marine, largely unstressed, equilibrium (K-selected) communities and shows a closer genetic affinity with the regional Viking parasequences than to the incised-valley fill assemblages.

9. Channel-fill facies associations are dominated by amalgamated subaqueous dunes, interstratified with flood-induced, sheet-flow sandstones. Successions may be burrowed or completely unburrowed. The presence of a trace fossil suite demonstrates that the channel complex accumulated in marine or marginal-marine conditions, although the degree of salinity-induced stress is difficult to determine. The main stress illustrated by the trace fossil suite appears to be related to migration of dunes with a subordinate influence imparted by high-energy sheet-flows with associated rapid deposition. The trace fossil suite reflects these stresses by the predominance of deeply penetrating, branching, and thickly-lined, dwelling structures. Burrowed successions are interpreted to reflect tidal channels, tidal inlets or transgressively-filled re-incised channels. Unburrowed successions are interpreted to reflect fluvial channels, distributary channels, or lowstand-generated, non-ma-

rine channels re-incised into earlier estuarine deposits.

10. The ichnology of estuarine valley systems in the Viking Formation is distinguished from fully marine regional Viking Formation successions only through careful analysis of the entire assemblage, including uniformity of burrowing, intensity of burrowing, the distribution of individual elements, the character of dominant elements, ethological interpretation of the organism behaviors, and assessment of trace fossil size, in addition to the cataloguing of the ichnogenera present. The wide range of environmental stresses imposed on organisms occupying Viking Formation estuaries results in a highly complicated ichnological record, but detailed analysis of the preserved suite permits a much enhanced interpretation of the depositional subenvironments comprising the incised-valley systems.

11. The complex nature of incised-valley systems requires the full integration of stratigraphy, sedimentology, and ichnology in order to recognize the depositional complexes and, ultimately, to resolve the depositional history of the successions. To date, ichnology has been under-utilized in such analyses, although its careful employment is currently proving to be invaluable.

ACKNOWLEDGMENTS

Funding has been gratefully received from Esso Resources Canada Ltd., Husky Oil Operations Ltd., Canadian Hunter Exploration Ltd., PanCanadian Petroleum Ltd., and Energy, Mines and Resources. Research support has also been made available through the Natural Sciences and Engineering Research Council of Canada, Grant No. A0816 to S.G. Pemberton, a Sir Izaack Walton Killam Memorial Scholarship, and a Province of Alberta Graduate Fellowship, both awarded to James A. MacEachern. Special thanks to Howard Brekke for his assistance both in the logging of cores and in the designing of the drafted figures; to Mike Ranger, who kindly permitted use of his computer program to draft the lithologs presented in this paper; and to Indraneel Raychaudhuri, who has been instrumental in our work on the *Glossifungites* ichnofacies. Helena Viveiros and Chandra Hodgkinson were exceedingly helpful summer assistants, and their help in core logging is greatly appreciated. We are also grateful to Brian Zaitlin and Gerry Reinson for their insights into the nature of incised-valley fills. Careful review and editing by R. Pickerill, M. Miller, R. Dalrymple, and D. Ulmer-Scholle greatly improved the manuscript.

REFERENCES

ALLEN, G. P., 1971, Relationship between grain size parameter distribution and current patterns in the Gironde Estuary (France): Journal of Sedimentary Petrology, v. 41, p. 74–88.

ALLEN, G.P., AND POSAMENTIER, H.W., 1993, Sequence stratigraphy and facies model of an incised valley fill: the Gironde Estuary, France: Journal of Sedimentary Petrology v. 63, p. 378–391.

BEYNON, B. M., PEMBERTON, S. G., BELL, D. D., AND LOGAN, C. A., 1988, Environmental implications of ichnofossils from the Lower Cretaceous Grand Rapids Formation, Cold Lake oil sands deposit, *in* James, D. P., and Leckie, D. A., eds., Sequences, Stratigraphy, Sedimentology: Surface and Subsurface: Calgary, Canadian Society of Petroleum Geologists Memoir 15, p. 275–290.

BEYNON, B. M., AND PEMBERTON, S. G., 1992, Ichnological signature of a brackish water deposit: an example from the Lower Cretaceous Grand Rapids Formation, Cold Lake oil sands area, Alberta, *in* Pemberton, S. G., ed., Applications of Ichnology to Petroleum Exploration, a Core Workshop: Tulsa, Society of Economic Paleontologists and Mineralogists Core Workshop 17, p. 199–221.

BOREEN, T., 1989, The sedimentology, stratigraphy and depositional history of the Lower Cretaceous Viking Formation at Willesden Green, Alberta, Canada: Unpublished M. Sc. Thesis, McMaster University, Hamilton, 190 p.

BOREEN, T., AND WALKER, R. G., 1991, Definition of allomembers and their facies assemblages in the Viking Formation, Willesden Green area, Alberta: Bulletin of Canadian Petroleum Geology, v. 39, p. 123–144.

BROMLEY, R. G., PEMBERTON, S. G., AND RAHMANI, R., 1984, A Cretaceous woodground: the *Teredolites* ichnofacies: Journal of Paleontology, v. 58, p. 488–498.

DALRYMPLE, R. W., ZAITLIN, B. A., AND BOYD, R., 1992, Estuarine facies models: conceptual basis and stratigraphic implications: Journal of Sedimentary Petrology, v. 62, p. 1130–1146.

DÖRJES, J., AND HOWARD, J. D., 1975, Estuaries of the Georgia coast, U.S.A.: Sedimentology and biology. IV. Fluvial-marine transition indicators in an estuarine environment, Ogeechee River-Ossabaw Sound: Senckenbergiana Maritima, v. 7, p. 137–179.

FREY, R. W., AND SEILACHER, A., 1980, Uniformity in marine invertebrate ichnology: Lethaia, v. 13, p. 183–207.

FREY, R. W., AND PEMBERTON, S. G., 1984, Trace fossil facies models, *in* Walker, R. G., ed., Facies Models (2nd ed.): St. John's, Geoscience Canada, Reprint Series 1, p. 189–207.

FÜRSICH, F. T., AND MAYR, H., 1981, Non-marine *Rhizocorallium* (trace fossil) from the Upper Freshwater Molasse (Upper Miocene) of southern Germany: Neues Jahrbuch für Geologie und Paläontologie, Monatshefte, H. 6, p. 321–333.

GLAISTER, P., 1959, Lower Cretaceous of southern Alberta and adjoining areas: American Association of Petroleum Geologists Bulletin, v. 43, p. 590–640.

HAQ, B. U., HARDENBOL, J., AND VAIL, P.R., 1987, Chronology of fluctuating sea levels since the Triassic: Science, v. 235, p. 1156–1166.

JUMARS, P. A., 1993, Concepts in Biological Oceanography: New York, Oxford University Press, 348 p.

LEVINTON, J. S., 1970, The paleoecological significance of opportunistic species: Lethaia, v. 3, p. 69–78.

MACEACHERN, J. A., PEMBERTON, S. G., RAYCHAUDHURI, I., AND VOSSLER, S. M., 1990, The *Glossifungites* Ichnofacies and discontinuity surfaces: Applications to sequence stratigraphy (abs.): Utrecht, 13th International Sedimentological Congress (Nottingham), International Association of Sedimentologists, p. 140.

MACEACHERN, J. A., PEMBERTON, S. G., AND RAYCHAUDHURI, I., 1991a, The substrate-controlled *Glossifungites* Ichnofacies and its application to the recognition of sequence stratigraphic surfaces: subsurface examples from the Cretaceous of the Western Canada Sedimentary Basin, Alberta, Canada, *in* Leckie, D. A., Posamentier, H. W., and Lovell, R. W. W., eds., 1991 NUNA Conference on High Resolution Sequence Stratigraphy (Programme, Proceedings and Guidebook): Banff, Geological Association of Canada, p. 32–36.

MACEACHERN, J. A., PEMBERTON, S. G., RAYCHAUDHURI, I., AND VOSSLER, S. M., 1991b, Application of the *Glossifungites* Ichnofacies to the recognition of sequence stratigraphic boundaries: Examples from the Cretaceous of the Western Canada Sedimentary Basin, Alberta, Canada (abs.): American Association of Petroleum Geologists Bulletin, v. 75, p. 626.

MACEACHERN, J. A., AND PEMBERTON, S. G., 1992, Ichnological aspects of Cretaceous shoreface successions and shoreface variability in the Western Interior Seaway of North America, *in* Pemberton, S. G., ed., Applications of Ichnology to Petroleum Exploration, a Core Workshop: Tulsa, Society of Economic Paleontologists and Mineralogists Core Workshop 17, p. 57–84.

MACEACHERN, J. A., BECHTEL, D. J., AND PEMBERTON, S. G., 1992a, Ichnology and sedimentology of transgressive deposits, transgressively-related deposits and transgressive systems tracts in the Viking Formation of Alberta, *in* Pemberton, S. G., ed., Applications of ichnology to petroleum exploration, a core workshop: Tulsa, Society of Economic Paleontologists and Mineralogists Core Workshop 17, p. 251–290.

MACEACHERN, J. A., RAYCHAUDHURI, I., AND PEMBERTON, S. G., 1992b, Stratigraphic applications of the *Glossifungites* Ichnofacies: Delineating discontinuities in the rock record, *in* Pemberton, S. G., ed., Applications of ichnology to petroleum exploration, a core workshop: Tulsa, Society of Economic Paleontologists and Mineralogists Core Workshop 17, p. 169–198.

McGOOKEY, D. P., HAUN, J. D., HALE, L. A., GOODELL, H. G., McCUBBIN, D. G., WEIMER, R. J., AND WULF, G. R., 1972, Cretaceous System, *in* Mallory, W. W., ed., Geologic Atlas of the Rocky Mountain Region, U.S.A.: Denver, Rocky Mountain Association of Geologists, p. 190–228.

MAGWOOD, J. P. A., AND PEMBERTON, S. G., 1990, Stratigraphic significance of *Cruziana* : new data concerning the Cambrian-Ordovician ichnostratigraphic paradigm: Geology, v. 18, p. 729–732.

OOMKENS, E., AND TERWINDT, J. H. J., 1960, Inshore estuarine sediments in the Haringvliet (Netherlands): Geologie en Mijnbouw, v. 39, p. 701–710.

PATTISON, S. A. J., 1991a, Sedimentology and allostratigraphy of regional, valley-fill, shoreface and transgressive deposits of the Viking Formation (Lower Cretaceous), Central Alberta: Unpublished Ph. D. Thesis, McMaster University, Hamilton, 380 p.

PATTISON, S. A. J., 1991b, Crystal, Sundance and Edson valley-fill deposits, *in* Leckie, D. A., Posamentier, H. W., and Lovell, R. W. W., eds., 1991 Nuna Conference on High Resolution Sequence Stratigraphy (Programme, Proceedings and Guidebook): Banff, Geological Association of Canada, p. 44–47.

PATTISON, S. A. J., 1992, Recognition and interpretation of estuarine mudstones (central basin mudstones) in the tripartite valley fill deposits of the Viking Formation, central Alberta, *in* Pemberton, S. G., ed., Applications of ichnology to petroleum exploration, a core workshop: Tulsa, Society of Economic Paleontologists and Mineralogists Core Workshop 17, p. 223–249.

PEMBERTON, S. G., AND FREY, R. W., 1984, Ichnology of storm-influenced shallow marine sequence: Cardium Formation (Upper Cretaceous) at Seebe, Alberta, *in* Stott, D. F., and Glass, D. J., eds., The Mesozoic of Middle North America: Calgary, Canadian Society of Petroleum Geologists Memoir 9, p. 281–304.

PEMBERTON, S. G., AND FREY, R. W., 1985, The *Glossifungites* ichnofacies:modern examples from the Georgia Coast, U. S. A., *in* Curran, H. A., ed., Biogenic Structures: Their Use in Interpreting Depositional Environments: Tulsa, Society of Economic Paleontologists and Mineralogists Special Publication 35, p. 237–259.

PEMBERTON, S. G., AND WIGHTMAN, D. M., 1992, Ichnological characteristics of brackish water deposits, *in* Pemberton, S. G., ed., Applications of Ichnology to Petroleum Exploration, a Core Workshop: Tulsa, Society of Economic Paleontologists and Mineralogists Core Workshop 17, p. 141–167.

PEMBERTON, S. G., MACEACHERN, J. A., AND FREY, R. W., 1992a, Trace fossil facies models: environmental and allostratigraphic significance, *in* Walker, R. G., and James, N., eds., Facies Models: Response to Sea Level Change: St. John's, Geological Association of Canada, p. 47–72.

PEMBERTON, S. G., MACEACHERN, J. A., AND RANGER, M. J., 1992b, Ichnology and event stratigraphy: The use of trace fossils in recognizing tempestites, *in* Pemberton, S. G., ed., Applications of Ichnology to Petroleum Exploration, a Core Workshop: Tulsa, Society of Economic Paleontologists and Mineralogists Core Workshop 17, p. 85–117.

PEMBERTON, S.G., REINSON, G. E., AND MACEACHERN, J. A., 1992c, Comparative ichnological analysis of late Albian estuarine valley-fill and shelf-shoreface deposits, Crystal Viking Field, Alberta, *in* Pemberton, S. G., ed., Applications of Ichnology to Petroleum Exploration, a Core Workshop: Tulsa, Society of Economic Paleontologists and Mineralogists Core Workshop 17, p. 291–317.

PIANKA, E. R., 1970, On r and k selection: American Naturalist, v. 104, p. 592–597.

RANGER, M. J., AND PEMBERTON, S. G., 1992, The sedimentology and ichnology of estuarine point bars in the McMurray Formation of the Athabasca Oil Sands Deposit, northeastern Alberta, Canada, *in* Pemberton, S. G., ed., Applications of Ichnology to Petroleum Exploration, a Core Workshop: Tulsa, Society of Economic Paleontologists and Mineralogists Core Workshop 17, p. 401–421.

REINSON, G. E., 1985, Facies analysis and reservoir geometry of the Crystal Viking field, Tp. 45 and 46, Rg. 3 and 4W5, central Alberta: Calgary, Geological Survey of Canada, Open File Report 1193, 168 p.

Reinson, G. E., Clark, J. E., and Foscolos, A. E., 1988, Reservoir geology of Crystal Viking Field, Lower Cretaceous estuarine tidal channel-bay complex, south-central Alberta: American Association of Petroleum Geologists Bulletin, v. 72, p. 1270–1294.

Remane, A., and Schlieper, C., 1971, Biology of Brackish Water: New York, Wiley, 372 p.

Roy, P. S., Thom, B. G., and Wright, L. D., 1980, Holocene sequences on an embayed high-energy coast: an evolutionary model: Sedimentary Geology, v. 26, p. 1–19.

Savrda, C. E., 1991a, Ichnology in sequence stratigraphic studies: An example from the Lower Paleocene of Alabama: Palaios, v. 6, p. 39–53.

Savrda, C. E., 1991b, *Teredolites,* wood substrates, and sea-level dynamics: Geology, v. 19, p. 905–908.

Stelck, C. R., and Koke, K. R., 1987, Foraminiferal zonation of the Viking interval in the Hasler Shale (Albian), northeastern British Columbia: Canadian Journal of Earth Sciences, v. 24, p. 2254–2278.

Vail, P. R., Mitchum, R. M., Jr., and Thompson, S., III, 1977, Seismic stratigraphy and global changes of sea level, part 3: Relative changes of sea level from coastal onlap; part 4: Global cycles of relative changes of sea level, *in* Payton, C. E., ed., Seismic Stratigraphy- Applications to Hydrocarbon Exploration: Tulsa, American Association of Petroleum Geologists Memoir 26, p. 63–97.

Van Veen, J., 1936, Onderzoekingen in de Hoofden, Landsdrukkerij, Den Haag, 252 p.

Wheatcroft, R. A., 1990, Preservation potential of sedimentary event layers: Geology, v. 18, p. 843–845.

Wightman, D. M., Pemberton, S. G., and Singh, C., 1987, Depositional modelling of the Upper Mannville (Lower Cretaceous), central Alberta. Implications for the recognition of brackish water deposits, *in* Tillman, R. W., and Weber, K. J., eds., Reservoir Sedimentology: Tulsa, Society of Economic Paleontologists and Mineralogists Special Publication 40, p. 189–220.

CONTROL OF ESTUARINE VALLEY-FILL DEPOSITION BY FLUCTUATIONS OF RELATIVE SEA-LEVEL, CRETACEOUS BEARPAW-HORSESHOE CANYON TRANSITION, DRUMHELLER, ALBERTA, CANADA

R. BRUCE AINSWORTH* AND ROGER G. WALKER

Department of Geology, McMaster University, Hamilton, Ontario, L8S 4M1, Canada

ABSTRACT: The transition from the Bearpaw to Horseshoe Canyon Formation (Campanian-Maastrichtian) is about 60 m thick and is exposed in three-dimensions along the Red Deer Valley near Drumheller, Alberta. These clastic marine to marginal-marine deposits are divided into seven allomembers (A to G) defined by marine to brackish flooding surfaces. The deposits of allomember B fill an incised valley over 50 km long, up to 12 km wide, and about 20 m deep. The incision was cut either during a fall in relative sea level or by avulsion of a deltaic distributary channel. The estuarine fill of the incision appears to be transgressive. In outcrop, two main facies associations are recognised; they are interpreted to represent (1) the estuarine-marine zone and (2) the paleoseaward end of the turbidity maximum zone. Within the estuary, there was lateral shifting of individual channels along with lateral accretion of inclined heterolithic stratification (IHS). The IHS includes centimeter and meter-scale alternating sandy and muddy strata. These probably reflect daily tidal cycles and the seasonal migration of the turbidity maximum zone up and down the estuary, respectively. Tidal bundle sequences in Facies Association 1 suggest a semi-diurnal tidal cyclicity.

The lateral juxtaposition of estuarine-marine filled channels with turbidity maximum zone filled channels indicates that the overall transgression was probably punctuated by higher frequency sea-level fluctuations. This makes it difficult to distinguish the products of allocyclic and autocyclic processes within the valley. The base of the incised valley is a candidate for a sequence boundary and the estuarine fill is assigned to a transgressive systems tract.

INTRODUCTION

There are very few easily accessible places in the world where several horizons of intertonguing marine, marginal-marine, and non-marine rocks can be observed in continuous outcrops of flat-lying strata. One such place is a few kilometres south of Drumheller, Alberta (Fig. 1), where a 50 to 60-m thick section can be continuously walked out for 15 km in the dip direction and 3.5 km in a strike direction. Six tongues of the marine Bearpaw Formation pinch out northwestward into marginal-marine and non-marine sediments of the Horseshoe Canyon Formation (the basal formation of the Edmonton Group; Fig. 2). These tongues define seven regressive successions and allow a detailed history of relative sea level and parasequence stacking patterns to be worked out (Ainsworth, 1992, 1994).

These marine to non-marine alternations occur in a significant stratigraphic position within the fill of the Alberta foreland basin, namely at the time when marine mudstones of the Bearpaw Formation (late Campanian, Maastrichtian) were about to be overwhelmed by more than 1000 m of non-marine sediments of the Edmonton Group. Similar marine to non-marine intertonguings also occur in the underlying clastic wedge at the contact between the marine Lea Park Formation and the dominantly non-marine Belly River Formation (early Campanian, Alberta; Al-Rawahi, 1993; Power, 1993). One of the purposes of this paper, therefore, is to document the vertical and horizontal facies changes within an incised valley near the base of a major, non-marine clastic wedge and to relate some of these changes to rapid fluctuations of relative sea level.

In order to follow the theme of this Special Publication, we will discuss a valley-fill succession that cuts into a prograding wave- and storm-influenced shoreface. The prograding shoreface represents an early advance of marginal-marine sediments into the Bearpaw sea; the estuary

fill represents a subsequent transgression. The valley fill is interpreted as tidally-dominated estuarine sediments overlain by tidal-flat deposits and a coal seam.

The sediments were first interpreted as deltaic (Shepheard and Hills, 1970) but more recently were re-interpreted by Rahmani (1988) as having formed in delta front and estuarine channel environments. We agree with Rahmani that much of the section is estuary fill but present different interpretations of the way in which filling took place and of the history of sea-level fluctuation.

Throughout the paper, we use the definition of Dalrymple and others (1992, p. 1132), namely that an estuary is "the seaward portion of a drowned valley system which receives sediment from both fluvial and marine sources and which contains facies influenced by both tide, wave and fluvial processes. The estuary is considered to extend from the landward limit of tidal facies at its head to the seaward limit of coastal facies at its mouth."

REGIONAL SETTING AND STRATIGRAPHY

The study area (Figs. 1, 2) is about 12 km south-east of Drumheller, Alberta. In late Cretaceous times, this area was part of the Western Interior Seaway which lay within a foreland basin that evolved during the Upper Jurassic as a response to the accretion of terranes in the cordillera to the west. The seaway contains rocks of Upper Jurassic to Paleogene age.

The study area lay at the head of a south-easterly oriented embayment with an actively rising cordillera to the west (Williams and Stelck, 1975). Rivers flowed north-eastward from the cordillera but joined to form major trunk distributaries that flowed parallel (from north-west to south-east) to the axis of the foreland basin, (Eisbacher and others, 1974; Rahmani and Lerbekmo, 1975). The regional shoreline trend in the study area was approximately NNE-SSW (Fig. 3; Rahmani, 1983; Ainsworth, 1991).

The Horseshoe Canyon Formation forms the base of a clastic wedge (the Edmonton Group) which is up to 1000

¹Present address: Shell Research, KSEPL, PO Box 60, 2280 AB, Rijswijk, The Netherlands.

Incised-valley Systems: Origin and Sedimentary Sequences, SEPM Special Publication No. 51

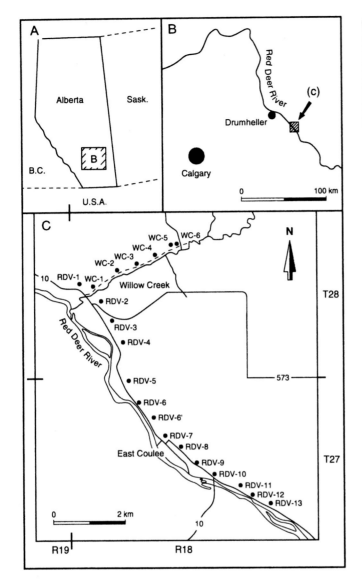

FIG. 1.—Location maps. In (C), RDV indicates Red Deer Valley sections and WC indicates Willow Creek sections; Highway 10 continues northwestward to the town of Drumheller. T = Townships, R = Ranges west of the Fourth Meridian.

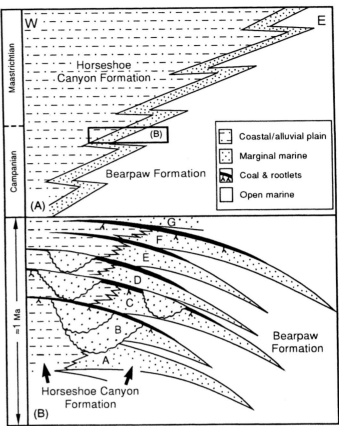

FIG. 2.—(A) Schematic diagram showing the southeastward-climbing diachronous contact between the marine Bearpaw shales and the marginal-marine deposits of the Horseshoe Canyon Formation, (B) a more detailed schematic section illustrating the seven informal allomembers identified (A to G). Allomember B represents the main subject of this paper.

m thick in the Foothills of the Rocky Mountains (Irish, 1970). The Horseshoe Canyon Formation intertongues southeastward with the Bearpaw Formation (marine shales) forming the Bearpaw—Horseshoe Canyon transition zone (Fig. 2; Shepheard and Hills, 1970). The diachronous contact between these formations becomes younger eastward and is in most places conformable (Gibson, 1977). The rocks are of Campanian-Maastrichtian age, but the precise location of the boundary in this area is still unresolved (Obradovich and Cobban, 1975; Lerbekmo and Coulter, 1985). The Bearpaw shales are assigned to the *Baculites compressus* Zone of the Pierre Shale succession (Williams and Stelck, 1975). The maximum northwestward flooding by the Bear-

paw sea occurred in the latest Campanian (*Baculites reesidei* Zone, Williams and Stelck, 1975).

The Drumheller area has been mentioned in numerous regional and stratigraphic studies (Allan and Sanderson, 1945; Irish, 1970; Gibson, 1977), and a local stratigraphy has been based on the mapping and correlation of fifteen major coal-bearing intervals in the Red Deer valley between East Coulee and Ardley (Fig. 1; Allan and Sanderson, 1945; Shepeard and Hills, 1970; Gibson, 1977; Rahmani, 1983). We have built on this scheme, recognizing additional coals and using *bounding discontinuities* (erosional bases of channels and transgressive surfaces of erosion) to erect an allostratigraphy (North American Commission on Stratigraphic Nomenclature, 1983). In the study area, we now recognize seven allomembers, informally lettered A through G (Fig. 4). All of these units have been described and interpreted by Ainsworth (1991, 1992, 1994), but this paper concerns only allomembers A and B. The top of allomember B is defined by Coal 0 (zero) (Fig. 4).

PREVIOUS WORK

The only detailed previous studies are those of Shepheard and Hills (1970) and Rahmani (1983, 1988, 1989). She-

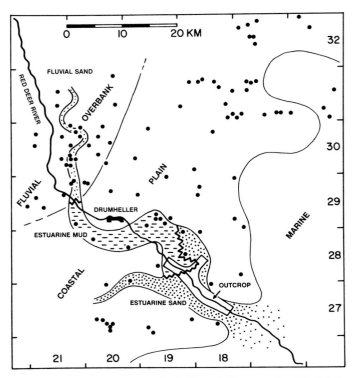

FIG. 3.—Map of the estuary in the Drumheller area, simplified from Rahmani (1988). Note outcrop area southeast of Drumheller, and core control (black circles) of facies in subsurface. Heavy stipple indicates estuarine sand supplied from the marine end of the valley, light stipple indicates fluvial sand, and dashes indicates central basin estuarine mud.

pheard and Hills (1970) suggested prodelta, delta front, distributary channel, beach, interdistributary bay, mudflat, open bay, and floodplain environments, and used the Mississippi Delta as a modern analog. The deposits were reinterpreted by Rahmani (1983) in terms of embayed shorelines, estuaries, and barrier island systems with the lower part (our allomember B, Fig. 4) as an estuarine channel fill. In outcrop, the channel trends northwest-southeast and is up to 3.5 km wide and 20 km long. The regional setting of the incision has been established by Rahmani (1988, p. 456) from outcrop and subsurface studies (Fig. 3). It can be traced in the subsurface (Rahmani, 1988, 1989) for at least 30 km northwestward where the channel gradually narrows from a maximum of 12 km to a minimum of 0.5 km in width.

Rahmani's maps (1988, 1989; Fig. 3) indicate that the estuarine valley is both sand- and mud-filled in the southeast (in outcrop) but becomes predominantly mud filled in the subsurface (for 21 km northwest of the end of the outcrop). The mud filling is up to 11 m thick and 3 km wide and overlies a cross-bedded unit which is up to 5 m thick. The muddy facies is replaced landward (northwestward) by a sandy facies 5 to 10 m thick. This lateral sand-mud-sand facies change within the estuary was interpreted by Rahmani (1988, 1989) to represent a tripartite estuarine system (Nichols and Biggs, 1985). The sandy channel fill that crops out in the south-eastern part of the study area was interpreted as a marine sand in the estuary mouth. The subsur-

face mud-filled portion of the channel represented the turbidity maximum zone of the estuary (Allen and others, 1980), and the sandy channel fill in subsurface, in the northwest, represented the estuarine to fluvial transition zone.

PROGRADING SHOREFACE DEPOSITS

The prograding shoreface of allomember A is not the main subject of this paper and is only described so that allomember B can be placed in context. The lower part of allomember A consists of interbedded sandstones and mudstones interpreted as offshore marine deposits (Rahmani, 1988; Ainsworth, 1991, 1992, 1994). They are overlain by a sandstone up to 14 m thick (Fig. 3) that is mostly swaley cross-stratified with in situ root traces in the top. The base of this sandstone is sharp in the northwest and becomes progressively more gradationally-based toward the southeast. It is interpreted as a prograding, storm-dominated, shoreface succession. In the northwest, the very sharp base, without a gradation from offshore to lower shoreface, suggests a forced regression (Plint, 1991, p. 415; Posamentier and others, 1992) with wave scouring of the offshore deposits before rapid progradation of the shoreface itself due to the small lowering of relative sea level. The shoreface then prograded without further lowering in sea level, resulting in a more gradational base.

ESTUARINE VALLEY-FILL DEPOSITS: DESCRIPTION

The deposits of allomember B form a fining-upward succession (Fig. 5) which has a maximum thickness of 20 m in the Willow Creek area (Fig. 4). The basal bounding discontinuity of the allomember consists of a series of coalesced channel-shaped erosion surfaces that cut into the shoreface sandstones and offshore transition zone deposits of allomember A. The true walls of the incised valley are not exposed and can only be approximately mapped from subsurface data (Fig. 3). Locally, the erosion surface is marked by a lag of sideritized mudstone clasts (Fig. 6), and has a maximum relief of 16 m. Flow directions inferred from cross-bedded sandstones within the valley fill are generally toward the north in the Willow Creek area (Figs. 7, 8) and in the Red Deer Valley (Fig. 8). No macrofossils or evidence of bioturbation were observed within this allomember.

Facies Association 1—Structureless to Cross-bedded Sandstone

This is the dominant facies association, occurring from RDV-13 to RDV-2 (Fig. 4). It also occurs in the southwesterly and north-easterly ends of Willow Creek (Fig. 4; channel fills 1, 3, 4).

Apparently structureless, poorly-cemented, and friable medium-to fine-grained sandstones are the predominant deposits of Facies Association 1. Planar tabular, planar tangential, and trough cross-stratification can be observed where the sandstones are better cemented. Sets range in thickness from 10 to 250 cm. Mud and carbonaceous drapes are common on foresets and muddy toesets (Fig. 9). Analysis of one set shows a pattern of mud drapes alternating consis-

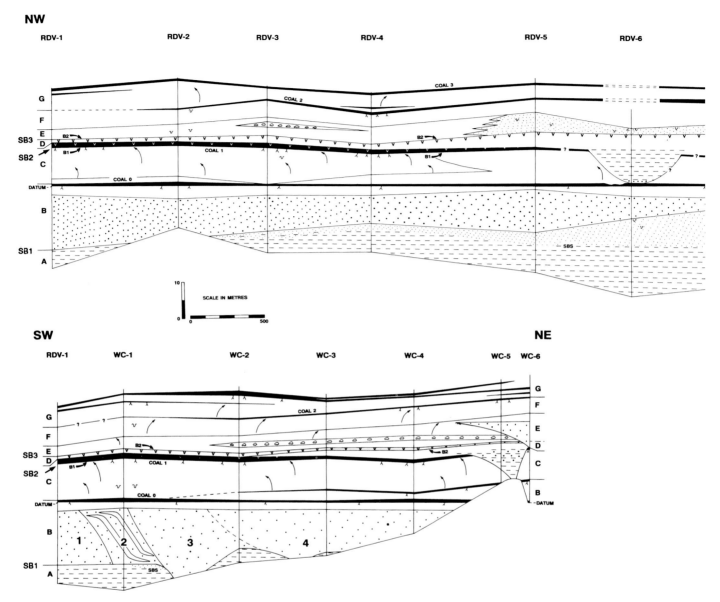

FIG. 4.—Red Deer Valley (RDV) (dip) and Willow Creek (WC) (strike) sections. Vertical lines show locations of measured sections (see Fig. B (Willow Creek section) represent discrete incisions within the estuarine fill. Vertical exaggeration 24x.

tently with sandy foresets. These foresets are up to 10 cm thick and are overlain by a mud drape. A thinner (up to 2 cm thick), fine sandstone layer overlies the mud drape and is in turn overlain by another mud drape. Over ninety of these alternations can be measured from one set near RDV-1 (Fig. 10).

Sideritised mud rip-up clasts (cm scale) are very common and occur in concentrations at the base of the allomember and in pods within the dominant sandstone lithology. They also occur sporadically throughout the sandy facies association and in concentrations at the base of small (meter scale) scours.

The sandstones of channel fill 1 (Fig. 4) contain many meter-scale *in situ* and displaced isolated blocks of hetero-

lithic strata (Fig. 11), composed of mm-scale laminae of sandstone, mudstone, and carbonaceous material. The blocks are irregularly distributed throughout the sandstones (Fig. 11); some are isolated and contorted (Fig. 11). Ripple cross-stratification is the dominant structure within the top 2 metres of the association.

Facies Association 2—Inclined Heterolithic Strata

The inclined heterolithic strata (IHS; Thomas and others, 1987) (Fig. 12A) consist of cm-scale triplets of fine sandstone, carbonaceous material, and mudstone. These are packaged into meter-scale units in which the triplets are composed dominantly of sandstone or mudstone. In many

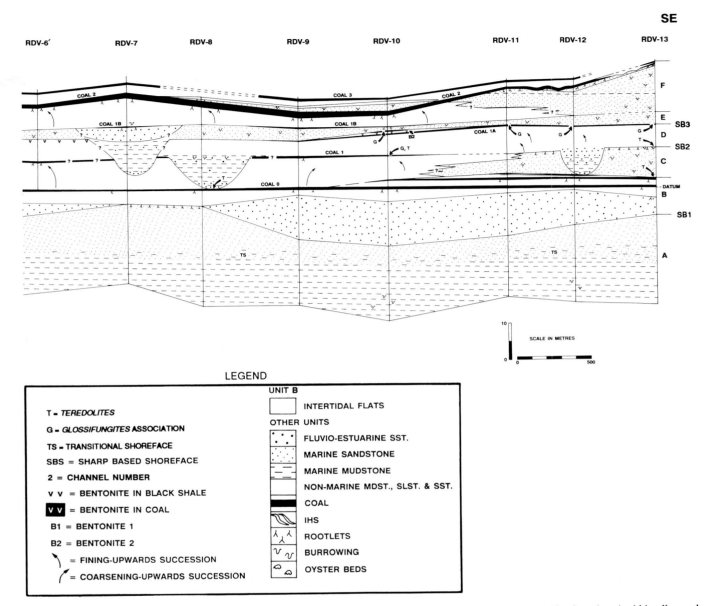

SE

RDV-6'   RDV-7   RDV-8   RDV-9   RDV-10   RDV-11   RDV-12   RDV-13

LEGEND

T = TEREDOLITES

G = GLOSSIFUNGITES ASSOCIATION

TS = TRANSITIONAL SHOREFACE

SBS = SHARP BASED SHOREFACE

2 = CHANNEL NUMBER

v v = BENTONITE IN BLACK SHALE

V V = BENTONITE IN COAL

B1 = BENTONITE 1

B2 = BENTONITE 2

↘ = FINING-UPWARDS SUCCESSION

↗ = COARSENING-UPWARDS SUCCESSION

UNIT B

☐ INTERTIDAL FLATS

OTHER UNITS

FLUVIO-ESTUARINE SST.

MARINE SANDSTONE

MARINE MUDSTONE

NON-MARINE MDST., SLST. & SST.

COAL

IHS

ROOTLETS

BURROWING

OYSTER BEDS

1C), and letters up the sides indicate allomembers. Allomember B is the estuarine deposit discussed in this paper. Numbers 1 to 4 within allomember

places, there is a progressive stratigraphic change upward from sand-rich to mud-rich triplets.

The IHS are best developed in channel 2 (Fig. 4) which is about 300 m wide. The channel fill has a maximum thickness of 12 m. The south-western contact with the sandstone fill of channel 1 is sharp (Fig. 12A). Toward the north-east, the IHS are cut out at the erosional edge of channel 3 (Fig. 13). The IHS association is also observed throughout the 3 km of exposure north-west of RDV-1. It is less well developed along the Red Deer Valley southeast of RDV-1 where it occurs in a few locations above the top of the sandy Facies Association 1, and has a maximum thickness of 2 m.

At the channel 2 location, the IHS dip at approximately 10° towards the north-east and grade laterally northeastward into cross-bedded, medium grained sandstones (Fig. 12A). Concave-upward erosion surfaces (Fig. 14) at many different scales occur within the IHS (Fig. 12B). Mud rip-up clasts are common on the erosion surfaces along with slump blocks up to 2 m long that commonly occur towards the toes of the erosion surfaces.

Centimeter-scale Triplets.—

These consist of interlaminated sandstone, carbonaceous material, and mudstone. The sandy bases of many triplets appear to be sharp, suggesting an overall grading from sand

FIG. 5.—Fining-upward succession of allomember B (arrowed). Prominent coal at tip of arrow is Coal 0. Allomember B is 13 m thick at this location (RDV-2).

FIG. 6.—Sideritized mud clasts (arrow at right) at the erosional base of allomember B. Hoodoo in foreground is approximately 2 m high; erosional base of allomember B is just above the bottom of the hoodoo (arrow at left) (Hoodoos Recreation Area, RDV-1).

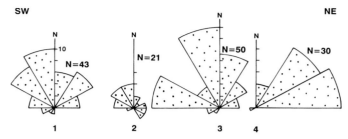

FIG. 7.—Allomember B paleocurrent rose diagrams from 2-D and 3-D cross-stratified sets over 15 cm in height in the Willow Creek area. Numbers 1 to 4 correspond to the channel numbers shown in Figure 4. Note paleoflow concentrations are towards the northern hemisphere (paleolandward). Also note the different paleocurrent patterns of channels 3 and 4.

The appearance of mud in the succession is indicated by the arrow in Figure 15A. Below this arrow, there are about 25 alternations of sandstone and carbonaceous laminations. Above the arrow, there is a consistent interlamination of sandstone, carbonaceous material, and mudstone (Fig. 15C). Stratigraphically upward, the triplets contain a smaller proportion of sandstone and a higher proportion of mudstone. Sandstone laminae may be only one or two grains in thickness (Fig. 15C), whereas the mudstone laminations thicken from a few mm to about 1 cm. The carbonaceous material maintains a consistent thickness of 2–3 mm throughout. There are 211 triplets above the arrow in Figure 15A, making a total of 236 triplets in the whole muddier-upward succession.

Meter-scale Alternations.—

Superimposed on the cm-scale triplets is a meter-scale alternation of sandier and muddier strata (Figs. 12, 15A). The paler colored IHS of channel 2 (Fig. 12) consists of triplets dominated by fine sandstone (Fig. 15B); the darker colors are due to triplets dominated by mudstones (Fig. 15C). Rahmani (1989, p. 22) suggested that the contacts between the sandier and muddier strata of the IHS are conformable (e.g., Fig. 15A) and therefore termed the meter-scale alternations "sandstone-shale doublets." However, the contacts are *not* always conformable, and in places the muddier strata overlie erosion surfaces that cut down into sandier strata (Figs. 12, 14). The sandier and muddier strata are *not* necessarily genetically related units as is implied by the term "doublets."

There are no marine body or trace fossils in this facies association. Rahmani (1983, p. 20) identified fresh and salt water palynomorphs in the Willow Creek area.

Overlying Facies

Throughout the study area, both facies associations are overlain by an interlaminated sandstone and mudstone facies (Fig. 16) which ranges from 0 to 3 m in thickness. The sandstones are very fine grained and commonly ripple cross-laminated. In places, they occur as isolated lenticles within the dark grey mudstone. Scours up to 1.5 m deep and filled with sand or IHS occur within this facies (RDV-3). The

to mud in each triplet. The proportions of these lithologies are variable and commonly change progressively upward through a succession of triplets.

The sandy triplets toward the base of a typical gradational succession (Fig. 15A) are 1–3 cm thick and consist dominantly of fine sandstone with regularly spaced, discrete, mm-thick interlaminations of carbonaceous material within the sandstone (Fig. 15B). Mm-scale rippled flasers of carbonaceous material also occur within the sandstone. In places, carbonaceous laminations are very closely spaced and are separated by mm- to cm-thick fine sand (Fig. 15B). Mudstone is extremely thin to absent.

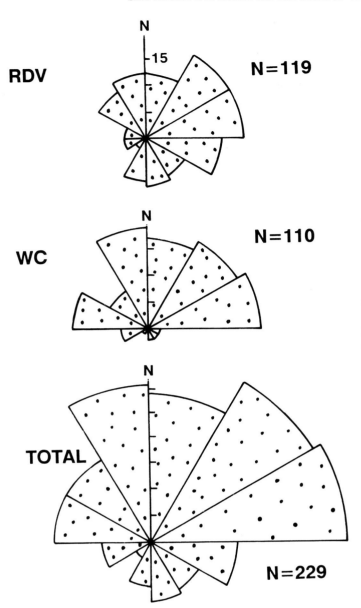

FIG. 8.—Allomember B paleocurrent roses from 2-D and 3-D cross-stratified sets over 15 cm in height; (RDV) readings from Red Deer Valley localities, (WC) readings from Willow Creek localities, (TOTAL) total readings from all localities. Note polymodal distribution of readings and predominant flow directions towards the northern hemisphere (paleolandward).

FIG. 9.—Mud and carbonaceous drapes on cross-bed foresets (Facies Association 1, channel 3). Scale bar (left center) is 10 cm.

ESTUARINE VALLEY-FILL DEPOSITS: INTERPRETATION

The spacing of the mud drapes in Facies Association 1 is clearly cyclic (Fig. 10B) indicating a tidal influence during the filling of the valley. Paleocurrents were directed predominantly towards the northern quadrants (Fig. 8) in a *paleo-landward* direction. This is *not* the orientation that would be expected if the cross-bedded sandstones in the valley were fluvial. Instead, the paleoflow data indicate onshore-directed (flood) tidal currents. The valley itself could be a tidal inlet, a tidally-influenced deltaic distributary, or an estuary. The valley can be traced for more than 50 km, eliminating a tidal inlet interpretation. We therefore suggest that the channel, whether originally cut as a river or deltaic distributary, has been *filled in an estuarine environment* (Dalrymple and others, 1992) with the fill consisting of a series of sand bars and a muddy central basin. The scarcity of ebb-directed cross-strata may be a function of the location of the outcrop with respect to original flood and ebb channels.

The channel is funnel shaped (open to the southeast and closing northwestward; Fig. 3; Rahmani, 1988, 1989) which is typical of many modern estuaries (e.g., the Gironde, France; Cobequid Bay, Canada). The absence of any macrofossils and trace fossils within the fill indicates a stressed environment, possibly due to strong tidal currents, high sedimentation rates, and possibly also semi-diurnal salinity fluctuations. Allen (1991) attributes the absence of burrowing fauna within the funnel zone of the Gironde Estuary (France) to high water turbidity and strong tidal currents. He also considers this lack of fauna to be distinctive of high-energy macrotidal estuaries. In this overall context, we can interpret the two facies associations in more detail.

Interpretation of Facies Association 1

The fining-upward facies succession of Association 1, together with the change from cross-bedding to ripple cross-lamination (in the upper 2 m) indicates a decrease in flow velocities. This decrease is probably related to lateral accretion of sand bodies during estuary filling and migration. The regular alternations of sand and mud (and carbonaceous) drapes on many individual foresets (Figs. 9, 10) is interpreted as tidal bundling and spring-neap tidal cyclicity

interlaminated sandstones and mudstones are overlain by a light grey mudstone that reaches 2.5 m in thickness in the south-eastern part of the area. Carbonaceous material is abundant and *in situ* root traces are common. This facies is overlain by a solitary coal (Coal 0) towards the north-west of the RDV profile (Fig. 4) and the south-west of the WC profile (Fig. 4). A split in Coal 0 occurs between RDV-9 and RDV-10, and farther to the south-east the muddy rooted facies is interbedded with thin coal seams (e.g., RDV-12). A similar split occurs between WC-1 and WC-2 (Fig. 4). Individual coal beds range from 10 to 70 cm in thickness.

(A)

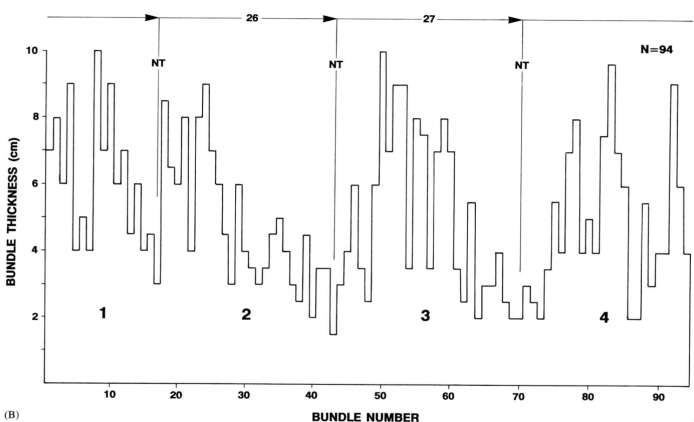

(B)

FIG. 10.—Tidal bundle sequence in Facies Association 1 at section RDV-1, (A) Cross-bedded set containing bundle sequences (N, neap; S, spring) analyzed in Figure 10B. Dark layers on foresets represent mud drapes. Hammer (right) for scale. (B) Plot of bundle thickness versus bundle number; note 26 and 27 bundles between neap tide periods (NT) indicating a semi-diurnal influence within the system.

(Visser, 1980; Boersma and Terwindt, 1981). In the estuary fill, there are 26 or 27 bundles deposited between neap tides (the thinnest bundles; Fig. 10B). Modern studies indicate that neap tides occur with a periodicity of 14.76 days. For 26 or 27 bundles to be formed in about 14 days, the tides must have been semi-diurnal. The thick-thin bundle alternations within neap-spring cycle 1 (Fig. 10) may represent diurnal inequalities (de Boer and others, 1989). The internal erosion surfaces within the sets of cross bedding are probably reactivation surfaces (de Mowbray and Visser, 1984) although they could also represent slight re-orientations of the direction of bedform propagation. Neap-spring

cycles 2 and 3 (Fig. 10) appear to be markedly asymmetrical with relatively thick bundles occurring early in the tidal cycle. The reason for this is unknown.

The numerous small scours and sideritised mud clast lags represent periods of erosion, probably related to peak strengths in the tidal currents, peak fluvial discharges, or storm enhanced tidal discharges.

The *in situ*, isolated and contorted heterolithic blocks described from channel 1 (Fig. 11) probably represent portions of collapsed channel walls. Alternatively, the isolated and contorted blocks may have been eroded from a mud rich point bar during periods of peak fluvial discharge or

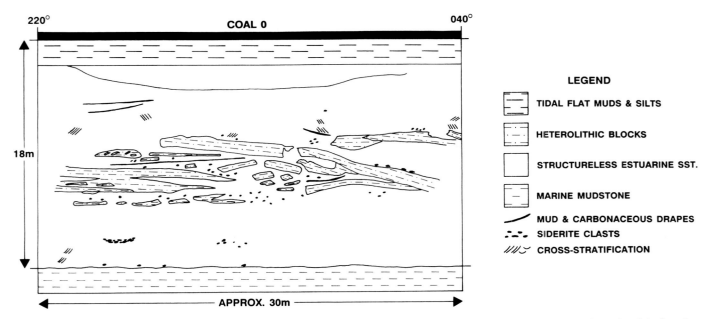

FIG. 11.—Facies Association 1 in channel 1 (see Fig. 4). Semi-schematic sketch (accurate vertical scale and schematic horizontal scale) of section perpendicular to flow direction (see Fig. 7). Note isolated and contorted nature of some of the heterolithic blocks within the structureless estuarine sandstone.

storm enhanced tidal discharges when large amounts of sand were also being transported through the system.

This facies association occurs exclusively at the seaward end of the valley fill as part of a tripartite (Nichols and Biggs, 1985) estuary fill. There is no preserved evidence for the exact nature of the estuary mouth environments, but these may have included tidal sand ridges, a partial spit or barrier across the estuary mouth, and channels through such a spit, as described in the Bay of Fundy by Dalrymple (1992) and Dalrymple and others (1991).

Interpretation of Facies Association 2

The inclined heterolithic strata in this facies association suggest lateral accretion on fluvial or estuarine point bars (Thomas and others, 1987). Deposits similar to the IHS of association 2 have been described from modern point bars within large tidal channels (Clifton, 1983; Smith, 1989). Because of their association with cross-bedded sandstones in which paleoflow is landward and in which there is good evidence of tidal currents, we interpret the IHS as having formed on gently dipping bars within an estuarine system.

Centimeter-scale Triplets.—

Each triplet indicates waning flow during deposition, with stronger flows depositing the sandstone laminations and progressively weaker flows depositing the carbonaceous material and the mudstone. The very regular stacking of sharp-based triplets suggests an equally regular repetition of flow conditions. In an estuarine tidal setting, these cyclically repetitive conditions could be related to (1) the semi-diurnal tides, (2) spring-neap changes in tidal-current velocities, or (3) annual fluctuations in the position of the turbidity maximum related to annual fluctuations in fluvial discharge.

Depositional conditions would be very variable during a monthly or annual cycle, and it is not easy to imagine how the monotonous sand-carbonaceous-mud laminations would form so consistently. We therefore suggest that the simplest interpretation of the cm-scale triplets (Fig. 15) is that they were formed by the semi-diurnal tidal currents. Sand would have been emplaced during peak flows, with deposition of carbonaceous material and (finally) mud during slack tides. Deposition of mud would have been enhanced at this location (the freshwater-saltwater transition) by flocculation due to increased salinities and also by the decrease in flow velocities at slack tides promoting settling of flocs and floc groups (Nichols and Biggs, 1985).

There is a suggestion in places that thicker and thinner triplets alternate, suggesting diurnal inequality of the tides; Nio and Yang (1991, p. 23) have used pictures supplied by Rahmani to illustrate this feature. In our experience of the outcrop, this systematic alternation is uncommon; in most places the triplets were probably formed two-per-day from either the ebb or flood tides. No paleocurrent determinations were possible within the triplets, but in channel 2 (Fig. 12) the IHS pass laterally into cross-bedded sandstones with up-estuary flow directions. It therefore seems most likely that the sand in the triplets was supplied from the marine end of the estuary. We therefore tentatively suggest that flood-tidal flows formed the triplets and that ebb flows moved through the estuary along different paths; any ebb flows in the study area were incapable of eroding the smooth mud layer at the top of each triplet.

Meter-scale Alternations.—

The larger-scale progression from sand-dominated to mud-dominated triplets (Fig. 15A) indicates longer term varia-

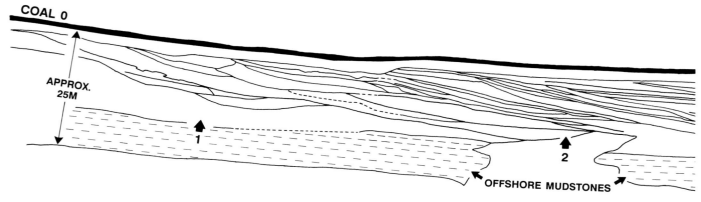

FIG. 12.—Inclined heterolithic stratification (IHS) of Facies Association 2 (channel 2) in the Willow Creek area (see Fig. 4). (A) Photomontage sections through the IHS. Black concave-up lines represent internal erosion surfaces.

tions in current strengths and sediment availability. Rahmani (1989) suggested that this reflected seasonal variations in fluvial discharge with the sandier portions being deposited during high river stage (with tidal fluctuations superimposed).

We suggest that the origin of the meter-scale alternations is more complex and is a product of up-channel and down-channel migrations of the turbidity maximum zone in response to variations in fluvial discharge (Fig. 17). The position of the turbidity maximum zone depends on the relative influences of fluvial and tidal flows, and sediment supply, such that during peak fluvial discharge, the turbidity maximum zone shifts *seaward*. Castaing and Allen (1981) have documented the seaward shift of the turbidity maximum in the Gironde estuary during high river flow. The effect of peak fluvial discharges in the Willow Creek area is to form a series of mud-dominated triplets due to: (1) the seaward shift of the turbidity maximum zone and (2) the more limited amount of sand transported *landward* up the estuary from the marine end. Rahmani's (1989) interpretation of the upward change from sandier to muddier triplets suggests decreasing fluvial discharge; our interpretation is the exact opposite, involving increasing fluvial discharge and a down-estuary shift in the zone of turbidity maximum (Fig. 17).

As noted above, the triplets pass laterally into cross-bedded sandstones with up-estuary paleoflow directions. It is therefore unlikely that the sand in the sand-dominated triplets was supplied from the *fluvial* end of the estuary as suggested by Rahmani's interpretation. To account for the upward progression into mud-dominated triplets, we therefore favor the down-estuary shift in the turbidity maximum zone.

In the successions that grade upward from sand- to mud-rich triplets (e.g., Fig. 15A), there appears to be a gradually increasing fluvial discharge (down-estuary shift of the turbidity maximum zone). In other places, mud-rich triplets erosively overlie sand-dominated triplets (Figs. 12, 14). This suggests some erosion of the lateral accretion surface during rising river stage. In other places, sand-rich triplets erosively overlie mud-rich triplets suggesting that as the turbidity maximum is forced back upstream during lower fluvial discharge, scouring takes place due to increasing tidal action.

We have so far interpreted the triplets in terms of deposition during semi-diurnal tidal fluctuations with superimposed (?seasonal) fluctuations in fluvial discharge. We have not been able to detect much evidence for a spring-neap cyclicity although one of Rahmani's photographs of possible spring-neap cyclicity has been published by Nio and Yang (1991, p. 22). In our experience, the triplets pro-

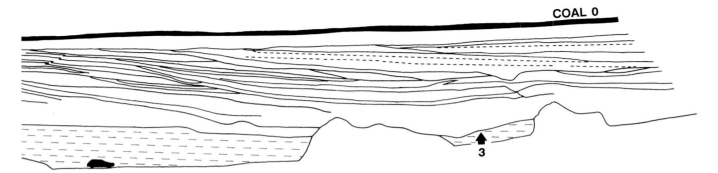

of IHS (note car in foreground for scale). (B) Photomontage overlay drawn in the field. Numbers 1 to 3 indicate locations of detailed measured

FIG. 13.—Erosional contact (arrowed) between muddy channel 2 (Facies Association 2; left) and sandy channel 3 (Facies Association 1; right) in the Willow Creek area (see Fig. 4). Channel 3 also cuts down through the offshore marine mudstones of allomember A. For scale, the cliff is approximately 60 m high.

FIG. 14.—Muddy heterolithic strata erosively overlying sandy strata within the IHS of Facies Association 2. Arrows show erosion surfaces and are about 2.5 m long.

gressively thin stratigraphically upwards (Fig. 15) with a concomitant increase in proportion of mud in each triplet rather than grouping themselves into packages of 14 or 28 layers. The thicknesses of sand, carbonaceous material, and mud in the triplets perhaps reflect sediment availability more

than slight spring-neap fluctuations in rate and amount of sediment transport.

Numerous internal erosion surfaces in the IHS (Figs. 12, 14) suggest that the semi-diurnal deposition from tidal currents was interrupted by periods of higher flow velocities. These may represent flood flows in the river as the turbidity

FIG. 15.—(A) Triplets in an overall thinner- and muddier-upward succession in Facies Association 2. Arrow marks first appearance of mudstone lithology. Scale bar is 10 cm. (B) Detail of sandy triplets from lower part of Figure 15A. Note the discrete mm-thick carbonaceous laminations within the fine sandstone. Arrows define a layer believed to be the deposit of one tidal cycle. Note also the thin sand laminations between the carbonaceous laminae and the rippled nature of the carbonaceous material within the sandy layers. (C) Detail of the upper muddier part of Figure 15A. By comparison with (B), note the large increase in proportion of mudstone to sandstone in each triplet.

maximum was displaced seaward and/or scour by tidal currents as the turbidity maximum was displaced landward. Slumping along the erosion surfaces may be the result of erosional oversteepening at the toe of the lateral accretion surfaces.

Interpretation of the Overlying Facies

The interlaminated, current-rippled sandstones and mudstones suggest intermittent sand transport and mud deposition. This facies conformably overlies the estuarine deposits; in this setting, the alternating lithologies suggest deposition in a tidal-flat environment. The sand- and IHS-

filled scours probably represent intertidal creeks similar to those described by de Mowbray (1983). The overlying carbonaceous shales with *in situ* root traces represent a muddy, vegetated environment lying between the intertidal flats and the overlying swamp environment suggested by the presence of Coal 0. On the basis of vitrinite reflectance, Rahmani (1989) suggests that Coal 0 is woody in origin.

DISCUSSION OF VALLEY ORIGIN AND ARCHITECTURE OF FILL

The channel complex is relatively straight (Fig. 3), at least 50 km long, up to 12 km wide, and about 20 m deep. It cuts into the prograding storm-dominated shoreface of

FIG. 16.—Parallel-laminated sandstone and mudstone of the tidal-flat facies.

allomember A. This channel-cutting-shoreface relationship could be autocyclic in origin, being simply due to a switch in channel position without any accompanying fluctuation of sea level. Alternatively, the relationship could be allocyclic. In this case, channel incision through the shoreface would be related to a continuation of the interpreted fall of relative sea level that first caused progradation of the sharp-based shoreface in allomember A. The fact that only one large channel complex is known at this stratigraphic horizon, along with the very large scale of the channel, makes an allocyclic (lowstand incision) origin a little more likely than simple autocyclic channel switching.

Subsurface work suggests that the estuary has a tripartite facies distribution (Rahmani, 1988, 1989). His well log and core cross section down the length of the valley (Rahmani 1988, his Fig. 26, p. 460) shows that estuarine muds occur between the outcrop area and the town of Drumheller and that these muds are underlain by about 5 m of estuarine sand.

Within the main channel in the Willow Creek area, the multiple smaller channel incisions (Fig. 4) are probably due to the constant shifting of several coeval flood channels. In the present Salmon River Estuary, Cobequid Bay, Nova Scotia (which is similar in scale to the Drumheller incision), co-existing flood and ebb channels have shifted position laterally during the last few decades (Dalrymple and others, 1990). These shifts result in channels that persistently erode previously deposited channel sediments.

Channel 2, which has a dominantly muddy fill (Fig. 4), is juxtaposed with channels 1 and 3, which are sand-filled (Fig. 12). Within channel 2, the tripartite estuary model can explain the seasonal/yearly juxtaposition of the meter-scale sandy and muddy strata. However, annual fluctuations in fluvial and tidal discharge alone cannot explain the lateral channeled juxtaposition of the seaward end of the turbidity maximum zone (channel 2) with the estuarine marine zone (sandy channels 1 and 3). This presumably represents a longer term, seaward shift of the turbidity maximum zone during channel switching which is most probably produced by a relative sea-level fall. The sandy fill of channel 1 is incised by the muddy fill of channel 2 implying a basinward shift of facies. The muddy fill of channel 2 is incised by the sandy fill of channel 3 implying a landward shift of facies

and re-establishment of marine estuary-mouth sand deposition. This landward shift may result from a rise in relative sea level.

CONTROLS ON ESTUARINE DEPOSITION

The incised valley was originally cut by a river or distributary and transformed into an estuary during a rise of relative sea level. The cutting and filling of the four separate channels may have been partly autocyclic (e.g., channel avulsions, seasonal changes in river discharge) although major landward and seaward shifts of the turbidity maximum zone (sandy channel 1 to muddy channel 2 and back to sandy channel 3) may have been caused by minor sea-level fluctuations. Toward the end of valley filling, the tidal flat and rooted facies spread from the valley to rest upon the paleo-shoreface of allomember A (Fig. 18; RDV-7, 8).

The spread of tidal-flat facies outside the estuary and onto the older shoreface suggests a continuation of relative sea-level rise after estuary filling. This rise may also have created the accommodation space for the peat that subsequently was compacted into coal 0. By this time, the river had presumably avulsed out of the study area; at the stratigraphic level of the coal, there is no evidence either of fluvial or estuarine facies in the area.

We have not identified any fluvial facies preserved within the channel and therefore suggest that during the first phase of transgression of the incised channel any fluvial sand was reworked into tidal sand bars, and any fluvial mud was washed away to sea. The geometry of the valley was also probably modified by tidal currents, and the paleocurrent data suggest that new sand was supplied from the marine end.

The fining-upward facies succession formed during the filling of the estuary which occurred in response to a relative sea-level rise. Although evidence for superimposed higher frequency relative sea-level fluctuations within the valley-fill are observed, the major facies trends are probably more controlled by lateral migration of channels and bars and autocyclic up- and down-estuary shifts in the position of the turbidity maximum zone.

IMPLICATIONS IN TERMS OF SEQUENCE STRATIGRAPHY

The incision at the base of allomember B is a good candidate for a sequence boundary. However, sequence boundaries should be represented by regionally extensive unconformities whereas the allomember B incision has so far only been traced over a relatively small area (50 × 12 km; Rahmani, 1988, 1989). The regional extent of this surface is unknown. A basinward shift in facies should also be observed at sequence boundaries at the base of incised valleys (van Wagoner and others, 1990). However, the basal erosion surface of this valley only cuts into offshore mudstones (with a distinct basinward shift in facies) in the north-west of the study area (Fig. 4; RDV-1) and farther toward the south-east (the area studied by Saunders, 1989). In most locations the channel erodes into shoreface sandstones, which may simply indicate a lateral rather than basinward shift in facies. It is unclear whether the channel eroded into a pre-existing shoreface or its own coeval shoreface.

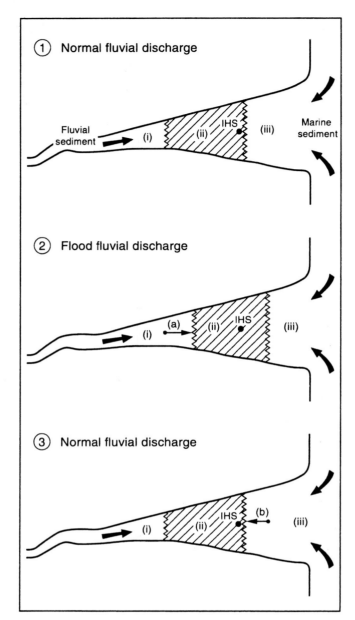

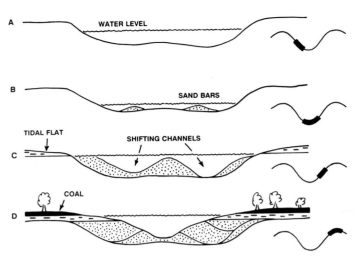

FIG. 18.—Relationship of valley incision and filling to changes in relative sea level. (A) Valley is incised during falling stage. (B) At lowstand, some sand bars begin to form within the valley. (C) During rising stage, individual channels shift autocyclically within the valley, which is now bordered by tidal flats. (D) Toward the end of rising stage and at highstand, more sandbars plug the estuary and coals begin to form around the valley margins. During this cycle of relative sea-level change, superimposed higher order falls and rises of relative sea level result in axial shifts of facies belts within the incised valley.

FIG. 17.—Explanation of the meter-scale alternations of Facies Association 2. Plan view of idealized estuary, with IHS indicating position of the IHS beds of Facies Association 2. Note position of the estuarine fluvial zone (i), turbidity maximum zone (ii), and estuarine marine zone (iii). With normal fluvial discharge (1), the IHS form at the marine end of the turbidity maximum zone, with sand supplied from the marine end of the system; sand-rich IHS are deposited. During flood fluvial discharge (2), the turbidity maximum zone moves downstream (arrow a). The IHS are now farther from the marine supply of sand and mud rich strata are deposited. With a return to normal fluvial discharge (3), the turbidity maximum zone shifts back landward (arrow b), and marine sand is supplied to the IHS again; sand-rich IHS are deposited.

Most of the palaeocurrents in the study area recorded from cross-bedding directly overlying the erosion surface, indicate up-estuary (landward) flows, and there appear to be no fluvial deposits directly overlying the erosion surface. If so, the surface of subaerial erosion (i.e., the *candidate se-* *quence boundary*) can no longer be identified; it has been erosionally modified by the flooding surface that lies at the base of the estuarine sand in the channel. The modification of the valley floor and the creation of an estuary from a pre-existing river or distributary both depend upon the initiation of transgression. We therefore, do not agree with some reports that all incised-valley fills be assigned to *lowstand* systems tracts. Instead, the data presented here supports the views of van Wagoner and others (1990, p. 31) who suggest that erosion of the valley and sediment by-pass occur during a relative fall of sea level and that deposition in the valleys occurs "in response to a relative rise in sea level, generally during the late lowstand or transgressive systems tracts."

CONCLUSIONS

The nature of the valley fill, particularly the paleoflow directions and IHS with tidally-influenced triplets, strongly indicates its estuarine origin. Tidal influences were strong as indicated by the tidal bundle sequences within cross-bed sets that exhibit semi-diurnal tidal cyclicity. The cm-scale, sand-mud alternations of the IHS probably reflect tidal cyclicities, and the meter scale, sand-mud alternations suggest axial migration of the turbidity maximum zone, probably due to seasonal fluctuations in fluvial discharge. The juxtaposition of channels that are predominantly sand- and mud-filled indicates that predominantly autocyclic processes were at times overprinted by fluctuations of relative sea level.

However, it is not clear how the incised valley originated; it may represent a falling stage and lowstand incision, but it might also have an autocyclic origin due to the switching of fluvial or deltaic distributary channels. Unfortunately, there is no outcrop (other than in the Red Deer River valley) to check for these other possible channels. If incision is related to a fall of relative sea level, the base of the valley was initially a sequence boundary. However, the preserved evidence suggests that the fluvially-cut surface has been modified during transgression and the overlying estuarine valley-fill deposits are probably associated with transgressive systems tract deposition. Thus the sequence boundary appears to have been modified into a transgressive surface of erosion. Finally, we conclude that because estuaries only form during transgressive conditions, it makes no sense for estuarine deposits to be assigned to a *lowstand* systems tract. Also, transgressive systems tract deposits *can* be identified without the preservation of an unmodified, underlying sequence boundary.

In a broader context, the sediments we have discussed occur at a critical point in the filling of the foreland basin, namely where a marine section (Bearpaw) is about to be overwhelmed by more than 1000 m of non-marine sediments (Edmonton Group). Despite the implied high rate of sediment input and rapid filling of accommodation space, fluctuations of relative sea level are still able to overprint autocyclic processes within the incised valley.

ACKNOWLEDGMENTS

We thank Ray Rahmani for his initial help in setting up the project, and the Natural Sciences and Engineering Research Council of Canada for funding. The staff of the Royal Tyrrell Museum in Drumheller were particularly helpful in making facilities available during the fieldwork. We are grateful to the referees, D. A. Leckie and J. R. Suter, for their helpful comments on the manuscript.

REFERENCES

AINSWORTH, R. B., 1991, Sedimentology and high resolution sequence stratigraphy of the Bearpaw-Horseshoe Canyon transition (Upper Cretaceous), Drumheller, Alberta, Canada: Unpublished M. Sc. Thesis, McMaster University, Hamilton, 213 p.

AINSWORTH, R. B., 1992, Sedimentology and Sequence Stratigraphy of the Upper Cretaceous, Bearpaw-Horseshoe Canyon transition, Drumheller, Alberta: Calgary, American Association of Petroleum Geologists Annual Convention, Field Trip Guidebook 7, 118 p.

AINSWORTH, R. B., 1994, Marginal marine sedimentology and high resolution sequence analysis; Bearpaw-Horseshoe Canyon transition, Drumheller, Alberta: Bulletin of Canadian Petroleum Geology, v. 42, p. 26–54.

ALLAN, J. A., AND SANDERSON, J. O. G., 1945, Geology of the Red Deer and Rosebud sheets, Alberta: Edmonton, Alberta Research Council, Report No. 13, 110 p.

ALLEN, G. P., 1991, Sedimentary processes and facies in the Gironde estuary; a recent model for macrotidal estuarine systems, in Smith, D. G., Reinson, G., Zaitlin, B. A., and Rahmani, R. A., eds., Clastic Tidal Sedimentology: Calgary, Canadian Society of Petroleum Geologists Memoir 16, p. 29–39.

ALLEN, G. P., SALOMON, J. C., BASSOULET, P., DU PENHOAT, Y., AND DE GRANDPRE, C., 1980, Effects of tides on mixing and suspended sediment transport in macrotidal estuaries: Sedimentary Geology, v. 26, p. 69–90.

AL-RAWAHI, Z. S., 1993, Sedimentology and allostratigraphy of the Basal Belly River Formation of central Alberta: Unpublished M. Sc. Thesis, McMaster University, Hamilton, 174 p.

BOERSMA, J. R., AND TERWINDT, J. H. J., 1981, Neap-spring tide sequences of intertidal shoal deposits in a mesotidal estuary: Sedimentology, v. 28, p. 151–170.

CASTAING, P., AND ALLEN, G. P., 1981, Mechanisms controlling seaward escape of suspended sediment from the Gironde; a macrotidal estuary in France: Marine Geology, v. 40, p. 101–118.

CLIFTON, H. E., 1983, Discrimination between subtidal and intertidal facies in Pleistocene deposits, Willapa Bay, Washington: Journal of Sedimentary Petrology, v. 53, p. 353–369.

DALRYMPLE, R. W., 1992, Tidal depositional systems, in Walker, R. G., and James, N. P., Facies Models: Response to Sea Level Change: St. John's, Geological Association of Canada, p. 195–218.

DALRYMPLE, R. W., KNIGHT, R. J., ZAITLIN, B. A., AND MIDDLETON, G. V., 1990, Dynamics and facies model of a macrotidal sand-bar complex, Cobequid Bay-Salmon River Estuary (Bay of Fundy): Sedimentology, v. 37, p. 577–612.

DALRYMPLE, R. W., MAKINO, Y., AND ZAITLIN, B. A., 1991, Temporal and spatial patterns of rhythmite deposition on mud flats in the macrotidal Cobequid Bay-Salmon River estuary, Bay of Fundy, Canada, in Smith, D. G., Reinson, G. E., Zaitlin, B. A., and Rahmani, R. A., eds., Clastic Tidal Sedimentology: Calgary, Canadian Society of Petroleum Geologists Memoir 16, p. 137–160.

DALRYMPLE, R. W., ZAITLIN, B. A., AND BOYD, R., 1992, Estuarine facies models; conceptual basis and stratigraphic implications: Journal of Sedimentary Petrology, v. 62, p. 1130–1146.

DE BOER, P. L., OOST, A. P., AND VISSER, M. J., 1989, The diurnal inequality of the tide as a parameter for recognizing tidal influences: Journal of Sedimentary Petrology, v. 59, p. 912–921.

DE MOWBRAY, T., 1983, The genesis of lateral accretion deposits in recent intertidal mudflat channels, Solway Firth, Scotland: Sedimentology, v. 30, p. 425–435.

DE MOBRAY, T., AND VISSER, M. J., 1984, Reactivation surfaces in subtidal channel deposits, Oosterschelde, southwest Netherlands: Journal of Sedimentary Petrology, v. 54, p. 811–824.

EISBACHER, G. H., CARRIGY, M. A., AND CAMPBELL, R. B., 1974, Paleodrainage pattern and late-orogenic basins of the Canadian Cordillera, in Dickinson, W. R., ed., Tectonics and Sedimentation: Tulsa, Society of Economic Paleontologists and Mineralogists Special Publication 22, p. 143–177.

GIBSON, D. W., 1977, Upper Cretaceous and Tertiary coal-bearing strata in the Drumheller-Ardley region, Red Deer River Valley, Alberta: Calgary, Geological Survey of Canada, Paper 76–35, 41 p.

IRISH, E. J. W., 1970, The Edmonton Group of South-Central Alberta: Bulletin of Canadian Petroleum Geology, v. 18, p. 125–155.

LERBEKMO, J. F., AND COULTER, K. C., 1985, Late Cretaceous to early Tertiary magnetostratigraphy of a continental sequence: Red Deer Valley, Alberta, Canada: Canadian Journal of Earth Sciences, v. 22, p. 567–583.

NICHOLS, M. M., AND BIGGS, R. B., 1985, Estuaries, in Davis, R. A., ed., Coastal Sedimentary Environments: New York, Springer Verlag, p. 77–186.

NIO, S. D., AND YANG, C. S., 1991, Diagnostic attributes of clastic tidal deposits; a review, in Smith, D. G., Reinson, G. E., Zaitlin, B. A., and Rahmani, R. A., eds., Clastic Tidal Sedimentology: Calgary, Canadian Society of Petroleum Geologists Memoir 16, p. 3–28.

NORTH AMERICAN COMMISSION ON STRATIGRAPHIC NOMENCLATURE, 1983, North American Stratigraphic Code: American Association of Petroleum Geologists Bulletin, v. 67, p. 841–875.

OBRADOVICH, J. D., AND COBBAN, W. A., 1975, A time-scale for the Late Cretaceous of the Western Interior of North America, in Caldwell, W. G. E., ed., The Cretaceous System in the Western Interior of North America: St. John's, Geological Association of Canada Special Paper 13, p. 31–54.

PLINT, A. G., 1991, High-frequency relative sea level oscillations in Upper Cretaceous shelf clastics of the Alberta foreland basin: possible evidence for a glacio-eustatic control, in McDonald, D. I. M., ed., Sedimentation, Tectonics and Eustacy: Oxford, International Association of Sedimentologists Special Publication 12, p. 409–428.

POSAMENTIER, H. W., ALLEN, G. P., JAMES, D. P., AND TESSON, M., 1992, Forced regressions in a sequence stratigraphic framework: concepts, examples, and exploration significance: American Association of Petroleum Geologists Bulletin, v. 76, p. 1687–1709.

POWER, B. A., 1993, Sedimentology and allostratigraphy of the Upper Cretaceous (Campanian) Lea Park-Belly River transition in central Alberta, Canada: Unpublished Ph. D. Dissertation, McMaster University, Hamilton, 411 p.

RAHMANI, R. A., 1983, Facies Relationships and Paleoenvironments of a Late Cretaceous Tide-dominated Delta, Drumheller, Alberta: Calgary, Canadian Society of Petroleum Geologists, Conference on the Mesozoic of Middle North America, Field Trip Guidebook 2, 36 p.

RAHMANI, R. A., 1988, Estuarine tidal channel and nearshore sedimentation of a Late Cretaceous epicontinental sea, Drumheller, Alberta, Canada, *in* de Boer, P. L., van Gelder, A., and Nio, S. D., eds., Tide-influenced Sedimentary Environments and Facies: Dordrecht, D. Reidel Publishing Company, p. 433–471.

RAHMANI, R. A., 1989, Cretaceous Tidal Estuarine and Deltaic Deposits, Drumheller, Alberta: Calgary, Canadian Society of Petroleum Geologists, Second International Research Symposium on Clastic Tidal Deposits, Field Guide, 55 p.

RAHMANI, R. A., AND LERBEKMO, J. F., 1975, Heavy mineral analysis of Upper Cretaceous and Paleocene sandstones in Alberta and adjacent areas in Saskatchewan, *in* Caldwell, W. G. E., ed., The Cretaceous System in the Western Interior of North America: St. John's, Geological Association of Canada, Special Paper 13, p. 607–632.

SAUNDERS, T. D. A., 1989, Trace fossils and sedimentology of a Late Cretaceous progradational barrier island sequence: Bearpaw-Horseshoe Canyon Formation transition, Dorothy, Alberta: Unpublished M. Sc. Thesis, University of Alberta, Edmonton, 170 p.

SHEPHEARD, W. W., AND HILLS, L. V., 1970, Depositional environments, Bearpaw-Horseshoe Canyon (Upper Cretaceous) transition zone, Drumheller "badlands," Alberta: Bulletin of Canadian Petroleum Geology, v. 18, p. 166–215.

SMITH, D. G., 1989, Comparative sedimentology of mesotidal (2 to 4 m) estuarine channel point bar deposits from modern examples and ancient Athabasca oil sands (Lower Cretaceous), McMurray Formation, *in* Reinson, G. E., ed., Modern and Ancient Examples of Clastic Tidal Deposits—A Core and Peel Workshop: Calgary, Canadian Society of Petroleum Geologists, Second International Research Symposium on Clastic Tidal Deposits, p. 60–65.

THOMAS, R. G., SMITH, D. G., WOOD, J. M., VISSER, J., CALVERLEY-RANGE, E. A., AND KOSTER, E. H., 1987, Inclined heterolithic stratification—terminology, description, interpretation and significance: Sedimentary Geology, v. 53, p. 123–179.

VAN WAGONER, J. C., MITCHUM, R. M. JR., CAMPION, K. M., AND RAHMANIAN, V. D., 1990, Siliciclastic Sequence Stratigraphy in Well Logs, Cores, and Outcrops: Tulsa, American Association of Petroleum Geologists, Methods in Exploration Series 7, 55 p.

VISSER, M. J., 1980, Neap-spring cycles reflected in Holocene subtidal large-scale bedform deposits: a preliminary note: Geology, v. 8, p. 543–546.

WILLIAMS, G. D., AND STELCK, C. R., 1975, Speculations on the Cretaceous palaeogeography of North America, *in* Caldwell, W. G. E., ed., The Cretaceous System in the Western Interior of North America: St. John's, Geological Association of Canada, Special Paper 13, p. 1–20.

STRATIGRAPHY AND DEPOSITIONAL HISTORY WITHIN INCISED-PALEOVALLEY FILLS AND RELATED FACIES, DOUGLAS GROUP (MISSOURIAN/VIRGILIAN; UPPER CARBONIFEROUS) OF KANSAS, U.S.A.

ALLEN W. ARCHER
Department of Geology, Kansas State University, Manhattan, Kansas 66506
WILLIAM P. LANIER
Department of Earth Sciences, Emporia State University, Emporia, Kansas 66801
AND
HOWARD R. FELDMAN
Kansas Geological Survey, Lawrence, Kansas 66047

ABSTRACT: The Douglas Group (Stephanian) of eastern Kansas contains several paleovalleys that were eroded during falling sea level and filled during lowstands and subsequent transgressions. One paleovalley exhibits 34 m of incision, is approximately 32 km in width, and can be laterally traced along outcrop and into the subsurface to the south for approximately 140 km. A fluvial to estuarine to marine facies mosaic can be delineated both laterally, from north to south, as well as within individual vertical sections.

Paleovalleys were filled with a fining upward succession; the lowest facies is cross-bedded conglomerate and sandstone. The conglomerate contains clasts and fossils eroded from older units exposed within the paleovalley. Sandstone beds exhibit large scale (up to 1 m thick) trough and tabular-planar cross beds. Paleocurrent directions are generally southwest and indicate deposition via large-scale fluvial systems that were constrained within the paleovalleys.

Overlying the fluvial sandstone is a diverse suite of lithofacies including planar-bedded sandstones and siltstones, heterolithic facies, sheet-like sandstone, bioturbated sandstones, and marine facies. The planar-bedded sandstones and siltstones can exhibit neap-spring tidal cycles which were formed in high-intertidal settings. Heterolithic facies are typically laminated and contain pinstripe laminations, starved ripples, and well-developed tidal cycles (cyclical tidal rhythmites). Neap-spring tidal cycles are common and range from 1 cm in thickness in heterolithic facies to as much as 1 m in thickness in planar-bedded siltstones. An interpretation invoking very high localized depositional rates is substantiated by the presence of buried upright trees, some of which have attached foliage. Tidal rhythmites are well developed in siliciclastic facies immediately overlying coals. The heterolithic and silty rhythmites were apparently developed within the estuarine turbidity maximum where high turbidity and locally high depositional rates resulted from estuarine circulation patterns and tidal amplification.

The sheet-like sandstone bodies are dominated by small-scale trough crossbedding and ripple- and planar laminations. Paleocurrents are bimodal to the southwest and northeast, reflecting ebb- and flood-tidal currents. Features such as flat-topped ripples, rain-drop imprints, and tetrapod trackways indicate deposition within the intertidal zone.

Estuarine to marine sequences contain progressively higher diversities of biogenic structures. "Flaggy" bioturbated sandstones indicate significant marine influences. These sandstones are capped by widespread marine shales and limestones that extend far beyond the limits of paleovalleys. Shales can be extensively bioturbated, lack laminations, and locally contain marine body fossils. Limestones form widespread lithostratigraphic markers and contain abundant marine fossils such as bivalves, fusulinids, brachiopods, crinoids, and bryozoans. Some of the limestones consist of shelly lags which indicate the development of transgressive surfaces of erosion.

There are two major sequences developed within the Douglas Group. The sequence boundaries can be placed at the contact between incised fluvial sandstones and eroded underlying, commonly marine, strata. The fluvial and estuarine facies were deposited during lowstand and subsequent sea-level rise. The highstand system includes marine shales and limestones which were erosionally incised during subsequent fall in sea level.

INTRODUCTION

In Upper Carboniferous strata of the United States, cyclical alternations of siliciclastics and carbonates (cyclothems) have been the focus of intense investigation, primarily concerning the relative contributions of glacio-eustatic oscillations, tectonic movements, and climatic cycles (e.g., Heckel 1986; Klein, 1992; Cecil, 1990). Emphasis on Upper Carboniferous cyclothems in the midcontinent U. S. has focused on interpreting black shale and carbonate lithologies (e.g., Heckel, 1977, 1983, 1986; Coveney and others, 1991). Thick siliciclastic parts of cycles have been relatively neglected in recent times, yet these units contain a complex array of facies that are not readily explainable by use of the commonly cited delta-progradation model. The Douglas Group (Missourian-Virgilian), which is the thickest siliciclastic unit within Missourian-Virgilian Kansas-type cyclothems, is the focus of this study.

A key element in understanding Upper Carboniferous siliciclastic sequences is the recognition of cyclical tidal rhythmites which are rhythmically bedded, muddy through sandy sediment in which the thicknesses of successive laminae and beds reflect differences in tidal heights forced by earth/moon/sun orbital geometries (Archer and others, 1991). Cyclical tidal rhythmites are now known from Upper Carboniferous rocks in the Appalachian Basin (Martino and Sanderson, 1991), Black Warrior Basin (Demko and others, 1991), Illinois Basin (Kvale and Archer, 1989, 1990, 1991; Kvale and others, 1989; Baird and others, 1986), Forest City Basin (Archer and others, 1994), and central Colorado (Archer, 1991). Yet despite these numerous examples of cyclical tidal rhythmites, and the great strides that have been made in matching lunar orbital periodicities to patterns of bed thicknesses, an understanding of the depositional environments of these rocks, especially regarding tidal ranges and positions within coastal environments, has remained incomplete. As discussed herein, however, much of the sedimentology of these rhythmite-bearing lithofacies can be explained in the context of fluvial to tidal-estuarine facies deposited within valley-fill sequences.

Incised-valley Systems: Origin and Sedimentary Sequences, SEPM Special Publication No. 51
Copyright © 1994, SEPM (Society for Sedimentary Geology), ISBN 1-56576-015-8

GEOLOGIC SETTING

Location Of Study Area

The surficial and subsurface stratigraphic setting for the Douglas Group has been well established (e.g., Bowsher and Jewett, 1943; Lins, 1950; Winchell, 1957; Sanders, 1959). The outcrop belt of the Douglas Group roughly parallels depositional dip, presenting an ideal opportunity to study the onlap of nonmarine-to-marine sequences in a structurally simple cratonic setting (Fig. 1). Previous work has concentrated on specific aspects of the Douglas Group, but no definitive overview and model of the diverse suite of lithofacies has been previously presented. Previous sedimentological studies of the Douglas sandstones (Bower, 1961; Griffith, 1981; Hamblin, 1964; Henning, 1985; Lins, 1950; Minor, 1969; Rutan, 1980; Sanders, 1959; Walton and Griffith, 1985) have delineated the major aspects of facies relationships. Comprehensive stratigraphic treatments of the section have also been performed (D. Ball, 1985; S. Ball, 1964; Bowsher and Jewett, 1943; Patterson, 1933; Winchell, 1957; Stephenson, 1958).

Characterization of the various major lithofacies described in this report are based upon several key localities and groups of closely spaced localities in specific counties (Fig. 2). In general, there is increased fluvial influence and decreased marine influence in the northern part of the outcrop belt in eastern Kansas. The fluvial components are especially well developed and exposed in Wyandotte, Leavenworth, and Douglas counties of northeastern Kan-

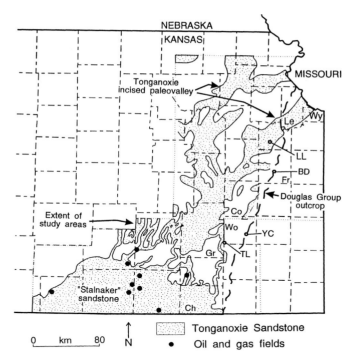

FIG. 2—Map of eastern Kansas showing outcrop belt of the Douglas Group and the limit of the Tonganoxie paleovalley and "Stalnaker" sandstone (adapted from Lins, 1950; Winchell, 1957; Sanders, 1959; Griffith, 1981). Open circles are localities discussed in the text. BD-Buildex quarry; Ch-Chautauqua County; Co-Coffey County; Fr-Franklin County; Gr-Greenwood County; Le-Leavenworth County; LL-Lonestar Lake (Douglas County); TL-Toronto Lake; Wo-Woodson County; Wy-Wyandote County; YC-Yates Center.

sas. Tidal rhythmites are best exposed in Douglas and Franklin counties of east-central Kansas. Sheet-like sandstones are well exposed around the Toronto Reservoir in Greenwood and Woodson counties, and marine-influenced sandstones are best exposed in Chautauqua County in southeastern Kansas.

Stratigraphy

The formalized lithostratigraphy of Pennsylvanian strata in Kansas is complex because many thin, marine stratigraphic units, particularly carbonates and black shales, can be laterally traced for considerable distances. Such widespread units, which have been given member to even formational rank, result in "layercake" geometries that characterize much of the northern midcontinent. The Douglas Group overlies and underlies such widespread carbonates and shales (Fig. 3); lateral facies variability and valley incision create a number of complexities within the Douglas Group regarding application of detailed lithostratigraphic nomenclature. Valley-fill relationships have long been recognized because of incision into underlying marine units (Lins, 1950). Our studies indicate that as much as 34 m of incision occurs within the subsurface (Fig. 4). During valley incision, lithified carbonates in the eroded stratigraphic units impeded downcutting of the paleovalleys. Thus, many of the paleovalleys exhibit a benched paleotopography (Fig.

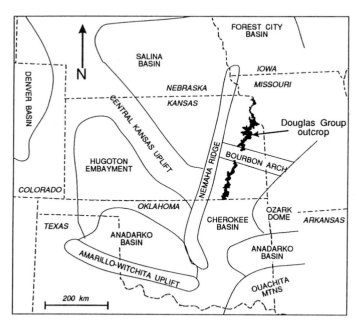

FIG. 1—Regional geological setting and structural features associated with outcrop belt of Douglas Group (solid black). To the north of the Bourbon Arch, fluvial facies dominant the valley-fill sequences whereas marine influences become more dominant south of this structural feature. Along the western edge of the paleodepositional systems, the Nemaha Ridge and Central Kansas Uplift served to confine the fluvial system during lowstands and direct paleoflow to the southwest. During highstands, the sedimentological effects of these structural features were much reduced.

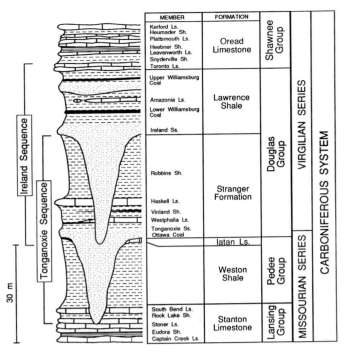

FIG. 3—Schematic stratigraphic section of the Douglas Group in the study area based primarily on well-logs and exposures in Leavenworth and Douglas Counties. The vertical section can be subdivided into two major unconformity-bounded sequences. Based upon Moore and others (1951).

4) whereby the lithified carbonates formed valley-wall erosional terraces and valley floors. Evidence for subaerial exposure of the valley walls includes the presence of *in situ* coals and paleosols (Goebel and others, 1989).

A number of formerly economic coals occur within the laterally variable, terrestrial facies that characterizes the Douglas Group (Fig. 5). Before and during World War II, there was extensive surface and underground mining of Douglas Group coals. Detailed analyses of Douglas Group stratigraphy during these mining operations (Bowsher and Jewett, 1943) provide much data on coal-bed distributions that is no longer readily available from existing surface exposures.

FACIES DESCRIPTIONS AND DEPOSITIONAL INTERPRETATIONS

The Douglas Group can be divided into seven major facies which are differentiated on the basis of lithology, sedimentary structures, paleocurrent distributions, and trace and body fossils. Within the proposed fluvial-estuarine-marine transition these facies include: (1) basal conglomerate and cross-bedded sandstones of a fluvial facies; (2) horizontally bedded, very fine-grained sandstones and siltstones of the fluvial to estuarine transitional facies; (3) "gray shale" facies characterized by lenticular and flaser bedded (heterolithic) mudstones and siltstones deposited within mid-estuary environments; (4) cross-bedded and horizontally bedded sandstones representing the estuarine-sandflat facies; (5) interbedded sandstone and mudstone with marine body and trace fossils representing the estuarine to marine transitional facies; (6) shell-lag bearing limestones related to transgressive surfaces of erosion (ravinement); and (7) fossiliferous shales, black, organic-rich shales, and open marine limestones formed upon a marine shelf. Coals also occur within

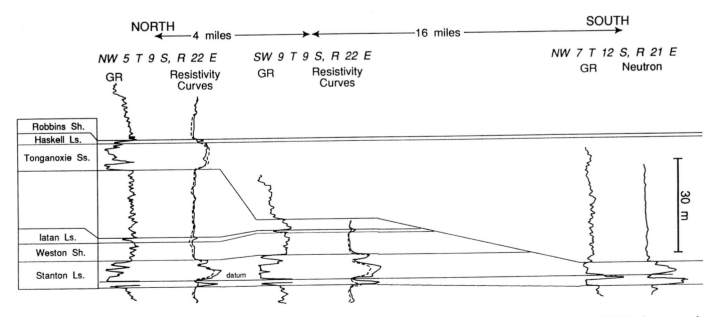

FIG. 4—North-south cross section through the northern half of the main Tonganoxie paleovalley that was mapped by Lins (1950) in Leavenworth County. The Haskell Limestone is projected to the south based on nearby outcrops and well-logs. In the southern-most well-logs, the South Bend Limestone and Rock Lake Shale Members of the Stanton Limestone have been removed by pre-Tonganoxie erosion. Resistivity curves are not shown above well fluid levels. GR-Gamma ray.

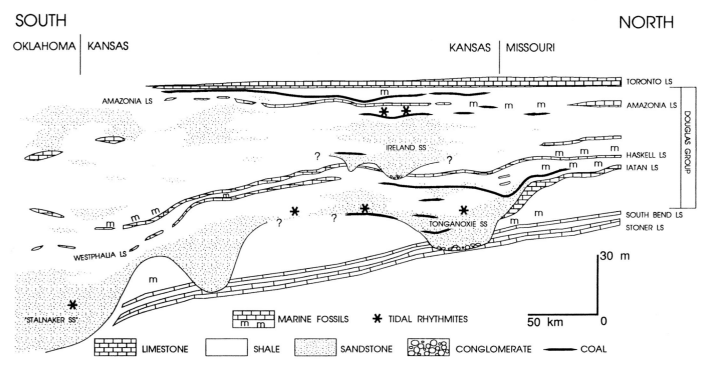

FIG. 5—Cross section of the Douglas Group along the outcrop belt illustrating lateral and vertical lithofacies variability and location of tidal rhythmites. The southern portion of the cross section extends westward into the subsurface in order to show the "Stalnaker" sandstone. Modified from Bowsher and Jewett (1943) and based upon additional information from S. Ball (1964).

the Douglas Group and are most commonly associated with fluvial to estuarine facies.

Basal Conglomerates and Crossbedded Sandstone Facies

This facies is dominated by thick, quartz arenitic to subarkosic, medium- to fine-grained sandstone and underlying, crossbedded conglomerate. In the Stranger Formation, this facies is represented by Tonganoxie Sandstone outcrops in Leavenworth, northwestern Wyandotte, and Douglas Counties. In Douglas and Franklin Counties, this facies includes exposures of the Ireland Sandstone.

In central and southern Leavenworth and northwestern Wyandotte Counties, the base of the Tonganoxie Sandstone is defined by conglomerates (locally absent to 3 m thick) that disconformably overlie shales and carbonates of the Stanton Formation and Weston Shale (Lins, 1950). Conglomerate is composed of limestone, fine-grained sandstone, mudstone pebbles and granules, and abraded invertebrate fossils. This composition reflects the derivation of the conglomerate from eroded, underlying stratigraphic units. Plant fossils are common and range upward in size to tree trunks with decimeter dimensions (Lins, 1950). The conglomerates are overlain and locally intercalated with up to 20 m of dominantly medium- to large-scale, trough crossbedded sandstones. Trough cross-bed coset thicknesses range from 0.1 to over a meter with widths of 1 to 4 meters and lengths up to 6 meters. Pebble lags commonly mark the lower, erosional, bounding surfaces of the trough cosets. Tabular cross-beds with tangential to planar foresets occur

in the upper portions of the sandstone outcrops in south-central Leavenworth County. Coset and bedset thickness for both trough and tabular cross-beds generally decrease vertically and exhibit an upward-fining sequence. In the upper parts of sandstone sections, planar foresets locally exhibit clay drapes. These sandstones contain abraded plant fossils, especially twig, branch, and log-sized materials. Invertebrate fossils are exceedingly rare, but the upper parts of sandstone units contain poorly preserved *Carbonicola*-type bivalves and associated trace fossils (*Lockeia* and associated vertically oriented escape structures). Similar association of bivalve trace fossils occur in Pennsylvanian sandstones of Indiana (Archer and Maples, 1984).

Subsurface and outcrop studies of the fluvial sandstone facies indicate elongate, channel-form rather than sheet-like geometries (Lins, 1950; Sanders, 1959; Rutan, 1980). Paleocurrent data collected for the present study as well as the analyses of Bower (1961) and Minor (1969) indicate dominant south to southwestward transport directions for the cross-bedded sandstones roughly paralleling the long axes of the Douglas paleovalleys.

Planar-bedded Sandstone and Siltstone Facies

Planar laminae to beds of very fine-grained sandstone and siltstone characterize this fluvial to estuarine transitional facies. Exceptional exposures of this facies in the Tonganoxie Sandstone are found at the Buildex Quarry locality (see Fig. 2). Rutan (1980, p. 42) describes a lithologically similar, "streaked siltstone" facies from the Lawrence Formation in southern Douglas County.

The Buildex Quarry exposures consist of five meters of sheet-like, vertically accreted, siltstones and sandy siltstones bounded above and below by thin coals and encasing upright plants with attached leaves. Beds and lamina throughout most of the vertical sequence are separated by thin clay drapes and generally non-erosive bounding surfaces (Fig. 6A). Strata range upward from submillimeter-thick, normally graded cyclical rhythmites in the lower 0.5 meter of the sequence to graded bedsets up to 12.5 centimeters thick composed of "Bouma-like" sequences (Fig. 6B). Synsedimentary convolutions and a variety of water escape structures such as flames and pillars are found in the thicker bedsets. Strata within the upper approximately two meters of the exposure are locally confined within channels that are conformable with underlying strata but onlap "channel levees." The "channel levees" are pervasively rooted and contain upright plants and trees with attached leaves. Bedding surfaces within the "channel levees" exhibit linguoid ripples, sinuous-crested ripples, or planar surfaces. Raindrop impressions occur as depressions on bed surfaces and casts on bed soles and are preserved on approximately 10% of the bedding planes. Other physical sedimentary structures include stick drag marks, microload structures, runzel marks, rille and runnel marks, runoff wash-outs, falling-water marks, starved wind ripples, and microstrandline marks in ripple troughs with raindrop impressions on the ripple crests (Lanier and others, 1993). Paleocurrent analyses indicate a dominant southwestwards vector mean with a minor, subordinant northeastwards mode. Detailed thickness measurements show a continuous gradational series of thickening and thinning with a well-developed periodicity between millimeter-scale lamina through decimeter-thick beds (Lanier and others, 1993). These periodicities indicate the presence of cyclical tidal rhythmites in this facies.

The planar-bedded siltstones contain abundant plant fossils and a diverse assemblage of trace fossils. Ichnofossils include the surface traces *Plangtichnus*, *Haplotichnus*, *and Treptichnus*, arthropod traces (including *Kopichnium*), fish-fin drag marks, and tetrapod trackways. This assemblage is similar to that described from laminated Pennsylvanian siltstones in Indiana (Archer and Maples, 1984) and Alabama (Demko and others, 1991). Vertical traces are rare, and this lithofacies is not significantly bioturbated. Plant fossils are also exceptionally well preserved and include upright lycopods, calamitids and pteridosperms, as well as the leaf/foliage genera *Annularia*, *Asterophyllites*, *Spherophillum*, *Aletopteris*, *Neuropteris*, *Cordalites*, and *Pecopteris*.

Heterolithic Facies

The mud-rich heterolithic lithofacies has been commonly termed "gray shale" and is interpreted to represent a mid-estuarine facies. In the Lawrence Formation, this facies is exposed at the Lone Star Spillway locality in Douglas County. Similar facies within the Stranger Formation outcrop south of Yates Center in Woodson County (see localities, Fig. 2). Exposures of this facies range up to 20 meters in thickness and consist largely of heterolithic, gray mudstone with flaser, lenticular and pinstripe bedding. The content of very fine-grained sand increases upwards through the vertical sequence. Lenticular and flaser bedding within this facies commonly exhibits tidal periodicities (Fig. 6F). Much of this facies exhibits little or no bioturbation although small-scale loading and convolutions are very common. Tool marks and oriented plant fossils are frequently preserved on bedding planes. This facies also contains small-scale, wedge-shaped slumps and small channels (ca. 5 cm by 40 cm) which contain an accretionary fill of lenticular-bedded mudstone.

The upper 4 m of this facies are characterized by laterally discontinuous, 1- to 5-cm-thick beds of very-fine grained, subarkosic sandstone and larger channels (6 m wide). Thin, discontinuous sandstone beds occur both within channelized and non-channelized parts of this facies and are capped by symmetrical and asymmetrical, sinuous to straight crested ripples, interference ripples, linguoid ripples, and rare flat-topped ripples. Polished, vertically oriented slabs exhibit bidirectional cross-lamination and common mud flasers. The major locus of sandstone deposition, however, was within well-defined channels ranging from 0.4–1.5 meters deep and 6–15 m wide that are filled with moderately inclined heterolithic bedding. Other somewhat smaller channels are completely mud-filled. At the Lone Star Lake spillway, the channels are stacked and offset in an en echelon pattern. Channel bases are invariably highly convoluted and characterized by load, slump, and ball-and-pillow structures. Sandstone beds within the channels are not bioturbated and contain unidirectional and bidirectional climbing ripple cross-lamination, rare but very well-developed, unidirectional climbing ripple cross-lamination, and climbing wave ripples (Fig. 6D). Paleoflow reversals are very common within individual sandstone beds. The sequence at the Lone Star Lake spillway is capped by a paleosol and a 30- to 40-cm-thick coal above which are large upright trees (Fig. 6C). Rhythmites exhibiting tidal periodicities (Fig. 6F) are well developed within the heterolithic facies that directly overlie this coal (Archer, 1991) and are similar to those described by Kvale and Archer (1990). Paleocurrent analyses indicate bimodal paleoflow with transport to the north-northeast and southwest.

The most common biogenic structure throughout the mid-estuarine facies is *Lockeia*, which was apparently produced by small burrowing bivalves. *Uchirities*, *Planolites*, *Scalarituba*, and other unidentified surface traces indicative of horizontal locomotion are also common. A single tetrapod footprint has also been found, suggesting that this facies was periodically emergent.

Sheet-like Sandstone Facies

Brown to gray, medium to fine-grained, quartz arenites and subarkoses are the dominant lithologies of the sheet-like sandstones which are interpreted to represent deposition within estuarine sandflats. This facies is best exposed at Toronto Lake in Woodson County (see Fig. 2) where the Ireland Sandstone has a sheet-like geometry and forms al-

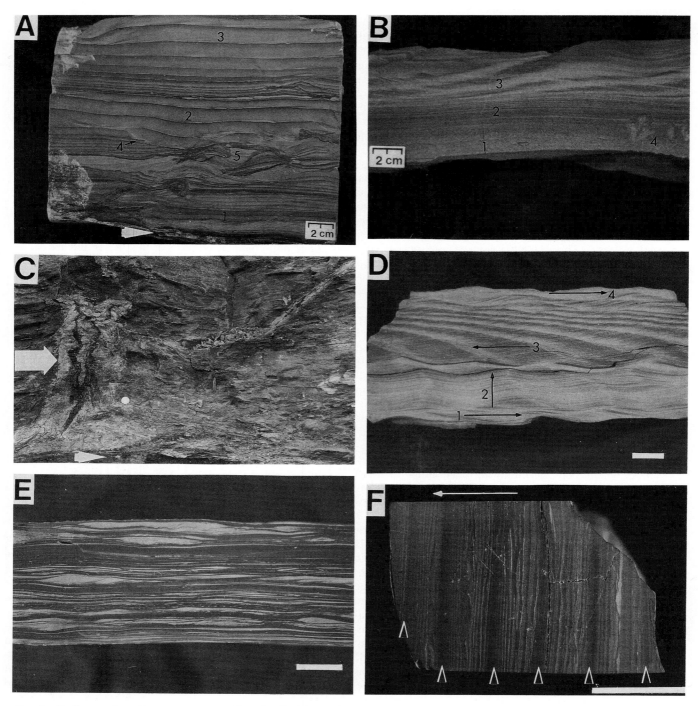

FIG. 6—Bedform-scale sedimentary structures from the fluvial-estuarine transitional facies and mid-estuarine, heterolithic facies of the Douglas Group. (A) Basal laminated (1) to very thinly bedded (2) tidal rhythmites from the fluvial-estuarine transition. Slab also shows a portion of the Ottawa Coal (lower arrow), incipient climbing siltwaves in thinly bedded laminites (3), erosional truncations of laminite sequences (4), and rhythmically laminated mud drapes which accumulated on plant materials (5). (B) "Bouma-like" sequence from the Buildex Quarry showing A (1), B (2), and C (3) subdivisions, and fluid-escape "feather" pillars (4). (C) Upright tree (large arrow) rooted in the lower Williamsburg Coal (lower arrow) from the mid-estuarine heterolithic facies. (D) Complex cross-lamination from a channel sandstone bed of the heterolithic facies. Unidirectional ripple cross-lamination (1), successively overlain by vertically aggrading, climbing wave ripple cross-lamination (2), climbing current ripple cross-lamination (3), and unidirectional ripple cross-lamination (4). Arrows indicate directions of transport. (E) Slab of typical "gray shale" from the heterolithic facies exhibiting lenticular and pinstripe bedding. (F) Tidal rhythmite sequence from the heterolithic facies above the lower Williamsburg Coal (see C). Up arrow at the top of print; other small arrows indicate sediments deposited during neap portions of the tidal cycles. Bar scales in D-F are 2 centimeters.

most continuous exposures along the modern shoreline of Toronto Lake. The sandstones are as much as 10 meters in thickness and extend over an area of about 20 square km. Parallel-bedded sandstone, ranging from 10 to 50 cm thick and parted by cm-thick mudstones, is dominant in the lower 3 to 5 m of most sections. The majority of sandstone beds are characterized internally by distinctive packages of horizontal laminations with parting lineation. Zones exhibiting primary current lineation are abruptly overlain by complex forms of ripple cross-lamination which commonly exhibit erosive bases. Ripples that climb at subcritical angles (Allen, 1984) are also common in the ripple cross-laminated zones. Ripple tops are commonly planated by the overlying, horizontally laminated sandstone (Fig. 7A). Bedding-plane exposures of this contact have isolated linguoid ripple troughs on an otherwise planated surface with primary current lineations (Fig. 7B). The upper surfaces of other beds preserve linguoid ripples, double-crested, asymmetric sinuous-crested ripples, rare straight-crested symmetric ripples, and stick drag marks that attain decimeter lengths. Lower bedding surfaces have tool marks, flute marks, and small-scale load structures.

Trough cross-bedding characterizes the upper 1 to 3 meters of the facies. Cosets range from 14 to 65 cm in thickness with widths of 1 to 10 meters and lengths up to 8 meters. Reactivation surfaces are common (Fig. 7C). These sandstones are locally highly convoluted. The sandstone beds define large, two-dimensional and three-dimensional bars with heights of several meters and decameter wavelengths. Small-scale bedforms found on bar tops and in the troughs between bars (Fig. 7D, E, F) include ripple fans with asymmetric ripples, straight- to sinuous-crested asymmetric and symmetrical ripples, linguoid ripples, rare rhombohedral ripples, flat-topped straight-crested symmetric ripples, and interference ripples showing equant hexagonal "brick and tile" (Allen, 1984) patterns. Symmetric-crested interference ripples are commonly superimposed on asymmetric crested ripple fans that characterize the bar tops, and many of these surfaces have a continuum of sedimentary structures from straight to sinuous to linguoid ripples. Large- and small-scale runoff washouts and runnels and comb-shaped rill marks have also been recorded. At one locality at Toronto Lake, the entire sequence is dissected by a 7.5-m-thick trough cross-bedded sandstone with a channel-shaped geometry.

Paleocurrents for the Ireland Sandstone at the Toronto Lake locality have a dominant north to northeastward mode although other localities exhibit a dominant northwestward or northeastward to eastward transport direction. Paleoflow reversals of 180 are well developed within bar-top bedforms.

The sheet-like sandstones do not contain marine body fossils although the relative degree of bioturbation and trace fossil abundances increase upwards through the vertical sequence. The sandstone is not generally internally bioturbated except upper parts of the bars that were extensively burrowed by forms such as *Chondrites*, *Asterosoma*, *Planolites*, and a bilobed form tentatively assigned to *Gyrochorte*. Plant fossils include abraded and transported calamitid and lycopod logs as much as 10 cm in diameter.

Bioturbated Sandstone Facies

The bioturbated sandstone facies is characterized by interbedded, fine-grained, quartz arenitic to subarkosic sandstones and shale that contain marine body fossils and a diverse assemblage of marine trace fossils. Exposures of this facies in both the Stranger and Lawrence Formations are found in Chautauqua County, Kansas (see Fig. 2) and reach a maximum thickness of 6 meters. Sandstones range from 30-cm-thick beds with small-scale trough cross-bedding and marine fossils to laterally discontinuous, "flaggy" sandstone beds up to 10 cm thick (Fig. 8A) which are slightly to moderately bioturbated. The interbedded shales average 60 centimeters in thickness and may contain marine fossils and are locally extensively bioturbated. Sandstone-rich zones of flaser or lenticular bedding are common within the shales; the sandstones exhibit flat-topped ripples (Fig. 8E). Bedforms associated with the "flaggy" sandstones include: asymmetric and symmetric, sinuous- to straight-crested ripples (Figs. 8B, F); flat-topped ripples (Figs. 8C, E); and a variety of interference ripples including ladder-back rippled bedforms (Fig. 8C). Rippled sandstone beds have unidirectional and bidirectional cross-lamination and wave ripple bedding (*sensu* Boersma, 1970 in Reineck and Singh, 1980). Runzel marks and large-scale eolian deflation surfaces are also very common (Fig. 8D). In Chautauqua County in southern Kansas, paleocurrents in the Lawrence Formation have a dominant northwest mode for unidirectional current-generated structures. Wave-generated sedimentary structures indicate south to southwestward transport and indicate prevailing winds from the northeast. Transport directions for the Stranger Formation were towards the north to northeast.

Plant fossils are rare in this facies and consist mostly of unidentifiable abraded debris. Trace fossils are common and diverse in this facies and include vertically oriented, U-shaped tubes (*Arenicolites*), oblique *Rhizocorallium* in sandstone-dominated units, and vertical escape burrows in very fine-grained sandstones. Lower surfaces of sandstone beds commonly exhibit trilobite-type traces including resting (*Rusophycus*) and crawling (*Cruziana*) forms. Upper surfaces of sandstone beds exhibit a variety of feeding and locomotion traces including *Olivellites* and *Gyrochorte*.

Shell-lag Carbonate Facies

The Westphalia Limestone, a thin, locally discontinuous, shell-lag bearing limestone, occurs within the upper Tonganoxie Sequence and appears to overlie a transgressive surface of erosion. The Westphalia Limestone, which has been interpreted as a widespread storm deposit (S. Ball, 1971), ranges from about 30 cm to 1.5 m in thickness and commonly contains a basal zone of abraded, single valves of thick-shelled myalinid bivalves. The upper part of the unit is characterized by a packstone to grainstone consisting of well-sorted fusilinids. In the northern part of the study area, the Westphalia consists of an ostracode-rich mudstone that erosionally overlies the Upper Sibley Coal.

In the Ireland Sequence, shell-lag limestones are not well developed. In the southern part of the study area, a limestone referred to as the "Amazonia" is locally developed

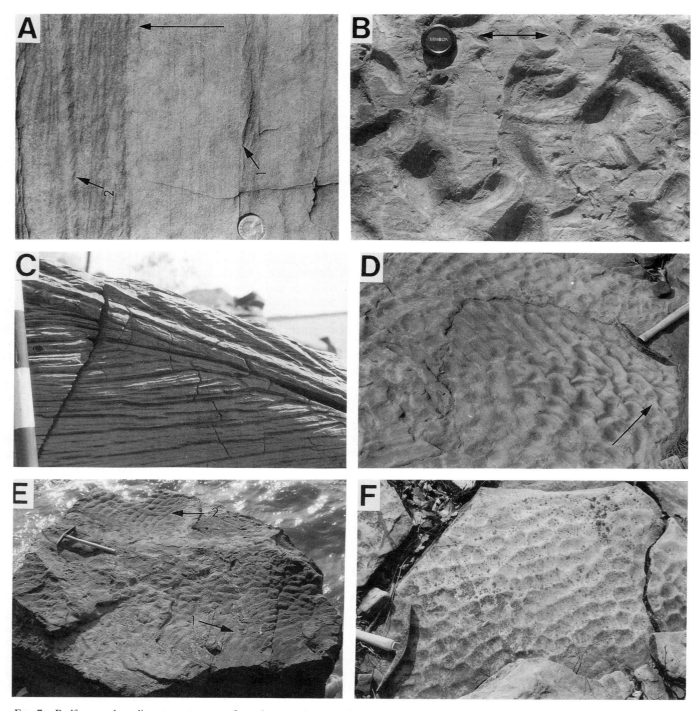

FIG. 7—Bedform-scale sedimentary structures from the estuarine sand flat facies of the Douglas Group. (A) Fine- to medium-grained sandstone showing planated ripple cross-lamination (1) overlain by parallel lamination grading into ripple cross-lamination with climbing ripples (2). (B) Planated linguoid ripples with a surface exhibiting primary current lineation. (C) Reactivation surface from cross-bedded sandstone of a large bar bedform; ripples climb up the bar slip face. (D) Bar-top bedforms showing a lateral transition from straight-crested asymmetrical ripples to linguoid ripples. Transport direction indicated by arrow. (E) Crest of bar-top (long axis of hammer) showing ripple fans (1) and rhombohedral ripples (2). (F) Bar-top interference ripple bedforms showing an equant "tile and brick" pattern. Hammer head in D-F is 26 centimeters; staff divisions in C are 10 centimeters.

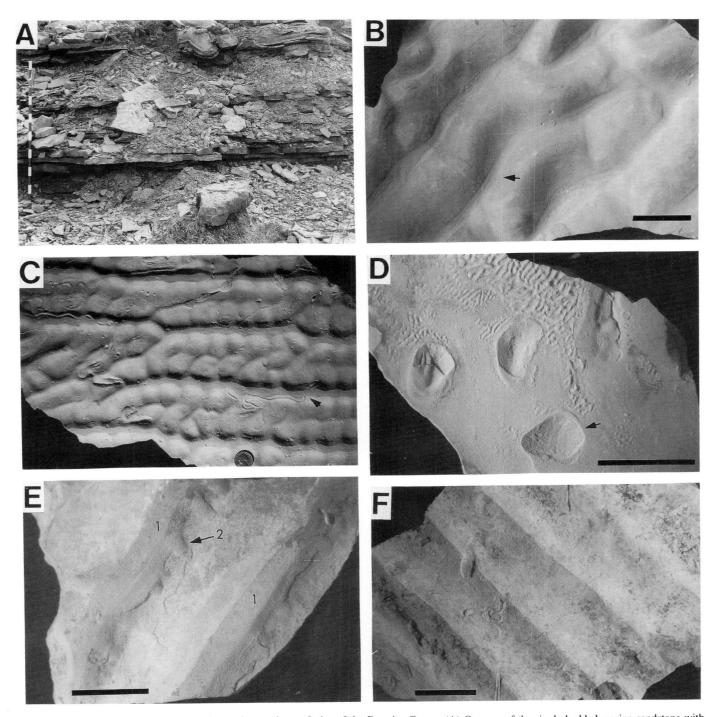

FIG. 8—Sedimentary structures from the marine sandstone facies of the Douglas Group. (A) Outcrop of the ripple-bedded marine sandstone with interbedded shales; (B) Symmetric, sinuous-crested ripples with rounded- to flat-tops, strandline marks (arrow), and a weakly-developed interference component. (C) Flat-topped ladder-back ripple bedform. Note that trace fossils are truncated at the ripple crests (arrow). (D) Deflated linguoid(?) rippled surfaces showing runzel marks and "aggradation lips" (arrow) at the margins of the stranded ripple troughs. (E) Flat-topped straight crested ripples (1) with small-scale washover lobes (2). (F) Trochoidal wave ripples. Bar scales in B, D-F are 2 centimeters.

and may represent a facies similar to the Westphalia. The stratigraphic placement and textures of these limestones are similar to the transgressive, ravinement-related carbonates that occur within Morrowan (Westphalian B) valley-fill sequences in western Kansas and Colorado (Wheeler and others, 1990).

Fossiliferous Shale and Limestone Facies

The shales and limestones within the upper parts of the sequences contain abundant marginal to normal marine trace- and body fossils and represent the most offshore deposits in the Douglas Group. Within the basal part of the Robbins Shale Member, Miller and Swineford (1957) described an assemblage of fish skulls and brain casts, nautiloids, and ammonoids associated with phosphate and geothite nodules that were interpreted as having formed in a restricted marine setting. This zone appears to represent a condensed section and probably the maximum-flooding surface of the Tongonoxie Sequence.

The thicker sandstone lamina within these marine shales commonly have flute casts and burrows on lower bedding surfaces, and analyses of clay mineralogy suggested deposition within generally restricted marine conditions (Jamkhindikar, 1969). Study of trace fossils by Hakes (1977) suggests generally low-energy, marine conditions for the upper half of the Lawrence Shale. These marine facies stratigraphically overlie and can be correlated beyond the incised-valley fills and thus represent a depositional system formed in nearshore brackish to open-marine conditions upon a shallow marine shelf.

DEPOSITIONAL MODEL

Modern Estuary Models

Estuaries are commonly sites of tidal amplification and tide-mediated deposition. In general, tidal bedding can be expected to be common within flooded-valley estuaries because: (1) fine-grained sediment is pumped into the middle estuary where high turbidity is maintained; (2) incised valleys provide accommodation space; (3) fluvial and marine currents are low in middle estuaries; and (4) specific estuarine geometries can lead to significant tidal amplification.

Estuarine circulation and the presence of a turbidity maximum can result in a tripartite facies distribution that is characterized by a fluvial to marine, coarse-fine-coarse pattern of sedimentation (Dorjes and Howard, 1975; Dyer, 1979; Rahmani, 1989; Allen, 1991; Dalrymple and others, 1991; Nichols and others, 1991). Coarse sediment is primarily deposited in the narrow upper parts of estuaries where cross-sectional areas are small, and fluvial processes begin to merge with estuarine processes. In the middle estuary, bottom currents are weak, turbidity is high, and the sediment is generally muddy. Much of the suspended mud is deposited during slack water at highest and lowest tides. As tidal velocity decreases, suspended sediment is deposited as normally graded layers. Muddy tidal flats can be well developed in the middle estuary; such flats can contain heterolithic bedding consisting of sand layers deposited during maximum tidal velocities and clay drapes formed during slack

water. In the bay mouth, bottom currents are higher, and marine processes such as waves and tides can deposit coarse marine sediment. During the post-glacial sea-level rise, estuarine sediments have been filling flooded river valleys along the northern Atlantic coasts. The sequence of facies begins with fluvial sand deposited on an incised surface, followed by sandy and muddy estuarine facies, and capped by marine sand (Nichols and others, 1991; Dalrymple and others, 1992). This is similar to sequences described herein within the Douglas Group.

Theoretical Constraints

In modern environments, many macrotidal systems can be related to basinal geometries that significantly amplify tidal ranges. In general, bays and estuaries that have a gradually decreasing width from the seaward to landward end, coupled with a concurrent decrease in depth, can result in tidal-height amplification. Such settings include the Severn River estuary in southwest England and the St. Lawrence River estuary in eastern Canada (Fig. 9). A number of related factors suggest that the rhythmites that occur within the Douglas Group valley-fill sequences were developed within zones that experienced significant tidal amplification. Simple equations can constrain the depth/length conditions in which resonance and tidal amplification can occur (see Tricker, 1964, p. 28). The results of such computations can be compared to inferred embayment lengths and depths that may have existed during development of the estuarine phase of the valley-fill sequences of the Douglas Group of Kansas (Fig. 10). Based upon inferences regarding the magnitude of sea-level oscillations that characterize such Carboniferous depositional cycles (cyclothems), maximal depths at the seaward end of the embayment could have reached values of approximately 100 m (Heckel, 1977, 1986). Given such depths, tidal resonance could occur within an embayment with a north-to-south length of approximately 290 km (Fig. 10). This type of theoretical information is of potential use to constrain the paleogeography of the study area.

Paleoenvironmental Interpretations

The depositional model of the Douglas Group is based upon the lateral and vertical relationships observed for the various lithofacies together with comparison to suitable modern analogs. The common occurrence of cyclical tidal rhythmites within upper parts of the valley-fill sequences suggests significant tidal activity. Given the thickness of individual depositional units (related to single tidal events) that occur within the fluvio-estuarine transitional facies (Tessier and others, 1992; Lanier and others, 1993), it is likely that a high tidal range, probably macrotidal, was operative during at least part of the deposition cycles. The presence of tidal periodicities but lack of paleontologic marine indicators suggests an estuarine setting. In the following discussion, the major lithofacies are compared to modern tidal estuarine models.

The locally developed conglomerates and large-scale trough crossbeds of the fluvial lithofacies, together with variable, but generally southwestward paleocurrents, are

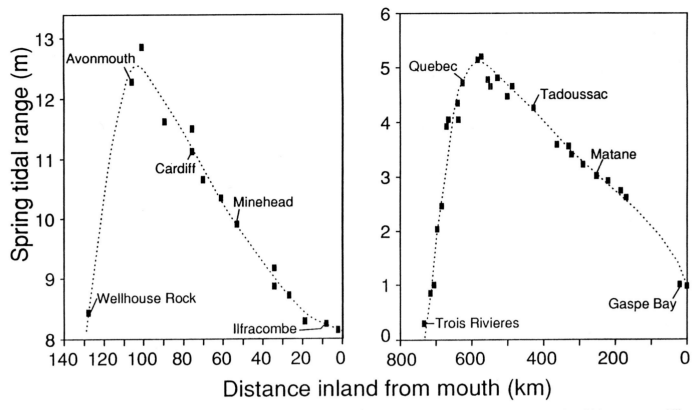

FIG. 9—(A) Tidal amplification within major estuarine systems. These diagrams were constructed by extrapolating spring-tidal ranges to a midline within the estuary. (A) Within the Severn Estuary of southwestern England, macrotidal coastal systems are amplified to a severely macrotidal system (data from Hoare and Haggett, 1979, p. 15 with additional information from NOAA, 1991a). (B) Amplification along St. Lawrence River Estuary increases coastal microtidal systems to a low macrotidal system. Note the amplification is maximized at a considerable distance from the "mouth" of the system (data from NOAA, 1991b).

strongly suggestive of a sand dominated, bedload controlled, fluvial system. The generally fining upward sequence (conglomerate to fine sandstone or siltstone) and general decrease in bedform thicknesses indicate that significant changes in flow characteristics occurred during the valley-fill sequences. In the upper parts of the sandstone bodies, abundant clay-draped foresets suggest tidal influences during deposition.

The laminated and bedded siltstones and fine-grained sandstones of the fluvio- to estuarine facies are clearly dominated by tidally modulated sedimentation. This facies was formed during the final phases of the incised-valley fill and overwhelmed peat swamps rapidly enough to bury *in situ*, upright trees. Such relationships could be interpreted as crevasse-splay deposition within a floodplain; however, the tidal periodicities that can be measured within successive bedform thicknesses indicate that a model invoking strictly fluvial overbank processes is not applicable. Estimated rates of vertical accretion, based upon analyses of neap-spring cycles within tidal rhythmites, suggest deposition within the turbidity maximum zone of a large, fluvio-estuarine system. Moreover, numerous biogenic (e.g., tetrapod trackways) and physical sedimentary structures (e.g., raindrop imprints and rill marks), which are present on virtually every bedding plane surface, indicate that exposure

was periodic and short term. The rhythmites that occur within this facies share a number of similarities to the modern analogs described from the Bay of Mont St. Michel in France (Tessier, 1990; Tessier and others, 1989) and from the upper reaches of the Bay of Fundy in Canada (Dalrymple and Makino, 1989; Dalrymple and others, 1991). These analogs include unusually high rates of vertical accretion as well as similarities in physical and biogenic sedimentary structures (Tessier and others, 1992). Invoking such analogs would suggest that this Douglas Group lithofacies may be related to deposition upon fluvio-tidal point bars developed within a highly meandering, uppermost estuarine system (Fig. 11).

Rhythmites exhibiting tidal periodicities occur locally within the mid-estuarine, heterolithic facies, especially when such facies directly overlie coals (Archer, 1991; Archer and others, 1994). This facies generally lacks significant bioturbation ; however, surficial trackways and trails do occur. The heterolithic facies was probably deposited within upper- and middle-estuarine environments and includes lateral mudflats as well as subtidal settings. Occurrence of tetrapod trackways indicates periodic emergence.

The lower part of estuarine facies includes sandflats and bars that contain a variety of features suggestive of tidal processes. In particular, the pervasive horizontal lamination and parting lineation are indicative of upper flow-regime

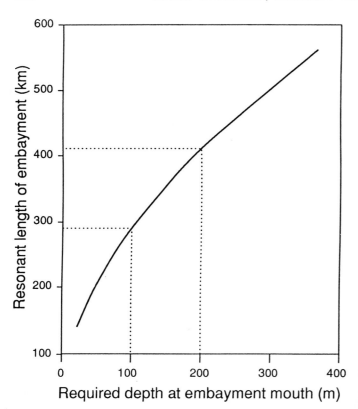

FIG. 10—Relationship of embayment depths and lengths required for a period of 12 hours (data from Tricker, 1964, p. 28) to simulate resonance effects of a semidiurnal tidal system. Dashed lines enclose reasonable depth fluctuations from lowstand to highstand as interpreted for midcontinental U. S. cyclothems; these depths suggest that reasonable lengths for tidal resonance could have been on the order of about 300 to 400 km.

FIG. 11—Facies model for valley-fill, estuarine-to-marine depositional sequences developed within the incised valleys in the Douglas Group of eastern Kansas. Numeric codes for facies are the same as used in the text. Paleoflow roses for the various facies are based upon the following localities (1) Leavenworth County, Kansas, (2) Buildex Quarry, (3) Lone Star Spillway, (4) Toronto Lake, and (5) Chautauqua County, Kansas. This reconstruction is intended to represent the lateral relationships of the six lithofacies developed during early to mid transgression. Adapted from models of Dalrymple and others (1992).

conditions and suggest similarities to the upper flow regime sand flats that occur in the Bay of Fundy (Dalrymple and others, 1990). In the Toronto Lake area, these sandstones tend to be overlain by trough crossbedded facies that commonly exhibit flat-topped ripples, bar-top ripple fans, and flow reversals similar to those described from tidal sand ridges from the Bay of Fundy (Dalrymple and others, 1990). Evidence for emergence includes large-scale runnels and rill marks. In the Bay of Fundy, the sand flats are most extensively developed landward of tidal sand ridges. Using this analog, the Toronto Lake sandstones suggest deepening water conditions with the seaward sand ridges stepping landward over the generally shallower sand flats. The occurrence of deeper-water trace fossils at the top of the sandstone sequences indicates that ultimately these tidal sand ridges were drowned by progressively deepening conditions and subsequently the upper few decameters were extensively bioturbated.

The trace- and body-fossil assemblage within the bioturbated sandstone facies indicates that such sandstones are the most open marine of all the Douglas Group sandstones in Kansas. In particular, the diversity of the trace fossils, especially the trilobite-related forms (such as *Cruziana* and *Rusophycus*), suggests that more-or-less normal marine sal-

inities were established during deposition of the sand. Associated body fossils, such as myalinid clams, further support such interpretations. Extensive surfaces of completely planated ripples, runzel marks, and large-scale eolian deflation surfaces indicate that a variety of depositional processes affected and modified the bedforms within this sandstone facies. Although heterolithic bedding is common within the sandstones, there is a lack of cyclical tidal rhythmites within this facies. In general, this facies yields abundant evidence of extensive wave reworking, and this together with the other marine indicators, suggests a placement either within the lowermost or even outside the estuarine embayment.

The shell-lag limestones were formed offshore of the marine sandstone facies in water depths sufficient to allow for significant bottom scour and concentration of marine shelly macrobenthos such as myalinid clams. These limestones can be correlated over relatively large areas and are not as constrained by the incised valleys as were the siliciclastic facies discussed above. Thus such limestones indicate that the incised paleovalleys were nearly or completely filled and no longer had a significant influence upon depositional topography.

Sequence Stratigraphic Model

Depending upon scale, the sequence stratigraphy of the Douglas Group could be defined several ways. At a larger scale, the entire Douglas Group can be considered as part of a terrestrial to marginal-marine, lowstand systems tract bounded by highstand carbonates and organic-rich black shales (Fig. 3). Thus the lower highstand tract would be represented by the Stanton Limestone and the upper by the Oread Limestone. However, the deeply incised paleovalleys developed within the Douglas Group are probably best interpreted as Type 1 sequence boundaries (Van Wagoner and others, 1990); thus the Douglas Group itself can be subdivided into depositional sequences.

The bases of these sequences are interpreted as sequence boundaries because fluvial facies directly overlie an unconformity developed upon older marine facies, and this indicates a basinward shift in facies (Fig. 12). Each sequence records successive stacking of more terrestrial to more marine depositional environments. Two major sequences can be recognized in the Douglas Group in the study area: the Tonganoxie Sequence ranges from the base of the Tonganoxie Sandstone up to the top of the Robbins Shale and the Ireland Sequence ranges from the base of the Ireland Sandstone up to the top of the Toronto Limestone (Fig. 3). The Tonganoxie Sequence is best delineated in the northeastern part of the study area where it forms a wide (32 km) paleovalley that can be traced from northeastern Leavenworth County (Lins, 1950) to western Coffey County (Sanders, 1959), a distance of approximately 140 km. The paleovalley is deeply incised into underlying marine shale and carbonate rocks cutting down as deeply as the Stanton Limestone. Paleovalley walls are rarely observed in outcrop, but in central Franklin County at the Buildex Quarry Locality, a rooted coal is developed on an erosional surface developed on the Weston Shale indicating that paleovalley walls were subaerially exposed.

Although the sequences are readily defined because of the extensive erosional surfaces, the precise delineation of systems tracts becomes problematic regarding the placement of the lower boundary of the transgressive systems tract. In this regard, there is an intrinsic conflict between the definitions of transgressive surface given for estuarine systems (Dalrymple and others, 1992) and for sequence stratigraphy of siliciclastics systems (Van Wagoner and others, 1990). Problems exist with the application of these two definitions to the sequences in the Douglas Group.

Because the paleovalley fills of the Douglas Group are generally similar to the model of estuarine valley fills described by Dalrymple and others (1992), their definitions are potentially applicable. Outcrops of the Tonganoxie Sequence in southern Leavenworth and northern Wyandotte Counties reveal fluvial crossbedded conglomerates and sandstones overlying marine rocks of the Stanton Limestone. The basinward shift in facies across this contact from marine limestone to fluvial sandstone and the evidence of subaerial exposure on paleovalley walls, clearly indicate a relative fall in sea level and development of a type 1 sequence boundary. The deposits of fluvial sediments within the incised paleovalley belong to the lowstand systems tract. Based upon the model of Dalrymple and others (1992), the onset of estuarine deposition can be based on the lowest occurrence of sandstones that exhibit clay-draped bedforms and may occur as low as 3 to 5 m above the base of Tonganoxie Sandstone. This occurrence of tidal influence could be interpreted as "marine" influence and be used to delineate the base of the transgressive systems tract (Fig. 12). However there is not a sharp boundary, and the transition from fluvial to estuarine deposits is gradational.

Conversely, widespread marine flooding is indicated by deposition of the shell-lag limestones such as the Westphalia Limestone that overlie the valley-fill facies (Fig. 12). This unit would appear to conform with the definitions of "transgressive surface" given by Van Wagoner and others (1990). This typically occurs approximately 30 m above the base of the Tongonoxie Sandstone where the thickness is measured in the deepest part of the valley-fill sections. If the shell-lag limestones mark the transgressive surface of erosion, then the overlying units, by definition, are part of the transgressive systems tract. This interpretation would be similar to the interpretations made by Wheeler and others (1990; their Fig. 15) for subsurface valley-fill sequences in the Pennsylvanian of western Kansas and eastern Colorado. Using this interpretation, most of the valley-fill facies are part of the lowstand systems tract (Fig. 12), which is in agreement with definitions of Van Wagoner and others (1990).

We do not currently have sufficient information regarding the parasequence stacking patterns within the valley-fill succession; however, the coals generally become thicker and more widespread within the higher parts of the valley fill. This could indicate progradation of parasequences during deposition of the lowstand systems tract and successive development of more landward facies. Conversely, localized environmental factors, such as coastal proximity and wetter microclimates, together with rising baselevels may all have served to enhance peat production within a generally retrogradational phase. The relative influence of these factors will not be easy to determine unless extensive coring of the interval can be undertaken.

The transgressive systems tract is defined as being bounded below by the transgressive surface and above by the maximum flooding surface and consists of a deepening upward succession of parasequences (Van Wagoner and others, 1990). A pattern of increasing marine influence occurs definitely above the Westphalia and into the Haskell Limestone and indicates a series of landward-stepping parasequences. The succession culminates with a condensed section in the lowermost Robbins Shale. The lower Robbins Shale contains phosphate nodules, fish-skull casts, and pelagic fossils such as ammonoids (Miller and Swineford, 1957), all consistent with deep-water, anoxic to dysaerobic conditions and represents the maximum water depth for the sequence (see Heckel, 1986; Boardman and others, 1984). Thus this zone represents a condensed section formed at the maximum flooding surface. The rest of the Robbins Shale appears to represent continued marine deposition within the

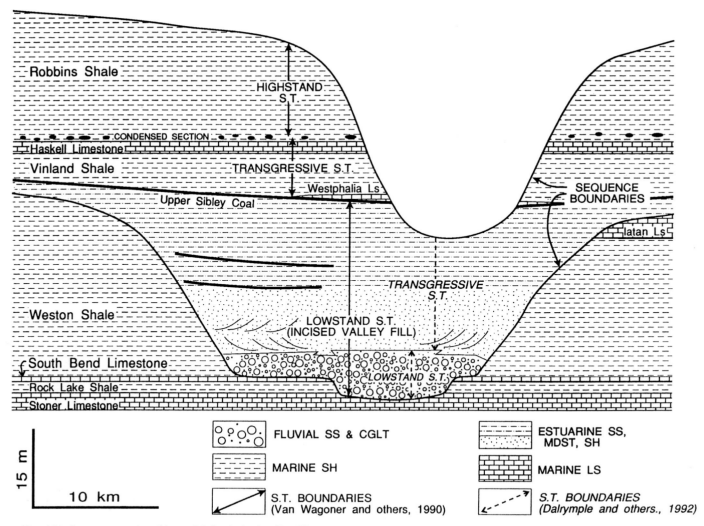

FIG. 12—Sequence stratigraphic model for incised valley-fill sequences developed within the Tonganoxie Sequence (lower Douglas Group) of Kansas. Placement of systems tract boundaries is shown based upon the definitions proposed by Van Wagoner and others (1990) and Dalrymple and others (1992). Depending on criteria used to establish the transgressive surface, the incised-valley fill can be placed into either the lowstand or transgressive systems tract.

highstand systems tract. Because the upper Robbins Shale is erosionally truncated by the overlying Ireland Sequence, it is not possible to adequately delineate parasequence stacking patterns within this part of the section.

The Ireland Sequence is less well-exposed and therefore more difficult to study, but the major sandstones were deposited in incised paleovalleys that truncate the Haskell Limestone and cut as deep as the Tonganoxie Sandstone estuarine sandstones and possibly into the Tonganoxie fluvial sandstones. The morphology of the paleovalley system is not well known; however, in the northern part of the study area they appear to be filled with a succession of facies similar to that of the Tonganoxie paleovalley, beginning with fluvial conglomerate and sandstone, overlain by estuarine sandstones and shale (including tidal rhythmites). Above these valley-fill facies, a series of discontinuous limestones ("Amazonia") indicate widespread marine transgression. A condensed section is not readily apparent

within this depositional sequence; however, the sequence appears to culminate with the Toronto Limestone. The paleosol on the upper surface of the Toronto Limestone represents the top of the Ireland Sequence. The paleosol features in the upper Toronto may have resulted from subaerial exposures and deep weathering that occurred after deposition of the overlying Snyderville Shale (Bush, 1991), in which case the top of the Ireland Sequence can be defined as the upper Snyderville Shale.

CONCLUSIONS

The Douglas Group consists of two major sequences that are composed of fluvial to estuarine to nearshore siliciclastic facies and marine shales and limestones. The sequences exhibit deep incision that resulted from lowering of relative sea level. In the northern part of the study area, sandstones in the thicker cycles are largely confined to paleovalleys. The best documented paleovalley fill is the Tonganoxie Sandstone, which is incised at least 34 m into underlying marine rocks and extends for at least 140 km downdip. The paleovalleys were filled during lowstand and transgression with a sequence of generally fining upwards facies that represent fluvial, estuarine, and finally marine environments.

Fluvial facies consist of crossbedded conglomerate and sandstone. Crossbeds are oriented predominantly to the south or basinward. Estuarine conditions are indicated by the widespread occurrences of cyclical tidal rhythmites in mudrocks and siltstones and bimodal sediment-transport directions. Similar tidal cycles are preserved in modern sediments in estuaries that are confined by bedrock valleys. The large tidal range that is required for deposition of these kinds of facies can probably only occur where funnel-shaped estuaries amplify tidal cycles.

In the upper parts of valley-fill sections and most well developed in the southern part of the study area, sandstone deposition was not confined to paleovalleys and reflects more marine influence. This includes wave ripples and more marine assemblages of trace fossils. Shell-lag limestones separate the upper parts of the valley-fill facies from the overlying, generally more open-marine facies. Sea-level highstand resulted in deposition of marine, bioturbated to fossiliferous shale and limestones that are widely distributed and not confined to paleovalleys.

ACKNOWLEDGMENTS

Analyses and interpretation of shale fabrics in the Douglas Group were funded by Kansas Department of Transportation (Grant K-TRAN: KSU-91–6). The Kansas Geological Survey provided partial field expenses during early phases of this study. Portions of the sedimentological research on modern analogs were funded by an NSF grant (EAR-9018079) to compare laminated shales within Carboniferous sites that exhibit well preserved and diverse fossil assemblages.

REFERENCES CITED

ALLEN, G. P., 1991, Sedimentary processes and facies in the Gironde estuary: a recent model for macrotidal estuarine systems, *in* Smith, D. G., Reinson, G. E., Zaitlin, B. A., and Rahmani, R. A., eds., Clastic Tidal Sedimentology: Calgary, Canadian Society of Petroleum Geologists Memoir 16, p. 29–40.

ALLEN, J. R. L., 1984, Sedimentary Structures: Their Characteristics and Physical Basis, Vol. 1: New York, Elsevier, 673 p.

ARCHER, A. W., 1991, Modeling of tidal rhythmites using modern tidal periodicities and implications for short-term sedimentation rates, *in* Franseen, E. K., Watney, W. L., Kendall, C. G. St. C., and Ross, W., eds., Sedimentary Modeling: Computer Simulations and Methods for Improved Parameter Definition: Kansas Geological Survey, Bulletin, v. 233, p. 185–194.

ARCHER, A. W., FELDMAN, H. R., KVALE, E. P., AND LANIER, W. P., 1994, Pennsylvanian (Upper Carboniferous) fluvio- to tidal-estuarine coal-bearing systems: delineation of facies transitions based upon physical and biogenic sedimentary structures. Palaeogeography, Palaeoclimatology, Palaeoecology, v. 106, p. 171–185.

ARCHER, A. W., KVALE, E. P., AND JOHNSON, H. R., 1991, Analysis of modern equatorial tidal periodicities as a test of information encoded in ancient tidal rhythmites, *in* Smith, D. G., Reinson, G. E., Zaitlin, B. A., and Rahmani, R. A., eds., Clastic Tidal Sedimentology: Calgary, Canadian Society of Petroleum Geologists Memoir 16, p. 189–196.

ARCHER, A. W., AND MAPLES, C. G., 1984, Pennsylvanian nonmarine trace-fossil assemblages: southwestern Indiana: Journal of Paleontology, v. 58, p. 448–466.

BAIRD, G. C., SROKA, S. D., SHABICA, C. W., AND KUECHER, G. J., 1986, Taphonomy of Middle Pennsylvanian Mazon creek area fossil localities, northeast Illinois; significance of exceptional fossil preservation in syngenetic concretions: Palaios, v. 1, p. 271–285.

BALL, D. S., 1985, The Pennsylvanian Haskell-Cass section, a perspective on controls of Midcontinent cyclothem deposition: Unpublished M.S. Thesis, University of Kansas, Lawrence, 147 p.

BALL, S. M., 1964, Stratigraphy of the Douglas Group (Pennsylvanian, Virgilian) in the northern Midcontinent region: Unpublished Ph.D. Dissertation, University of Kansas, Lawrence, 674 p.

BALL, S. M., 1971, The Westphalia Limestone of the northern midcontinent: a possible storm deposit: Journal of Sedimentary Petrology, v. 41, p. 217–232.

BOARDMAN, D. W., II, MAPES, R. H., YANCEY, T. E., AND MALINKY, J. M., 1984, A new model for the depth-related allogenic community succession within North American Pennsylvanian cyclothems and implications on the black shale problem *in* Hyne, N. J., ed., Limestones of the Midcontinent: Tulsa, Tulsa Geological Society Special Publication No. 2, p. 141–182.

BOWSHER, A. L., AND JEWETT, J. M., 1943, Coal resources of the Douglas Group in east-central Kansas: Kansas Geological Survey Bulletin, v. 43, 94 p.

BOWER, R. R., 1961, Dispersal centers of sandstones in the Douglas Group (Pennsylvanian) of Kansas: Unpublished M.S. Thesis, University of Kansas, Lawrence, 19 p.

BUSH, D. C., 1991, Evidence of subaerial exposure in the Toronto Limestone, Oread Formation (Pennsylvanian) near St. Joseph, Missouri: Transactions, Missouri Academy of Science, v. 25, p. 131.

CECIL, C. B., 1990, Paleoclimatic controls on stratigraphic repetition of chemical and siliciclastic rocks: Geology, v. 18, p. 533–536.

COVENEY, R. M., JR., WATNEY, W. L., AND MAPLES, C. G., 1991, Contrasting depositional models for Pennsylvanian black shale discerned from molybdenum abundances: Geology, v. 19, p. 147–150.

DALRYMPLE, R. W., KNIGHT, R. J., ZAITLIN, B. A., AND MIDDLETON, G. V., 1990, Dynamics and facies model of a macrotidal sand bar complex, Cobequid Bay-Salmon River estuary (Bay of Fundy): Sedimentology, v. 37, p. 577–612.

DALRYMPLE, R. W., AND MAKINO, Y., 1989, Description and genesis of tidal bedding in the Cobequid Bay-Salmon River estuary, Bay of Fundy, Canada, *in* Taira, A., and Masuda, F., eds., Sedimentary Facies in the Active Plate Margin: Tokyo, Terra Scientific Publishing Company, p. 151–177.

DALRYMPLE, R. W., MAKINO, Y., AND ZAITLIN, B. A., 1991, Temporal and spatial patterns of rhythmite deposition on mud flats in the macrotidal Cobequid Bay—Salmon River estuary, Bay of Fundy, Canada, *in* Smith, D. G., Reinson, G. E., Zaitlin, B. A., and Rahmani, R. A., eds., Clastic Tidal Sedimentology: Calgary, Canadian Society of Petroleum Geologists Memoir 16, p. 137–160.

DALRYMPLE, R. W., ZAITLIN, B. A., AND BOYD, R., 1992, Estuarine facies models: Conceptual basis and stratigraphic implications. Journal of Sedimentary Petrology, v. 62, p. 1130–1146.

DEMKO, T. M., JIRIKOWIC, J., AND GASTALDO, R. A., 1991, Tidal cyclicity in the Pottsville Formation, Warrior Basin, Alabama: sedimentology and time-series analysis of a rhythmically laminated sandstone-mudstone interval (abs.): Geological Society America, Abstracts with Programs., v. 23, p. A287.

DORJES, J., AND HOWARD, J. D., 1975, Estuaries of the Georgia coast, U. S. A.: Sedimentology and biology. IV. Fluvial-marine transition indicators in an estuarine environment, Ogeeche River—Ossabaw Sound: Senckenbergia Maritima, v. 7, p. 137–179.

DYER, K. R., 1979, Estuaries and estuarine sedimentation, *in* Dyer, K. R., ed., Estuarine Hydrography and Sedimentation: New York, Cambridge University Press, p. 1–18.

GOEBEL, K. A., BETTIS, E. A., AND HECKEL, P. H., 1989, Upper Pennsylvanian paleosol in Stranger Shale and underlying Iatan Limestone, southwestern Iowa: Journal Sedimentary Petrology, v. 59, p. 224–232.

GRIFFITH, G. L., 1981, The Tonganoxie Sandstone in portions of Sedgwick, Butler, and Greenwood counties, Kansas: Unpublished M.S. Thesis, Wichita State University, Wichita, 54 p.

HAKES, W. G., 1977, Trace fossils in Late Pennsylvanian cyclothems, Kansas: Geological Journal, Special Issue 9, p. 209–226.

HAMBLIN, W. K., 1964, Rhythmic laminations within some seemingly homogeneous sandstones of Kansas and Oklahoma: Kansas Geological Survey Bulletin, v. 169, p. 183–189.

HECKEL, P. H., 1977, Origin of phosphatic black shale facies in Pennsylvanian cyclothems of mid-continent North America: American Association of Petroleum Geologists Bulletin, v. 661, p. 1045–1068.

HECKEL, P. H., 1983, Diagenetic model for carbonate rocks in Midcontinent Pennsylvanian eustatic cyclothems: Journal of Sedimentary Petrology, v. 53, p. 733–759.

HECKEL, P. H., 1986, Sea-level curve for Pennsylvanian eustatic marine transgressive-regressive depositional cycles along the Midcontinent outcrop belt, North America: Geology, v. 14, p. 330–334.

HENNING, L. G., 1985, Study of the Ireland Sandstone (Douglas Group, Upper Pennsylvanian) in east-central Kansas: Unpublished M.S. Thesis, Wichita State University, Wichita, 103 p.

HOARE, A. G., AND HAGGETT, P., 1979, Tidal power and estuary management-a geographical perspective, *in* Severn, R. T., Dineley, D. L., and Hawker, L. E., eds., Tidal Power and Estuary Management, 30th Symposium of the Colston Research Society: Dorchester, John Wright and Sons, p. 14–25.

JAMKHINDIKAR, S. M., 1969, Petrography and clay mineralogy of the Lawrence Shale formation (Pennsylvanian) in Kansas: Unpublished Ph.D. Dissertation, University of Kansas, Lawrence, 140 p.

KLEIN, G. deV., 1992, Climatic and tectonic sea-level gauge for Midcontinent Pennsylvanian cyclothems: Geology, v. 20, p. 363–366.

KVALE, E. P., AND ARCHER, A. W., 1989, Recognition of tidal processes in mudstone-dominated sediments, Lower Pennsylvanian, Indiana, *in* Cobb, J. C., ed., Geology of the Lower Pennsylvanian in Kentucky, Indiana, and Illinois: Illinois Basin Studies 1: Lexington, Illinois Basin Consortium, p. 29–44.

KVALE, E. P., AND ARCHER, A. W., 1990, Tidal deposits associated with low- sulfur coals, Brazil Fm. (Lower Pennsylvanian), Indiana: Journal of Sedimentary Petrology, v. 60, p. 563–574.

KVALE, E. P., AND ARCHER, A. W., 1991, Characteristics of two Pennsylvanian-age semidiurnal tidal deposits in the Illinois Basin, U.S.A., *in* Smith, D. G., Reinson, G. E., Zaitlin, B. A., and Rahami, R. A., eds., Clastic Tidal Sedimentology: Calgary, Canadian Society Petroleum Geologists Memoir 16, p. 179–188.

KVALE, E. P., ARCHER, A. W., AND JOHNSON, H. R., 1989, Daily, monthly, and yearly tidal cycles within laminated siltstones of the Mansfield Formation (Pennsylvanian) of Indiana: Geology, v. 17, p. 365–368.

LANIER, W. P., FELDMAN, H. R., AND ARCHER, A. W., 1993, Tidally modulated sedimentation in a fluvial to estuarine transition, Douglas Group, Missourian-Virgilian, Kansas: Journal of Sedimentary Petrology, v. 63, p. 860–873.

LINS, T. W., 1950, Origin and environment of the Tonganoxie Sandstone in northeastern Kansas: Kansas Geological Survey Bulletin, v. 86, p. 105–140.

MARTINO, R. L., AND SANDERSON, D. D., 1991, Rhythmic sedimentation in a tide-dominated marginal marine setting, Breathit Formation (Pennsylvanian), eastern Kentucky (abs.): Geological Society America, Abstracts with Programs, v. 23, p. A461.

MILLER, H. W., AND SWINEFORD, A., 1957, Paleoecology of the nodulose zone at the top of Haskell Limestone (Upper Pennsylvanian) in Kansas: American Association of Petroleum Geologists Bulletin, v. 41, p. 2012–2036.

MINOR, J. A., 1969. Petrology of the Tonganoxie Sandstone (Pennsylvanian), Kansas-Missouri: Unpublished M.S. Thesis, University of Missouri, Columbia, 98 p.

MOORE, R. C., FRYE, J. C., JEWETT, J. M., WALLACE, L., AND O'CONNOR, H. G., 1951, The Kansas rock column: Kansas Geological Survey Bulletin 89, 132 p.

NICHOLS, M. M., JOHNSON, G. H., AND PEEBLES, P. C., 1991, Modern sediments and facies model for a microtidal coastal plain estuary, the James estuary, Virginia: Journal of Sedimentary Petrology, v. 61, p. 883–899.

National Oceanic and Atmospheric Administration, 1991a, Tide Tables 1992, High and Low Water Predictions, Europe and West Coast of Africa including the Mediterranean Sea: Riverdale, NOAA, 204 p.

National Oceanic and Atmospheric Administration, 1991b, Tide Tables 1992, High and Low Water Predictions, East Coast of North and South America, including Greenland: Riverdale, NOAA, 289 p.

PATTERSON, J. M., 1933, The Douglas Group of the Pennsylvanian system in Douglas and Leavenworth counties, Kansas: Unpublished M.S. Thesis, University of Kansas, Lawrence, 35 p.

RAHMANI, R. A., 1989, Cretaceous tidal estuarine and deltaic deposits, Drumheller, Alberta. Field trip guide: Second international research symposium on clastic tidal deposits: Calgary, Canadian Society of Petroleum Geologists, 55 p.

REINECK, H.-E., AND SINGH, I. B., 1980, Depositional Sedimentary Environments, With References to Terrigenous Clastics: New York, Springer-Verlag, 549 p.

RUTAN, D., 1980, The environment of deposition of the Ireland Sandstone member and related strata: Unpublished M.S. Thesis, University of Kansas, Lawrence, 120 p.

SANDERS, D. T., 1959, Sandstones of the Douglas and Pedee Groups in northeastern Kansas: Kansas Geological Survey Bulletin, v. 134, p. 125–159.

STEPHENSON, L. G., 1958, Pedee and Douglas groups (Pennsylvanian) of southeastern Nebraska and adjacent region: Unpublished M.S. Thesis, University of Nebraska, Lincoln, 213 p.

TESSIER, B., 1990, Enregistrement des cycles tidaux en accretion verticale dans un milieu actuel (la baie du Mont-Saint-Michel), et dans une formation ancienne (la molasse marine miocene du bassin de Digne). Mesure de temps et application a la recontitution des paleoenvionments: Unpublished Ph.D. Dissertation, University Caen, Caen, 122 p.

TESSIER, B., ARCHER, A. W., AND FELDMAN, H. R., 1992, Comparison of Carboniferous tidal rhythmites (eastern and western Interior Basins, U. S. A.) with modern analogues (the Bay of Mont-Saint-Michel) (abs.): Courier Forschungsinstitut Senckenberg, v. 151, p. 84–85.

TESSIER, B., MONTFORT, Y., GIGOT, P., AND LARSONNEUR, C., 1989, Enregistrement des cycles tidaux en accretion verticale, adaption d'un outil de traitement mathmatique: Examples en baie du Mont-Saint-Michel et dans la molasse marine miocene du bassin de Digne: Bulletin Societe Geologie France, v. 8, p. 1029–1041.

TRICKER, R. A. R., 1964, Bores, Breakers, Waves, and Wakes, An Introduction to the Study of Waves on Water: London, Mills and Boon Limited, 250 p.

VAN WAGONER, J. C., R. M. MITCHUM, K. M. CAMPION, AND V. D. RAHMANIAN, 1990, Siliciclastic sequence stratigraphy in well logs, cores, and outcrops: Concepts for high-resolution correlation of time and facies: Tulsa, American Association of Petroleum Geologists, Methods in Exploration Series, No. 7, 55 p.

WALTON, A. W., AND GRIFFITH, G., 1985, Deltaic deposition in the Tonganoxie or "Stalnaker" Sandstone (Stranger Formation, Virgilian); TXO Robison C-1, Harper County, Kansas: Lawrence, Kansas Geological Survey, Subsurface Geology Series 6, p. 145–160.

WHEELER, D. M., SCOTT, A. J., CORINGRATO, V. J., AND DEVINE, P. E., 1990, Stratigraphy and depositional history of the Morrow Formation, southeast Colorado and southwest Kansas, *in* Sonnenbery, S. A., Shannon, L. T., Rader, K., von Drehle, W. F., and Martin, G. W., eds., Morrow Sandstones of Southeast Colorado and Adjacent Areas: Denver, Rocky Mountain Association of Geologists, p. 9–35.

WINCHELL, R. L., 1957, Relationship of the Lansing Group and the Tonganoxie ("Stalnaker") Sandstone in south-central Kansas: Kansas Geological Survey Bulletin, v. 127, p. 123–152.

EVOLUTION OF LOWER PENNSYLVANIAN ESTUARINE FACIES WITHIN TWO ADJACENT PALEOVALLEYS, ILLINOIS BASIN, INDIANA

ERIK P. KVALE AND MARK L. BARNHILL

Indiana University, Indiana Geological Survey, Bloomington, Indiana, 47405

ABSTRACT: The lower Pennsylvanian strata in Indiana, Illinois, and western Kentucky rests unconformably on Mississippian to Devonian deposits within the midcontinent Illinois Basin. These deposits fill a complex drainage network of sub-Pennsylvanian paleovalleys with as much as 140 m of shale, sandstone, coal, and mudstone. Paleovalley widths are variable ranging from a kilometer to several kilometers wide and trend roughly northeast to southwest. Timing of valley incision is difficult to constrain and may have been diachronous. Filling of the southern reaches of the drainage system commenced during earliest Pennsylvanian while incision may have continued in the more northern (upland) reaches in Indiana.

The paleovalleys progressively filled from south to north during an overall transgressive sea-level rise. During sea-level rise, these valleys became the sites for estuarine deposition. Two relatively small paleovalleys (1 to 1.5 km wide) have been studied in detail in south-central Indiana. Lithofacies can be mapped down the valleys for several kilometers by using subsurface and outcrop data. Within these valleys, conglomerate and conglomeratic sand-dominated inner (upper) estuarine, mud-dominated estuarine central basin, and sand-dominated outer (lower) estuarine deposits can be identified. Central basin sediments overlie fluvial deposits. Direct evidence of tidal influence within the central basin deposits can be recognized by the presence of intertidal rhythmites that exhibit well developed neap-spring cycles. Outer estuarine deposits overlie the central basin deposits and accumulated during the final stages of valley-filling.

INTRODUCTION

The contact of the basal Pennsylvanian strata in most of the Illinois Basin (Fig. 1) of the east-central United States is marked by an unconformity of considerable relief. Detailed maps of this unconformity in Indiana reveal that the surface formed on Mississippian to Devonian strata and consists of deeply incised, interconnected paleovalleys and interfluve areas formed by the incision of rivers flowing towards the southern margin of the basin (Fig. 2). Incision spanned an interval of time from latest Mississippian to early Pennsylvanian (Droste and Keller, 1989).

The formation of the unconformity was coincident with the withdrawal of the Mississippian seaway from virtually the entire North American craton (see summary discussion in Nelson and others, 1991). Paleovalleys as deep as 140 m and as wide as 30 km have been reported in the southern end of the basin. These dimensions decrease to the north. Sea-level rise in the early Pennsylvanian initiated back-filling of these paleovalleys to the south with the onlap of younger sediments filling valleys to the north.

The origin of the Pennsylvanian fill sequences is generally unknown. Nelson and others (1991) noted the presence of fluvial sandstones at the base of many of the paleovalleys and cited the work of several detailed studies. Droste and Keller (1989) proposed that the paleovalleys contain at least some estuarine sediments but provided no direct evidence to support this contention. Howard and Whitaker (1990) offered the first documentation of a bedrock confined, fluvial estuarine valley fill in the Illinois Basin. This study in southeastern Illinois is particularly noteworthy because it demonstrates the association of significant hydrocarbon accumulations within these deposits. However, these papers focus on the sandstone within the fill facies without much regard to the characteristics of the finer grained units. Yet, it is the mudstone and not the sandstone that is often the most volumetrically important of the fill succession. Moreover, the sedimentology and ichnology of the mudstone may, in fact, be the key to recognizing estuarine environments in the rock record. As an example, the estuarine interpretation of Howard and Whitaker (1990)

is based largely on the presence of a few acritarchs in a thin shale that overlies a basal sandstone. However, not a single study has yet provided direct evidence of tidal processes within an Illinois Basin valley-fill sequence.

Recent studies of modern and ancient estuaries provide significant insight into Pennsylvanian valley-fill sequences in the Illinois Basin. Estuaries are natural sinks for fluvial and marine sediments and are a natural consequence of the marine drowning of bedrock defended valleys. This paper provides the first detailed sedimentological and biological evidence of Pennsylvanian estuarine facies filling an Illinois Basin paleovalley and supports the contention that such processes were very important in these valley-fill sequences.

BACKGROUND

The study area occupies the eastern portion of the Naval Surface Warfare Center (NSWC), Crane, Indiana (herein referred to as "Crane") (Fig. 2). The delineation of the facies relationships and sedimentology of the basal Pennsylvanian was an outgrowth of a geologic investigation of potential groundwater aquifers done by the Indiana Geological Survey in cooperation with the U. S. Army Corps of Engineers.

Fourteen coreholes were drilled in the study area that penetrated the Pennsylvanian/Mississippian unconformity. Gamma-ray logs were available for eleven of these holes. Regional stratigraphic correlations by L. Furer (pers. commun., 1992) have determined the section to be approximately equivalent to the Mansfield Formation (Fig. 3).

Field mapping of Crane, the fourteen coreholes mentioned above, and unpublished IGS field notes and maps from outside the Crane facility provided a data base for a sub-Pennsylvanian map that clearly shows the existence of two, subparallel, north-south trending paleovalleys each of which is 1 to 1.5 km wide (Fig. 4). These paleovalleys are likely tributaries to the much larger Shoals paleovalley mapped by Droste and Keller (1989) to the south (Fig. 2). Locally, the relief on the unconformity exceeds 30 meters.

Three cross sections were constructed oriented perpendicular to the paleovalleys (Figs. 4, 5, 6, 7). The sections

Incised-valley Systems: Origin and Sedimentary Sequences, SEPM Special Publication No. 51

FIG. 1.—Map showing the outcrop distribution (cross hatched area) of Pennsylvanian-age rocks in the Illinois Basin.

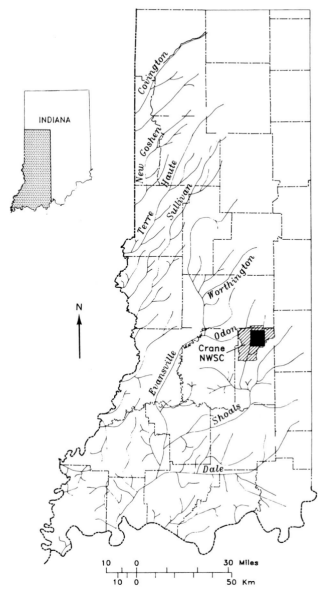

FIG. 2.—Map showing the major channels of the drainage system developed on the sub-Pennsylvanian surface (from Droste and Keller, 1989). Crane NSWC is highlighted by the broadly spaced hatchures north of the "Shoals Paleovalley" with the study area delineated by the solid pattern within Crane. The only modern drainage depicted on this map is the portion of the Wabash River that forms the western border of Indiana and the Ohio River that forms the southern border of Indiana.

were correlated from a Pennsylvanian datum (L4) at the base of a fine-grained interval dominated by a grey shale that can be correlated from the study area westward to the Illinois-Indiana border (L. Furer, pers. commun.), a distance of approximately 60 kilometers. Its lateral extent and fine-grained character suggests that it is a transgressive marine unit. As such it represents a suitable marker for regional correlation. Samples from this unit are currently being processed for marine microfossils.

The cross sections include both outcrop and subsurface data. Locations of measured sections of outcrops are shown on Figure 4. The sections were described during mapping of the NSWC. Unfortunately, heavy vegetation tends to obscure most of the fine-grained deposits within the study area; thus, most exposures described are of the coarser grained facies. The locations and elevations of small abandoned coal mines within the area were also noted. Without the subsurface control, regional and even local facies correlations would be difficult. However, coreholes are scattered throughout the study area and interspersed with the outcrop measured sections. Thus, areas covered by vegetation can be convincingly correlated to fine-grained deposits present in nearby wells. Therefore, regional correlations are possible.

To facilitate facies comparisons, three lines of correlation were drawn parallel to the datum. These lines of correlation are numbered L1, L2, L3, and L4 from bottom to top with L4 representing the datum. They are presented as an aid to the discussion of lateral facies. Generalized maps of facies present along these lines utilizing outcrop and subsurface data were constructed to visualize the broader facies evolution through time.

Regionally, the Pennsylvanian has an average dip of 3.8 to 5.7 m/km (20 to 30 ft/mi) to the southwest in Indiana (Hutchison, 1967). However within the study area, two monoclinal flexures appear to be present (Fig. 4). In the central portion of the study area Pennsylvanian dips change from horizontal east of a north-south line separating holes IGS 3 (Fig. 4, well 3) and IGS 4 (Fig. 4, well 4), to approximately 2.8 m/km (15 ft/mi) of apparent dip to the southwest between holes IGS 4 and WES-6C-1 (Fig. 4, well C-1), to perhaps as much as 11 m/k (60 ft/mi) of apparent

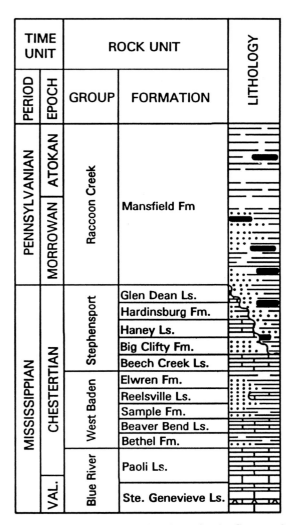

FIG. 3.—Generalized stratigraphic column for the Crane study area. The thick solid bars signify coal-bearing horizons. The Pennsylvanian/ Mississippian unconformity is denoted by the inclined, sinusoidal line.

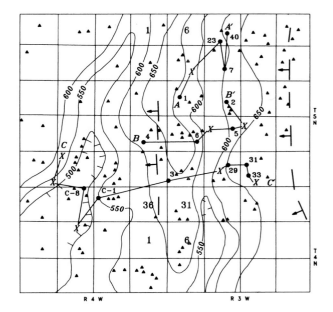

EXPLANATION

x Location of measured outcrop used in cross section

⌐ Monoclinal flexure showing dip direction

²⁹• Location of corehole

▲ Location of measured outcrop

FIG. 4.—Sub-Pennsylvanian paleovalleys on Crane. The contours reflect elevation (in feet above mean sea level) of the Pennsylvanian-Mississippian surface. The study area includes portions of four Townships within the U.S. Public Land Survey system, which each consist of 36 square miles. The corner sections of the Townships are denoted by the large numbers and are one mile (1.6 km) on each side. The cross-section lines correspond to the cross-sections in Figures 5, 6, and 7.

dip to the west between holes WES-6C-1 and WES-6C-8 (Fig. 4, well C-8). Thus, while the average regional dip of the Pennsylvanian may be 3.8 to 5.7 m/km (20 to 30 ft/ mi), the local dip may be twice that. In fact, another westward-dipping, northward-trending monoclinal flexure just east of the easternmost paleovalley can be demonstrated from outcrop mapping of the Mississippian units where Pennsylvanian outcrops are not present or are very thin (Kvale, 1992). It therefore appears that the paleovalleys may be localized by these folds. Furer (1992) presents evidence that this type of feature in the Illinois Basin may be related to reactivated basement faulting.

LITHOFACIES AND ENVIRONMENTS OF DEPOSITION

Pennsylvanian rock types filling the paleovalleys at Crane can be grouped into seven major lithofacies (Barnhill, 1992). These are: (1) shale, (2) wavy- and flaser-bedded sandstone and mudstone, (3) ripple-bedded and parallel-laminated sandstone, (4) massive and large-scale cross-bedded sandstone, (5) rhythmic-bedded siltstone, (6) conglomerate and conglomeratic sandstone, and (7) coal and rooted mudstone, siltstone, and sandstone. These lithofacies record deposition within bedrock confined paleovalleys that were progressively drowned and filled during an overall marine transgression.

Shale Lithofacies

Description.—

The shale lithofacies is volumetrically the most important of all the lithofacies and can be subdivided into two groups: a dark gray shale and a lenticular bedded shale. Both of these units are slope formers in outcrop and are usually heavily vegetated. The dark gray shale is the most common in the valley-fill sequences and is generally micaceous, structureless to platy, waxy, and sometimes silty with finely disseminated plant fragments along parting planes. Siderite bands (nodules?) 30 cm or more thick are common. Trace fossils are rare but may include small (mm-diameter), *Chondrites*-like, horizontal tubes in the siltier intervals. Body

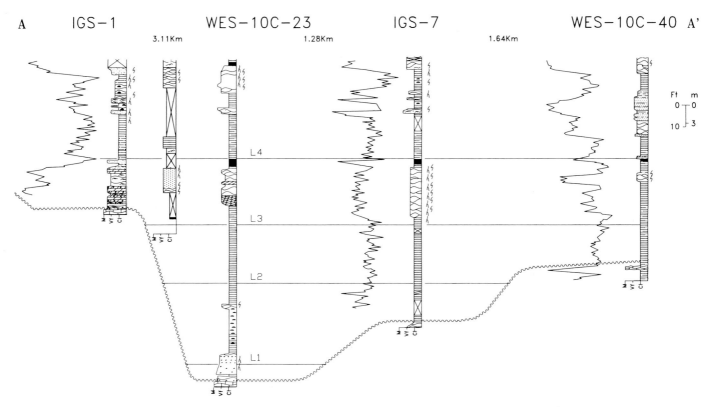

Fig. 5.—Cross-section A-A'. Labeled columns (eg., IGS 1) refer to coreholes (and associated gamma-ray logs where available). Unlabeled columns are the graphic depictions of measured outcrop sections. See Figure 4 for location of coreholes and outcrops. Grainsize is noted at the base of each column (M -medium grained sandstone; vf—very fine grained sandstone; cl—clay). Interval distance (in km) between coreholes is noted. Datum (L4) is the base of a regionally correlatable shale. See text for discussion of L1-L3. Refer to Figure 7 for the explanation of symbology.

fossils are also rare, but a single small (<1 cm across) spiriferid brachiopod was observed within the east paleovalley fill approximately 4.6 m above the unconformity in IGS 7 (Fig. 5 cross-section A-A').

The lenticular bedded shale is generally micaceous and silty but contains isolated lenses or streaks of very fine-grained, quartz-rich sandstone. Trace fossil diversity is low but can be locally intense within this facies and includes traces such as *Planolites*, and *Chondrites*.

Interpretation.—

The shale lithofacies occurs primarily in two contexts within the study area: (1) as part of the valley-fill succession (below L3) and (2) as a stratigraphically younger, regionally correlatable unit present across southwestern Indiana that caps the paleovalley-fill succession (above L4). In both contexts, the general absence of sandstone and the abundance of dark shales within this facies indicates a low energy, low oxygen, and organic-rich environment. This is consistent with a very low diversity, ichnofossil assemblage that includes *Chondrites* (Bromley and Ekdale, 1984). The regional extent of the uppermost shale suggests that it is a transgressive marine deposit reflecting normal marine salinities and maximum water depth during the overall transgression. Marine body fossils have yet to be identified in the regionally extensive marine unit; however, this shale

is known primarily from the subsurface and has only recently been identified in outcrop.

The spiriferid brachiopod found within the paleovalley-fill shale is indicative of normal marine salinities (A. Horowitz, pers. commun., 1992); however, the occurrence of siderite bands within this facies suggests a mixing of iron rich freshwater and marine water (Woodland and Stenstrom, 1979). The identification of only a single specimen suggests that this fossil is allochthonous rather than autochthonous.

The discontinuous nature of the paleovalley-fill shale, the presence of siderite nodules, and its position lateral to coals and rooted tidal-flat deposits (see below) suggest brackish water conditions.

Wavy and Flaser-bedded Sandstone and Mudstone Lithofacies

Description.—

The wavy-bedded sandstone lithofacies is the most common of the observed sandstone facies which are gradational with one another. It consists of light gray, well sorted, subangular to subrounded, very fine grained quartz arenite that is intercalated with medium to dark gray, carbonaceous, micaceous mudstone drapes (Fig. 8). Ripple forms are generally asymmetric, very sinuous, and with rounded crests.

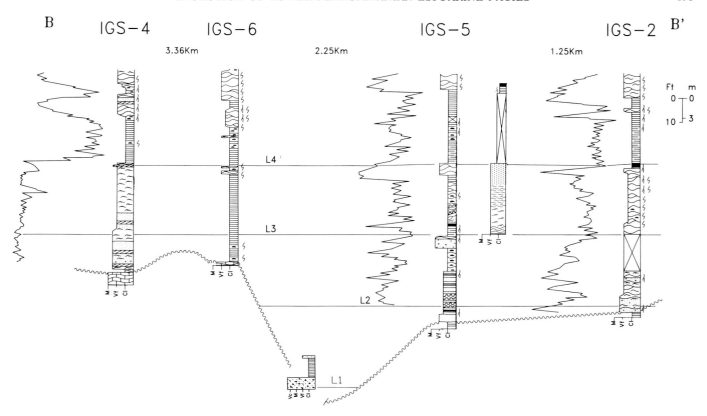

Fig. 6.—Cross-section B-B'. Datum, grainsize, and symbols as for Figure 5.

The clay drapes are typically 1 to 4 mm thick but range up to 1 cm or more in thickness.

Plant fragments may be finely disseminated through the mudstone drapes with sideritized zones and patches also commonly preserved. Bioturbation can be locally intense with the traces *Planolites, Teichichnus*, and possibly *Lochiea* present within this facies.

Flaser bedding is less common within the fill succession than wavy bedding. Texturally, it is very similar to the sandstones in the wavy-bedded facies. Drapes are confined to the ripple troughs.

Interpretation.—

Wavy- and flaser-bedding, although not clearly diagnostic, are characteristic of tidal settings (eg., Reineck and Wunderlich, 1968; Clifton, 1982). The abundance of these structures in core and outcrop exposures supports a depositional interpretation of a mixed sand and mud tidal flat. The lack of evidence of subaerial exposure such as drying cracks, drain features such as rills, or raindrop impressions indicates a lower intertidal to subtidal setting for the deposits. The limited bioturbation and relatively low diversity of trace fossils, the absence of marine body fossils, and the presence of siderite bands and nodules suggest a brackish environment for this facies.

Ripple-bedded and Parallel-Laminated Sandstone Lithofacies

Description.—

The ripple-bedded and parallel-laminated lithofacies is primarily restricted to a fairly continuous, sheet-like deposit that occurs near the top of the valley-fill sequence (Figs. 5, 6, 7, between L3 and L4). Texturally, it resembles the sandstones in the flaser- and wavy-bedded facies. Locally it grades laterally into the wavy- and flaser-bedded lithofacies and commonly overlies the massive and trough cross-bedded lithofacies. Rounded mudstone rip-up clasts, an average of 1 cm in diameter, are occasionally contained within the facies. In outcrop, the parallel-laminated sandstone typically exhibits primary current lineations (PCL) on bedding plane surfaces. In fact, in some outcrops PCL is the dominant primary structure. Ripple forms are generally asymmetrical and highly sinuous crested. Locally, bedding plane exposures exist of very straight crested ripple forms with ripple indices of 15 or greater indicating formation by wind generated wave currents in shallow water. Herringbone cross-stratification has also been observed in core and outcrop (Fig. 9). Trace fossils observed in both the ripple-bedded sandstone (and some flaser-bedded sandstones) include a diverse assemblage including *Teichichnus, Zoophyco*s, *Planolites, Conosticu*s (Fig. 10), and *Rhizocorallium*. The first three trace fossils are thought to have been made by infaunal deposit-feeding annelids that existed in generally lower energy conditions (Devera, 1989). *Conosticus* is a resting/dwelling structure of a sea anemone and is common in Pennsylvanian sequences interpreted to have been deposited in normal to near-normal marine salinities (Chamberlin, 1971; Devera, 1989; Martino and Sanderson, 1993). Evidence of bioturbation was not found in the parallel-laminated sandstone probably because of high

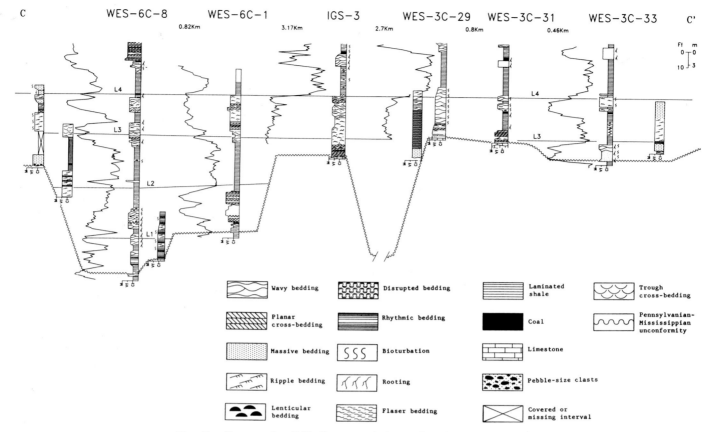

Fig. 7.—Cross-section C-C'. Datum, grainsize, and symbols as for Figure 5.

current velocities in the upper flow regime resulting in excessive rates of sediment movement and reworking.

Interpretation.—

This facies is interpreted as the product of intertidal to subtidal sandflat deposition. This interpretation is supported by the lateral extent of the lithofacies, a general absence of dunes and an abundance of horizontally stratified sandstone ripples and parallel-laminated sandstone, a general absence of subaerial exposure features, and a lateral association with tidal bedding features such as wavy- and flaser-bedded sandstones and herringbone cross-stratification. Normal or near normal marine salinities are indicated by the diverse assemblage of trace fossils including *Conosticus* (Devera, 1989; Martino and Sanderson, 1993).

Massive and Cross-bedded Sandstone Lithofacies

Description.—

Massive and cross-bedded sandstones are grouped together into one facies because they are commonly associated and very similar texturally. The facies is a quartz arenite that is light gray to tan, very fine to fine grained, well sorted, subangular to subrounded, and micaceous. The massive sandstone locally exhibits dewatering pipes and highly contorted bedding. In most cases, however, the unit is totally structureless.

Within the cross-bedded sandstone, sets are generally small to medium (7 to 40 cm thick) with tangential lower contacts. Locally, this lithofacies is often observed as a single set within the ripple-bedded and parallel-laminated lithofacies. One- to three- centimeter diameter mudstone rip-up clasts are common near basal contacts of the facies or along foreset boundaries. Basal contacts are normally erosive. One to three meter thick channel packages consisting of stacked trough, cross-bedded sets (set thickness generally ranging from 30 cm to 1.5 m) overlain by ripple-bedded and parallel-laminated sandstone occur locally. Reactivation surfaces are very common in the cross-bedded facies (Fig. 11), some of which have a pronounced sigmoidal form. Fresh or unweathered exposures of the reactivation surfaces reveal that the trough cross-bedded sets are commonly organized into large-scale tidal bundles. Clay draped packages of large-scale foresets (dominant-flow deposits) are capped by reversely dipping ripple sets (subordinate flow deposits) which are in turn draped by clay (Fig. 12). These large-scale structures are very similar to those described by Boersma (1969) and Visser (1980). Bioturbation was not observed within the facies.

Interpretation.—

The massive and cross-bedded sandstone lithofacies is interpreted as a tidal channel-fill facies that formed within a tidal sandflat environment dominated by the ripple-bedded

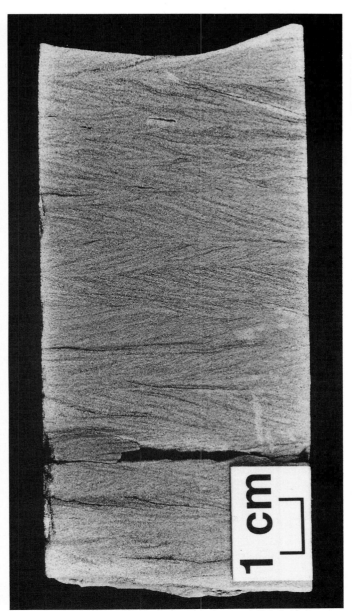

FIG. 8.—Photo of slabbed core of wavy-bedded sandstone and mudstone. Note small, horizontal, tube-like structures at the base of several of the ripple beds.

FIG. 9.—Photo of slabbed core of herringbone ripple-lamination.

and parallel-laminated lithofacies. Dewatering of the facies is possibly related to the migration of tidal channels and subsequent bank collapse or perhaps from dewatering of underlying mud into the sand as a result of sediment density gradients.

The individual or isolated trough cross-bedded sets represent the migration of single sandwaves across the tidal sandflat. The presence of double clay drapes in the large-scale tidal bundles suggest a predominantly sub-tidal origin for this facies.

The absence of bioturbation reflects a high sediment mobility and current energy within the original depositional system. However, association with the bioturbated ripple-bedded and parallel-laminated lithofacies also suggests a normal or near normal marine salinity for this environment.

Paleocurrent Trends

Description.—

Paleocurrent directions were measured from ripple faces, trough axes, and reactivation surfaces in the ripple-bedded and parallel-laminated sandstone lithofacies (tidal sandflat) and the massive and cross-bedded sandstone lithofacies (tidal channel). The results can be subdivided into an eastern and western zone separated by a north-south trending line that

FIG. 10.—Inverted bedding plane view of *Conosticus* burrows. *Conosticus* is a resting/dwelling structure of a burrowing sea anemone (Chamberlin, 1971). Ruler is 15 cm long. Specimen was collected from ripple-bedded sandstone present above large-scale tidal bundles depicted in Figure 11.

FIG. 11.—Large-scale tidal bundles preserved in the western part of the study area. Inclined reactivation surfaces are weathering along goethite-cemented mudstone drapes. Paleoflow is flood-tide dominated (to the east or landward).

separates wells WES-3C-29 and IGS 3 (Fig. 4, wells 29 and 3). Paleoflows within both zones are strongly bipolar (Figs. 13, 14). The eastern zone is bipolar in a northeast-southwest direction whereas the western zone is bipolar in a more east-west direction. Trough axes and reactivation surfaces of large-scale tidal bundles tend to have a more easterly paleoflow orientation in the western zone. Similar primary structures vary from northerly paleoflow trends to southerly paleoflow trends in the eastern zone.

Interpretation.—

Pennsylvanian paleoshorelines of Indiana have been extrapolated largely from the regional distribution patterns of Pennsylvanian sandstones considered to be totally fluvial. This distribution suggests that over time paleoshorelines trended north-northwest to south-southeast in this part of Indiana (Potter, 1962). However during initial transgression of the paleovalleys, the shoreline was likely highly irregular. In general, however, north- or east-oriented paleoflows would be landward directed (flood-tide oriented) whereas west- or south-orientations would be seaward directed (ebb-tide oriented). Thus, in the western zone flood tides were the dominant flow based on the preferred orientation of the large-scale trough cross-beds. In the eastern zone flood or ebb tides dominated depending on the outcrop.

Conglomerate and Conglomeratic Sandstone Lithofacies

Description.—

This lithofacies was encountered in the study area in only two sites, but both occupy the same stratigraphic position near the base of the east paleovalley. The first site is within 3 meters of the base of WES-10C-23 (Fig. 5) and consists of a conglomeratic sandstone with mudstone and ironstone pebble-size clasts. The unit is rooted at the top. The second site is in a measured outcrop section between IGS 6 and IGS 5 (Fig. 6). It consists of a clast-supported conglomerate with clasts of blade-shaped mudstone and iron-cemented mudstone (ironstone). In addition, one very weathered limestone clast of probable Mississippian age was found. Clast sizes range from 1 to 5 cm. The conglomerate fines upwards to a conglomeratic sandstone consisting of mudstone and ironstone clasts with large weathered plant fragments in a matrix of fine- to medium-grained quartz sandstone. The unit is massive.

Interpretation.—

Limited exposure and an absence of primary structures make a depositional interpretation of this lithofacies difficult. The large clasts indicate current competence beyond anything observed in the rest of the succession. Its position at or very near the bottom of the paleovalley suggests a fluvial depositional system that transported large tree branches and incorporated preexisting Mississippian bedrock and intraformational deposits into its bedload.

Rhythmic-bedded Siltstone Lithofacies

Description.—

The rhythmically bedded siltstone lithofacies is present within the paleovalley-fill sequences of two holes (ISG 5, Fig. 6 and WES-6C-8, Fig. 7) and crops out in the immediate vicinity of both. It consists of rhythmically laminated, well-sorted siltstone to very fine-grained sandstone with intercalated dark gray silty mudstone (Figs. 15, 16). Finely disseminated plant material is common along bedding planes. Although not apparent through most of this facies, decimeter thick zones of progressively thickening and thinning, vertically accreted laminae (tidal rhythmites

FIG. 12.—Outcrop photo of toe-sets of large-scale tidal bundles preserved in the eastern part of the study area. The arrow in the lower right-hand corner of the photo is pointing to stratigraphic up. The nearly horizontal reactivation surfaces are weathering along goethite-cemented mudstone drapes. Dominant paleoflow is to the right (southward or ebb-direction). Note the subordinate-flow (flood-oriented) ripple (small arrow) that is separated from a smaller ebb-oriented ripple (large arrow) by a clay drape. The smaller ebb-oriented ripple is in turn capped by a clay drape.

or small-scale tidal bundles) are present (Figs. 17, 18). These correspond to deposition during neap-spring-neap-tidal cycles. Thick siltstone lamina alternate with thin lamina in the IGS 5 core suggesting the possibility of semidiurnal tidal events. Alternatively, the thick-thin couplets in the IGS 5 core may reflect flood-ebb cycles in a diurnal system. Similar couplets are uncommon in the WES-6C-8 core suggesting predominantly diurnal tidal deposition.

Fine plant rootlets are present in the upper portions of IGS 5 and WES-6C-8. These are short structures, a fraction of a millimeter wide, that exist at highly oblique angles to the bedding and occasionally are observed to be branching (Fig. 19). Raindrop impressions were also observed along a mud parting of one of the lamina in the same core (Fig. 20). Traces are all horizontal and include *Plangtichnus* and *Haplotichnus* (interpreted as insect trackways by Maples and Archer, 1987), small arthropod trackways, and possible fish fin drag marks.

Interpretation.—

The preservation of neap-spring tidal cycles and the evidence of subaerial exposure, including horizontal track-

ways made by insects and arthropods plus raindrop impressions, support an intertidal tidal-flat interpretation for this lithofacies. The facies is very similar to the Indiana Hindostan Whetstone beds (Kvale and others, 1989; Archer and Kvale, 1989; Kvale and Archer, 1991), which are of comparable age and located south of the Crane NSWC, in terms of texture, primary structures, and trace fossil assemblage. Archer and Kvale (1989) documented nearly continuous cycles of daily, semidaily, semimonthly, monthly, seasonal, and yearly tidal sedimentation in six meters of stacked laminated siltstones in the Whetstone beds. Sedimentation rates of as much as 1 m/yr were calculated for the Whetstone beds based on the recognition of these cycles.

Deposition of the Crane rhythmites was not nearly as continuous as deposition in the Whetstone beds as revealed by the truncated and amalgamated neap-spring cycles preserved in these cores. This is probably the result of periodic reworking of the tidal flats. Still, intervals are preserved which record sedimentation rates of four to five centimeters per month.

The existence of rootlets in the rhythmites indicates that these tidal flats were vegetated at least in their upper por-

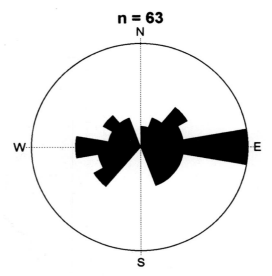

n = 63

FIG. 13.—Rose plot of paleoflow directions recorded in the western zone of the study area. See text for definition of western zone. Plot includes measurements from trough-axes, ripple foresets, and directions of inclination of reactivation surfaces of large-scale tidal bundles.

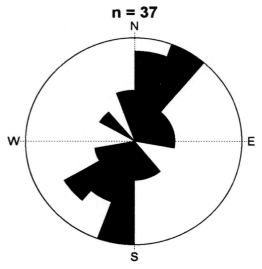

n = 37

FIG. 14.—Rose plot of paleoflow directions recorded in the eastern zone of the study area. See text for definition of eastern zone.

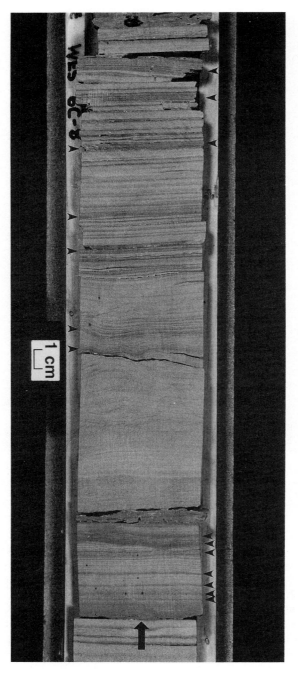

FIG. 15.—Photo of slabbed core from WES-6C-8 showing rhythmically laminated siltstones. Small horizontal arrows mark mudstone-rich neap-tide deposits. The large vertical arrow is indicating stratigraphic up.

tions. Frey and Howard (1986) note that the character of vegetated tidal flats prior to the introduction of "grassy" angiosperms is poorly known. They suggest that well-vegetated tidal flats may be a relatively recent phenomenon. The rooting in the rhythmites strongly supports the idea that vegetated tidal flats did exist prior to the Cretaceous although the plants were likely rush-like as suggested by Frey and Howard (1986).

The general absence of vertical or infaunal bioturbation within this facies suggests brackish to freshwater salinities. With the exception of the fish fin drag marks, the noted trace fossils were probably generated during low tide. High

rates of sedimentation may also have been at least partially responsible for the exclusion of infaunal activity.

*Coal and Rooted Mudstone, Siltstone,
and Sandstone Lithofacies*

Description.—

Rooting can be found locally in all of the major lithofacies. Generally, rooting is not apparent in much of the

FIG. 16.—Photo of slabbed core from IGS 5 showing rhythmically laminated siltstones. Small horizontal arrows mark the thinner laminated neap-tide deposits. Note the thick-thin couplets preserved in the central part of the core. These are bounded by very thin claystone drapes. The large vertical arrow is indicating stratigraphic up. The section of core missing just above the vertical arrow contains raindrop impressions preserved along a bedding plane (see Fig. 20).

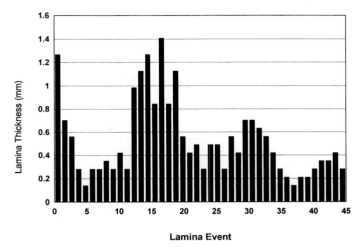

FIG. 17.—Histogram plot of thickness variability of lamina in a portion of WES-6C-8. Note the cyclic variability related to neap-spring tidal events.

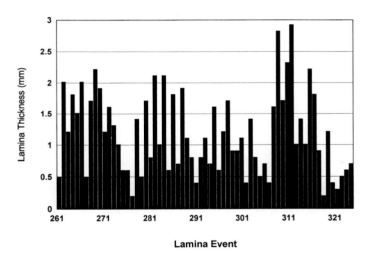

FIG. 18.—Histogram plot of thickness variability of lamina in a portion of IGS 5. Note the cyclic variability related to neap-spring tidal events. Approximately two months of deposition (two neap and two spring events) is represented by this diagram.

dark gray shale facies unless it is in near proximity to an overlying coal. In such cases, the dark gray shales grade into greenish underclays. Rooting occurs at the top of the sheet-like sandstone deposit comprised of the massive and cross-bedded sandstone lithofacies and the ripple-bedded and parallel-laminated lithofacies, which are present in the upper part of the valley-fill succession. Rooting is also present in relatively thin massive sandstones located on top of or very close to the Pennsylvanian and Mississippian unconformity such as in WES-3C-33 (Fig. 7), WES-10C-23 (Fig. 5), and IGS 5 (Fig. 6). Rooting is fairly common in the wavy bedded sandstone facies but not to the extent that bedding is completely destroyed. Segments of the rhythmically bedded siltstone facies are also rooted as in IGS 5 (Fig. 6).

Coals are discontinuous in the paleovalley-fill succession and are found in proximity to the paleovalley walls (eg., outcrop section between IGS 1 and WES-10C-23, Fig. 5, near the base of WES-6C-1, Fig. 7, near the base of IGS 2, Fig. 6) . They can not be traced beyond the outcrop or core holes in which they are identified. Thus, coal-forming

FIG. 19.—Photo of polished core from IGS 5 showing the preservation of rootlets (small arrows). The large horizontal arrows mark thin, neap-tide laminae. The top of the photo is stratigraphic up.

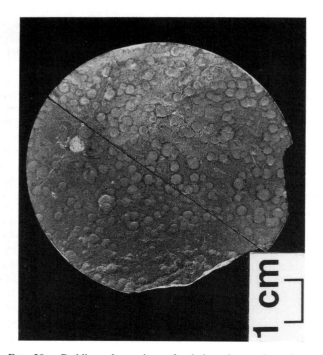

FIG. 20.—Bedding plane view of raindrop impressions from the rhythmically laminated siltstone in IGS 5. Refer to Figure 16 for view perpendicular to bedding of this section of core.

peat development within the paleovalleys was patchy and isolated. In some cases, however, coals can be correlated laterally over short distances to rooted horizons. It is not until the stratigraphic interval above the paleovalley fills that either the coals or rooted facies become more regionally correlatable.

The coals within the paleovalley fills are predominantly clarains and vitrains with smaller amounts of durain and are of bituminous rank. The presence of underclays beneath the coals indicates they are all autochthonous.

Interpretation.—

Rooting occurs in the tidal rhythmites of IGS 5 and within wavy-bedded sandstone also thought to be of tidal origin. The presence of rootlets within these facies suggests that vegetated tidal-flats existed periodically during valley-fill.

Outcrop mapping and corehole information indicate that rooting may be more common in deposits present along the unconformity. For example, rooting is present in sandstone that directly overlies or is in close proximity to the unconformity in IGS 5 (Fig. 6), IGS 2 (Fig. 6), and WES-10C-23 (Fig. 5). Rooting is also present beneath a coal that formed adjacent to the unconformity in WES-6C-1 (Fig. 7). Deposits adjacent to paleovalley walls are logical positions to expect rooting since this is where upper intertidal and supratidal flats would be best developed.

The coals are clearly freshwater mire deposits. Their association with deposits of a tidal origin indicates that these are supratidal deposits. Apparently they formed along the paleovalley walls in wetland areas slightly elevated above the highest tide level.

ESTUARINE FACIES MODELS

Traditionally, the almost complete lack of marine body fossils and the presence of plant fossils, coals, and rooted horizons through the various lithofacies would have meant that much of the facies associated with the paleovalley-fill succession would have been interpreted as nonmarine (fluvial-lacustrine). However, when examined in detail, only the coals are clearly nonmarine in origin. The conglomerate and conglomeratic sandstone present in the basal part of the succession are also likely nonmarine. Marine influence is indicated by the tidal rhythmites, tidal bedding, the brachiopod-bearing shale, and the bioturbated horizons. Even the rooted horizons not associated with coals (i.e., those within the tidal rhythmites and tidal bedding) can be interpreted to have formed on silty or mixed sand and mud tidal flats.

An overall upward increase in salinity is suggested from lithologic evidence, primary sedimentary structures, and preserved trace fossil assemblages. A basal fluvial system is suggested by the presence of the relatively thin conglomeratic deposits in the eastern paleovalley. A mix of fluvial and marine processes produced a stressed, perhaps brackish water environment, as indicated by the sparse and patchy bioturbation, the presence of siderite, and the almost complete lack of marine body fossils within the mud-dominated portion of the fill succession. Tidal currents were a major influence during this phase of sedimentation as indicated by the presence of tidal rhythmites and tidal bedding. It is not until the thick, more laterally continuous sandstone is encountered at the top of the succession that bioturbation diversity and primary sedimentary structures indicate a more fully marine influence.

From a geological point of view, estuaries can be defined as the marine-influenced, seaward portion of drowned valleys that receive sediment from both fluvial and marine sources and show evidence of fluvial, wave, and or tidal influence (Dalrymple and others, 1992). In this context, the deposits occupying the paleovalleys on Crane can be interpreted as estuarine.

Estuarine facies models have received a great deal of attention recently. Two conceptual models of estuarine sedimentation have been proposed by Dalrymple and others (1992) and Reinson (1992). Both of these classifications recognize the importance of wave and tidal influences in the lower reaches of the estuary and fluvial influence in the upper reaches. In general, both classifications recognize outer estuarine, central basin, and inner estuarine zones, which are characterized by marine (wave and or tide), mixed, lower-energy tidal and fluvial, and fluvial currents respectively. In wave-dominated estuaries, a tripartite axial facies zonation exists where the marine and fluvial zones tend to be sand-dominated, whereas the central basin tends to be muddy and generally corresponds to the turbidity maximum in the fluvial-tidal transition zone. In tide-dominated estuaries, the tripartite facies zonation is not as well defined, and sands can occur along the entire estuary. However, at the fluvial-tidal transition channels become quite sinuous and sediments are mud-rich (Dalrymple and others, 1992).

The volumetric importance of any of the facies and the extent to which they are developed and preserved in the rock record is a function not only of the processes that move and deposit the sediments but also on the availability of sediment at both the fluvial and marine ends of the system and on rates of sea-level rise (Amos and others, 1991; Dalrymple and others, 1992; Shanley and others , 1992; Allen and Posamentier, 1993). Thus, a rapid sea-level rise within an estuarine system could result in little, if any, fluvial sediments being preserved if rates of fluvial sediment influx are small.

LITHOFACIES ASSOCIATIONS

The three east-west cross sections presented are correlated from a datum (L4) at the base of a regionally extensive shale that appears to represent a transgressive marine unit over a rooted/coal horizon (Figs. 5, 6, 7). As references for discussion of lithofacies development through time, three other lines of correlation were drawn (L1-L3). In a channel-fill succession, time lines will dip into the channel (eg., Fletcher and others, 1990). Thus, given the uncertainties of how much dip to apply to the correlation lines plus the problems of variable compaction ratios, L1-L3 are only approximate isochronous surfaces.

The cross sections reveal that the two paleovalleys are incised to approximately the same depth relative to the datum (L4). The oldest fill sediments observed (at L1 and below) are in coreholes WES-6C-8 (Fig. 7) and WES-10-

23 (Fig. 5) and in the outcrop exposure depicted on Figure 6 between IGS 6 and IGS 5. In the western paleovalley (Fig. 7, bottom of WES-6C-8) these deposits include a dark gray shale that contains a thin coal spar (probable branch fragment). The shale coarsens upwards to rhythmically bedded siltstones of intertidal-flat origin. This is overlain by more shale and eventually a wavy-bedded sandstone and mudstone that are rooted at the L1 level.

The oldest sediments encountered in the eastern paleovalley include wavy-bedded sandstone which is overlain by a thin shale and a massive conglomeratic sandstone with a sharp basal contact (Fig. 5, bottom of WES-10C-23). The conglomeratic sandstone (L1 level) is the same unit as the basal conglomerate and conglomeratic sandstone that is depicted in the stratigraphically lowest outcrop section in Figure 6. This conglomeratic facies is probably fluvial in origin and contrasts with tidal deposits at the same stratigraphic level in the western paleovalley. Rooting is present at the L1 level in both the eastern and western paleovalleys.

Above L1 and below L2, shales occupy the deepest parts of the eastern paleovalley with sandstone and mudstone occupying the same position in the western paleovalley. These units appear to be at least brackish water deposits with the sandstone exhibiting tidal bedding (wavy- or flaser-bedding). A single marine spiriferid brachiopod found less than 2 meters below L2 in IGS 7 indicates a connection to normal marine waters. In IGS 5, a laterally discontinuous deposit of coal, probably representing a supratidal peat mire, is present along the valley flank and was eventually transgressed by intertidal-flat deposits of rhythmically bedded siltstones (Fig. 6).

The interval between L2 and L3 is dominated by brackish water subtidal shales in the center of both paleovalleys with tidal-flat deposits of ripple-(Fig. 7, outcrop west of WES-6C-8,) wavy- to flaser-bedded sandstone and mudstone (Fig. 6, IGS 2) and rhythmically-bedded siltstone (Fig. 6, IGS 5) generally confined to the paleovalley walls. Rooting in the tidal-flat deposits (IGS 5 and IGS 6) suggests that they were vegetated and intertidal.

Trough to planar cross-stratified sandstone present below L3 in IGS 3 (Fig. 7) and IGS 4 (Fig. 6) and exposed in the outcrop depicted to the west of WES-3C-29 (Fig. 7), indicates tidal channels developed some time after deposition of the shales along the C-C' cross-section (L3 level) and scoured out previously existing, finer grained deposits in a bedrock high between the east and west paleovalleys. Little of the original Mississippian surface was exposed at the L3 level. By this time, the paleovalleys were nearly filled with sediment.

The sandstone at the L3 level and above comprises most of the ripple-bedded, parallel-laminated, massive, and cross-bedded sandstone lithofacies observed in outcrop and core. It is much more extensive than any sandstone observed at lower stratigraphic levels and is predominantly marine in origin. This is indicated by its diverse trace fossil assemblage, common occurrence of large-scale tidal bundles, and bipolar paleocurrent indicators.

This sandstone is interpreted as a tidal sandflat that was dissected by tidal channels. The paleoflow indicators show that some of these channels were flood oriented while others were ebb oriented. Most of the larger channels examined in the vicinity of the western paleovalley are flood oriented (eastward directed). Those associated with the eastern paleovalley are either flood oriented (north directed) or ebb oriented (south directed).

Between L3 and L4, the paleovalleys were completely filled. This interval is dominated by the marine sandstone (tidal sandflat) in the southern part of the study area (Fig. 7, crossed by the C-C' cross-section) but is replaced (interfingers?) to the north with rooted, wavy-bedded sandstone (vegetated, intertidal sand and mud flat) and brackish water subtidal shale (Figs. 5, 6, cross-sections B-B' and A-A').

Just below L4 an extensive coal and rooted or weathered horizon is present and probably reflects a local(?) drop in base level. The L4 level marks the base of a marine transgression that buried the coal and rooted or weathered horizon. No evidence of a transgressive lag was found at the base of this deposit. However this may simply reflect a rapid transgression of a low-energy, muddy marine environment across a coastal wetland resulting in the deposition of primarily mud-rich deposits.

DISCUSSION OF CRANE VALLEY-FILL SEQUENCE

The stratigraphic succession indicates an overall transgressive event during filling of the two Crane paleovalleys and the formation and filling of a bedrock defended estuary system. Fluvial sedimentation is confined to the deepest part of the eastern paleovalley with the deposition of the conglomerate and conglomeratic sandstone. However, this facies was not encountered in the western paleovalley. Instead deposits of probable intertidal origin occur at the same stratigraphic interval. This suggests an active, bedload-transporting fluvial system (and associated deposition) existed only in the eastern paleovalley and not in the western paleovalley at this time. It is possible that fluvial deposits do exist in the western paleovalley and that the deepest part of the western paleovalley was not penetrated by core and was missed during field mapping because of extensive vegetative cover. However, it is also possible that if a fluvial system did exist in the western paleovalley, it may not have transported a significant bedload or its deposits were removed by erosion. Thus, during sea-level rise the western paleovalley would have been a site of non-deposition at the same time fluvial sediments were accumulating in the eastern paleovalley. As base level continued to rise, tidal deposits began to fill the western paleovalley.

In general, brackish water, subtidal shale facies dominate the fill with patches of coarser and sometimes rooted, intertidal facies and supratidal, coal-forming peat mires confined to the valley walls (Fig. 21, L2). Not until the final stages of fill do sub- to inter-tidal sandstones become more extensive when they dominate deposition over the interfluve separating the two paleovalleys and across the southern part of the study area along the C-C' cross-section (Fig. 21, L3).

A relative base-level drop is marked by an extensive horizon, which is penetrated by roots and locally overlain by coals (Fig. 21, L4). This horizon was transgressed by a regionally extensive marine shale.

The vertical change from conglomeratic sandstone (present in the eastern paleovalley), to a mudstone-dominated facies (present in both paleovalleys), to a still younger sandstone-dominated facies (deposited as both paleovalleys were overfilled and buried) and the associated changes in sedimentary bedding features and body and trace fossil contents suggest a major shift in depositional environments through time. In a vertical sense, the environments change from a fluvial system (dominated by coarse-grained deposits) to that of a quiet water, brackish, subtidal environment flanked by mixed intertidal flats (some vegetated) and supratidal mires (coals) to one of higher-energy, sub- to intertidal flats dissected by tidal channels with a more normal marine salinity. This change indicates a shift from a fluvially dominated, inner estuarine setting, to a mixed fluvial-tidal, central-basin estuarine setting, to a marine-dominated outer estuarine setting.

The fluvial sediments are volumetrically the least important of the fill deposits whereas the central basin sediments constitute the volumetrically most important. The central basin remained relatively fixed within bedrock confined walls during sea-level rise until the final stages of fill (upper few meters). At this point, with very little local relief within the paleovalleys, the outer estuarine tidal sandflat transgressed the central basin estuarine deposits.

Facies development within a central basin is a function of the relative strengths of fluvial versus marine currents. In a very general sense, these processes essentially nullify each other generating a relatively low energy environment of deposition. The central basin facies remained essentially fixed within the confines of the Crane bedrock walled paleovalleys because an equilibrium was reached between the effects of the mixing of fluvial and marine processes and the effect of sea level rise. Thus, rates of sedimentation within the central basin equalled the rate of sea-level rise within the estuary preventing the central basin from shifting up or down the paleovalleys until the bedrock-confined valleys were nearly filled. At this point, the effects of bedrock confinement were minimized, and outer estuary facies transgressed the central basin facies.

The highest-energy, tidal depositional systems appear to have been localized over the interfluve high and possibly reflect, at least initially, a tidal shoal area between the east and west paleovalleys. These outer estuarine sandstones thin to the north over several kilometers as the interval becomes muddier. This indicates the northward extent of the outer estuary during transgression.

According to the facies models of Dalrymple and others (1992) and Reinson (1992), the development of a mud-dominated central basin suggests a barred, wave-influenced estuary. In such settings, tidal ranges tend to be mesotidal or less. The barriers effectively reduce wave and storm influences within the central basin resulting in a lower energy environment where deposition from suspension is much more important than in tide-dominated estuaries where strong tidal currents are effectively propagated well into the central basin. Thus, the dominance of mudstone within the Crane central basin deposits suggests that this may have been a wave-dominated estuary with a barrier positioned somewhere south to southwest of the study area.

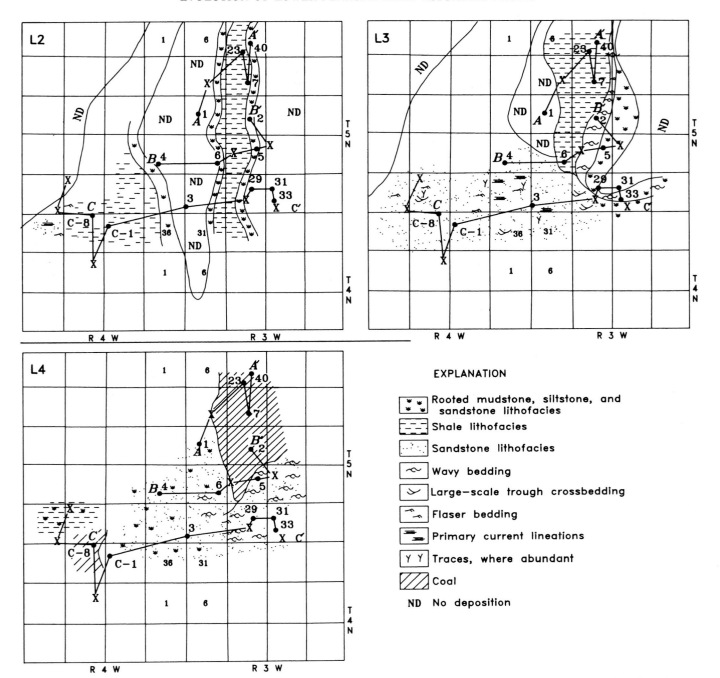

Fig. 21.—Generalized diagrams illustrating the development of facies at levels L2, L3 and L4. Interpretations incorporate data from the cross sections and outcrop information not included in the cross sections.

While this is a plausible interpretation, evidence of wave activity in the Crane sandstones is equivocal. Oscillatory ripples are commonly seen in fresh exposures of the sandstone but are of the form that could have been generated by asymmetric tidal currents as well as waves. It should be pointed out that all of the facies described from the Crane paleovalley-fill successions probably formed within an estuary, landward of any estuary-mouth barrier. In such settings wave and storm effects would be minimal. In general, however, storm and wave deposits including barrier bars, washover deposits, spit deposits, hummocky cross stratification, and shell lags have not been commonly recognized in Lower Pennsylvanian units of the Illinois Basin. The absence of storm deposits may be explained by the Illinois Basin's equatorial setting during Early Pennsylvanian time (Scotese and others, 1979) and its likely position in the intertropical convergence zone. Thus, strong storm activity was unlikely.

The best modern analogs for early Pennsylvanian environments of deposition may be found in the equatorial tropical climates of coastal Malaysia and Indonesia (eg., Cecil and others, 1985; Cecil, 1990; Staub and Esterle, 1992). Recent work by Staub and Esterle (1993) has shown that in the Rajang River delta (which experiences macro- to mesoscale tides) in Sarawak, East Malaysia significant volumes of suspended load material are delivered to estuaries by fluvial systems. Once the suspended sediment load reaches the fluvial-tidal transition zone, it is flocculated and becomes bedload material. The result is that, in general, estuarine channel bottom sediments in the Rajang River delta are dominated by mud. Thus, it may be possible that muddy central basins can develop in nonbarred estuaries, particularly those formed in mud-dominated tropical environments such as in present day Sumatra, Malaysia, and Borneo. In such settings, however, the mud reflects deposition in the central basin not from suspension but from bedload.

The absence of thick fluvial deposits within the paleovalleys (and perhaps total absence in the western paleovalley) suggests that sea level rise was very rapid relative to fluvial sedimentation rates. It is possible that fluvial systems carried very little coarse clastic material in the Illinois Basin at this time. Cecil (1990) has suggested that during Morrowan times, when coals were forming, the climate of the eastern U. S. would have been ever-wet. According to his model, such a climate would have allowed for the development of dense vegetation in the Illinois Basin that would have been a deterrent to fluvial erosion within the Illinois Basin. Thus, most of the material transported and deposited during this time may have been generated locally by the reworking of the Mississippian Chesterian siliciclastic and carbonate units by marine processes or transported by fluvial systems to the Illinois Basin from the rising Appalachian Mountains to the east or Canadian Shield area to the northeast.

CONCLUSIONS

Estuarine sedimentation can be documented in two relatively narrow paleovalleys in south-central Indiana. The paleovalleys were tributaries to a major drainage network that developed during latest Mississippian to early Pennsylvanian time. Sedimentation within the paleovalleys occurred during an early Pennsylvanian sea-level rise.

Although vertical and lateral facies relationships are complex, inner estuarine, central basin, and outer estuarine deposits can be recognized within the valley fill. Fluvial deposits constitute a minor portion of the paleovalley-fill succession and are dominated by intraformationally derived conglomerate and conglomeratic sandstone. Subtidal central-basin deposits are dominated by shale that is locally bioturbated (low diversity) and in one site was found to contain a single marine bivalve. The shale grades laterally into vegetated intertidal flats characterized by rooted sandstones and siltstones near the valley walls. Coal-forming supratidal peat mires also formed along the valley walls flanking the central basin. Tidal processes can be directly demonstrated within the central basin deposits through the recognition of tidal rhythmites within the intertidal laminated-siltstones.

Outer estuarine facies are characterized by sub- to intertidal sandflat deposits. Tidal processes appear to have dominated this interval with wave activity generally absent. This facies developed during the final stages of paleovalley filling. A relative drop in base level across the study area allowed for the development of a coastal wetland identified by an extensive rooted and coal-bearing horizon. This was immediately followed by transgression of a regional marine shale across the study area.

ACKNOWLEDGEMENTS

Funding for this investigation was provided by the U.S. Department of the Navy, the U. S. Geological Survey CO-GEOMAP program, and the Indiana Geological Survey. We thank Jeff Ciocco of the Department of the Navy and Bill Murphy of the U.S. Army Corps of Engineers for their helpful cooperation and support in providing valuable subsurface information. We also thank Lloyd Furer (Indiana Geological Survey) for his discussions on the regional aspects of this study and Joe Devera (Illinois State Geological Survey) for discussions regarding the significance of the ichnofacies. Helpful reviews were provided by R. Dalrymple, R. Cheel, and C. von der Borch. Drafting services were provided by Kim Sowder, Kari Lancaster, and Licia Weber. Photographic plates were prepared by Barb Hill and John Day.

The views and conclusions contained in this document are those of the authors and should not be interpreted as necessarily representing the official policies, either expressed or implied, of the U. S. Government.

REFERENCES CITED

ALLEN, G. P., AND POSAMENTIER, H. W., 1993, Sequence stratigraphy and facies model of an incised valley fill: the Gironde Estuary, France: Journal of Sedimentary Petrology, v. 63, p. 378–391.

AMOS, C. L., TEE, K. T., AND ZAITLIN, B. A., 1991, The post-glacial evolution of Chignecto Bay, Bay of Fundy, and its modern environment of deposition, in Smith, D. G., Reinson, G. E., Zaitlin, B. A., and Rahmani, R. A., eds., Clastic Tidal Sedimentology: Calgary, Canadian Society of Petroleum Geologists Memoir 16, p. 59–90.

ARCHER, A. W., AND KVALE, E. P., 1989, Seasonal and yearly cycles within tidally laminated sediments: an example from the Pennsylvanian of Indiana, U.S.A., in Cobb, J. C., ed., Geology of the Lower Pennsylvanian in Kentucky, Indiana, and Illinois: Bloomington, Illinois Basin Studies 1, Illinois Basin Consortium (Indiana Geological Survey, Illinois State Geological Survey, Kentucky Geological Survey), p. 45–56.

BARNHILL, M. L., 1992, Subsurface sedimentology of the Pennsylvanian (Mansfield) rocks, Naval Surface Warfare Center, Crane, Indiana: Bloomington, Indiana Geological Survey, Open File Report 92–15, 93 p.

BOERSMA, J. R., 1969, Internal structure of some tidal megaripples on a shoal in the Westerschelde estuary, The Netherlands—a report of a preliminary investigation: Geologie en Mijnbouw., v. 48, p. 409–414.

BROMLEY, R. G., AND EKDALE, A. A., 1984, Chondrites: a trace fossil indicator of anoxia in sediments: Science, v. 224, p. 872–874.

CECIL, C. B., 1990, Paleoclimate controls on stratigraphic repetition of chemical and siliciclastic rocks: Geology, v. 18, p. 533–536.

CECIL, C. B., STANTON, R. W., NEUZIL, S. G., DULONG, F. T., RUPPERT, L. F., AND PIERCE, B. S., 1985, Paleoclimate controls on late Paleozoic sedimentation and peat formation in the central Appalachian basin (U.S.A.): International Journal of Coal Geology, v. 5, p. 195–230.

CHAMBERLIN, C. K., 1971, Morphology and ethology of trace fossils from the Ouachita Mountains, southeast Oklahoma: Journal of Paleontology, v. 45, p. 212–246.

CLIFTON, H. E., 1982, Estuarine deposits, *in* Scholle, P. A., and Spearing, D., eds., Sandstone Depositional Environments: Tulsa, American Association of Petroleum Geologists Memoir 31, p. 179–189.

DALRYMPLE, R. W., ZAITLIN, B. A., AND BOYD, R., 1992, Estuarine facies models: conceptual basis and stratigraphic implications: Journal of Sedimentary Petrology, v. 62, p. 1130–1146.

DEVERA, J. A., 1989, Ichnofossil assemblages and associated lithofacies of the Lower Pennsylvanian (Caseyville and Tradewater Formations), Southern Illinois, *in* Cobb, J. C., ed., Geology of the Lower Pennsylvanian in Kentucky, Indiana, and Illinois: Bloomington, Illinois Basin Studies 1, Illinois Basin Consortium (Indiana Geological Survey, Illinois State Geological Survey, Kentucky Geological Survey), p. 57–83.

DROSTE, J. B., AND KELLER, S. J., 1989, Development of the Mississippian-Pennsylvanian unconformity in Indiana: Bloomington, Indiana Department of Natural Resources Geological Survey Occasional Paper 55, 11 p.

FLETCHER, C. H., KNEBEL, H. J., AND KRAFT, J. C., 1990, Holocene evolution of an estuarine coast and tidal wetland: Geological Society of America Bulletin, v. 102, p. 283–297.

FREY, R. W., AND HOWARD, J. D., 1986, Mesotidal estuarine sequences: a perspective from the Georgia Bight: Journal of Sedimentary Petrology, v. 56, p. 911–924.

FURER, L. C., 1992, Basement tectonics in the eastern Illinois Basin and their affect on early Paleozoic sedimentation: American Association of Petroleum Geologists Bulletin, v. 76, p. 1274.

HOWARD, R. H., AND WHITAKER, S. T., 1990, Fluvial-estuarine valley fill at the Mississippian-Pennsylvanian unconformity, Main Consolidated Field, Illinois, *in* Barwis, J. H., McPherson, J. G., and Studlick, R. J., eds., Sandstone Petroleum Reservoirs: New York, Springer-Verlag, p. 319–341.

HUTCHISON, H. C., 1967, Distribution, structure, and mined areas of coals in Martin County, Indiana: Bloomington, Preliminary Coal Map 11, Indiana Geological Survey.

KVALE, E. P., 1992, Surface geological mapping of Naval Surface Warfare Center, Crane, Indiana: Bloomington, Indiana Geological Survey, Open File Report 92–10, 4 p.

KVALE, E. P., ARCHER, A. W., AND JOHNSON, H. R., 1989, Daily monthly, and yearly tidal cycles within laminated siltstone of the Mansfield Formation (Pennsylvanian) of Indiana: Geology, v. 17, p. 365–368.

KVALE, E. P. AND ARCHER, A. W., 1991, Characteristics of two, Pennsylvanian-age, semidiurnal tidal deposits in the Illinois Basin, U.S.A., *in* Smith, D. G., Reinson, G. E., Zaitlin, B. A., and Rahmani, R. A., eds., Clastic Tidal Sedimentology: Calgary, Canadian Society of Petroleum Geologists Memoir 16, p. 179–188.

MAPLES, C. G., AND ARCHER, A. W., 1987, Redescription of Early Pennsylvanian trace-fossil holotypes from the nonmarine Hindostan Whetstone beds of Indiana: Journal of Paleontology, v. 61, p. 890–897.

MARTINO, R. L., AND SANDERSON, D. D., 1993, Fourier and autocorrelation analysis of estuarine tidal rhythmites, lower Breathitt Formation (Pennsylvanian), eastern Kentucky, USA: Journal of Sedimentary Petrology, v. 63, p. 105–119.

NELSON, W. J., TRASK, C. B., JACOBSON, R. J., DAMBERGER, H. H., WILLIAMSON, A. D., AND WILLIAMS, D. A., 1991, Absaroka Sequence, Pennsylvanian and Permian Systems, *in* Leighton, M. W., Kolata, D. R., Oltz, D. F., and Eidel, J. J., eds., Interior Cratonic Basins: Tulsa, American Association of Petroleum Geologists Memoir 51, p. 143–164.

POTTER, P. E., 1962, Regional distribution patterns of Pennsylvanian sandstones in Illinois Basin: American Association of Petroleum Geologists Bulletin, v. 46, p. 1890–1911.

REINECK, H., AND WUNDERLICH, F., 1968, Classification and origin of flaser and lenticular bedding: Sedimentology, v. 11, p. 99–104.

REINSON, G. E., 1992, Transgressive barrier island and estuarine systems, *in* Walker, R. G., and James, N. P., eds., Facies Models: St. Johns, Geological Association of Canada, p. 179–194.

SCOTESE, C. R., BAMBACH, R. K., BARTON, C., VAN DER VOO, R., and ZIEGLER, A. M., 1979, Paleozoic base maps: Journal of Geology, v. 87, p. 217–233.

SHANLEY, K. W., McCABE, P. J., and HETTINGER, R. D., 1992, Tidal influence in Cretaceous fluvial strata from Utah, USA: a key to sequence stratigraphic interpretation: Sedimentology, v. 39, p. 905–930.

STAUB, J. R., AND ESTERLE, J. S., 1993, Provenance and sediment dispersal in the Rajang River delta/coastal plain system, Sarawak, East Malaysia: Sedimentary Geology, (in press).

STAUB, J. R., AND ESTERLE, J. S, 1992, Evidence for a tidally influenced Upper Carboniferous ombrogenous mire system: upper bench, Beckley Bed (Westphalian A), southern West Virginia: Journal of Sedimentary Petrology, v. 62, p. 411–428.

VISSER, M. J., 1980, Neap-spring cycles reflected in Holocene subtidal large-scale bedform deposits: a preliminary note: Geology, v. 8, p. 543–546.

WOODLAND, B. G., AND STENSTROM, R. C., 1979, The occurrence and origin of siderite concretions in the Francis Creek Shale (Pennsylvanian) of northern Illinois, *in* Nitecki, M. H., ed., Mazon Creek Fossils: New York, Academic Press, p. 69–103.

SEQUENCE STRATIGRAPHY OF AN INCISED-VALLEY FILL: THE NEOPROTEROZOIC SEACLIFF SANDSTONE, ADELAIDE GEOSYNCLINE, SOUTH AUSTRALIA

IAN A. DYSON AND CHRISTOPHER C. VON DER BORCH

School of Earth Sciences, Flinders University of South Australia, Bedford Park SA 5042, Australia

ABSTRACT: The Neoproterozoic Seacliff Sandstone occurs as a series of incised-valley fill deposits in the Adelaide Geosyncline of South Australia. It is the basal formation of an unconformity-bounded depositional sequence, formally referred to as the Sandison Subgroup, and is composed of a succession of interbedded sandstone, siltstone, and dolostone. A number of well exposed sections were measured to interpret the sedimentology, geometry, and cyclicity of the Seacliff Sandstone and to present a sequence-stratigraphic model of the incised-valley fill deposits.

An unconformity at the base of the incised valley is interpreted as a sequence boundary formed by subaerial exposure and fluvial incision during a major fall of relative sea level. The incised-valley fill is composed of lowstand and transgressive facies that are separated by a transgressive surface. The lowstand facies consists of a basal-fluvial lag overlain by estuarine and shallow marine sandstone. Above the transgressive surface, *a ragged transgressive blanket* consisting of several backstepping parasequences was deposited as relative sea level continued to rise.

Each parasequence of the *ragged transgressive blanket* consists of resedimented facies that commonly overlie a basal, decimeter-thick dolostone and passes upwards into mature sandstone deposited above storm wave base. The resedimented facies represent possible deposition of sandstone beds, derived from longshore drift, down the side of a progressively drowning paleovalley. Sandstone at the top of the uppermost parasequence is normally capped by a several metre-thick dolostone, deposited on a maximum flooding surface. The top of this dolostone marks the change from transgressive to regressive sedimentation. All dolostone beds within the incised-valley fill are assigned to the regionally occurring Nuccaleena Formation. They are interpreted to overlie marine flooding surfaces and represent background carbonate deposition below storm-wave base on sediment-starved hiatal surfaces.

The interpretation of incised-valley fills within the Seacliff Sandstone may lead to a better understanding of the geometry and reservoir characteristics of similar sandstone bodies in hydrocarbon-prospective basins. Potential exists to find reservoir-quality sandstone within the *ragged transgressive blanket* and is dependent on differentiating between the transgressive surface and maximum flooding surface, and mapping the distribution of each parasequence to understand differences in reservoir quality.

INTRODUCTION

Incised-valley fills, which commonly range in width from a few kilometres to tens of kilometres and in depth from tens to hundreds of metres, are thought to form in two temporally distinct phases (Van Wagoner and others, 1990). The first phase consists of erosion into coastal-plain and/or shelf sediments in response to a relative sea-level fall, accompanied by sediment bypass through the eroded valleys and deposition at the lowstand shoreline. The second phase consists of deposition of dominantly fine-grained fluvial, estuarine or marine sediments within the valleys in response to a relative rise in sea level. The base of a typical incised-valley succession is normally marked by a basinward shift in facies and in sequence stratigraphy terminology is classified as a type 1 sequence boundary (Van Wagoner and others, 1988). Shallow marine strata, such as upper shoreface and distributary mouth bar deposits, are absent adjacent to valley edges (Van Wagoner, 1991).

Regional aspects of incised valleys were originally defined on seismic sections (Vail and others, 1977). Such sections typically provide large-scale overviews of the geometries of these features. More recently, incised valleys have been identified and subjected to high resolution studies in outcrop and subsurface (e.g., Wood and Hopkins, 1989; Shannon, 1990; Wheeler and others, 1990). It is now recognised that incised-valley fills have the potential to host significant hydrocarbon reservoirs. For example, detailed outcrop studies, like those in the San Juan Basin of New Mexico (Jenette and others, 1991) and the Book Cliffs section in Utah (Van Wagoner, 1991), lead to enhanced predictive capabilities in petroleum exploration.

A series of unusually deep (to 1 km) incised valleys have been identified and described from a Neoproterozoic

succession in Australia (von der Borch and others, 1989; Christie-Blick and others, 1990). More recently Dyson (1992a) demonstrated that a unit termed the Seacliff Sandstone represents an additional unit of incised-valley fill in the same basin. This paper examines details of the sedimentology, geometry, and cyclicity of the Seacliff Sandstone and possible mechanisms for its formation are discussed.

STUDY AREA, DATA, AND METHOD

The Seacliff Sandstone crops out in a limited number of localities within the Mount Lofty and Flinders Ranges of South Australia. These occurrences are confined to a narrow belt which extends from Loud Hill to Wilmington (Fig. 1) within and east of the Torrens Hinge Zone (Thomson, 1969; Parker and others, 1990). Equivalents of the Seacliff Sandstone have also been mapped elsewhere (e.g., Forbes, 1975), but there does not appear to be lateral continuity between them (Preiss, 1987). Attention in this study focuses on well exposed sections of this unit at Kulpara, Wilmington and at the type section of Thomson (1966) at Hallett Cove (Fig. 1). Sequence stratigraphic analysis of the Seacliff Sandstone is based on previous studies by Dyson (1986, 1992a) and Dyson and von der Borch (1986).

STRATIGRAPHY AND GEOLOGIC SETTING

The Seacliff Sandstone is located in the upper part of a Neoproterozoic succession that is as much as 15 km thick and widely exposed in the Flinders and Mount Lofty Ranges of South Australia (Fig. 1). The sedimentary basin containing these strata is commonly referred to, in a non-genetic sense, as the Adelaide Geosyncline (Mawson and Sprigg, 1950). Preiss (1982) divided the Neoproterozoic

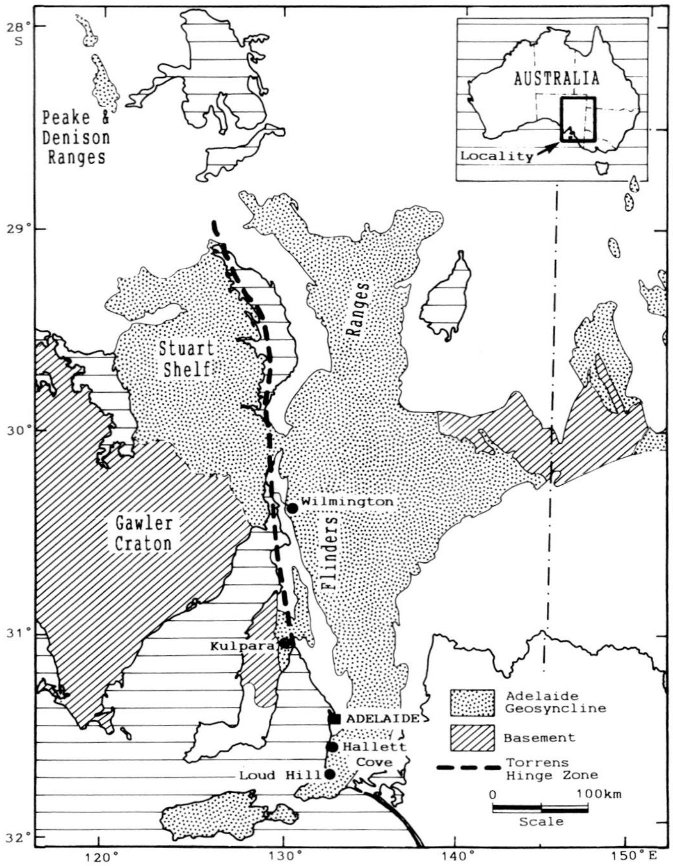

FIG. 1.—Location map of the Adelaide Geosyncline and measured sections.

TABLE 1.—THE STRATIGRAPHIC POSITION OF THE SEACLIFF SANDSTONE WITH RESPECT TO SELECTED LITHOSTRATIGRAPHIC UNITS OF THE ADELAIDE GEOSYNCLINE (MODIFIED FROM CHRISTIE-BLICK AND OTHERS, 1990; PREISS, 1987). NO TIME OR THICKNESS IMPLIED.

	MORALANA SUPERGROUP	HAWKER GROUP		EARLY CAMBRIAN		
NEOPROTEROZOIC	HEYSEN SUPERGROUP	WILPENA GROUP	POUND SUBGROUP	MARINOAN	'EDIACARIAN'	ADELAIDEAN
			Wonoka Formation Bunyeroo Formation			
			SANDISON SUBGROUP			
			ABC Range Quartzite Brachina Formation Nuccaleena Formation Seacliff Sandstone			
		UMBERATANA GROUP	▲ ▲ ▲ ▲ ▲ ▲ ▲ ▲ ▲ ▲ ▲ ▲ ▲ ▲	STURTIAN		
	WARRINA SUPERGROUP	BURRA GROUP		TORRENSIAN		
		CALLANNA GROUP		WILLOURAN		
	ARCHEAN AND PALEOPROTEROZOIC COMPLEXES			Pre - ADELAIDEAN		

(Adelaidean) and Cambrian stratigraphy of the Adelaide Geosyncline into three major lithostratigraphic units bounded by regional unconformities (Table 1). The classification emphasised the distinction between early Adelaidean, late Adelaidean, and Cambrian tectonic and depositional styles (Preiss, 1987) and suggested passive margin development in late Sturtian or early Cambrian time (von der Borch, 1980; Christie-Blick and others, 1990).

Deposition of the early Adelaidean Warrina Supergroup (Table 1) was confined to rifted troughs within the Geosyncline where it consists of thick accumulations of mixed evaporites, clastics, and carbonates deposited under non-marine to shallow marine conditions. The late Adelaidean Heysen Supergroup represents a change in tectonic style and paleogeography and was possibly influenced by initial rifting followed by extensional and salt tectonics (Christie-Blick and others, 1990). The Heysen Supergroup consists of shallow marine clastics with minor carbonates and diamict sediments. It also contains evidence of two major glaciations (Table 1) within the Umberatana Group.

Incised valleys of the Seacliff Sandstone along with the kilometer-deep Wonoka "canyons" (von der Borch and others, 1989; Christie-Blick and others, 1990) and overlying incised valleys are located in the Wilpena Group and overlying Uratanna Formation (Table 1). The lowermost Wilpena Group is thought to represent the sediments of a major, post-glacial transgression (Preiss, 1987) and contains a number of transgressive-regressive cycles.

SEQUENCE STRATIGRAPHIC FRAMEWORK

The term Sandison Subgroup incorporates the unconformity-bounded depositional sequence at the base of the lower Wilpena Group (Dyson, 1992a) and consists of the Seacliff Sandstone, Nuccaleena Formation, Brachina Formation, and ABC Range Quartzite (Fig. 2). The stratigraphic units of the Sandison Subgroup are genetically related rather than strictly lithostratigraphic in nature and conform to the systems tracts of Van Wagoner and others (1987). The base of the Seacliff Sandstone is regarded by Dyson (1992b) as a sequence boundary. This boundary corresponds to one of seven regional unconformities recognised within or bounding the Wilpena Group in the Flinders Ranges (von der Borch and others, 1988; Christie-Blick and others, 1990). The base of the Nuccaleena Formation (Fig. 3) was interpreted by these authors to represent a marine transgression across a nearly planar erosion surface developed on top of the Umberatana Group.

PREVIOUS WORK

At Kulpara, about 120 km north of Hallett Cove (Fig. 1), Horwitz (1959) mapped a white, coarse-grained feldspathic quartzite overlying the Reynella Siltstone Member of the Elatina Formation with a sharp contact. The quartzite was originally correlated with the ABC Range Quartzite, but it was later identified as Seacliff Sandstone by Thomson (1966) who correlated it with the basal member of the Brachina Formation at Hallett Cove. Plummer (1978), in contrast, regarded the unit as the uppermost part of the Umberatana Group because, he argued, arenaceous sediments that underlie the dolostone at the base of the Brachina For-

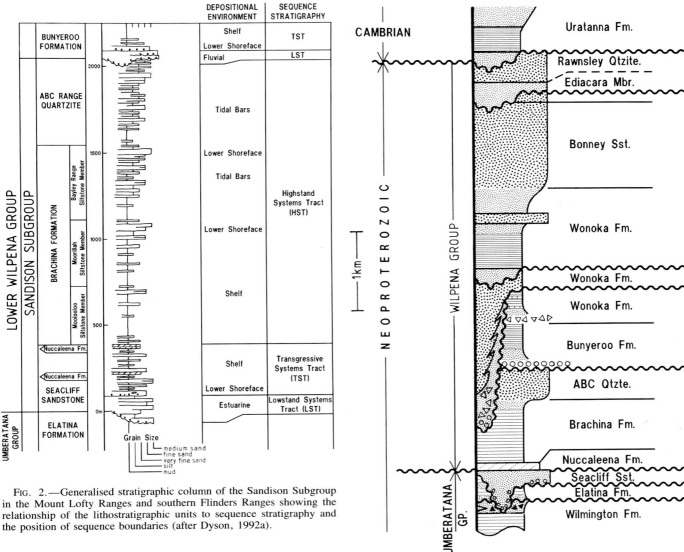

FIG. 2.—Generalised stratigraphic column of the Sandison Subgroup in the Mount Lofty Ranges and southern Flinders Ranges showing the relationship of the lithostratigraphic units to sequence stratigraphy and the position of sequence boundaries (after Dyson, 1992a).

FIG. 3.—Generalised stratigraphic section for the Wilpena Group of the central Flinders Ranges (modified from Christie-Blick and others, 1990). The incised valleys of the Seacliff Sandstone correspond with the proposed sequence boundary at the base of the Wilpena Group (Christie-Blick and others, 1990). Glacigenic units of the Umberatana Group are represented by solid triangles.

mation should be included in the Elatina Formation (Fig. 3). A three-fold classification of the underlying glaciogenic Elatina Formation by Lemon and Gostin (1990) also placed the Seacliff Sandstone at the top of the Umberatana Group. Forbes (1982) argued that the lithology of the Seacliff Sandstone, composed of sandstone-siltstone-dolostone, allowed it to be distinguished from the overlying Brachina Formation and proposed its elevation to formation status.

Forbes and Preiss (1987) considered dolostone lenses within the type Seacliff Sandstone at Hallett Cove to be tongues of the Nuccaleena Formation and regarded the Seacliff Sandstone and Nuccaleena Formation as partial lateral equivalents occurring at the base of the Wilpena Group. The upper Seacliff Sandstone appeared to intertongue with the Brachina Formation at Kulpara and Wokurna, suggesting the Seacliff Sandstone was sedimentologically related to the Wilpena Group (Forbes and Preiss, 1987).

Thomson and others (1976) suggested a deltaic, shallow-water environment of deposition for the Seacliff Sandstone. Dyson (1986) and Dyson and von der Borch (1986) sug-

gested the unit was deposited in a shallow shelf to slope environment. The Nuccaleena Formation was thought to have been deposited under shallow subtidal to supratidal conditions (Plummer, 1979) and was considered unlikely by Forbes and Preiss (1987) to represent deposition in water deeper than that in which the Seacliff Sandstone was deposited.

The localised sandstone bodies of the Seacliff Sandstone were interpreted by Dyson (1992a) to fill incised valleys cut during a major fall in relative sea level. The incised valleys were also interpreted to contain a basal lowstand systems tract overlain by the retrogradational lithofacies of a transgressive systems tract. The intertonguing relationship of sandstone, dolostone, and shale was explained by the occurrence of upward-shallowing cycles or parasequences in an overall transgressive regime. Nuccaleena-type dolostone beds within the Seacliff Sandstone were interpreted to mark the base of successive, upward shallowing cycles, possibly representing background carbonate deposition on sediment-starved, hiatal surfaces.

SEQUENCE STRATIGRAPHY

The sequence stratigraphy of the Seacliff Sandstone is illustrated in Figures 2 and 4. Figure 2 shows the Seacliff Sandstone to be the basal formation of the unconformity-bounded depositional sequence formally referred to as the Sandison Subgroup. Figure 4 is a cross-section from Hallett Cove to Wilmington with the line of section representing approximately 280 km.

The incised-valley fill of the Seacliff Sandstone consists of a basal lowstand systems tract and upper transgressive systems tract (Dyson, 1992a). The thickness of the sandstone facies within the valley fill ranges from 60–175 m and is compared with other localities in Figure 4. The lowstand systems tract is defined as all the strata from the sequence boundary to the transgressive surface. The overlying transgressive systems tract is overlain by a maximum flooding surface that separates transgressive facies from the regressive facies of the Brachina Formation. Details of the sequence boundary, lowstand systems tract facies, transgressive surface, and the transgressive systems tract are described in detail below.

Sequence Boundary

The base of the Seacliff Sandstone is interpreted to be a sequence boundary (Dyson, 1992b). A deep paleovalley was mapped over a strike of some 6 km in a locality 5-km south of Kulpara (Fig. 5) where the base of the Seacliff Sandstone (Fig. 6) cuts down through the Reynella Siltstone into the Wilmington Formation with relief of some 150 m. A gravel lag, 15–20 cm thick, is present on top of the sequence boundary and contains quartz, sandstone, and siltstone grains up to 1 cm in diameter.

About 10 km further south, the Seacliff Sandstone appears to erode into the Wilmington Formation below the level of gritty limestone, interpreted by Preiss (1983) to belong to the Etina Formation. This suggests that the minimum width of the paleovalley may be of the order of 20–30 km along the depositional strike, accompanied by possible erosional relief of some 300–500 m at the base of the Seacliff Sandstone. Outcrop is either poor or inaccessible in this area and further field studies are planned. The erosional relationship with underlying and adjacent strata is consistent with the sharp, irregular basal contact of the Seacliff Sandstone at Hallett Cove.

Lowstand Systems Tract

Overlying the basal lag on top of the sequence boundary at Kulpara is a succession of interbedded sandstone and shale. Low in the succession, fine to medium-grained sandstone is thick-bedded and aggradational in character and contains abundant pink feldspar clasts of medium to coarse sand size.

The sandstone commonly exhibits tangential cross-bedding with unidirectional reactivation surfaces and occasional bidirectional cross-bedding and sigmoidal cross-bedding. Supermature, fine-grained sandstone units display symmetrical ripples and low angle cross-stratification. Higher in the succession, sandstone beds are commonly arranged into 5m-thick cycles where basal, hummocky cross-stratified sandstone is overlain by sandstone displaying tangential cross-bedding. At Hallett Cove, basal, fine-grained sandstone commonly displays small-scale ripple cross-lamination, trough cross-bedding and hummocky cross stratification (Fig. 4).

The fine and medium-grained sandstone is interpreted to have been deposited in an estuarine environment where wave and tidal processes were prominent. Estuarine deposits are classified as wave- or tide-dominated on the basis of the dominant marine process, but the two types are often intergradational (Dalyrymple and others, 1992). Sigmoidal cross-bedding (Kreisa and Moiola, 1986) and herringbone cross-bedding strongly suggest a tidal influence. Low-angle cross-stratification and symmetrical wave ripples suggest deposition on the lower shoreface. Hummocky cross-stratification is formed under combined flow conditions at or above storm wave base (Dyson, 1983; Swift and others, 1983; Nottvedt and Kreisa, 1987; Myrow and Southard, 1991). The tidal- and wave-formed deposits are assigned to the lowstand systems tract. Basinward, in an easterly direction, these facies are interpreted to pass into inner shelf sandstone that is characterised by hummocky cross-stratification.

A subsidiary section of the Seacliff Sandstone was measured at Wilmington (Figs. 1, 4) where a basal 3.5 m-thick dolostone overlies pebbly diamictite of the Reynella Siltstone Member. The base of the dolostone is interpreted to be a sequence boundary. A number of initially progradational parasequences in turn overlie the dolostone and become increasingly aggradational upsection. These parasequences together represent a lowstand wedge that has the transgressive surface as its upper boundary. The lowstand wedge is composed of one or more progradational parasequence sets and is restricted seaward of the shelf break where it onlaps the slope of the preceding sequence (Van Wagoner and others, 1990). The proximal part of the lowstand wedge consists of the incised-valley fill and associated lowstand-shoreline deposits on the shelf or upper slope.

Transgressive Surface

The transgressive surface is interpreted to overlie fine-grained sandstone of the lowstand systems tract at Hallett Cove where it is defined by a surface of well-defined symmetrical wave ripples, the crests of which show a north-south orientation. This surface is the first significant marine-flooding surface within the Seacliff Sandstone at Hallett Cove and is overlain by a 15 cm-thick, hummocky, cross-stratified sandstone containing a lag accumulation of sandstone and dolostone clasts (Figs. 7, 8). The lag is in turn overlain by immature sandstone and mudstone that pass upwards into a 1 m-thick dolostone (Fig. 8).

At Kulpara, the transgressive surface is also defined by large-scale symmetrical wave ripples with crests oriented

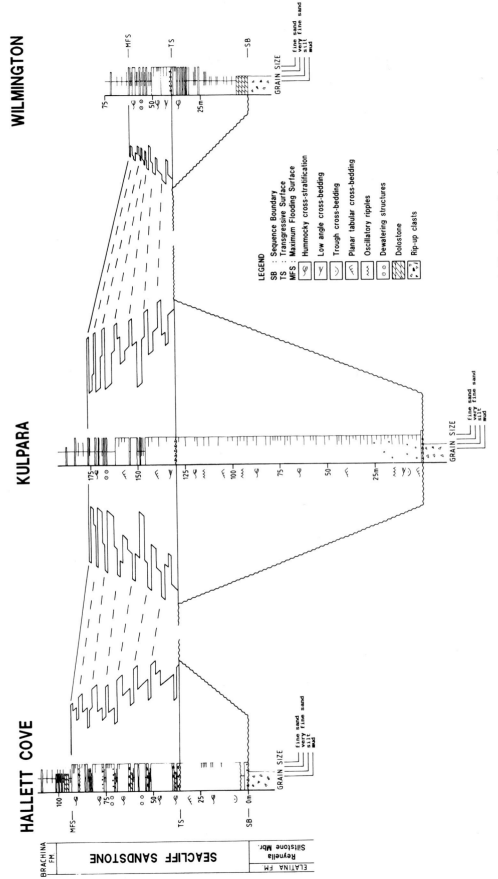

FIG. 4.—Summary sections of the Seacliff Sandstone from Hallett Cove, Kulpara, and Wilmington. Localities are shown in Figure 1. The line of section is 280 km, but no scale is intended for width of the paleovalleys.

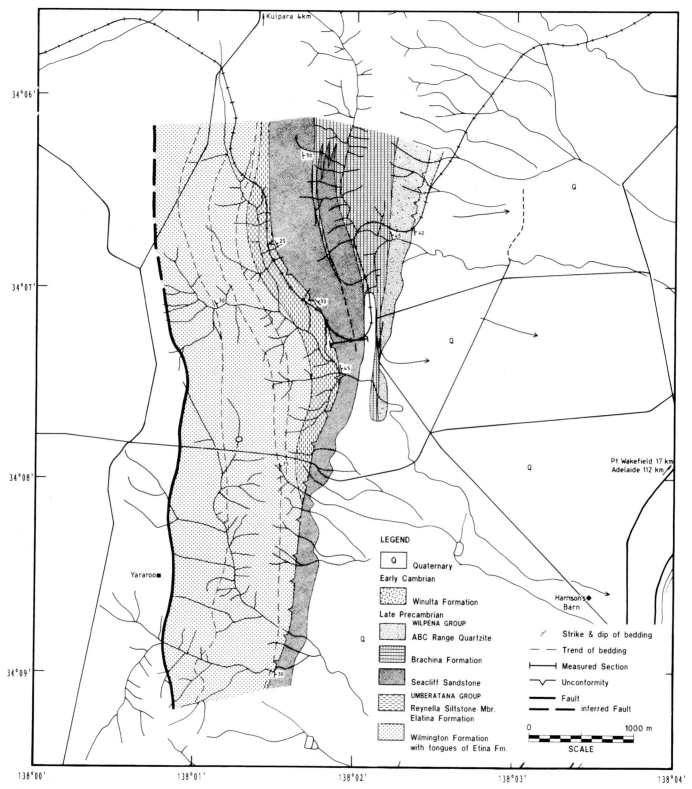

FIG. 5.—Geological map of the Seacliff Sandstone at Kulpara. Note the apparent intertonguing relationship of the upper Seacliff Sandstone with the Brachina Formation.

FIG. 6.—Sequence boundary at the base of the Seacliff Sandstone (marked by dashed lines) overlying the Reynella Siltstone Member of the Elatina Formation in a rail cut exposure at Kulpara. Relief on the erosional surface, shown in Figure 5, is of the order of 150 m.

FIG. 8.—Dolostone, about 1 m thick at the base of a parasequence at Hallett Cove and displaying centimeter-thick alternations of carbonate and shale. The dolostone is overlain by a hummocky cross-stratified sandstone that contains abundant clasts of dolostone, interpreted to be storm rosettes. Float from this unit is shown supporting the geological hammer.

FIG. 7.—Transgressive surface at the base of a dark-colored sandstone showing heavy mineral laminae and hummocky cross-stratification overlying wave ripples developed on top of lowstand facies, Hallett Cove section. Note abundant, imbricate dolostone clasts. Brunton compass sits on transgressive surface.

Transgressive Systems Tract

Several, thin dolostone beds, previously interpreted to be tongues of the Nuccaleena Formation, are cyclically interbedded with Seacliff Sandstone at Hallett Cove (Dyson and von der Borch, 1986). The dolostone beds, commonly less than 1 m thick (Fig. 8), are characterised by parallel lamination, occasional, asymmetrical-ripple cross-lamination and rare, pinch-and-swell-ripple cross-lamination. Stable carbon ($\delta^{13}C$) and oxygen ($\delta^{18}O$) isotope measurements from the dolostone beds are distinctly negative, ranging from -2 to -3.5% for $\delta^{13}C$ and from -4 to -10% for $\delta^{18}O$. Preliminary results suggest increasingly negative $\delta^{13}C$ values for upper dolostone beds in the Seacliff Sandstone. The dolostone beds are often overlain by an erosive based, thin sandstone (c. 20–50 cm) containing dolostone clasts that often lie at high angles to the base of the sandstone. This sandstone is in turn overlain by interbedded shale and thin, micaceous, parallel-laminated and current-rippled sandstone. Current directions derived from asymmetrical ripples are dominantly towards the east and south-east. A thick (3–5 m) sharp-based, mature sandstone, commonly displaying hummocky cross-stratification and basal clasts of sandstone and shale, caps the cycle.

The intertonguing relationship of sandstone, shale, and dolostone in the Seacliff Sandstone (Forbes, 1982) can be explained by the occurrence of upward-shallowing cycles or parasequences (Fig. 10) in an overall transgressive regime (Dyson, 1992a). Dolostone beds commonly overlie marine flooding surfaces where they are deposited below storm-wave base. Each dolostone in a typical cycle was interpreted to represent background carbonate deposition on sediment-starved, hiatal surfaces by Dyson and von der Borch (1986), who suggested the dolostones were partly diagenetic and partly detrital in origin. Negative $\delta^{13}C$ values suggest a possible diagenetic origin in the presence of anoxic pore waters. The apparent increase of $\delta^{13}C$ in dolostones higher in the section at Hallett Cove may reflect a decrease

in a north-south direction. Again, a lag accumulation of well-rounded, sandstone clasts, commonly 1–5 mm in size, rests on what is interpreted to be a ravinement surface. Sandstone overlying the rippled surface contains abundant horizontal-planar stratification and small-scale unidirectional and, less commonly, bidirectional cross-bedding. Along strike, north of the rail cut (Fig. 5), the transgressive surface is overlain by mudstone and siltstone.

The transgressive surface marks the base of the interpreted retrogradational parasequence set of the Seacliff Sandstone. The strike of wave-ripple crests on the transgressive surface at Hallett Cove and Kulpara suggests a north-south shoreline. Dolostone beds within the Seacliff Sandstone are interpreted to form on flooding surfaces that coalesce basinward (Fig. 9).

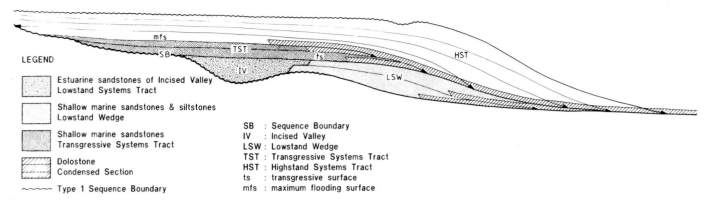

FIG. 9.—Stratal patterns of the depositional sequence represented by the Sandison Subgroup. Dolostones of the incised-valley fill are developed on flooding surfaces and in condensed sections where stratal surfaces converge. Note the maximum flooding surface (surface of maximum starvation, Baum and Vail, 1988) and transgressive surface are nearly coincident in a basinward direction.

FIG. 10.—Two parasequences of the transgressive systems tract exposed in the coastal cliffs at Hallett Cove. Each parasequence is about 9 m thick.

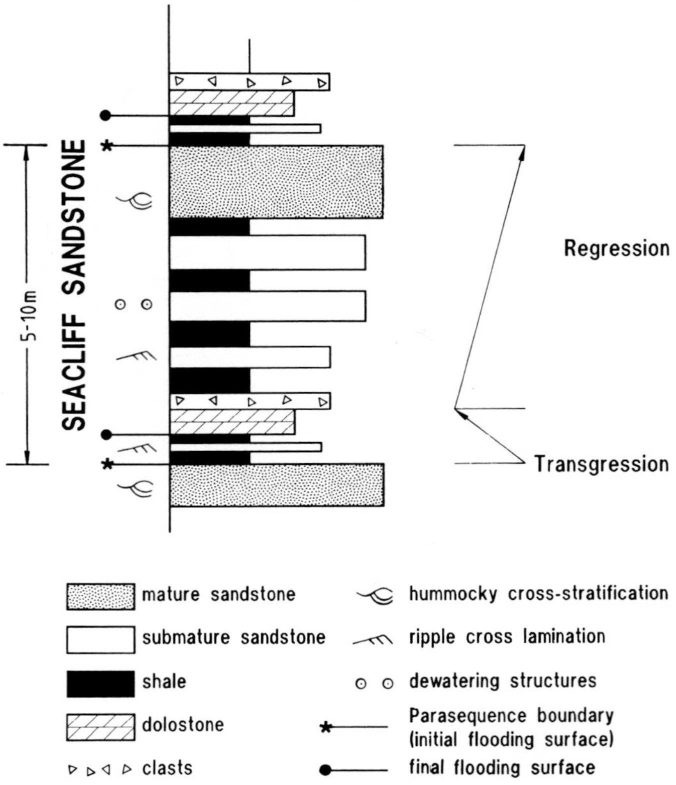

FIG. 11.—Idealised parasequence of the transgressive systems tract consisting of a basal transgressive unit overlain by a thicker regressive unit. The dolostone at the base of the parasequence is interpreted to have been deposited on a flooding surface below storm-wave base.

in sedimentation rates. Similar trends were reported for anoxic dolomites by Pisciotto and Mahoney (1981), who demonstrated a possible relationship between sedimentation rate and $\delta^{13}C$ of authigenic dolomite. The greater range in $\delta^{18}O$ values may be due to post-burial effects. Alternatively, they could reflect possible changes in palaeotemperature, suggesting that deposition of the parasequences was, at least in part, affected by climate change. Further isotopic work is in progress.

Sandstone that overlies the basal dolostone often contains edgewise clasts of dolostone, herein referred to as storm rosettes. Similar orientations have been attributed to oscillatory currents produced during storms (Sepkoski, 1982). The base of this sandstone (Fig. 11) marks the transition from transgressive to regressive sedimentation within an individual parasequence (Dyson, 1992a). The overlying, interbedded, thin sandstone and shale are interpreted as slope facies that prograded into a deeper water environment towards the east and south-east. Parallel-lamination and current ripples are suggestive of Bouma (1962) sequences in

classical turbidites. Alternatively, these sandstone beds may have been deposited as distal facies in a storm-dominated environment where pure oscillatory flow was dampened by unidirectional or combined flow currents near storm-wave base. Similar structures were reported by Dyson (1983) in the basal Brachina Formation (Fig. 2) where fine-grained sandstone beds resembled classical, thin-bedded turbidites.

A typical cycle (Fig. 12) is capped by an erosive-based, hummocky, cross stratified sandstone deposited above storm wave base. Cycles did not aggrade to sea level along the line of section, but each cycle is inferred to have terminated in deeper water than the preceding cycle, evidenced by the observation that each of the seven cycles thins successively up section (Fig. 4). Seven backstepping (onlapping) parasequences, each formed in response to a minor sea-level fall or stillstand, have also been identified above the transgressive surface at Kulpara. These parasequences combine to form a *ragged transgressive blanket*. Along the depositional strike, the *ragged transgressive blanket* pinches and swells, passing laterally into shales that are normally associated with the Brachina Formation (Fig. 5). The edge of the blanket is referred to as "ragged" because in outcrop it appears to interfinger with Brachina shales. At Wilmington, the transgressive surface is also overlain by several parasequences which progressively thin upsection. The Seacliff Sandstone gradationally passes upwards into mudstone of the Brachina Formation (Fig. 4).

Maximum Flooding Surface

The uppermost and thickest dolostone (about 2.5 m thick) at Hallett Cove was interpreted by Dyson and von der Borch (1986) to have been deposited by hemipelagic sedimentation. This dolostone, similar to previously described, thinner dolostone beds associated with underlying cycles, is now considered likewise to represent carbonate precipitation on a hiatal surface developed during a time of limited terrigenous influx. Its base is a possible maximum flooding surface of the type described by Vail and others (1991) or surface of maximum starvation as defined by Baum and Vail (1988) and marks the change from transgressive to regressive sedimentation. The dolostone itself is contained within an interpreted, condensed section. The dolostone passes upwards into a 4 m-thick unit of thinly interbedded, fine-grained sandstone and dolostone. The thin (5–10 cm), graded sandstone beds exhibit undulatory and ripple-cross lamination

FIG. 12.—Close-up of the upper parasequence shown in Figure 10. Note the m-thick dolostone near the base of the parasequence and to the right of the steps overlain by interbedded shale and immature sandstones. A 3 m-thick hummocky cross-stratified sandstone caps the parasequence.

of combined flow origin and are interpreted to be distal tempestites deposited near storm wave base. This interbedded unit then grades upwards into shale, siltstone, and fine-grained sandstone of the Brachina Formation with an accompanying decrease in dolomitic interbeds. The sediments overlying the surface of maximum starvation represent the upper, condensed section.

DISCUSSION

Erosional Phase

The unconformity at the base of the Seacliff Sandstone is interpreted as a type 1 sequence boundary of Van Wagoner and others (1988), formed during a relative fall of sea level. It is marked by a basinward shift in facies where interpreted estuarine sandstone overlies shallow marine siltstone and very fine-grained sandstone of the Reynella Siltstone Member. The lateral extent of the basal erosive surface at Kulpara suggests that it probably was not cut during a single downcutting event but may represent a composite surface of two or more unconformities of slightly different ages. Possible erosional relief of some 500 m suggests that the relative fall in sea level is too great to be eustasy-driven.

There is no compelling evidence, such as paleosol horizons, to suggest subaerial exposure. However, subsequent sea-level rise and accompanied ravinement may have removed most of the evidence of subaerial deposition at Kulpara. Alternatively, the lag may represent a channel bottom deposit at the base of a sand-rich estuary.

Valley Filling Phase

The sequence boundary at the base of an incised-valley fill is normally separated from the transgressive ravinement surface by a succession of fluvial and estuarine facies (Nummedal and Swift, 1987; Van Wagoner and others, 1990; Wheeler and others, 1990). The apparent lack of lowstand fluvial deposits at Kulpara suggests that they should be sought further updip.

The development of the transgressive systems tract is dependent on sediment supply, basin subsidence, the rate of relative sea-level rise, and the nature of the transgressive surface (Carter and others, 1991). Major regressions punctuate the transgressive systems tract of the Seacliff Sandstone and result in the development of upward-coarsening parasequences that are thought to be connected by thin sandstone sheets. In a classic study, Hollenshead and Pritchard (1961) described a series of thick sandstone benches connected by thin passage sands in the Cretaceous Point Lookout Sandstone. The thicker sands corresponded to places where the shoreline remained stationary for longer periods of time. Swift (1968) attributed the sandstone benches to a balance between subsidence and sediment supply, and the passage sandstones to an excess of subsidence over sediment supply. Similar sandstone bodies have been attributed to alternating transgression and stillstand (e.g., Devine, 1991; Donselaar, 1989). Pauses in transgression often resulted in incised shoreface profiles as fluvial sediment was supplied to the shoreface (Niedoroda and others, 1985; Nummedal and Swift, 1987; Pattison and Walker, 1992). In transgressive-regressive cycles, the transgressive part is commonly thinner than the regressive part (Fischer, 1961). Wells (1960) suggested that this reflected the time involved where transgression was thought to occur more rapidly than regression. Figure 11 suggests that these concepts can be applied to the transgressive systems tract of the Seacliff Sandstone at the parasequence scale where the transgressive unit is much thinner than the overlying regressive unit. Facies architecture of the *ragged transgressive blanket* is controlled by the distribution of parasequences confined within the incised valley. The *ragged transgressive blanket* contains up to 7 upward-coarsening parasequences that range in thickness from 15 m to less than 4 m (Fig. 4). The parasequences thin and shale out along the depositional strike where they appear to intertongue with fine-grained facies of the Brachina Formation.

Hummocky cross-stratified sandstone that caps these parasequences often displays an erosive base. It may simply reflect normal progradation of inner shelf sands over more distal facies. Alternatively, deposition of this event sandstone may have resulted from a relative fall of sea level. In this situation, a lowstand deposit overlies a highstand succession of interbedded sandstone and shale that was deposited as distal tempestite facies or in a slope environment. This interpretation is supported by the progressive upward-thinning of the hummocky cross-stratified sandstone that caps upward-coarsening cycles. Also, relief at the base of the hummocky cross-stratified sandstone in successive cycles is increasingly less prominent. If this interpretation is correct, then the *ragged transgressive blanket* consists of several sequences containing a basal lowstand unit that is overlain by transgressive and highstand units. The marine flooding surface and dolostone would then be contained within each sequence and not at the base of each parasequence as shown in Figure 12. These sequences conform to the original definition of a sequence, defined as a relatively conformable succession or genetically related strata bounded by unconformities or their correlative conformities (Mitchum and others, 1977), and may be analogous to the high-frequency sequences of Mitchum and Van Wagoner (1991). Therefore, the *ragged transgressive blanket* may consist of a transgressive sequence set in the terminology of Mitchum and Van Wagoner (1991).

Valley Flooding Phase

The maximum flooding surface is represented by fine-grained, deeper water facies (Fig. 13) or a thick, uppermost dolostone (Fig. 9) and is contained within the condensed section. In areas of high sedimentation, the maximum flooding surface and the transgressive surface are separated by the *ragged transgressive blanket* but may be nearly coincident in areas with low sedimentation rates. Adjacent to incised valleys, the sequence boundary and the condensed section are almost coincident, as described elsewhere by Loutit and others (1988). Condensed sections are a thin, marine stratigraphic unit and occur where stratal surfaces converge. They consist of pelagic to hemipelagic sediments characterised by very low sedimentation rates (Loutit and others, 1988). Condensed sections also contain a possible

downlap surface (Vail and others, 1984; Van Wagoner and others, 1987) upon which distal toes of the highstand systems tract downlap. The downlap surface observed in seismic sections may correspond to the time of maximum flooding (Vail and others, 1984).

The Nuccaleena Formation at the base of the Wilpena Group or locally the uppermost dolostone of the Seacliff Sandstone is a very useful marker for inter-regional sequence correlation in the Adelaide Geosyncline (Coats and Blissett, 1971). However, where there are multiple dolostone horizons or the Nuccaleena Formation underlies the Seacliff Sandstone, for example at Yunta (Forbes, 1975) and Wilmington, its usefulness as a chronostratigraphic marker is questionable.

Significance of Deep Water Carbonates in Transgressive Systems Tracts

Dolostones within the incised-valley fill of the Seacliff Sandstone overlie marine flooding surfaces and represent background carbonate deposition on sediment-starved hiatal, surfaces. Below the surface of maximum starvation, each dolostone represents a mini-condensed section. They possibly coalesce basinward over a thin interval near the distal toes of the lowstand wedge where they are confined between the correlative conformity of the sequence boundary and the surface of maximum flooding (Fig. 9). Dolostone of the Seacliff Sandstone may have formed along surfaces of downlap, onlap, and on erosional unconformities or on transgressive ravinement surfaces.

Where the Nuccaleena Formation is not associated with facies of the Seacliff Sandstone, such as in the central Flinders Ranges, the base of the dolostone is a sequence boundary and its upper boundary represents the surface of maximum flooding. Adjacent to the incised valley where sedimentation is low, the sequence boundary, transgressive surface, and surface of maximum flooding are almost coincident (Fig. 9). Plummer (1979) interpreted the Nuccaleena Formation in the central Flinders Ranges to have been deposited under shallow subtidal to supratidal conditions where its base is locally disconformable upon the Umberatana Group. This dolostone facies was possibly deposited on a ravinement surface overlying former shelf deposits of the Elatina Formation as the shoreface retreated over the surface of subaerial exposure.

DEPOSITIONAL MODEL FOR INCISED VALLEY FILLS OF THE SEACLIFF SANDSTONE

The schematic diagram in Figure 13 illustrates the key surfaces and associated facies of the Seacliff Sandstone valley-fill deposits. The valley-fill deposits are aggradational in nature and are related to relative sea-level rise following a sea level lowstand. The complete depositional succession consists of a basal lag overlain by estuarine sandstone. Aggradational fluvial sandstone, though not observed in outcrop, was either not deposited or deposited updip in the axis of the valley. A transgressive surface was developed on top of the estuarine deposits as sedimentation failed to keep pace with increased relative sea-level rise. Dolostone deposited in a shallow subtidal environment may have formed

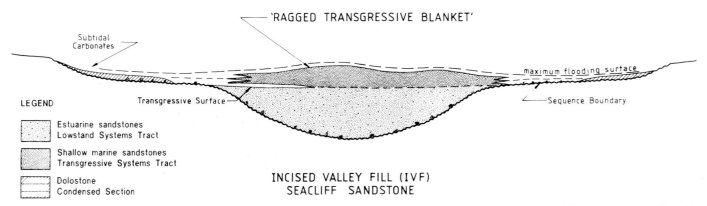

FIG. 13.—Schematic diagram of the Seacliff Sandstone valley fill at Kulpara illustrating the major boundaries within a sequence stratigraphic framework. Parasequences of the transgressive systems tract combine to form the *ragged transgressive blanket* that was developed on the transgressive surface during a rise in relative sea level and overlies estuarine lowstand facies. Note dolostone on the ravinement surface adjacent to the *ragged transgressive blanket*.

on the ravinement surface where the sequence boundary was coincident with the transgressive surface (Fig. 13). Above the transgressive surface, deposition of the *ragged transgressive blanket* resulted from fluvial sedimentation at the shoreline, leading to the development of aggradational estuarine and mouth bar facies as sea level continued to rise.

The *ragged transgressive blanket* is interpreted to consist of a series of back-stepping parasequences. Each parasequence in turn consists of resedimented facies (immature sandstones) that commonly overlie a basal dolostone. The resedimented facies, which contain shale and dolostone clasts and exhibit water escape structures, were interpreted by Dyson and von der Borch (1986) to be turbidites that passed through a stage of fluidised flow. For turbidites of this type to form, a submarine slope is required in proximity to a sediment source. Figure 14 is one possible model for this

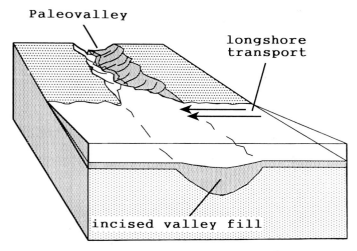

FIG. 14.—Proposed model for facies of the transgressive systems tract deposited within a progressively drowning paleovalley. Longshore transport of sand is deposited down the side of the paleovalley as resedimented facies. Above storm-wave base, the resedimented facies are reworked into mature, hummocky cross-stratified sandstones.

situation in which longshore transport of sand is redeposited down the side of a progressively drowning paleovalley. For such a mechanism to operate, sediment trapping in the advancing fluvial and estuarine phase would have been minor in comparison to longshore delivery in order to maintain a significant slope into the valley in the nearshore zone. Above storm wave base, resedimented facies of the incised-valley fill may have been reworked into mature, hummocky cross-stratified sandstone.

Sedimentation adjacent to and within the La Jolla and Scripps submarine canyons off the coast of California (Shepard and Dill, 1966) may be a partial modern analogue of the processes interpreted to be responsible for deposition within the Seacliff Sandstone incised-valley fill. Recent shelf sediments surrounding the Scripps Canyon are different in composition to those found within the canyon head. The shelf sediments are composed of relatively clean, homogenous, fine-grained sand. In comparison, the canyon-fill sediments are a heterogeneous mixture of micaceous silty sands and organic matter. The main sources of sand-sized sediment are derived from rivers in the region and nearshore and beach deposits. Sediment is transported by longshore drift in the outer surf zone until it is intercepted by the head of the submarine canyon, less than 200 m from the shoreline. Micaceous grains are kept in suspension longer and are transported farther downslope than the well sorted quartz grains. According to Shepard and Dill (1966), the net result of this differential suspension is the separation of the nearshore sands into two distinct zones: (1) a highly micaceous sand primarily confined within the canyon head and (2) a shallower sand dominantly composed of quartz grains.

IMPLICATIONS FOR EXPLORATION AND DEVELOPMENT
OF INCISED VALLEY FILLS

The description and interpretation of incised-valley fills within the Neoproterozoic Seacliff Sandstone may help with recognising individual components of other valley fills and lead to a better understanding of the geometry and reservoir characteristics of similar sandstone bodies in hydrocarbon-prospective basins. Incised valleys are commonly filled with composite sandstone reservoirs that have a potential to form abundant stratigraphic traps.

The lowstand system tract of incised-valley fills consists of a high percentage of sandstone that is likely to form prominent reservoirs in shallow marine to fluvial settings. They consist of a variety of sandstone types including estuarine, deltaic, shoreline, and fluvial sandstones (Van Wagoner and others, 1990). Transgressive surfaces above lowstand systems tracts rarely underlie reservoir quality strata but instead they commonly control seal distribution (Van Wagoner, 1991). Normally, deep water facies of backstepping parasequences or high frequency sequences rest directly above the transgressive surface.

However, potential exists to find reservoirs updip within the *ragged transgressive blanket* of Seacliff-type incised-valley fills where the great number of individual sandstone bodies offers multiple stacked reservoir targets. Above the transgressive surface, the facies are wave-dominated and the shoreline is found some distance up depositional dip. Laterall y, the sandstone bodies pinch out into shales of the condensed section creating an effective lateral seal. Each parasequence or high-frequency sequence is a time-stratigraphic unit that may have an estuarine or shoreface deposit located along its landward pinch-out into fine-grained lagoonal or continental facies. Further down depositional dip, open marine sandstone becomes interbedded with marine shale.

The backstepping nature of the *ragged transgressive blanket* tends to produce interbedded sandstone and shale, resulting in the development of multiple pay reservoirs that are interbedded with potential hydrocarbon source units. Reworking by coastal processes also tends to redistribute reservoir-quality sand into widespread trends that parallel the paleoshoreline. Continuity of the sandstone units is typically good along depositional strike but may vary widely in the depositional dip direction. The *ragged transgressive blanket* is overlain by a continuous shale seal of the condensed section that may also be a hydrocarbon source.

The stratigraphic complexity of the *ragged transgressive blanket* may be reduced by careful correlation of parasequence and high-frequency sequence boundaries and by differentiating between the transgressive surface and surface of maximum flooding. Orientation of the paleoshoreline is important in delineating the depositional strike of the shallow marine facies. The widespread marine shale or dolostone of the condensed section is a useful chronostratigraphic marker. It would also be necessary to map the distribution and facies of individual parasequences or high-frequency sequences within the *ragged transgressive blanket* to understand differences in reservoir quality.

CONCLUSIONS

1. The sequence boundary at the base of the Seacliff Sandstone may represent a composite erosional surface. A deep paleovalley was cut into underlying strata with a relief of some 150 m and may be of relevance to the understanding of similar incised valleys higher in the Wilpena Group.

2. The incised-valley fill consists of lowstand and transgressive systems tracts separated by a transgressive surface. The lowstand facies of the incised-valley fill consists of estuarine and shallow marine strata. The absence of fluvial deposits suggests that they were not deposited or are located some distance updip along the axis of the paleovalley.

3. The *ragged transgressive blanket*, which is a significant component of the Seacliff Sandstone valley fill, overlies the transgressive surface and is composed of a set of seven parasequences. Commonly within each parasequence is an immature sandstone containing abundant clasts which marks the transition from transgressive to regressive sedimentation; each retrogradational parasequence is interpreted to consist of transgressive and highstand units.

4. Dolostone beds within the incised-valley fill represent carbonate precipitation on hiatal surfaces developed during times of limited terrigenous influx. The dolostone overlying sandstone of the uppermost parasequence is interpreted to have formed on the maximum flooding surface. Below this surface of maximum starvation, each dolostone was deposited on marine flooding surfaces that coalesce basinward where they are confined between the correlative conformity of the sequence boundary and the maximum flooding surface.

5. Potential exists to find reservoirs within the *ragged transgressive blanket* of Seacliff-type incised-valley fills where the great number of individual sandstone bodies offers multiple stacked reservoir targets.

ACKNOWLEDGEMENTS

This paper summarizes part of a Ph.D. thesis undertaken by I. A. Dyson at Flinders University. We thank N. Christie-Blick, R. Dalrymple, J. Jago, J. Lorenzo, and W. Preiss for comments on this and earlier versions of the manuscript. We also thank Inara Stuart and Gail Jackson for typing and drafting respectively. The manuscript was critically reviewed and improved by referees R. Boyd, J. Grotzinger, and J. Lindsay.

REFERENCES

BAUM, F. R., AND VAIL, P. R., 1988, sequence stratigraphic concepts applied to Paleogene outcrops, Gulf and Atlantic basins, *in* Wilgus, C. W., Hastings, B., Kendall, C. G. St. C., Posamentier, H. W., Ross, C. A., and Van Wagoner, J. C., eds., Sea-level Changes: An Integrated Approach: Tulsa, Society of Economic Paleontologists and Mineralogists Special Publication 42, p. 309–327.

BOUMA, A. H., 1962, Sedimentology of Some Flysch Deposits: Amsterdam, Elsevier, 168 p.

CARTER, R. M., ABBOTT, S. M., FULTHORPE, C. S., HAYWICK, D. W., AND HENDERSON, R. A., 1991, Application of global sea-level and sequence stratigraphy models in Southern Hemisphere Neogene strata from New Zealand, *in* MacDonald, D. I. M., ed., Sedimentation, Tectonics and Eustasy: Sea-level Changes at Active Margins: Oxford, Blackwell Scientific, International Association of Sedimentology Special Publication 12, p. 41–65.

CHRISTIE-BLICK, N., VON DER BORCH, C. C., AND DIBONA, P. A., 1990, Working hypotheses for the origin of the Wonoka Canyons (Neoproterozoic), South Australia: American Journal of Science, v. 290-A, p. 295–332.

COATS, R. P., AND BLISSETT, A. H., 1971, Regional and economic geology of the Mount Painter Province: Bulletin of the Geological Survey of South Australia, v. 43, 426 p.

DALRYMPLE, R. W., ZAITLIN, B. A., AND BOYD, R., 1992, Estuarine facies models: conceptual basis and stratigraphic implications: Journal of Sedimentary Petrology, v. 62, p. 1130–1146.

DEVINE, P. R., 1991, Transgressive origin of channelled estuarine deposits in the Point Lookout Sandstone, Northwestern New Mexico: a model for upper Cretaceous, cyclic regressive parasequences of the U. S. western interior: American Association of Petroleum Geologists Bulletin, v. 75, p. 1039–1063.

DONSELAAR, M. E., 1989, The Cliff House Sandstone, San Juan Basin, New Mexico: model for the stacking of 'transgressive' barrier complexes: Journal of Sedimentary Petrology, v. 59, p. 13–27.

DYSON, I. A., 1983, The significance of hummocky cross-stratification in the late Precambrian Brachina Subgroup, Hallett Cove, South Australia (abs.): Geological Society of Australia Abstracts, v. 10, p. 49–50.

DYSON, I. A., 1986, Geology of the late Precambrian Brachina Subgroup at Hallett Cove, South Australia (abs.): Geological Society of Australia Abstracts, v. 15, p. 232.

DYSON, I. A., 1992a, Stratigraphic nomenclature and sequence stratigraphy of the lower Wilpena Group, Adelaide Geosyncline: the Sandison Subgroup: Quarterly Geological Notes, Geological Survey of South Australia, v. 122, p. 2–13.

DYSON, I. A., 1992b, Sedimentology and stratigraphy of the Reynella Siltstone Member, Elatina Formation: a late Proterozoic glacigenic sequence in the Adelaide Geosyncline (abs.): Geological Society of Australia Abstracts, v. 32, p. 155–156.

DYSON, I. A., AND VON DER BORCH, C. C., 1986, A field guide to the geology of the late Precambrian Wilpena Group, Hallett Cove, South Australia, in Parker, A. J., ed., Eighth Australian Geological Convention, One Day Geological Excursions of the Adelaide Region: Adelaide, Geological Society of Australia, p. 17–40.

FISCHER, A. G., 1961, Stratigraphic record of transgressing seas in light of sedimentation on the Atlantic coast of New Jersey: American Association of Petroleum Geologists Bulletin, v. 45, p. 1656–1666.

FORBES, B. G., 1975, Stratigraphic sections through the uppermost Umberatana Group near Yunta and Mannahill, South Australia: Adelaide, Department of Mines and Energy, Report Book, 75/13, 12 p.

FORBES, B. G., 1982, Minor changes in stratigraphic nomenclature, Adelaide System, late Proterozoic: Quarterly Geological Notes, Geological Survey of South Australia, v. 82, p. 2–3.

FORBES, B. G., AND PREISS, W. V., 1987, Stratigraphy of the Wilpena Group, in Preiss, W. V., compiler, The Adelaide Geosyncline—Late Proterozoic Stratigraphy, Sedimentation, Palaeontology and Tectonics: Geological Survey of South Australia Bulletin, v. 53, p. 211–254.

HOLLENSHEAD, C. T., AND PRITCHARD, R. L., 1961, Geometry of producing Mesa Verde sandstones, San Juan Basin, in Peterson, J. A., and Osmond, J. C., eds., Geometry of Sandstone Bodies: Tulsa, American Association of Petroleum Geologists Symposium, p. 98–118.

HORWITZ, R. C., 1959, The geology of the Wakefield military sheet: Adelaide, Geological Survey of South Australia, Report of Investigations, v. 18, 32 p.

JENETTE, D. C., JONES, C. R., VAN WAGONER, J. C., AND LARSEN, J. E., 1991, High resolution sequence stratigraphy of the upper Cretaceous Tocito Sandstone: the relationship between incised valleys and hydrocarbon accumulation, San Juan Basin, New Mexico, in Van Wagoner, J. C., Jones, C. R., Taylor, D. R., Nummedal, D., Jenette, D. C., and Riley, G. W., eds., Sequence Stratigraphy Applications to Shelf Sandstone Reservoirs: Outcrop to Subsurface Examples: Tulsa, American Association of Petroleum Geologists Field Conference, September 21–25, 1991, unpaginated.

KREISA, R. D., AND MOIOLA, R. J., 1986, Soigmoidal tidal bundles and other tide-generated sedimentary structures of the Curtis Formation, Utah: Geological Society of America Bulletin, v. 97, p. 381–387.

LEMON, N. M., AND GOSTIN, V. A., 1990, Glacigenic sediments of the late Proterozoic Elatina Formation and equivalents, Adelaide Geosyncline South Australia, in Jago, J. B., and Moore, P. S., eds., The Evolution of a Late Precambrian-Early Paleozoic Rift Complex: the Adelaide Geosyncline: Sydney, Geological Society of Australia Special Publication 16, p. 149–163.

LOUTIT, T. S., HARDENBOL, J., VAIL, P. R., AND BAUM, G. R., 1988, Condensed sections: the key to age determination and correlation of continental margin sequences, in Wilgus, C. W., Hastings, B., Kendall, C. G. St. C., Posamentier, H. W., Ross, C. A., and Van Wagoner, J. C., eds., Sea-level Changes: An Integrated Approach: Tulsa, Society of Economic Paleontologists and Mineralogists Special Publication 42, p. 183–213.

MAWSON, D., AND SPRIGG, R. C., 1950, Subdivision of the Adelaide System: Australian Journal of Science, v. 13, p. 69–72.

MITCHUM, R. M., JR., VAIL, P. R., AND THOMPSON, S., III, 1977, Seismic stratigraphy and global changes of sea level, Part 2: the depositional sequence as a basic unit for stratigraphic analysis, in Payton, C. E., ed., Seismic Stratigraphy—Applications to Hydrocarbon Exploration: Tulsa, American Association of Petroleum Geologists Memoir 26, p. 53–62.

MITCHUM, R. M., JR., AND VAN WAGONER, J. C., 1991, High-frequency sequences and their stacking patterns: sequence-stratigraphic evidence of eustatic cycles: Sedimentary Geology, v. 70, p. 131–160.

MYROW, P. M., AND SOUTHARD, J. B., 1991, Combined-flow model for vertical stratification sequences in shallow marine storm-deposited beds: Journal of Sedimentary Petrology, v. 61, p. 202–210.

NIEDORODA, A. W., SWIFT, D. J. P., FIGUEIREDO, A. G., JR., AND FREEDMAN, G. L., 1985, Barrier island evolution, middle Atlantic shelf, U. S. A. Part II: evidence from the shelf floor: Marine Geology, v. 63, p. 363–396.

NOTTVEDT, A., AND KREISA, R. D., 1987, Model for the combined-flow origin of hummocky cross-stratification: Geology, v. 15, p. 357–361.

NUMMEDAL, D., AND SWIFT, D. J. P., 1987, Transgressive Stratigraphy at sequence bounding unconformities: some principles derived from Holocene and Cretaceous examples, in Nummedal, D., Pilkey, O. H., and Howard, J. D., eds., Sea-level Fluctuation and Coastal Evolution: Tulsa, Society of Economic Paleontologists and Mineralogists Special Publication 42, p. 241–259.

PARKER, A. J., COWLEY, W. M., AND THOMSON, B. P., 1990, The Torrens Hinge Zone and Spencer Shelf with particular reference to early Adelaidean volcanism, in Jago, J. B., and Moore, P. S., eds., The Evolution of a Late Precambrian-Early Paleozoic Rift Complex: the Adelaide Geosyncline: Sydney, Geological Society of Australia Special Publication 16, p. 129–148.

PATTISON, S. J., AND WALKER, R. G., 1992, Deposition and interpretation of lond narrow sandbodies underlain by a basinwide erosion surface: Cardium Formation, Cretaceous Western Interior, Alberta, Canada: Journal of Sedimentary Petrology, v. 621, p. 292–309.

PISCIOTTO, K. A., AND MAHONEY, J. J., 1981, Isotopic survey of diagenetic carbonates, Deep Sea Drilling Project Leg 63, in Yeats, R. S., Haq., B. U., Barron, J. A., Bukry, D., Crouch, J., Denham, C., Douglas, A. G., Grechinb, V. I., Leinen, M., Niem, A., Verma, S. P., Poore, R. Z., Shibata, T. and Wolfart, R., eds., Initial Report DSDP, Leg 63: Washington D.C., United States Government Printing Office, p. 595–609.

PLUMMER, P. S., 1978, Stratigraphy of the lower Wilpena Group (Late Precambrian), Flinders Ranges, South Australia: Transactions of Royal Society of South Australia, v. 102, p. 25–38.

PLUMMER, P. S., 1979, Note on the paleoenvironmental significance of the Nuccaleena Formation (upper Precambrian), central Flinders Ranges, South Australia: Journal of Geological Society of Australia, v. 25, p. 395–402.

PREISS, W. V., 1982, Supergroup classification in the Adelaide Geosyncline: Transactions of Royal Society of South Australia, v. 106, p. 81–83.

PREISS, W. V., 1983, compiler, Adelaide Geosyncline and Stuart Shelf: Precambrian and Paleozoic geology, Geological Atlas Special Series, 1:60,000: Adelaide, Geological Survey of South Australia.

PREISS, W. V., 1987, Stratigraphic nomenclature and classification, in Preiss, W. V., compiler, The Adelaide Geosyncline—Late Proterozoic Stratigraphy, Sedimentation, Paleontology and Tectonics: Geological Survey of South Australia Bulletin, v. 53, p. 29–34.

SHANNON, L. T., 1990, Clifford Field: a fluvial valley-fill reservoir, Lincoln County, Colorado, in Sonnenberg, L., Shannon, T., Rader, K., von Drehle, W. F., and Martin, G. W., eds., Morrow Sandstones in Southeast Colorado and Adjacent Areas: Denver, Rocky Mountain Association of Geologists, p. 101–110.

SEPKOSKI, J. J., JR., 1982, Flat pebble conglomerates, storm deposits, and the Cambrian bottom fauna, *in* Einsele, G., and Seilacher, A., eds., Cyclic and Event Stratification: Berlin, Springer-Verlag, 536 p.

SHEPARD, F. P., AND DILL, R. F., 1966, Submarine Canyons and Other Sea Valleys: Chicago, Rand McNally and Company, 231 p.

SWIFT, D. J. P., 1968, Coastal erosion and transgressive stratigraphy: Journal of Geology, v. 76, p. 444–456.

SWIFT, D. J. P., FIGUEIREDO, A. G., FREELAND, G. L., AND OERTEL, G. F., 1983, Hummocky cross-stratification and megaripples: A geological double-standard?: Journal of Sedimentary Petrology, v. 53, p. 1295–1317.

THOMSON, B. P., 1966, Stratigraphic relationships between sediments of Marinoan age-Adelaide region: Quarterly Geological Notes, Geological Survey of South Australia, v. 9, p. 1–3.

THOMSON, B. P., 1969, Precambrian crystalline basement, *in* Parkin, L. W., ed., Handbook of South Australian Geology: Adelaide, Geological Survey of South Australia, p. 49–83.

THOMSON, B. P., DAILY, B., COATS, R. P., AND FORBES, B. G., 1976, Late Precambrian and Cambrian Geology of the Adelaide "Geosyncline" and Stuart Shelf, South Australia: Excursion Guide 33A: Sydney, 25th International Geological Congress, 56 p.

VAIL, P. R., AUDEMARD, F., BOWMAN, S. A., EISNER, P. N., AND PEREZ-CRUZ, C., 1991, The stratigraphic signatures of tectonics, eustasy and sedimentology—an overview, *in* Einsele, G., Ricken, W., and Seilacher, A., eds., Cycles and Events in Stratigraphy: Berlin, Springer-Verlag, p. 617–659.

VAIL, P. R., HARDENBOL, J., AND TODD, R. G., 1984, Jurassic Unconformities, Chronostratigraphy and Sea Level Changes from Seismic Stratigraphy and Biostratigraphy: Tulsa, American Association of Petroleum Geologists Memoir 36, p. 129–144.

VAIL, P. R., MITCHUM, R. M., JR., AND THOMPSON, S., III, 1977, Seismic stratigraphy and global changes of sea level, part 4: Global cycles of relative changes of sea level, *in* Payton, C. E., ed., Seismic Stratigraphy- Applications to Hydrocarbon Exploration: Tulsa, American Association of Petroleum Geologists Memoir 26, p. 83–97.

VAN WAGONER, J. C., 1991, High frequency stratigraphy and facies architecture of the Sego Sandstone in the Book Cliffs of Western Colorado and Eastern Utah, *in* Van Wagoner, J. C., Jones, C. R., Taylor, D. R., Nummedal, D., Jenette, D. C., and Riley, G. W., eds., Sequence Stratigraphy Applications to Shelf Sandstone Reservoirs: Outcrop to Subsurface Examples: Tulsa, American Association of Petroleum Geologists Field Conference, September 21–28, 1991, unpaginated.

VAN WAGONER, J. C., MITCHUM, R. M. JR., CAMPION, K. M., AND RAHMANIAN, V. D., 1990, Siliciclastic Sequence Stratigraphy in Well Logs, Cores and Outcrops: Concepts for High-resolution Correlation of Time and Facies: Tulsa, American Association of Petroleum Geologists, Methods in Exploration Series 7, 55 p.

VAN WAGONER, J. C., MITCHUM, R. M. JR., AND POSAMENTIER, H. W., 1987, Seismic stratigraphy using sequence stratigraphy, part 2: key definitions of sequence stratigraphy, *in* Bally, A. W., ed., Volume 1, Atlas of Seismic Stratigraphy: Tulsa, American Association of Petroleum Geologists Studies in Geology 27, p. 11–14.

VAN WAGONER, J. C., POSAMENTIER, H. W., MITCHUM, R. M. JR., VAIL, P. R., SARG, J. F., LOUTIT, T. S., AND HARDENBOL, J., 1988, An overview of the fundamentals of sequence stratigraphy and key definitions, *in* Wilgus, C. W., Hastings, B., Kendall, C. G. St. C., Posamentier, H. W., Ross, C. A., and Van Wagoner, J. C., eds., Sea-level Changes: An Integrated Approach: Tulsa, Society of Economic Paleontologists and Mineralogists Special Publication 42, p. 39–45.

VON DER BORCH, C. C., 1980, Evolution of late Proterozoic to early Paleozoic Adelaide Foldbelt, Australia: comparisons with post-Permian rifts and passive margins: Tectonophysics, v. 70, p. 115–134.

VON DER BORCH, C. C., CHRISTIE-BLICK, N., AND GRADY, A. E., 1988, Depositional sequence analysis applied to the late Proterozoic Wilpena Group, Adelaide Geosyncline: Australian Journal of Earth Sciences, v. 35, p. 59–71.

VON DER BORCH, C. C., GRADY, A. E., EICKHOFF, K. H., DIBONA, P., AND CHRISTIE-BLICK, N., 1989, Late Proterozoic Patsy Springs canyon, Adelaide Geosyncline: submarine or subaerial origin?: Sedimentology, v. 36, p. 777–792.

WELLS, A. J., 1960, Cyclic sedimentation: a review: Geological Magazine, v. 97, p. 389–403.

WHEELER, D. M., SCOTT, A. J., CORINGRATO, V. J., AND DEVINE, P. E., 1990, Stratigraphy and depositional history of the Morrow Formation, southeast Colorado and southwest Kansas, *in* Sonnenberg, L., Shannon, T., Rader, K., von Drehle, W. F., and Martin, G. W., eds., Morrow Sandstones in Southeast Colorado and Adjacent Areas: Denver, Rocky Mountain Association of Geologists, p. 9–35.

WOOD, J. M., AND HOPKINS, J. C., 1989, Reservoir Sandstone Bodies in Estuarine Valley Fill: Lower Cretaceous Glauconitic Member, Little Bow Field, Alberta, Canada: Tulsa, American Association of Petroleum Geologists Bulletin, v. 73, p. 1361–1382.

SEGMENT 2—TRANSGRESSIVE-LIMIT ESTUARY

TRANSGRESSIVE FACIES AND SEQUENCE ARCHITECTURE IN MIXED TIDE- AND WAVE-DOMINATED INCISED VALLEYS: EXAMPLE FROM THE GIRONDE ESTUARY, FRANCE

GEORGE P. ALLEN

TOTAL Centre Scientifique et Technique, 78470 St. Remy les Chevreuse, France

AND

HENRY W. POSAMENTIER

ARCO Exploration and Production Technology, 2300 West Plano Parkway, Plano, Texas 75075

ABSTRACT: A study of the Holocene deposits within the Gironde estuary incised valley indicates that a significant proportion of the valley fill has accumulated during transgression in the form of backstepping estuarine deposits. This incised valley was subjected to a mixed wave- and tidal-energy regime, and the transgressive fill was deposited in three major depositional environments: (1) the tide-dominated *inner estuary*, extending between the estuary mouth and the bayline, (2) the mixed tide and wave *estuary mouth*, and (3) the landward-migrating wave-dominated *shoreface*. The sediments deposited within each environment are bounded by valley-wide stratigraphic discontinuities and together comprise the *transgressive systems tract*.

Each depositional environment develops a specific facies assemblage, and the transgressive fill occurs in three successive phases. *Phase 1* occurs at the onset of transgression, when the incised alluvial valley is converted into an estuary by marine flooding. At this time, inner-estuary tidal sands and muds onlap the lowstand alluvial profile at the bayline.

Phase 2 occurs when the spit-constricted estuary-mouth tidal channel migrates landward over the inner-estuary sands and muds. This results in tidal currents scouring deeply into the underlying phase 1 estuarine sediments, forming a highly erosional *tidal ravinement surface* overlain by massive estuary-mouth sands.

As the wave-dominated shoreface migrates landward across the incised valley and its interfluves, the *wave-ravinement surface* is formed. The transgressive shoreface sands and marine muds overlying this surface constitute *phase 3* of the transgressive incised-valley fill. These deposits subsequently are capped by the Maximum Flooding Surface which marks the upper bounding surface of the *Transgressive Systems Tract*.

The shoreline at the time of maximum flooding forms a regional facies limit within the incised valley. Landward of this limit, the transgressive tract comprises primarily inner-estuary tidal sands and muds. Seaward of this limit the valley fill is more sand-prone and contain thick estuary-mouth sands.

INTRODUCTION

Present-day coastal estuaries furnish excellent analogues to study the sedimentary infill of incised fluvial valleys. The eustatic sea-level fall which occurred during the late Pleistocene resulted in the formation of deeply incised fluvial valleys on all of the coastlines of the world. Subsequent marine flooding during the Holocene sea-level rise converted them into estuaries. Several studies have shown that a significant portion of the sedimentary fill of these incised valleys accumulated during transgression (Allen and others, 1970; Kraft and others, 1987; Allen and Posamentier, 1993). This relative importance of the transgressive component of late-Pleistocene incised-valley fills is possibly biased by the fact that these studies concern primarily the proximal portions of the incised valleys. However, a number of studies in ancient incised valleys have indicated that transgressive deposits also form an important component of incised-valley fills in the Mesozoic and Cenozoic (e.g., Reinson and others, 1988; Rhamani, 1988; Allen and Posamentier, 1991; Pattison, 1992).

The Gironde estuary in SW France (Fig. 1) has been the subject of numerous studies during the past 25 years. Early studies of the abundant boreholes available within the estuary by Fabre (1939), Allen and others (1970), Feral (1970), and Assor (1972), indicated that the modern estuary overlies a late-Pleistocene, fluvial incised-valley fill comprising a wide variety of facies types. In a review of these studies and more recent borehole data, Allen (1991), and Allen and Posamentier (1993) showed that this facies variability is accompanied by a number of key stratigraphic surfaces indicating that a complex succession of events occurred during transgression. These events appear to be related to the

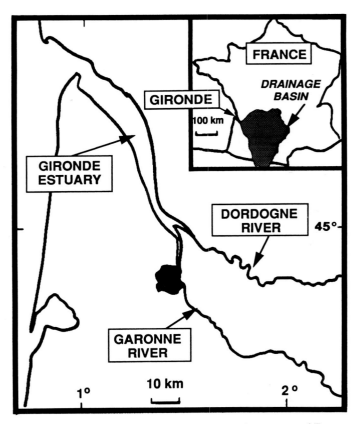

FIG. 1.—Location of Gironde estuary on the southwest coast of France.

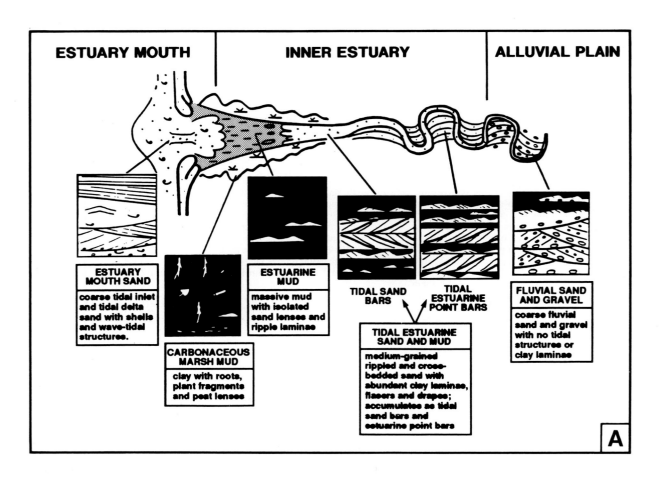

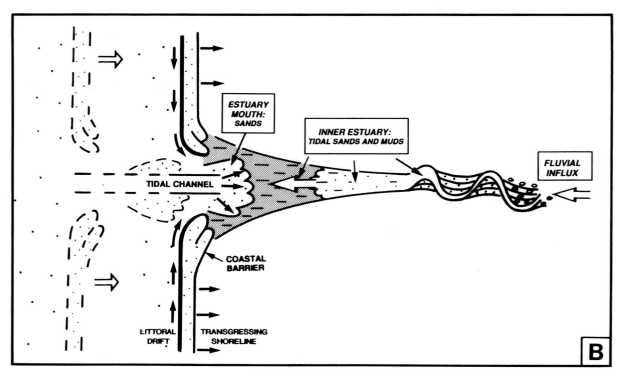

mixed wave and tide processes that predominated during transgression. This suggests that incised valleys which are subjected to both high-energy waves and tides undergo considerable sediment reworking during transgression which enhances the volumetric importance of the Transgressive Systems Tract and the facies variability within the incised-valley fill.

The objective of this paper is to develop a sequence-stratigraphic model of the transgressive deposits within incised valleys in mixed, high-energy, wave- and tide-dominated settings. This model is based on the facies and stratal architecture of the Gironde incised-valley fill and synthesizes the sedimentological and stratigraphic data available on this estuary, published in numerous papers including Fabre (1939), Allen and others (1970, 1976, 1980), Feral (1970), Assor (1972), Castaing (1981), Castaing and Allen (1981), Collotte (1985), Allen (1991), and Allen and Posamentier (1993).

MORPHOLOGY AND FACIES PATTERNS IN MIXED-ENERGY, TIDE- AND WAVE-DOMINATED ESTUARIES

During transgression, an incised valley is converted into a drowned river mouth estuary. Studies on the U. S. east coast and European Atlantic coasts (Allen and others 1970; Hayes, 1975; Wright, 1977; Dalrymple and others 1992) have shown that estuaries affected by high energy waves and tides exhibit characteristic morphological and facies patterns (Fig. 2). These estuaries commonly exhibit a seaward-opening funnel shape, with an abrupt narrowing at the coastline due to the deposition of wave-built, coastal sand barriers. During transgression, there are two major sources of sediments available to fill an incised-valley estuary: fluvial sediments from the hinterlands, and sediments sourced from the shelf and adjacent shorelines by wave erosion and tidal currents. Consequently, during transgression in wave- and tide-dominated settings, incised valleys can be filled from both ends (Fig. 2).

The Gironde estuary is characterized by a macrotidal regime, and spring-tide amplitudes attain 6 m. Wave energy on the coast and in the estuary mouth is high with an average significant wave height of about 1.3 m, and winter storm-wave heights that can exceed 7 m (Castaing, 1981). The average yearly fluvial sediment load has been evaluated by various authors (Migniot, 1971; Castaing, 1981) at 2.2×10^6 tons of suspended silt and clay, and about 0.7×10^6 tons of bedload sand and gravel. For a detailed discussion of the hydrological and sedimentological parameters affecting the Gironde, see Allen and others (1976, 1980), Castaing (1981), and Allen (1991).

In the upstream extremity of tide-dominated estuaries, the funnel shape narrows to one or more sinuous tide-domi-

nated channels (Fig. 2). These channels form tidal-estuarine point bars composed of muddy sand with heterolithic inclined stratification (Smith, 1988; Rahmani, 1989), and exhibit a variety of tide-dominated facies and structures (Allen and Truilhé, 1987). In the Gironde, the landward extremity of tidal-estuarine facies coincides with the *bay-line,* where the seaward-sloping alluvial profile joins the practically flat tidal-estuarine coastal plain (see discussion in Posamentier and Vail, 1988; Allen and Posamentier, 1993). The transition between the fluvial and estuarine channel sediments is very pronounced and marked by a decrease in grain size, an increase in mud laminae, and a disappearance of alluvial flood deposits (Allen and Truilhé, 1987).

Further downstream, the Gironde estuary widens into a funnel-shaped channel containing linear tidal sand bars in the upstream end which grade downstream into massive estuarine mud deposits (Fig. 3). Both the sinuous upper-estuary channels and the mid-estuary funnel are effectively sheltered from waves which affect only the estuary mouth and adjacent coast. In contrast, tidal and density currents are the dominant modes of sediment transport in this setting and produce a highly efficient sediment trap (Harleman and Ippen, 1969; Allen and others, 1980; Nichols and Biggs, 1985). Most of the fluvial sediment influx accumulates in this zone, and at the present time only a relatively small volume of suspended silt and clay escapes the estuary and attains the shelf (Castaing and Allen, 1981; Castaing, 1981). Consequently, landward-supplied fluvial sediments typically fine seaward within the upper part of the estuary funnel.

These fluvial-sourced sediments form a prograding and seaward-fining, "estuarine" bayhead delta within the estuary (Fig. 3). This tide-dominated, delta-like sediment wedge has been gradually filling the estuary since the end of the rapid Holocene eustatic rise (c. 4000 years BP). At its distal extremity, it merges with seaward-sourced estuary-mouth sands. During the past several thousand years, the limit between these two convergent depositional systems has been migrating seaward (Feral, 1970) and is presently located about 10 km from the estuary mouth.

The estuary mouth is constricted by coastal barriers which focus tidal currents, resulting in the erosion of a deep tidal inlet-like channel (Fig. 4). The thalweg depth of this estuary-mouth tidal channel varies between 20–30 meters, which is considerably deeper than the thalweg in the mid-estuary funnel and upper-estuary channels (Fig. 5).

The sediments within the estuary mouth consist of medium to coarse clean sand (Figs. 2, 3). This sand is furnished by wave erosion of older nearshore marine and dune deposits from the adjacent coasts and accumulates as estuary-mouth tidal-channel and tidal-delta deposits. Because

---

FIG. 2.—(A) Schematic facies model for a tide-dominated estuary on a high wave energy coastline, based on the Gironde and other estuaries (see text for references; modified from Allen, 1991). (B) Schematic illustration of the converging sedimentary systems within an incised-valley estuary undergoing transgression. The fluvially-sourced sediments accumulate in the inner estuary as an estuarine bayhead delta (see Fig. 3), while the seaward-sourced sands eroded from the shoreface and adjacent coasts accumulate in the estuary mouth as tidal-channel and tidal-delta deposits. At the present time, the bayhead delta is filling the estuary so that the facies limit at the convergence of these two systems is migrating seaward. However, since no fluvial sand is reaching the coast, the oceanic shoreline is still undergoing wave erosion.

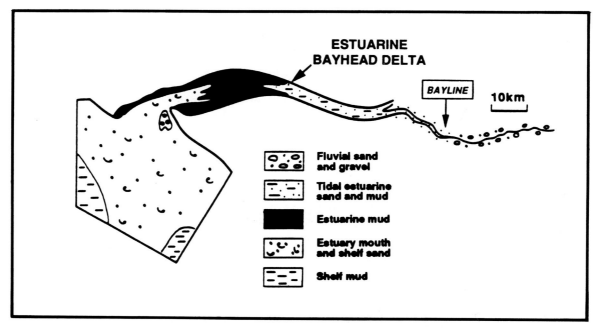

FIG. 3.—Surface-sediment distribution within the present Gironde estuary, Garonne river and adjacent shelf (from Allen, 1991). The estuarine bayhead delta constitutes a regressive tide-dominated sediment prism that is progressively filling the estuary.

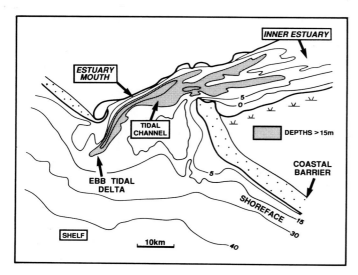

FIG. 4.—Present morphology of the Gironde estuary mouth, illustrating the deeply eroded estuary-mouth tidal channel (thalweg depths up to 30 meters). The distal end of the tidal channel terminates in a large ebb-tidal delta sand shoal, while the landward extremity of the channel extends some 10–15 km into the inner estuary.

the regressive estuarine bayhead delta has not yet reached the mouth of the estuary, no fluvial sand is presently supplied to the shorelines outside the estuary. Consequently, although the inner estuary funnel is filling with sediment, the coast is still retreating due to wave erosion (Fig. 2). Until fluvial sand can attain the coast, wave erosion will result in continued transgression of the estuary mouth and adjacent shoreline.

The continental shelf seaward of the estuary mouth and interfluve shoreline slopes gently offshore to the shelf/slope break. Surface coring on the shelf has shown that it is blanketed by a thin (commonly less than 2 m) cover of early-Holocene transgressive sand and gravel derived by wave reworking from subjacent Pleistocene deposits (Colotte, 1985).

These morphological and sedimentological patterns are typical of mixed wave and tidal estuaries undergoing transgression. The sediment facies within this type of estuary can be grouped into 3 distinct facies associations (Fig. 2): (1) *inner-estuary tidal sands and muds,* which accumulate in the wave-sheltered upper estuary channels and mid-estuary funnel; (2) *mixed tide- and wave-dominated estuary-mouth sands,* which form thick tidal-delta and tidal-inlet deposits of clean and frequently coarse-grained sand; and (3) *wave-dominated shoreface sand and shelf mud,* which accumulate seaward and lateral to the estuary mouth.

TRANSGRESSIVE FACIES WITHIN THE GIRONDE
INCISED-VALLEY FILL

A wide variety of lithologies occur within the incised-valley fill. As shown in Figures 5 and 6, the fill is composed of coarse fluvial sands and conglomerates in the valley thalweg, overlain by estuarine and shelf deposits similar to the facies that occur within and adjacent to the present estuary. The fluvial deposits which form the base of the valley fill are identical to the modern fluvial sands and gravels that are accumulating landward of the bayline about 115 km inland from the estuary mouth. Similar facies successions also have been described in ancient incised-valley fills (Reinson and others, 1988; Rahmani, 1989; Pattison, 1992).

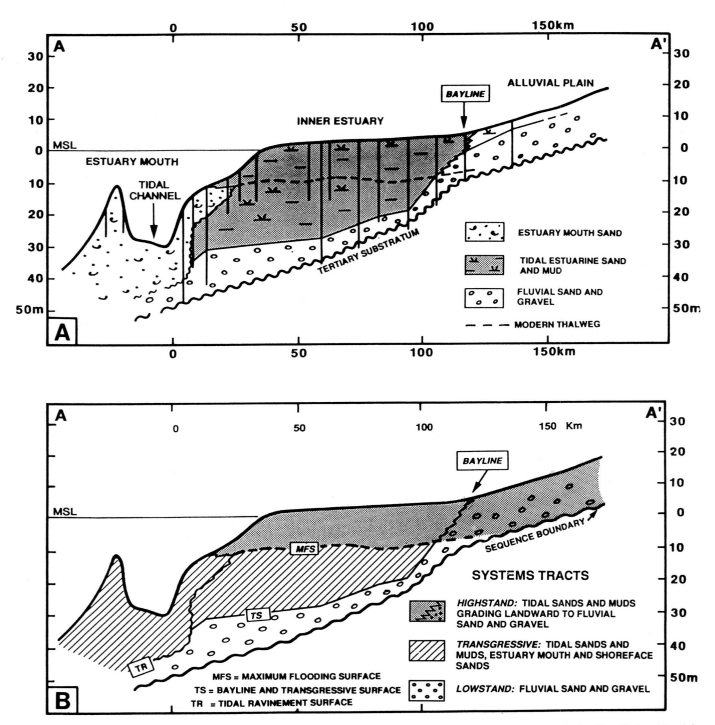

FIG. 5.—(A) Lithofacies distribution and borehole control along an axial section through the Gironde estuary incised-valley fill (see Fig. 6 for the location of the section). The cores and borings have been compiled from several authors (see text for references), and the section is drawn along the deepest observed substratum (from Allen and Posamentier, 1993). (B) Depositional systems tracts as they are interpreted along the same longitudinal section, illustrating the transgressive Holocene estuarine valley fill overlying lowstand fluvial sand and gravel in the valley axis. The Highstand Systems Tract is composed of tidal sand and mud similar to the transgressive inner-estuary deposits. Also shown are the major stratigraphic surfaces which punctuate the different phases of transgression. Since the section is drawn along the axis of the estuary, the wave ravinement surface is not shown (see Fig. 9 for a complete schematic longitudinal section).

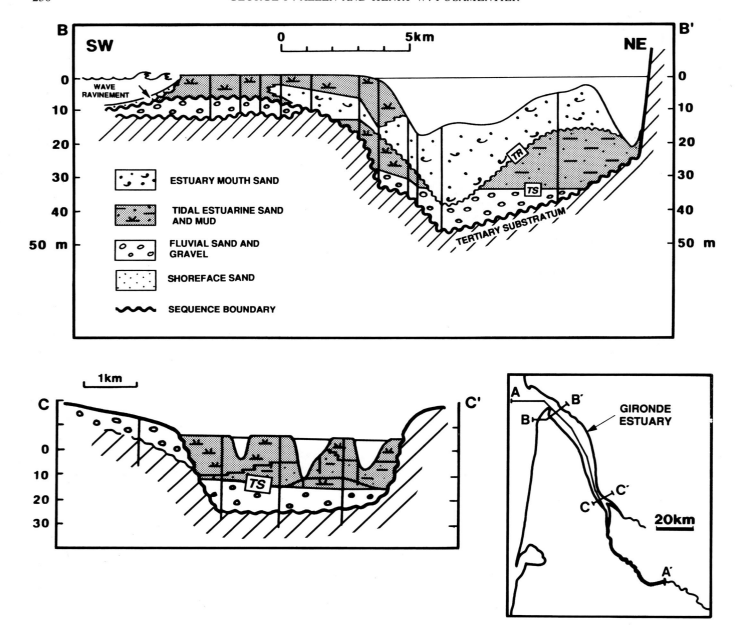

FIG. 6.—Lithofacies and borehole locations on two transverse sections within the Gironde estuary. Section B-B′ is located at the mouth of the present estuary, and section C-C′ is located 75 km upstream in the inner-estuary zone. TR and TS represent the Transgressive and Tidal Ravinement Surfaces respectively. Note the presence of thick, erosive-based estuary-mouth sands in the distal section and the wave ravinement on the transgressing shoreline adjacent to the estuary in section B-B′. The uppermost tidal flat and marsh deposits in section B-B′ represent the regressive estuarine bayhead delta which is prograding over the transgressive estuary, mouth sands. The base of these tidal sands and muds constitute the Maximum Flooding Surface within the estuary. Further upstream (section C-C′) this surface would be difficult to detect. The coarse fluvial deposits on the left interfluve of both sections represent older, Pleistocene highstand fluvial terraces.

The fluvial sand and gravel is continuous along the valley thalweg and merges landward with the modern fluvial deposits (Fig. 5). These sediments form the base of the incised-valley succession and their thickness (c. 10 m) is equivalent to the one-channel thick, present-day fluvial section that overlies the tertiary substrate landward of the bayline (Fig. 5). This suggests that little or no fluvial aggradation occurred in the alluvial plain landward of the bayline

during the Pleistocene lowstand or Holocene transgression. These one-channel thick fluvial deposits form the *Lowstand Systems Tract* within the incised-valley fill (for a more complete discussion, see Allen and Posamentier, 1993).

The fluvial deposits are overlain by a thick wedge of tidal estuarine sands and muds identical to the sediments of the present-day inner estuary (Figs. 5, 6). These sediments represent the *Transgressive Systems Tract* of the valley fill and

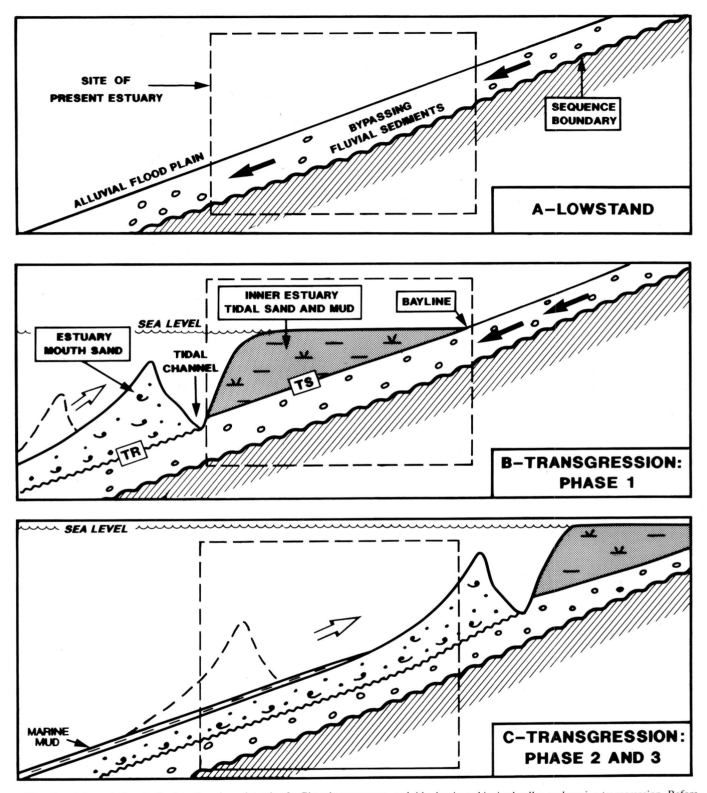

FIG. 7.—Schematic longitudinal section along the axis of a Gironde-type wave- and tide-dominated incised valley undergoing transgression. Before the incised fluvial valley is transgressed (section A), fluvial sediments bypassed the valley. During the initial phase of transgression (section B), estuarine point bars and tidal flats onlap landward onto the alluvial plain. The lack of fluvial aggradation landward of the bayline suggests that fluvial sediments bypassed the alluvial plain and accumulated within the estuarine channel in the vicinity of the bayline and the aggrading estuarine coastal plain. In the final phases of transgression (section C), tidal ravinement along the axis of the estuary erode most or all of the underlying inner-estuary sands and muds. For an illustration of the stratigraphic evolution during transgression on a transverse section, see Figure 8.

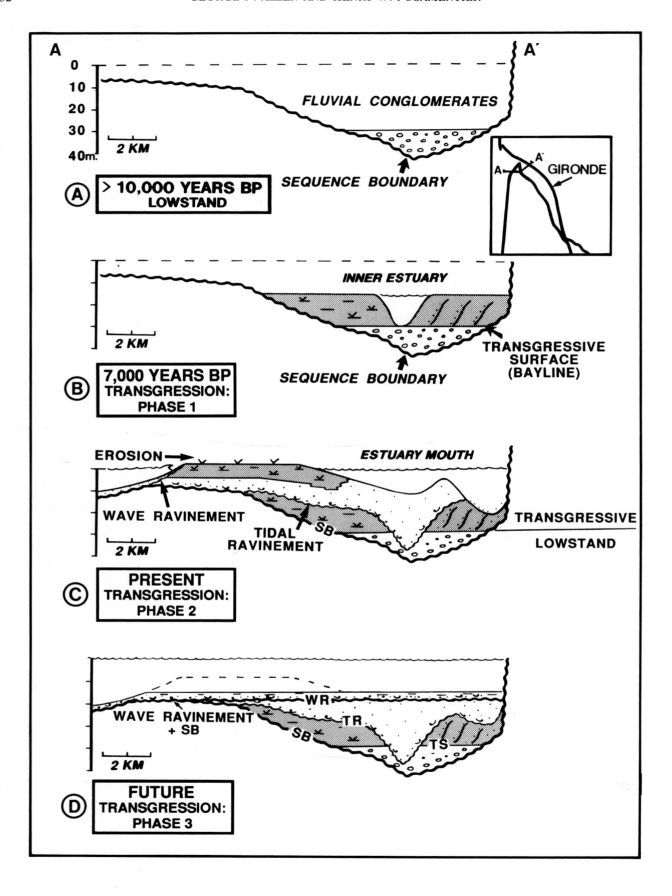

comprise estuarine point bars, tidal flats and marshes that accumulated over the fluvial deposits when the Holocene sea-level rise flooded the alluvial valley and progressively converted it into an estuary. The estuarine sediments onlap landward onto the alluvial profile, burying and preserving the underlying fluvial deposits. This stratigraphic discontinuity represents the *Transgressive Surface* separating the fluvial Lowstand Systems Tract from the overlying Transgressive Systems Tract (Posamentier and others, 1988).

In the distal extremity of the incised valley beneath the present estuary, the tidal estuarine sands and muds are overlain by massive, well-sorted medium to coarse-grained sand. The base of the sand constitutes a major erosional surface within the incised valley, incising into older inner-estuarine sands and muds, and locally down into the basal fluvial deposits (Fig. 6). The maximum thickness of these sands is variable, attaining more than 20 m in the axis of the incised valley. Similar thick sands have been described in other Holocene and ancient estuarine valley fills affected by waves and tides (Kraft and others,1987; Zaitlin and Schultz, 1990; Pattison, 1992; Dalrymple and others, 1992). These sediments are interpreted as estuary-mouth, tidal-channel and tidal-delta sand deposits that accumulated at the mouth of the transgressing estuary. The deeply incised erosional surface at the base of these sands results from tidal scour within the constricted estuary-mouth tidal channel and is referred to as the *tidal ravinement surface* (Allen, 1991). This surface extends landward about 10 km within the present Gironde.

As the estuary continues to be transgressed, the retreat of the adjacent shoreline results in wave erosion of the upper 5–10 meters of sediment. At the estuary mouth, this wave erosion removes the upper part of the incised-valley fill; however, lateral to the estuary the erosion removes older highstand interfluve deposits. This erosional surface (Fig. 6) comprises the *wave ravinement surface* (Swift, 1968; Swift and others, 1972), which is commonly overlain by a transgressive veneer of shoreface sands and shelf muds. This erosion surface and accompanying transgressive deposits have been observed on the continental shelf by several authors (e.g., Swift and others, 1972; Demarest and Kraft, 1987; Ashley and others, 1991). The wave ravinement surface commonly is paved with a thin shell and gravel lag (Demarest and Kraft, 1987). The modern landward limit of this surface in the Gironde estuary coincides with the present shoreline.

Within the modern estuary funnel, the transgressive deposits are capped by a regressive estuarine unit that has been prograding seaward into the estuary since the end of the rapid Holocene eustatic rise about 4000 years BP. The contact between these regressive deposits and the underlying transgressive deposits represents the *maximum flooding surface*. The regressive deposits comprise estuarine sands

and muds that are identical to the older transgressive estuarine deposits and constitute the "estuarine" bayhead delta mentioned previously. This unit is currently prograding down the estuary, sourced by the present discharge from the rivers, and comprises the early *Highstand Systems Tract* of the still-developing Würm depositional sequence. Historical records (Migniot, 1971) and bathymetric studies (Castaing, 1981) have shown that these highstand deposits are gradually filling the estuary and reducing its volume and width.

The different facies associations that comprise the transgressive estuarine sediment wedge are sufficiently contrasted as to be readily distinguishable in outcrops and cores, and possibly well logs. The development of these different facies associations results from the succession of sedimentary depositional environments during the progressive flooding of the fluvially-incised valley. The boundaries between the facies associations form mappable stratigraphic discontinuities within the valley fill that can be used to analyze and correlate the deposits within the incised valley.

DISCUSSION

Evolution of the Gironde Incised-Valley Fill During Transgression

The facies patterns described above indicate that during the Holocene transgression, the Gironde incised valley was subjected to 3 distinct phases of sedimentation. Each phase records a specific depositional environment as the transgression migrated landward across the alluvial profile. These environmental phases are: (1) *inner estuary* (2) *estuary-mouth tidal delta and inlet channel* and (3) *open-marine shoreface to shelf*. In any given section within the incised valley, these successive environmental phases result in the characteristic vertical and longitudinal facies relationships described in the previous section.

The sequence of events related to these three depositional phases is illustrated schematically in Figures 7 and 8. Prior to the Holocene transgression, the incised valley was a zone of sedimentary bypass for sediments en route to the river mouth (Figs. 7A, 8A). At the onset of eustatic rise at about 18,000 years BP, the distal extremity of the incised fluvial valley was transgressed and converted into an estuary. When this happened, most of the fluvial sediments were trapped within the estuary, reducing to nearly zero the volume of sand supplied to the adjacent shorelines. This resulted in coastal erosion by waves which further accelerated the transgression of the shoreline. As relative sea level continued to rise, estuarine conditions migrated landward up the incised valley, resulting in the deposition of an onlapping and aggrading wedge of tidal sands and muds over the coarser-grained lowstand fluvial deposits (Figs. 7B, 8B). These sediments accumulated between the estuary mouth

FIG. 8.—Schematic transverse section within the same incised-valley estuary illustrated on Figure 7, showing the facies and stratal patterns developed during transgression. Section C is based on the present Gironde estuary which represents a stillstand with the regression of the estuarine bayhead delta. Section D represents a hypothetical valley-fill section that would result after renewed relative sea-level rise and transgression of the estuary.

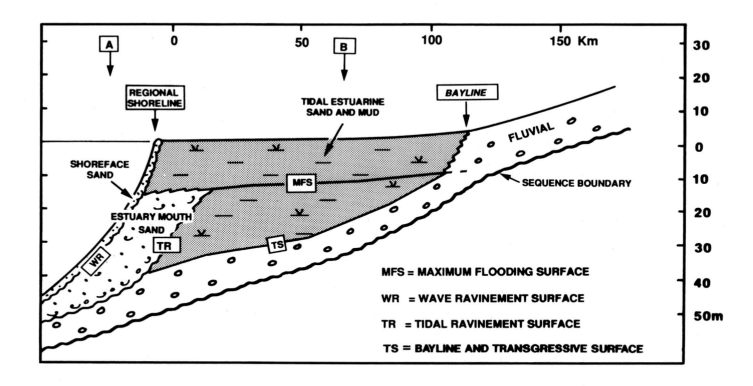

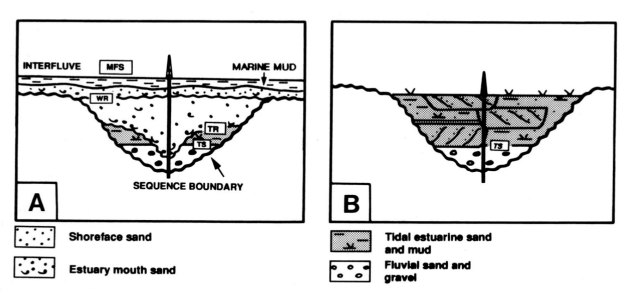

FIG. 9.—(A) Regional, longitudinal stratigraphic section in a completely filled incised valley on a high tide- and wave-energy coastline. The section represents the situation during the early Highstand Systems Tract when the regressive estuarine bayhead delta has entirely filled the incised-valley estuary. Note the different facies preserved to either side of the estuary mouth; this facies boundary is located somewhat landward from the maximum transgressive shoreline and separates a proximal, sand and mud estuarine valley fill from a more sand-prone, distal valley fill (see discussion in text). (B) Schematic transverse sections through the distal (section A) and proximal (section B) zones of the incised valley. The maximum flooding surface would be difficult to detect in the proximal incised-valley fill. The vertical lines on each section represent the location of the columnar facies sections illustrated on Figure 10.

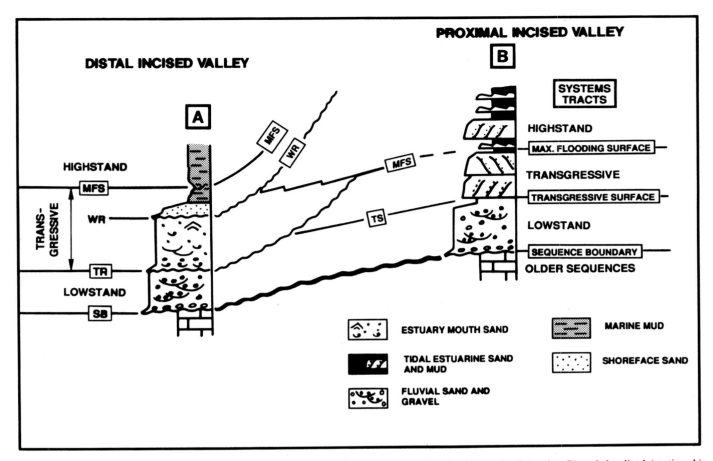

FIG. 10.—Schematic facies sections and stratigraphic correlations between two sections in the proximal (section B) and the distal (section A) zones of a Gironde-type, wave- and tide-dominated incised valley. The sections are assumed to be in the axis of the incised valley (see Fig. 9 for location of the sections). Note that the maximum flooding surface within the proximal part of the incised valley is truncated by the wave ravinement surface. In the proximal valley fill the transgressive surface forms an abrupt facies boundary between fluvial and tidal-estuarine deposits, whereas in the axis of the distal valley fill this surface is highly erosional, with estuary-mouth sand directly overlying fluvial deposits. The maximum thickness of the section in the valley thalweg varies from 10–50 m.

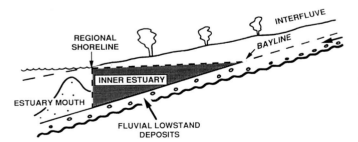

FIG. 11.—Schematic longitudinal section along the axis of a Gironde-type incised valley, illustrating the space available for inner estuary deposits during transgression. The space available will extend between the regional shoreline and the bayline. The regional shoreline occurs at the intersection between the interfluves surface and sea level, whereas the location of the bayline will be a function of the depth of incision and the valley slope.

and the bayline and constitute the first phase of transgression and represent the lowermost unit of the Transgressive Systems Tract. The sharp contact between these sediments and the underlying coarser fluvial deposits forms a *bayline flooding surface* which constitutes the *Transgressive Surface* separating the Lowstand and Transgressive Systems Tracts (Posamentier and Vail, 1988). Similar transgressive estuarine deposits have been documented in other Holocene incised valleys (e.g., Kraft and others, 1987).

As sea level continued to rise, the shoreline and estuary mouth migrated landward over the inner estuary sands and muds (Fig. 8C). Tidal currents in the estuary-mouth tidal channel scoured deeply into the older, phase 1, inner-estuary sands and muds, depositing thick tide-dominated estuary-mouth sands.

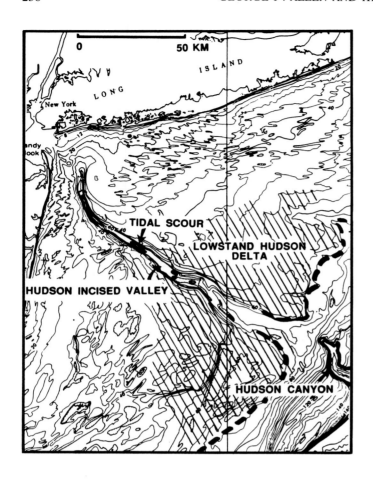

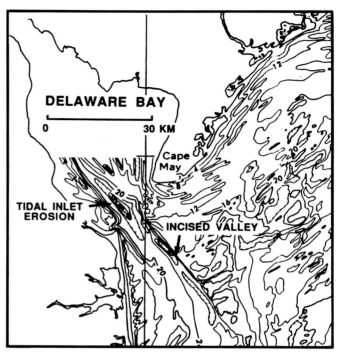

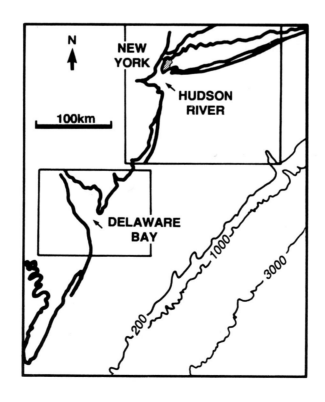

The erosional surface formed by the landward-migrating tidal-inlet channel constitutes the *tidal ravinement surface* described previously. In contrast with the overlying *wave ravinement surface,* the tidal ravinement surface forms only within the incised valley and forms an irregular surface that scours deeply into underlying inner-estuary sands and muds, and even the lowstand fluvial deposits (Fig. 8C). This surface is commonly paved by a coarse gravel lag and could be mistaken for another fluvially-incised surface and possibly a sequence boundary within the incised valley. This tidal ravinement surface and the overlying estuary-mouth sands constitute the *second phase* of the transgressive incised-valley fill and results in a typically narrow, channel-like sand deposit in the distal extremity of the transgressive valley fill (Fig. 8C). The thickness of this sand can exceed 10–15 meters and would be of excellent reservoir quality. These estuary-mouth deposits are a characteristic feature of estuaries affected by strong wave energy at their mouth, and similar sediments have been described in other tide- and wave-dominated estuarine valley fills (Kraft and others, 1987; Desmarest and Kraft, 1987; Dalrymple and others, 1992).

The *third phase* of the transgressive valley fill results from the landward migration of the shoreline and shoreface over the estuary-mouth deposits and adjacent interfluves (Fig. 8D). Wave erosion and shoreface retreat removes the upper 5–10 meters of the estuary-mouth sands and an equivalent thickness of sediments from older sequences in the interfluves. This results in formation of the well-documented *wave ravinement surface.* This surface generally is of low relief and is commonly widespread, extending over the incised valley as well as the interfluves (Fig. 8D), in contrast with the tidal ravinement surface, which is restricted to the incised valley. On the interfluves, the wave ravinement surface erodes the subaerially formed unconformity, removing any evidence of former subaerial exposure. Consequently, on interfluves in high wave-energy settings, the sequence boundary is merged with the wave ravinement surface and has the attributes of this latter surface (Fig. 8D).

The wave ravinement surface is overlain by wave- and storm-dominated, transgressive shoreface sands and thin offshore muds which constitute the deposits of phase 3. These deposits are usually thin, and in the case of the shelf adjacent to the Gironde, they form a thin sand and gravel veneer over the entire shelf (Colotte, 1985). They will eventually be capped by the *Maximum Flooding Surface* which separates the Transgressive and Highstand Systems Tracts. Figure 8D illustrates the final transgressive valley fill resulting when the shoreline has retreated over the estuary. As shown, the upper part of the phase 2 transgressive fill as well as the interfluves are truncated by wave erosion.

Factors Controlling Regional Facies Patterns

Facies partitioning and stratal geometries within wave- and tide-dominated incised valleys similar to the Gironde will be controlled by the interaction of several factors: volume of river influx, tidal range, coastal wave energy, rate of relative sea-level rise, and valley morphology. As shown by the present Gironde, during transgression most of the fluvially-supplied sediment is trapped within the inner estuary, between the bayline and the landward-retreating estuary mouth, accumulating as a landward stepping wedge of tidal sands and muds (Fig. 7). These deposits are subsequently eroded by the landward-migrating estuary-mouth tidal channel and partially replaced by thick, estuary-mouth sands. When the rise of relative sea level stops and highstand regression begins, the phase 1 sediments of the inner estuary landward of the regional shoreline and estuary-mouth tidal channel at the time of maximum flooding will be preserved and overlain by deposits of the regressive estuarine bayhead delta which are identical to the phase 1 transgressive deposits.

Different facies patterns will occur to either side of the maximum-flooding regional shoreline and estuary mouth (Fig. 9). Landward of this limit, the transgressive valley fill will be composed primarily of inner-estuary tidal sand and muds. Seaward of the maximum-flooding shoreline however, thick estuary-mouth sands predominate in the valley axis and are capped by the shoreface sands and offshore muds of phase 3 (Fig. 10). These different facies patterns on either side of the maximum-flooding regional shoreline determine a *proximal* and a *distal* paleogeographic zonation within the incised-valley fill (Fig. 10).

In the case of the Gironde incised valley, the inner estuarine deposits in the proximal part of the incised-valley system landward of the regional maximum-flooding shoreline extend about 80 kilometers inland and form a 2- to 15-km wide belt of sand and mud deposited in estuarine point bars and tidal flats. This deposit is 10 to 30 m thick and extends up to the fluvial-tidal contact at the bayline (Fig. 9).

At any time during the transgression, the longitudinal extent of the inner-estuary deposits will depend on the distance between the landward limit of tidal effects on sedimentation (i.e., the bayline in the case of the Gironde), and the mouth of the estuary. This distance is a function of the slope of the regional interfluves and the depth and slope of the incised-valley thalweg (Fig. 11). Whether or not this potential space is totally or partially filled with inner-estuary deposits will depend, however, on the ratio between the rate of relative sea-level rise and the fluvial-sediment flux.

F<small>IG</small>. 12.—Bathymetry of the continental shelf adjacent to Delaware Bay and the Hudson river (depths in meters). Note the partially-filled Pleistocene incised shelf valleys which extend from the mouth of both estuaries across the shelf. The locally deeper zones in their thalweg could represent unfilled areas or possible zones of more pronounced erosion within the retreating estuary-mouth tidal channel during periods of temporary stillstand during the transgression. Note the similarity of these deeper zones to the morphology of the tidal channel at the mouth of the present Delaware Bay estuary. The presence of a lowstand Hudson delta is conjectural and based on the cuspate-like morphology of the depth contours.

If the rate of relative sea-level rise is very rapid with respect to the fluvial-sediment influx, the incised valley will be flooded rapidly and the rate of accommodation added will overwhelm the rate at which fluvial sediment is supplied to the estuary. This would result in little sediment escaping the proximal area of the inner estuary. The same effect of restricting sedimentation to the extreme inner estuary would be achieved if the rate of fluvially-sourced sediment supply is very low. In either case, phase 1 deposits will be thin and poorly developed. Consequently, continued transgression could result in the tidal ravinement surface and estuary-mouth sands directly overlying the lowstand fluvial deposits with no intervening inner-estuary deposits.

If the ratio between relative sea-level rise and fluvial influx is low, then an aggrading estuarine coastal plain is maintained landward of the transgressing estuary mouth and shoreline. This results in the deposition of an elongate belt of inner-estuary tidal sands and muds progressively onlapping the fluvial fill at the base of the incised valley landward of the shoreline. These phase 1 deposits will be totally preserved landward of the shoreline and estuary-mouth tidal channel at the time of maximum flooding (Fig. 9).

The depth of scour of the estuary-mouth tidal channel will determine the preservation potential of the inner-estuary sands and muds of phase 1, *seaward* of the maximum-flooding shoreline, as well as the maximum thickness of the estuary-mouth sands of phase 2. This depth of incision will vary directly with tide range and coastal wave energy. As tidal range increases, a deeper tidal channel is required to accommodate the tidal prism, and the greater the coastal wave energy, the more constricted is the inlet, and the deeper the tidal currents will scour.

If the relative sea-level rise during transgression is punctuated by short periods of stillstand, deeper and more widespread erosion by a laterally migrating inlet could occur at the location where the estuary mouth remains fixed for a certain time interval. This could form zones of wider and deeper scour of the tidal ravinement surface. Such zones appear to exist in late-Quaternary incised valleys (e.g., Hudson Incised Valley, Delaware Incised Valley, etc.) on the U. S. east coast shelf (Fig. 12). This also could result in zones of locally thicker estuary-mouth sands that would be laterally continuous with shoreline sand deposits. This is possibly the situation in some of the incised valleys within the upper Cretaceous Viking Formation, Canada, as described by Pattison (1992) and Allen and Posamentier (1992).

The depth of shoreface erosion by waves will in turn determine the depth of erosion associated with the wave ravinement surface. The depth of this erosion, however, will usually be less than the maximum depth of the tidal ravinement surface so that the lower part of the estuary-mouth sand deposits should always be preserved. Consequently, the transgressive fill of an incised valley seaward of the maximum-flooding shoreline may comprise little more than the lower part of estuary-mouth tidal-channel deposits, overlain by transgressive offshore sediments (Fig. 7).

CONCLUSIONS

This study documents the facies associations and stratal architecture of an incised-valley fill in a mixed, high wave-

and tide- energy coastal setting. This type of environment is conducive to the development of thick and complex valley-fill successions, the bulk of which occurs within the transgress ive systems tract. In these settings, lowstand systems tract deposits commonly are thin and highstand systems tract deposits would be most common on the interfluves outside the valley.

The facies patterns that characterize the transgressive systems tract in this type of coastal setting are controlled by the morphology and processes of the estuary created within the incised valley as it is transgressed. The influence of waves and tides is expressed in terms of both facies partitioning and the types of stratal discontinuities that punctuate the valley fill.

The deposition of the transgressive incised-valley fill occurs in three distinct phases characterized by specific facies associations separated by regionally continuous stratigraphic discontinuities.

Phase 1—Inner-estuary Mud and Sand Point Bars and Tidal Flats.—These deposits consist of fluvially-supplied sediments which accumulate as tide-dominated, muddy point bars and tidal flats, and accumulate between the bayline and the regional shoreline. They directly overlie either lowstand fluvial deposits along the axis of the valley, or the underlying sequence below the sequence-bounding unconformity along the margins of the incised valley. Where they overlie lowstand deposits within the valley, the stratal discontinuity is a low-relief onlap surface. Geometrically, these deposits form a landward-tapering wedge that pinches out at the bayline.

Phase 2—Estuary-mouth Sands.—These deposits commonly comprise massive and relatively clean, tidal-channel and flood-tidal delta sands that are sourced from the seaward end of the estuary and are continuous with adjacent shoreface deposits of the regional shoreline. The basal contact of these deposits is a *tidal ravinement surface* that is characterized by irregular relief and is widely correlatable within the portion of the incised valley seaward of the-maximum flooding shoreline. This surface can be confused with fluvially-cut incisions that occur at the base of sequences. Consequently, this misinterpretation may lead to the erroneous conclusion that relative sea level fell, causing renewed fluvial downcutting, when in fact this surface merely subdivides the transgressive systems tract into two sub-units.

Phase 3—Shoreface Sands and Marine Muds.—These sediments overly a regional, low-relief, erosional *wave ravinement surface* and commonly comprise a relatively thin, widespread and sheet-like deposit. Locally, these sediments can be reworked by wave action subsequent to transgression to form ridges on the open shelf (Swift and others, 1972). Another important feature of incised-valley fills in high-energy wave and tide settings is the facies variations that occur to either side of the regional maximum-flooding shoreline. Landward of this paleogeographic limit, the predominant facies of the transgressive valley fill will consist of inner-estuarine tidal deposits deposited during the first phase of transgression. These proximal part of the incised-valley fill will be overlain by regressive tidal deposits of the highstand bayhead delta. In certain cases, such as in the landward extremity of the incised valley, it will be difficult to locate the maximum flooding surface since it will occur between similar transgressive and regressive tidal-estuarine point-bar deposits.

Seaward of the maximum-flooding shoreline, in the distal zone of the incised valley, the inner-estuary deposits of phase one will be partially eroded by the tidal ravinement surface and overlain by thick, longitudinally continuous, estuary-mouth tidal-inlet sands. These will form excellent reservoir prospects and will be overlain by the shoreface sands and marine muds of phase 3. These marine muds can form a regional seal over the estuary-mouth and shoreface sands.

ACKNOWLEDGMENTS

We wish to express our appreciation to P. Castaing, A. Feral and G. Truilhe for having furnished us with abundant data on the Gironde and for the many stimulating discussions with them on the sedimentology of the Gironde estuary. We would also like to acknowledge the helpful suggestions of the reviewers of this paper, R. Boyd, R. Dalrymple, G. Ashley, and P. Roy. Permission from TOTAL S. A. Centre Scientifique et Technique and ARCO Exploration and Production Technology to publish this paper is also acknowledged.

REFERENCES

ALLEN, G. P., 1991, Sedimentary processes and facies in the Gironde estuary; a Recent model for macrotidal estuarine systems, *in* Smith, D. G., Reinson, G. E., Zaitlin, B. A., and Rahmani, R. A., eds., Clastic Tidal Sedimentology: Calgary, Canadian Society of Petroleum Geologists Memoir 16, p. 29–40.

ALLEN, G. P., CASTAING, P., FERAL, A., KLINGEBIEL, A., AND VIGNEAUX, M., 1970, Contribution à l'étude des faciès de comblement et interprétation paléogéographique de l'évolution des milieux sédimentaires récents et actuels de l'estuaire de la Gironde: Bulletin de l'Institut de Géologie du Bassin d'Aquitaine, v. 8, p. 99–155.

ALLEN, G. P., SALOMON, J.C., DUPENHOAT, C., AND DE GRANDPRE, C., 1980; Effects of tides on mixing and suspended sediment transport in macrotidal estuaries: Sedimentary Geology, v. 26, p. 62–80.

ALLEN, G. P., SAUZAY, G., CASTAING, P., AND JOUANNEAU, J. M., 1976, Transport and deposition of suspended sediment in the Gironde estuary, France, *in* Wiley, M., ed., Estuarine Processes: New York, Academic Press, p. 63–81.

ALLEN, G. P., AND TRUILHE, G., 1987, Stratigraphic and facies model of a transgressive estuarine valley fill in the Gironde estuary (France), *in* James, D. P., and Leckie, D. A., eds., Sequences, Stratigraphy, Sedimentology, Surface and Subsurface: Calgary, Canadian Society of Petroleum Geologists Memoir 15, p. 575.

ALLEN, G. P., AND POSAMENTIER H. W., 1991, Facies and stratal patterns in incised valley complexes: examples from the Recent Gironde Estuary (France), and the Cretaceous Viking Formation (Canada) (abs.): American Association of Petroleum Geologists Annual Convention, Dallas, TX, April 7–10, 1991, American Society of Petroleum geologists Bulletin, v. 75, p. 534.

ALLEN, G. P., AND POSAMENTIER, H. W., 1992, On the origin and subsequent modification of incised valleys: American Association of Petroleum Geologists Annual Convention, Calgary, Canada, July 20–24, Abstracts with Programs, p. 70.

ALLEN, G. P., AND POSAMENTIER H. W., 1993, Sequence stratigraphy and facies model of an incised valley fill: the Gironde estuary, France, Journal of Sedimentary Petrology, v. 63, p. 378–392.

ASHLEY, G. M., WELLNER, R. M., ESKER, D., AND SHERIDAN, R. E., 1991, Clastic sequences developed during late Quaternary glacio-eustatic sea-level fluctuations on a passive margin: Example from the inner continental shelf near Barnegat Inlet, New Jersey: Geological Survey of America Bulletin, v. 103, p. 1607–1621.

ASSOR, R., 1972, Interpretation paléogéographique des terrains sédimentaires de la presqu'île du Médoc: Unpublished Thèse de Doctorat 3ème Cycle, Université de Bordeaux I, no. 146, Bordeaux, 258 p.

CASTAING, P., 1981, Le transfer à l'océan des suspensions estuariennes; cas de la Gironde: Unpublished Thèse Doctorat ès Sciences, Université de Bordeaux I, no. 701, Bordeaux, 530 p.

CASTAING, P., AND ALLEN, G. P., 1981, Mechanisms controlling seaward escape of suspended sediment from the Gironde, a macrotidal estuary in France: Marine Geology, v. 40, p. 101–118.

COLLOTTE, P., 1985, Le plateau central nord-Aquitain: characterisation morpho-sédimentaire et interpretation dynamique des dépôts Holocenes: Unpublished Thèse de Doctorat d' Océanologie, Université de Bordeaux I, no. 2069, Bordeaux, 277 p.

DALRYMPLE, R. W., ZAITLIN, B. A., AND BOYD, R., 1992, Estuarine facies models: conceptual basis and stratigraphic basis: Journal of Sedimentary Petrology, v. 62, p. 1130–1146.

DEMAREST, J. M., AND KRAFT, J. C., 1987, Stratigraphic record of Quaternary sea levels: implications for more ancient strata, *in* Nummedal, D., Pilkey, O. H., and Howard, J. D., eds., Sea-level Fluctuations and Coastal Evolution: Tulsa, Society of Economic Paleontologists and Mineralogists Special Publication 41, p. 223–239.

FABRE, A., 1939, Les terrains de revetement du Médoc: Bordeaux, Imprimerie E. Drouillard, 344 p.

FERAL, A., 1970, Interprétation sédimentologique et paléogéographique des formations alluviales de l'estuaire de la Gironde et de ses dépendances marines: Thèse de Doctorat 3ème cycle, Faculté des Sciences, Université de Bordeaux, no. 806, Bordeaux, 158 p.

HARLEMAN, M., AND IPPEN, A. T., 1969, Salinity intrusion effects in estuary shoaling: Proceedings of the American Society of Civil Engineers, Journal of the Hydraulics Division, v. 25, p. 9–27.

HAYES, M. O., 1975, Morphology of sand accumulation in estuaries: an introduction to the symposium, *in* Cronin, L. E., ed., Estuarine Research, Vol. II: New York, Academic Press, p. 3–22.

KRAFT, J. C., CHRZASTOWSKI, M. J., BELKNAP, D. F., TOSCANO, M. A., AND FLETCHER, C. H., 1987, The transgressive barrier-lagoon coast of Delaware: morphostratigraphy, sedimentary sequences and responses to relative rise in sea level, *in* Nummedal, D., Pilkey, O., and Howard, J., eds., Sea-level Fluctuation and Coastal Evolution: Tulsa, Society of Economic Paleontologists and Mineralogists, Special Publication 41, p. 129–143.

MIGNIOT, C., 1971, L'évolution de la Gironde au cours des temps: Bulletin de l'Institut de Géologie du Bassin d'Aquitaine, v. 11, p. 221–281.

NICHOLS, M. M., AND BIGGS, R. B., 1985, Estuaries, *in* Davis, R. A., ed., Coastal Sedimentary Environments (2nd ed.): New York, Springer-Verlag, p. 77–186.

PATTISON, S. A. J., 1992, Facies relationships and stacking patterns of valley fill deposits in the Viking formation, central Alberta: example of tripartite facies zonations: American Association of Petroleum Geologists Annual Convention, Calgary, Canada, June 21–24, Abstracts with Programs, p. 101–102.

POSAMENTIER, H. W., AND VAIL, P. R., 1988, Eustatic controls on clastic deposition II—sequence and systems tract models, *in* Wilgus, C. K., Hastings, B. S., Kendall, C. G. St. C., Posamentier, H. W., Ross, C. A., and Van Wagoner, J. C., eds., Sea-level Change- An Integrated Approach: Tulsa, Society of Economic Paleontologists and Mineralogists, Special Publication 42, p. 125–154.

POSAMENTIER, H. W., JERVEY, M. T., AND VAIL, P. R., 1988, Eustatic controls on clastic deposition I—conceptual framework, *in* Wilgus, C. K., Hastings, B. S., Kendall, C. G. St. C., Posamentier, H. W., Ross, C. A., and Van Wagoner, J. C., eds., Sea-level Change- An Integrated Approach: Tulsa, Society of Economic Paleontologists and Miberalgists, Special Publication 42, p. 110–124.

RAHMANI, R. A., 1988, Estuarine tidal channel and nearshore sedimentation of a late Cretaceous epicontinental sea, Drumheller, Alberta Canada, *in* de Boer, P. L., Van Gelder, A., and Nio, S. D., eds., Tide-influenced Sedimentary Environments and Facies: Boston, D. Riedel Publishing Company, p. 433–481.

RAHMANI, R. A., 1989, Cretaceous tidal estuarine and deltaic deposits, Drumheller, Alberta: Calgary, Canadian Society of Petroleum Geologists, Second International Research Symposium on Clastic Tidal Deposits, Field Trip Guide Book, 55 p.

REINSON, G. E., CLARK, J. E., AND FOSCOLOS, A. E., 1988, Reservoir geology of Crystal Viking Field, Lower Cretaceous estuarine tidal channel-bay complex, south-central, Alberta: American Association of Petroleum Geologists Bulletin, v. 72, p. 1270–1294.

SMITH, D. G., 1988, Modern point bar deposits analogous to the Athabasca oil sands, Alberta, Canada, *in* Boer, P. L., van Gelder, A., and Nio, S. D., eds. Tide-Influenced Sedimentary Environments and Facies: Dordrecht, D. Reidel Publishing Company, 530 p.

SWIFT, D. J. P., 1968, Coastal erosion and transgressive stratigraphy: Journal of Geology, v. 76, p. 444–456.

SWIFT, D. J. P, KOFOED, J. W., SAULSBURY, F. P., AND SEARS, P., 1972, Holocene evolution of the shelf surface, central and southern Atlantic shelf of North America, *in* Swift, D. J. P., Duane, D. B., and Pilkey, O. H., eds., Shelf Sediment Transport: Process and Pattern: Stroudsbourg, Dowden, Hutchinson and Ross, p. 499–574.

WRIGHT, L. D., 1977, Sediment transport and deposition at river mouths, a synthesis: Bulletin of the Geological Society of America, v. 88, p. 857–868.

ZAITLAN, B. A., AND SCHULTZ, B. C., 1990, Wave-influenced estuarine sand body, Senlac heavy oil pool, Saskatchewan, Canada, *in* Barwis, J. H., McPherson, J. G., and Studlick R. J., eds., Sandstone Petroleum Reservoirs: New York, Springer-Verlag, p. 363–387.

HOLOCENE ESTUARY EVOLUTION—STRATIGRAPHIC STUDIES FROM SOUTHEASTERN AUSTRALIA

PETER S. ROY

Geological Survey of New South Wales, Department of Mineral Resources, c/o Department of Geography, The University of Sydney, New South Wales 2006 Australia

ABSTRACT: Stratigraphies and radiocarbon age structures of four estuaries in SE Australia are described. Two different estuary types, wave-dominated barrier estuaries and more tidally-influenced drowned valley estuaries, are represented, each with examples showing contrasting river catchments and sediment discharges that control the rate the estuaries infill with sediment. Primary differences that arise from geological inheritance and mainly affect estuary-mouth conditions were established on this coast at the end of the postglacial marine transgression once sea levels stabilised about 6.5 ka ago. Since then, up to 50 m of Holocene sediments have been deposited in some estuaries. Central basin muds are most extensive in barrier estuaries behind bay barriers with constricted tidal inlets and have accumulated at rates ranging from 0.1 to 15.0 mm yr^{-1}, an upper limit imposed by rising sea level. Barrier estuaries experience most rapid environmental changes at mature stages of development as terrestrial flood plains spread seawards over shallow estuarine basins. Surprisingly, their flood-tide delta deposits seem to have grown little under stillstand conditions. In contrast, drowned-valley estuaries with open mouths and full tidal ranges contain large tidal-delta sand bodies that have grown landwards at rates of 1–4 m yr^{-1} during both rising sea-level and highstand conditions. As these estuaries approach maturity they discharge fine sediment to the sea thus retarding subsequent infilling. Estuaries with good flushing characteristics at their mouths, therefore, experience less radical environmental fluctuations due to both natural and man-induced changes than do estuaries with impeded tidal exchange.

INTRODUCTION

This paper explores the rate and nature of physical changes in SE Australian estuaries from a geological standpoint by documenting sedimentation patterns in various environments in estuaries of different types. Throughout their evolution, estuaries have experienced rapid environmental changes, and their inherent variability is reflected by sharp changes in lithologies over short distances and by estuarine life forms which have evolved a greater resilience to fluctuating natural conditions (salinity, water temperature, etc.) than most other communities. Thus, in evaluating the recent impact of man on estuarine ecosystems, the baseline concept of a pristine, natural estuary must incorporate the idea of continuing change.

The evolution of present-day estuaries in SE Australia can be traced back to the beginning of the Holocene epoch when rising sea level began drowning this bedrock-controlled coast. Here, embayments of various sizes are exposed to a relatively high-energy ocean wave climate and tidal ranges of less than 2 m (Roy and others 1980; Roy and Thom 1981; Chapman and others 1982). The continental shelf is narrow (less than 60 km wide), and 70 percent of it is deeper than 50 m: It is mostly sand-covered and, unlike areas with large tidal ranges and muddy inner shelves (e.g., NW Australia, Wright and others 1973), the microtidal embayments in New South Wales (NSW) are dominated by wave-induced sand movements on the open coast. The climate is temperate with an erratic rainfall pattern that is not strongly seasonal. Thus, estuaries here do not experience the marked annual cycle of salinity and water level change typical of areas with a Mediterranean climate as is the case in SW Australia (Hodgkin, 1978; Hesp, 1984). NSW coastal rivers have perennial flow interspersed with occasional floods. With headwaters in the eastern highlands less than 150 km inland and catchments areas less than 50,000 km^2, their sediment discharge is small by world standards. This, together with the deep, high-energy shelf, accounts for the absence of protruding fluvial deltas at the coast (Roy and others 1980; Roy and Thom, 1981), although somewhat subdued ebb tide deltas comprising simple river mouth bars do occur at the mouths of the larger rivers (Floyd and Druery, 1976).

Superimposed on this physical setting is a postglacial sea-level history which for eastern Australia is characterised by a period of rapid sea-level rise (the postglacial marine transgression-PMT) prior to 6.5 ka, followed by a stillstand of the sea (Thom and Chappell, 1975; Thom and Roy, 1983). With few exceptions, the Holocene estuaries occur in drowned valleys incised into bedrock and Pleistocene valley fill. Inundation commenced at the present coast 9–10 ka and, because of the margins' tectonic stability (Bryant and others, 1988), it terminated when sea level stabilized. Present-day, estuarine water bodies are located behind deposits of marine sand-barriers and tidal deltas—in the mouths of the drowned valleys. These sand deposits are intersected by inlet channels which, unlike the more mobile tidal inlets of barrier islands on coastal-plain coasts (e.g., United States East Coast: Boothroyd, 1978; Kraft, 1978), became fixed against headlands.

Previous geological investigations of estuaries in SE Australia have led to the development of a classification in which three basic estuary types evolve along characteristic pathways as they infill with sediment (Roy, 1984). Differences, firstly in estuary types and secondly in rates of infilling, account for the diversity of present day estuaries along this coast. The primary character of valley morphology and catchment size was inherited in early Holocene time at the end of the PMT when large subaqueous tidal delta sand bodies accumulated in the mouths of deep, **drowned-valley estuaries**; coastal sand barriers intersected by narrow, tidal-entrance channels isolated **barrier estuaries** and, in valleys with very small rivers, barriers with ephemeral inlets impounded **saline coastal lagoons** (Roy, 1984). Since sea level stabilised, the estuaries have continued to infill with immature fluvial sand and mud from the land and with quartzose marine sand from the sea. In addition, biogenic material has been produced internally. The degree to which depositional environments and lithofacies are developed varies between the different estuary types and

Incised-valley Systems: Origin and Sedimentary Sequences, SEPM Special Publication No. 51

also according to their stage of infilling (i.e., their maturity) (Roy, 1984, Table 1).

While being biologically distinctive, saline coastal lagoons on this coast are geologically similar to barrier estuaries and are not discussed further here. Differences between drowned-valley and barrier estuaries on this coast can be largely attributed to inherited geological properties of the local rock types. Drowned-valley estuaries are found in central NSW where the massive Hawkesbury Sandstone of the Permo-Triassic Sydney Basin forms prominent cliffs at the coast and has been eroded by rivers into particularly steep sided and deep valleys. Barrier estuaries, on the other hand, are more widespread and typically occupy paleo-valleys that are less rugged and deeply incised. The valleys are occupied by wave-formed barrier sand bodies at the coast, and there is a sharp transition from open marine to protected estuarine conditions at the estuary mouth. In contrast, the mouths of drowned-valley estuaries are transitional, bay environments with shoaling beds a kilometre or more in width that reduce incident wave energy by refraction and friction. As a result, energy conditions away from the bay area in the estuary itself tend to be dominated by tidal processes most of the time. Thus barrier estuaries originate in wave-dominated settings but drowned-valley estuaries, although located on a microtidal coast, are more strongly influenced by tidal processes.

METHODS

The evolutionary reconstructions described below are based on three principal methods: lithofacies analysis, seismic stratigraphy, and radiocarbon dating. Previous estuary studies have related modern sediment types to specific estuary sub-environments and dynamic conditions (e.g., Roy, 1980; Roy and Peat 1975, 1976; Roy and Crawford, 1981). Lithologies of the sands and their relationships to source rocks were determined by microscopic examination, and typical sedimentary structures were described by Nichol (1991) from a range of estuary environments in southern NSW. The geometry of the estuary fill has in most cases been mapped from high-resolution, seismic reflection profiling followed by reverse-circulation drilling and vibrocoring to obtain sediment samples. Drilling to depths of up to 60 m delineates estuarine deposits of Pleistocene age and shows that estuarine conditions have recurred on this coast throughout the late Quaternary (sub-bottom depths quoted in the report are referenced to approximate mean sea level).

Radiocarbon dating of fragmented shells and wood from drill hole and vibrocore samples has been used extensively to establish Holocene chronologies in the four estuaries discussed here, but in few cases can the material be considered to be truly insitu. Of the 140 samples analysed, the most reliable dates are on thin-walled shell species such as *Notospisula trigonella* from the mud basin facies. In tidal and fluvial delta sands, the biogenic material clearly has been reworked, and its radiometric age predates the time of deposition of the sediments (Roy 1991). Time lags of up to 1.5 ka occur in some environments due to a combination of mechanisms: reworking, transportation, and mixing with relict material. Attempts at using mixing models to correct

for these effects have proved of limited success (Nielson and Roy, 1981). Consequently, specific age relationships have not been determined in a rigorous manner between individual samples, but rather, large numbers of dates have been used to establish general trends and patterns.

DEPOSITIONAL ENVIRONMENTS AND LITHOFACIES

Although estuarine environments are extremely diverse, they can be grouped into three main categories: fluvial-estuarine river delta, central mud basin, and marine-dominated estuary mouth (Roy, 1984; Nichol, 1991; Dalrymple and others, 1992). The last category is associated with coastal sand barriers (dune, beach, nearshore, and backbarrier deposits) which, while not strictly estuarine environments, play an important role in estuary evolution (Roy and others, 1980). The most complex association of sub-environments, sediment types, and ecological habitats are found within **fluvial-estuarine delta** environments where rivers and streams enter microtidal to almost non-tidal, estuarine water bodies and conditions range from subaqueous (saline to brackish) through intertidal to terrestrial. Subenvironments include river and distributary channel beds, mid-channel shoals and delta mouth bars, levee banks and crevasse splays, delta top platforms and delta-front slopes, inter-distributary bays, freshwater and brackish swamps, and flood plains. Intertidal areas are often limited by the small tidal ranges (c. 5–15 cm) in barrier estuaries (Roy, 1984). They are colonised by mangrove and salt-marsh communities, although salt-marsh peats, used extensively in other parts of the world to date relative sea-level change, are poorly developed in NSW. Subtidal deposits are often shelly and are covered by seagrasses, in shallow areas. The composition of the sediments, which typically comprise immature, lithic-rich gravel, sand and mud in poorly sorted admixtures and with variable amounts of organics, is determined by the bedrock lithologies and weathering characteristics of the local catchments. The sediments occur in two stratigraphic settings: transgressive and regressive. Sandy transgressive deposits were laid down in back-stepping deltas during early Holocene deposition as the rising sea inundated the valleys. These deposits are now blanketed by estuarine muds which, depending on the maturity of the estuary, may be overlain in turn by regressive channel, delta, and overbank deposits that have built seaward during the stillstand.

Central mud basins are uniform, low-energy environments in the deeper or quieter parts of estuaries where fine river sediment, supplied mainly during floods, settles from suspension; they are the estuarine equivalents of pro-delta lithofacies. The resulting deposits are dark-grey to black muds, rich in estuarine shells, foraminifera, and organic material. They are extensively bioturbated by polychaetes, and fecal pellets often make up a large proportion of the sediment; virtually all small-scale primary sedimentary structures are destroyed (Nichol, 1991). Physical conditions are essentially placid with slow, wind-induced circulations in deeper areas and wave-stirring in water shallower than about 2m. Except for scattered biohermal shell banks (Peat and Roy, 1975) and small mounds produced by burrowing organisms, the mud surface is planar. Sandy shoreline facies around the estuary sides are the product of wave reworking and shoreline erosion and grade into the basin muds. Holocene muds experience considerable compaction, especially when loaded with thick, transgressive sand deposits, and pre-Holocene muds that have been exposed to sub-areal weathering are oxidised and semi-lithified with zones of iron oxide concretions produced by soil forming processes.

Marine-dominated estuary-mouth environments contain shelly quartzose (shelf) sands deposited by waves and tidal currents. During the PMT, sand on the continental shelf was most likely reworked and laid down in transgressive sheets as the rising sea overwashed the barrier surfaces and carried sand into deepening estuary mouths (Thom, 1984; Roy and others, 1994). The transgressive sand sheets onlap or interdigitate with muddy estuarine sediments to landward; in shallow valleys (c. <30 m deep), they usually lie directly on the pre-Holocene substrate, but in deeper valleys where estuarine conditions were initiated well seawards of the present coast, they overlie Holocene estuarine muds. Shelf sands that continued to accumulate in the estuary mouths after sea level stabilised form characteristic flood-tide deltas. In barrier estuaries, they occur as lobes at the landward ends of active tidal channels, but they reach their maximum development in drowned-valley estuaries, where deep mud basin environments provide the tidal deltas with accommodation space to prograde by slip-face accretion. Modern environments in barrier estuaries include broad, subtidal sand flats, often seagrass covered and muddy, intersected by tidal channels with shell lags on their beds and bordered by storm or dune ridges elevated above normal water levels. In drowned-valley estuaries, however, the delta ramp comprises a relatively shallow, landward-shoaling bay bed composed of clean sand that experiences reworking by ocean storm waves. It rises to a shallow sill area, often with well-developed tidal channels and sand banks; seagrass beds occur in protected sites (Bryant, 1980).

ESTUARINE STRATIGRAPHIES: CASE STUDIES

In this section, rates of physical change are documented for individual examples from central NSW of drowned-valley estuaries and barrier estuaries that have infilled with sediment at different rates. Examples of the former are the Hawkesbury River and Port Hacking; barrier estuaries are represented by the Shoalhaven delta and Lake Macquarie. Their catchments are compared in Figure 1 and their estuarine water bodies and the adjacent Quaternary coastal deposits are shown in Figure 2. Port Hacking and Lake Macquarie with small river inflows contrast sharply with the Hawkesbury estuary and the Shoalhaven delta, which are fed by much larger river systems.

Port Hacking

The Hacking estuary occupies a narrow, steep-sided, bedrock valley typical of the drainage systems incised into massive sandstones of the Sydney Basin. The inflowing streams are small; the largest is the Hacking River (Fig. 3). Open-ocean tidal ranges extend throughout the estuary which is fully saline except for short periods during floods when

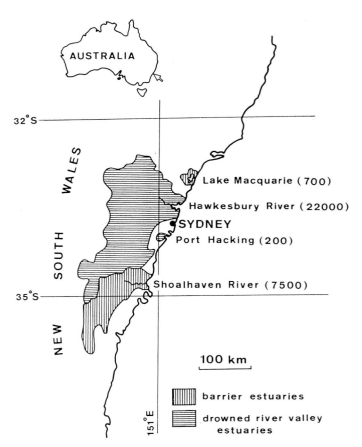

FIG. 1.—Location map showing river catchments of estuaries discussed in text. Numbers in brackets are catchment areas in km^2.

stratified conditions develop (Godfrey and Parslow, 1976). Bate Bay, in the drowned-valley mouth, is a marine-dominated, semi-enclosed bay environment with water depths of 5–10 m exposed to ocean waves. The bed of Port Hacking shoals landwards into a central zone characterised by inter-tidal and shallow, sub-tidal sand flats intersected by tidal channels 2–3 m deep. Basins up to 20 m deep occur in the upper estuary and its tributary arms. Small fluvial deltas have formed in the heads of the drowned valleys with the largest at the mouth of the Hacking River.

The depositional environments and simplified stratigraphy of the Hacking estuary are shown in Figure 3. At the estuary mouth where the bedrock valley is 90 m deep (Albani and others, 1978), Holocene sediments extend to −50 m and overlie eroded and weathered remnants of Pleistocene deposits. Lithofacies are dominated by estuary-mouth sands that form a large, flood-tide delta sand body up to 40 m thick. It occupies about 60 percent of the estuary including the mouths of some tributary bays (Fig. 3), and on its surface small barrier beaches have formed in embayments along the estuary's southern shoreline. Seismic profiling shows steep (15–25°), landward-dipping reflectors over the inner half of the sand body that parallel the depositional slope on active delta fronts. Clean sands with minor shell (<5 percent) and low angle bedding occur in its seaward

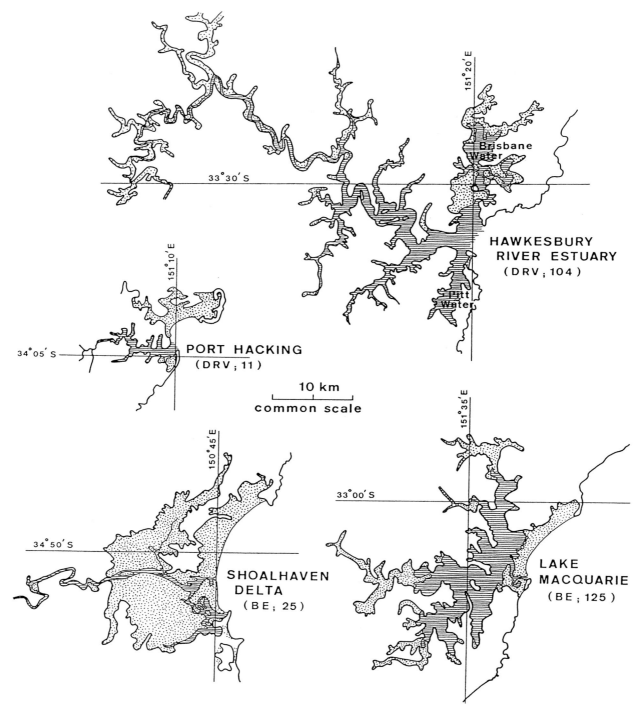

Fig. 2.—Quaternary sediments (stippled) and water bodies (hatched) of estuaries discussed in text compared at a common scale. Estuary type and water area in km² are shown in brackets. (DRV = drowned-river valley estuary; BE = barrier estuary).

part; the sands become more calcareous (up to 50 percent) in a landward direction and more muddy with depth (Nielsen and Roy, 1981; Thom and others, 1986).

Clean fluvial sands occur in the channels of inflowing streams and, at the mouth of the Hacking River, a shallow, sub-tidal delta lobe extends about 1.0 km into the estuary (Fig. 3). The delta lobe, which is approximately 10 m thick (the base was not penetrated by coring), is composed of sands, in part muddy, with layers of organic detritus of terrestrial origin. In the central basin between the tidal and fluvial deltas, shelly, organic-rich estuarine muds reach thicknesses of 10–20 m. These extend beneath both of the

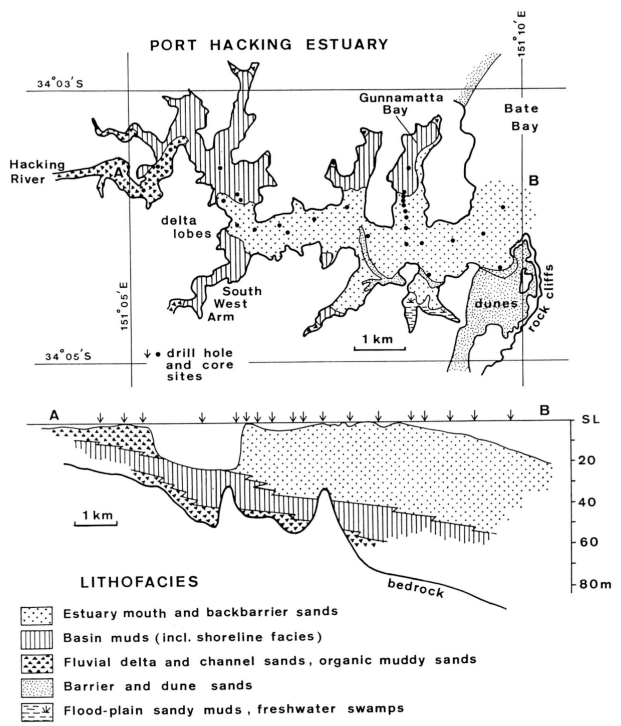

FIG. 3.—Port Hacking estuary showing simplified lithofacies in plan (A) and axial section (B).

highstand, delta sand bodies and overlie transgressive fluvial sands in the axis of the palaeo-valley (Fig. 3).

In Figure 4C, radiocarbon dates on comminuted, calcareous material from the estuary-mouth sand body have been used to construct time lines and are plotted against cumulative sediment volumes determined from seismic profiling and drilling. These data confirm a landward-building mode of deposition for tidal deltaic sediments younger than about 8 ka, but the low-shell sand and gently dipping seismic reflectors in the seaward part of the sand body suggest a somewhat different, aggradational mode of emplacement during the PMT. A regression line drawn through the data

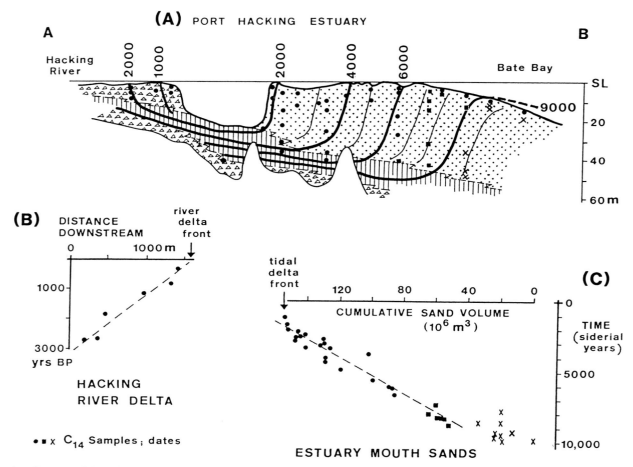

FIG. 4.—Constructed time lines based on radiocarbon dates superimposed on the stratigraphic section in the axis of Port Hacking estuary (A). Time lines in the tidal-delta sand body are displaced landwards due to contamination with old reworked shell (see text). Age/distance and age/ volume plots show rates of accretion of the fluvial (B) and tidal deltas (C) respectively. Dates shown by solid circles and squares have been calibrated to sidereal years (Clark, 1975); crosses indicate uncalibrated dates. Dates for the samples in the tidal delta are reported in Nielsen and Roy (1981).

points in Figure 4C indicates a constant rate of deposition at the delta front of about 16,000 m^3 yr^{-1} since mid Holocene time. Similar, although slightly higher, sediment transport rates have been determined from sand tracing experiments and calculations based on bed-form measurement (c. 20,000 m^3 yr^{-1}; B. Druery, pers. commun., 1988). These dating results suggest that, throughout the stillstand, the delta front advanced about 0.5 m yr^{-1} and increased its surface area by about 500 m^2 yr^{-1} although short-term measurements on fixed bed markers located at the terminus of the flood tide channel document vertical and horizontal accretion on the delta front of 1.27 and 2.82 m yr^{-1} respectively. In Gunnamatta Bay, a tributary arm on the northern side of the estuary (Fig. 3), radiocarbon dates indicate a much slower rate of sand supply (c. 1,500 m^3 yr^{-1}). Calibrated ages ranging from 700 to 1400 years BP on four surface samples from the actively prograding delta fronts in the main estuary and Southwest Arm confirm Nielsen and Roy's (1981) contention that the dates in Figure 4C have been age-shifted (i.e., are older than the enclosing sediment) due to the inclusion of old shell reworked from further seaward. An attempt to correct for this contamination factor was made

by Nielsen and Roy (1981), but no adjustments to the C$_{14}$ dates have been included in Figure 4.

Dates on wood fragments from the Hacking River delta, when plotted against distance downstream (Fig. 4B), show that the delta front has prograded about 1,500 m horizontally (c. 0.5 m yr^{-1}) over the last 2.7 ka. The wood is transported and the C$_{14}$ ages are somewhat older than the enclosing sediment, but the catchment is small and steep sided, so the residence time for the organics is not thought to be large. Sediment transport rates at the river mouth are not precisely known but are clearly only a fraction (<10 percent) of those in the estuary mouth.

Less data exists to document accumulation rates in the mud basins. Just upstream from the main delta front, 18 m of mud has accumulated since about 9,000 years BP at an average rate of 2.0 mm yr^{-1}. In Gunnamatta Bay rates range from 1.2 to 2.9 mm yr^{-1} in two drill holes.

Hawkesbury River

The Hawkesbury River is the largest drowned valley estuary on the east coast and is characterised by a sinuous, deeply-incised, bedrock valley extending about 50 km inland to its tidal limit (Fig. 5). Except at its mouth, the sediments are fluvial-deltaic in character with channel deposits predominating; flood plains and typical delta morphologies are poorly developed in the estuarine reach because of the narrow valley (Fig. 2). Besides occasional river floods, the estuary experiences moderately strong spring tidal flows of 0.5–1.0 m sec^{-1} (Dyson and Druery, 1985). Its lower reaches, which are the subject of the following discussion, contain drowned tributary valleys that are infilled to varying degrees depending on the sizes of their individual catchments (Roy, 1983). Broken Bay at the river mouth is a marine-dominated bay environment similar in many respects to Bate Bay at the mouth of the Hacking estuary. Its landward shoaling bed ranges from 20 m to less than 10 m deep and is exposed to refracted open-ocean waves. The Woy Woy beachridge plain, at the mouth of the Brisbane Water valley (Fig. 5), forms the northern shoreline of the Bay (Thom and others, 1978; Roy and others, 1980; Roy, 1983). Quaternary sediments and radiocarbon dates in Broken Bay and the Lower Hawkesbury estuary are described in Roy (1983); Figure 5 shows the location of drill holes in the lower estuary and on the Woy Woy beachridge plain. Additional data includes seismic reflection profiling in the lower estuary and drilling at bridge and pipeline crossing sites further upstream. Tidal-delta sands in the estuary mouth extend upstream for a distance of 8 km in the subsurface (but, because of blanketing by fluvial sediments, their surface extent is somewhat less, Fig. 5B). Muds principally occur in deep basins in the tributary valleys; in the axis of the main river channel, muds grade laterally into more sandy deposits forming marginal shoals and sub-aqueous point bars. Fluvial channel sands are coarse and gravelly above the tidal reach and become increasingly muddy and finer grained in a downstream direction (Neville, 1976; A. Jones, pers. commun., 1979). Just inside the estuary mouth they intermix with marine sands on the tidal delta surface and form a surficial mixed layer on the bed of northern Broken Bay (Fig. 5B). The bedrock valley of the Hawkesbury River is 125 m deep at its present mouth (Albani and Johnson, 1974). In it, Holocene sediments occur to about −60 m and overlie weathered Pleistocene deposits (Roy, 1983). Figure 5B shows a 30-m thick estuarine mud sequence overlying transgressive, fluvial sands at −50 to −60 m. A tidal-delta sand body onlaps the muds; it ranges from 30 m thick at the estuary mouth to less than 20 m at its inner edge, and seismic records in Broken Bay show steep, landward-dipping reflectors. Clean, shelly sands occur in its upper and outer part and become finer and more muddy downwards and in a landward direction. Its inner margin is overlain by sandy fluvial sediments less than 5 m thick which, further upstream, reach thicknesses of 10–15 m and grade into estuarine muds (Fig. 5B). Detailed coring and drilling in the channel 30 km upstream at a pipeline crossing (Dames and Moore, 1979, unpublished data) encountered complex interbedded sands and muds rich in organics and shells. A similar juxtaposition of rippled sand and cohesive mud characterises the present channel bed at this site and elsewhere in the central estuary upstream of the bridge in Figure 5.

Radiocarbon dates on shell and charcoal from scattered drill hole samples along the axis of the main estuary are shown in Figure 6. This time/depth plot documents mud sedimentation rates of 10–15 mm yr^{-1} between 10 ka and 8 ka BP that parallel the postglacial, sea-level rise over the same period. The transition from mud to sandy sediment at -21 m just upstream of the tidal delta front marks the beginning of fluvial-deltaic sedimentation in the lower estuary at about 8 ka BP. Tidal-delta growth prior to this time was extremely rapid although dates at the base of the sand body are undoubtedly age-shifted due to the inclusion of transported (old) shell. A radiocarbon date on *in situ* shells from the base of the fluvial sediments onlapping the delta's inner surface provide a minimum age of about 3.4 ka on tidal-delta growth in the main estuary. Here, delta-front accretion terminated once the mud basin infilled level with the tidal-delta surface (c. −14 m), which, from the sedimentation curve in Figure 6, was probably achieved around 7 ka BP. In the mouth of Pitt Water, however, the tidal delta was in place by 7 ka BP, but the delta front is still slowly accreting into the deep, Pitt Water basin (Roy, 1983). In the last 3 ka, up to 5 m of fine, fluvial-muddy sand has aggraded on the inner, tidal-delta surface in the main estuary. Thirty kilometres further upstream, a similar build-up (c. 5 m) of somewhat coarser sand and mud has occurred on the channel bed over the same time period (Dames and Moore, 1979, unpublished data). These late Holocene rates of upward accretion average 1–2 mm yr^{-1} but undoubtedly include numerous erosional events; they are almost an order of magnitude slower than during the PMT.

Contrasting styles of estuary evolution are illustrated on either side of Broken Bay; Brisbane Water on its northern side is a barrier estuary with tidal exchange restricted by a narrow entrance channel; Pitt Water to the south of Broken Bay is a drowned-valley-type estuary with an open mouth and a full tidal range (Fig. 5A). Sediment supplies to these sub-basins are similar, but their exposure to open-ocean waves which mainly come from the southeast differs markedly. This factor together with the shallow Pleistocene substrate is responsible for barrier building by waves in the south-facing mouth of the Brisbane Water valley but not in the more protected and deeper mouth of Pitt Water where tidal currents are a more important sand transporting agent (Roy, 1984). In northern Broken Bay, beach ridge progradation was initiated once sea level stabilised with sand reworked from the tidal delta surface (Fig. 6C). Radiocarbon dating of drill hole samples from the transect shown in Figure 5 suggest that 85 percent of the barrier formed 7–4 ka BP (Thom and others, 1981) (Fig. 6C). Subsequent growth was slower, and despite C$_{14}$ ages in excess of 1.3 ka near the beach, the possibility of present-day barrier progradation cannot be ruled out (Roy, 1983).

Lake Macquarie

Lake Macquarie is a barrier estuary 125 km^2 in area occupying a number of coalescing bedrock valleys with small river catchments (Fig. 1). The present estuary basin, located behind a coastal sand complex, ranges from 5 to 11 m deep and is one of the deepest estuaries of its type in

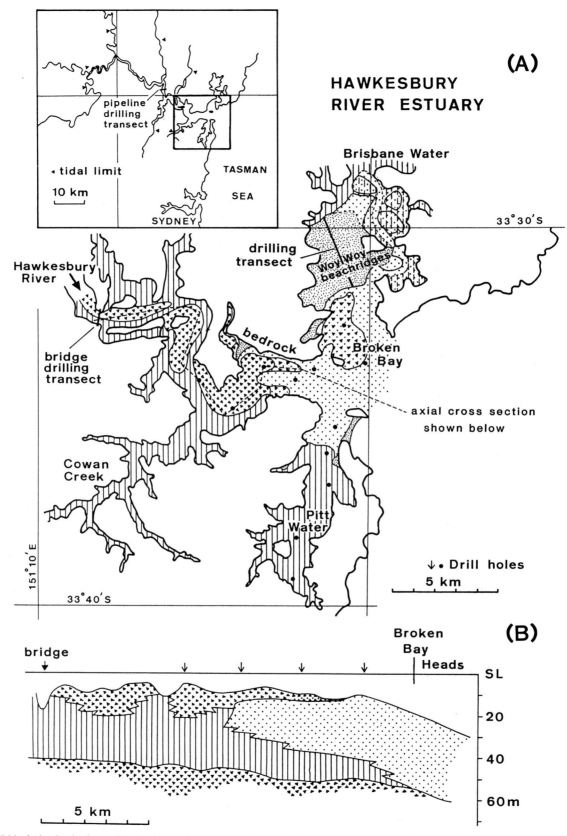

FIG. 5.—Lithofacies in the lower Hawkesbury River, Broken Bay, Pitt Water and the mouth of Brisbane Water (A). A dashed line shows the position of the stratigraphic section (B) in the main estuary (lithofacies symbols as shown in Fig. 3).

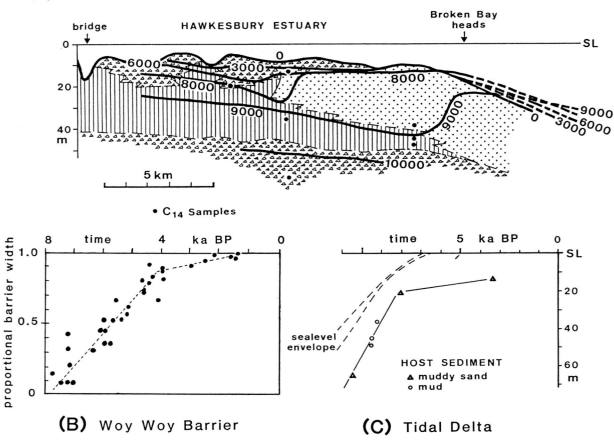

(A) Axial Cross Section

FIG. 6.—Time lines superimposed on the stratigraphic section in the Hawkesbury River (A) based on uncalibrated radiocarbon dates reported in Roy (1983). The dates plotted against depth in (B) indicate approximate accumulation rates of estuarine mud and fluvial-muddy sand in the lower estuary; the Postglacial sea-level envelope is from Thom and Roy (1984). The age structure of the Woy Woy beach ridge barrier (C) is based on data in Thom and others (1981) (lithofacies symbols as shown in Fig. 3).

NSW (Roy and Peat, 1976). Its entrance channel is narrow and tidal ranges are attenuated to less than 10 cm in the lake, which is saline under most conditions (Roy and others, 1980; Roy and Crawford, 1984).

The pattern of surface sediments shown in Figure 7A synthesizes work reported by Roy and Peat (1975). Shelly muds and sandy shoreline deposits that thinly mantle the bedrock valley sides cover about 90 percent of the estuary basin. The valley heads contain small flood plains and at the mouths of the larger creeks (e.g., Dora Creek), delta lobes protrude into the estuary. Drilling in the coastal sand complex shows it to be a composite feature comprising a core of leached, Pleistocene marine and aeolian sand onlapped by a Holocene barrier of the receded type with associated transgressive dunes (B. G. Thom, pers. commun., 1987). Estuary mouth sands forming tidal inlet and delta deposits at the barriers' southern end cover an area of approximately 13 km².

The stratigraphies illustrated in Figures 7B and 7C are based on detailed, seismic reflection profiling (Ringis and others, 1974) and drilling in the estuary, on the coastal sand

complex and in the delta of Dora Creek. The bedrock valley extends to about −60 m at the present coast but is substantially infilled with pre-Holocene deposits. Holocene sediments range from 10 to 27 m thick in the valley axes and are thickest beneath the estuary mouth (Fig. 7C). Here, shelly marine sands directly overlie an eroded, Pleistocene barrier surface and appear to have been emplaced by washover processes as sea level was rising. Unlike other estuaries, the tidal-delta complex in Lake Macquarie is not underlain by a transgressive mud unit except in a localised area around the present channel outlet into the lake. Here, the tidal delta overlies 5 m of mud, and delta face accretion apparently postdates the main phase of estuary mouth infilling; it may be partly of anthropomorphic origin.

Holocene muds in the estuary basin contain an abundant estuarine shell fauna (Roy, 1981; Roy and Crawford, 1984). They rarely exceed thicknesses of 10 m and overlie weathered Pleistocene sediments (oxidised clays and fluvial sands) that make-up more than 50 percent of the paleo-valley fill. Towards the present river deltas, muds grade into regressive fluvial-channel sands and underlie levee deposits com-

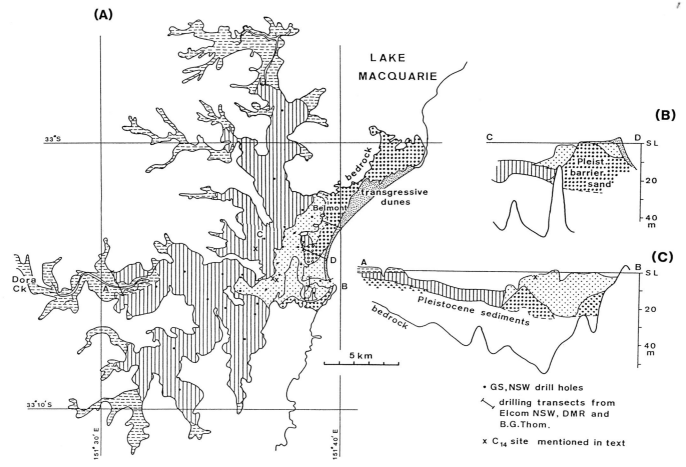

FIG. 7.—Lithofacies in Lake Macquarie and the adjacent barrier complex (A). Stratigraphic sections A-B and C-D are based on a synthesis of drilling data in the estuary and on the barrier; their horizontal scale is only approximate. The mouth of the present entrance channel is near "B" (lithofacies symbols as shown in Fig. 3).

posed of mud and fine sand up to 3.5 m thick (Electricity Commission of New South Wales, unpublished drilling data).

Age relationships of the Holocene deposits in Lake Macquarie are poorly documented in terms of radiocarbon dates, and the time lines depicted in Figure 8 rely in part on post-glacial sea-level changes proposed by Thom and Roy (1983). Most dates were obtained as part of a study of trace metal contamination in the upper part of the basin muds (Roy and Crawford, 1984). Here, insitu estuarine shells (mainly *Notospisula*) range in age from 0.5–4.7 ka BP and indicate

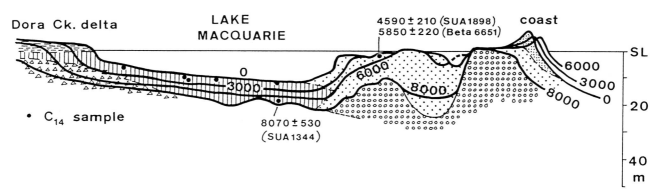

FIG. 8.—Inferred time lines superimposed on a diagrammatic east-west section in Lake Macquarie. Radiocarbon ages are calibrated according to Klein and others (1982).

an average sedimentation rate of 0.26 mm yr^{-1} (range 0.14—0.86 mm yr^{-1}, 8 samples). A date of about 8 ka BP at -16 m near the base of the mud sequence (Fig. 8) indicates an overall sedimentation rate of 0.83 mm yr^{-1} and, when compared with the sea-level curve, suggests that the estuary was at least 5 m deep at this time. Calibrated ages, ranging from 4.5—5.9 ka BP on *Anadara* shells from 1–2 m below the tidal delta surface near its inner edge at the site shown in Figures 7C and 8, suggest that the bulk of the tidal-delta sand body had been emplaced by the beginning of the stillstand.

Shoalhaven Delta

An extensive floodplain, approximately 125 km^2 in area between Nowra and the coast, occupies what was once a large, barrier estuary at the mouth of the Shoalhaven River (Fig. 9A). The delta plain lies behind an extensive beach-ridge barrier at the present coast (Thom and others, 1981); it is intersected by the river mouth at Shoalhaven Heads and by the Crookhaven estuary at the southern end of Shoalhaven Bight (Wright, 1970). The river has a coarse sand bed and, downstream of Nowra, flows between levee banks; other levees border Broughton Creek and mark prior river courses in the floodplain (Fig. 9A). At present, estuarine conditions exist only in the seaward part of the delta channels. Under low-flow conditions, the Shoalhaven River enters the sea at Crookhaven Heads via a man-made cut in the levee; the main river mouth at Shoalhaven Heads is often blocked by beach deposits and is only breached by flood discharge (Wright, 1977).

Drilling in the barrier and delta region shows that the floodplain is underlain by up to 27 m of shelly, organic-rich estuarine mud (Thom and others, 1981) (Fig. 9B). The mud sequence extends to near present mean sea level, and in the eastern part of the embayment, it encloses a seaward-thickening tongue of marine sand and muddy sand. A transgressive backbarrier (washover and estuary mouth) origin is inferred for the sand body which grades into and underlies, prograded barrier deposits at the present coast (Comerong Island) (Fig. 9B). Muddy, organic-rich overbank and backswamp deposits forming the subaerial floodplain overlie the estuarine muds and are generally less than 2 m thick, increasing to about 5 m beneath levees. Basal fluvial sands up to 20 m thick occur in the deeper parts of the palaeovalley, and younger and somewhat thinner channel sands intersect the upper part of the estuarine mud sequence (Fig. 9B).

Radiocarbon dates on insitu shells (*Notospisula trigonella*) and transported charcoal fragments from two drill holes in the estuarine mud unit provide an indication of the sequence of depositional events (Thom and others, 1981) (Fig. 10A). Calibrated ages plotted against depth in Figure 10B, show that low-energy, estuarine conditions were initiated about 9 ka BP behind a landward-retreating (transgressive) barrier complex. A date of about 9.5 ka BP on shell fragments from -11 m at the inner edge of these sands is abnormally old and indicates reworking of old shell from further seawards (Fig. 10B).

Drilling and dating in the main beachridge sequence just north of Shoalhaven Heads shows that the shoreline stabilised and barrier progradation commenced about 6.5 ka BP (Thom and others, 1981; Chapman and others, 1982). This would have coincided with the transition from active washover deposition to placid mud basin conditions in the seaward part of the estuary, and, accordingly, in Figure 10 the muds blanketing the estuary-mouth sand sheet are shown to be less than 6 ka old. Mud deposition was rapid (about 4–5 mm yr^{-1}) until about 4 ka BP, then slowed until about 2 ka BP (Fig. 10B). Initially fast rates of infilling decreased as the mud basin expanded to its maximum dimension at the end of the PMT, but by this time, muds had infilled the estuary to within 8 m of present sea level. In the next 3–4 ka, they built up to near present sea level, and over the last 2–3 ka, they have been superseded almost everywhere by terrestrial floodplain deposits. The Crookhaven estuary is a remnant of the former Shoalhaven estuary that escaped rapid infilling by the tendency of the river under flood to bypass it and discharge its sediment load directly to the sea at Shoalhaven Heads.

ESTUARY EVOLUTION

In this section, the various lines of stratigraphic data described in the previous section for each estuary are used to reconstruct individual histories of estuary development spanning the Holocene epoch. Lithofacies distributions are illustrated by maps at selected time intervals to show the evolution of the main depositional environments. The emphasis is on the movement of sediment from sources to sinks and the rates and times at which deposition occurred in the four estuaries. Port Hacking and the lower Hawkesbury River (Broken Bay) exemplify a dichotomy in drowned valley estuaries that, because their inflowing rivers differ markedly in size, have infilled slowly and rapidly respectively. Lake Macquarie and the Shoalhaven Estuary are barrier estuaries that exhibit the same dichotomy.

Drowned Valley Estuaries

The Hacking Estuary.—

At the beginning of the Holocene epoch (Fig. 11A), estuarine sedimentation was confined to the axial region of the Hacking valley where estuary-mouth sands, basin muds, and fluvial sands formed a succession of onlapping, transgressive deposits in an upstream direction. Dunes composed of marine sand are diagrammatically shown transgressing headlands on either side of the estuary mouth, which during the Last Glacial was joined by the paleo-Georges River in the region of Bate Bay (Roy and Crawford, 1981). Possible marine sand sources were interstadial barriers or aeolian sand ramps (the "protobarrier" in Fig. 11A) located seawards of the present coast. By 6 ka BP (Fig. 11B) the Hacking estuary had attained its present dimensions and the former mouth of the Georges River was blocked by a prograded (beach ridge) barrier on the northwestern side of Bate Bay (Roy and Crawford, 1981). Most likely, reworked remnants of the "proto-barrier" in Bate Bay acted as a source of low-shell sand for the estuary-mouth sand body which probably through a process of storm overwash had built upwards and into the estuary about 2 km by this

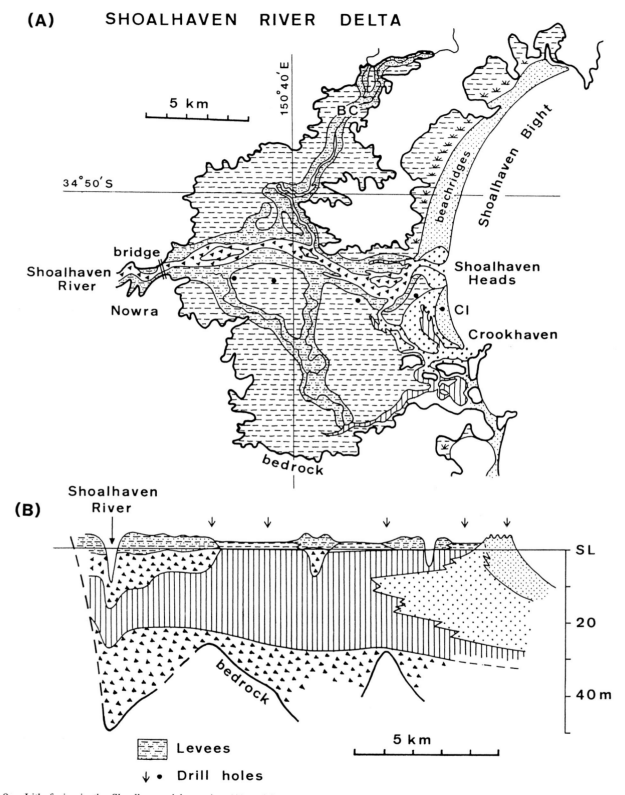

(A) SHOALHAVEN RIVER DELTA

5 km

150°40′E

34°50′S

BC

beachridges

Shoalhaven Bight

bridge

Shoalhaven River

Nowra

Shoalhaven Heads

CI

Crookhaven

bedrock

(B)

Shoalhaven River

SL

20

40 m

bedrock

▦ Levees

↓ • Drill holes

FIG. 9.—Lithofacies in the Shoalhaven delta region (A) and in an east-west cross section (B) are based on data reported in Thom and others (1981) supplemented by drilling at the Shoalhaven River bridge. Lithofacies symbols as shown in Figure 3 (BC = Broughton Creek; CI = Comerong Island).

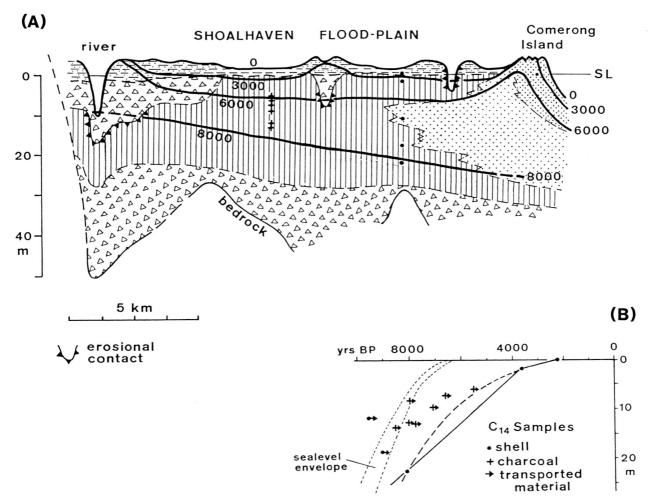

Fig. 10.—Time lines superimposed on the east-west stratigraphic section through the Shoalhaven delta (A) are based mainly on inferred mud accumulation rates indicated in the age/depth plot (B). Determinations of sedimentation are inaccurate due to the transported nature of much of the dated material.

time. In the following 6 ka (Figs. 5C, D), refracted ocean waves formed small barriers and spits, initially just inside the estuary mouth (Jibbon Beach) and progressively further upstream (Bundeena Beach and Deeban Spit most recently).

During the early stillstand, the principle source of sand for the tidal delta was from Bate Bay and the open coast immediately to the south of Port Hacking. As the tidal delta continued to grow upstream in the main estuary and into the mouths of tributary arms it converted approximately 3 km² of mud basin environment to shallow sand flats. While this accretional trend had little impact on tidal or salinity regimes, it dramatically changed biological environments and habitats in the central estuary. For example, the transition from deep mud basin to shallow sand flat took place over an interval of 75–150 years. The present delta-front morphology suggests that tidal-delta growth is non-uniform. Deposition is fastest at the terminus of the main flood-tide channel where the delta front develops a lobate planform (Figs. 3, 11D). Meandering and switching of the tidal channel in time and space has probably caused the delta

front to continuously change shape. A similar lobate morphology is also shown by the fluvial delta at the mouth of the Hacking River. Here, sediment transport and deposition presumably is confined to a jet stream emanating from the river mouth during floods. Throughout the last 3 ka, the fluvial delta lobe has prograded over an area of about 100 m² annually while at the same time fine suspended sediments and biogenic material have slowly accumulated in deep basins marginal to the delta. While the central basin remains unfilled, both deltas will continue to grow inwards.

Radiocarbon dates plotted in Figure 4 indicate that rates of tidal delta growth have not changed significantly during the late Holocene. However, the calculations are based on total sediment which in the latter part of the Holocene has become increasingly calcareous in composition with correspondingly less quartz. The only source of quartz sand for the tidal delta is from Bate Bay and the open coast and clearly this source has diminished over time. Biogenic material, on the other hand, grows on the sandy bed of the estuary, and the production of this material has apparently

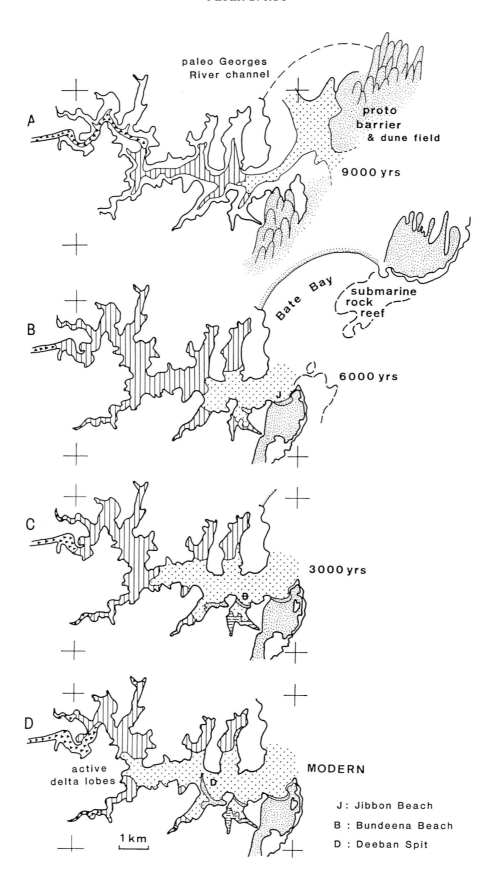

paleo Georges
River channel

A

proto
barrier
& dune field

9000 yrs

Bate Bay

submarine
rock
reef

B

6000 yrs

J

C

3000 yrs

B

D

active
delta lobes

MODERN

D

1 km

J : Jibbon Beach

B : Bundeena Beach

D : Deeban Spit

increased as the surface area of the tidal delta has expanded. Probably the present-day supply of sand is mainly from erosion of the delta ramp in the estuary mouth. Here, a superficial layer of charcoal and shell rich sand represents a zone of modern wave reworking. Ages of the shell detritus range from 3.2–2.6 ka (5 dates), and the contribution of this "relict" shell to the modern delta front largely explains the 1.5 ka time lag of the contemporary deposits (Fig. 4). Historical evidence that the estuary mouth has deepened by up to 3 m over the last 100 years supports a model of the tidal delta "feeding on itself"; however, some present-day contribution of "new" sand from offshore cannot be ruled out. Marine sand deposits located further seaward in Bate Bay and extending along the base of the coastal cliffs to the south are stirred by storm waves to depths of at least 50 m and may also experience net alongshore and onshore transport (Field and Roy, 1984).

Lower Hawkesbury River-Broken Bay.—

Like the Hacking estuary, the deeply incised Hawkesbury River valley was drowned and began infilling with sediment well before sea level reached its present position. Sea level 9 ka ago (Fig. 12A) was 15–20 m below its present level (Thom and Roy, 1985) and deep basin environments existed landwards of rapidly accreting tidal deltas in the mouths of the Hawkesbury and Brisbane Water paleovalleys. The basins acted as settling sites for the relatively large suspended sediment load carried by the Hawkesbury River during floods. Rates of deposition were extremely fast (>10 mm yr^{-1}) and possibly matched that at which sea level was rising during the PMT. As a result, fluvial-deltaic deposits progressively encroached downstream into the mud basin environments, and by 8 ka BP (Figs. 6A, 12B), sandy channel sediments had reached the lower estuary. Simultaneously, massive inputs of marine sand were responsible for rapid upstream growth of the tidal delta. Like the Hacking estuary, the primary sand source was offshore which involved erosion on the delta's seaward face (Fig. 6A). Approximate rates of upstream accretion at the delta front were in the order of 2–4 m yr^{-1} about 5 times faster than in Port Hacking. From 10 ka to about 7 ka BP about 8 km^2 of the lower estuary were converted from a placid mud basin environment to a clean sand substrate reworked by tidal currents and refracted ocean waves. Rapid deposition of the thick mud sequence was followed by equally rapid burial by the tidal-delta sand body. Compaction of the mud would have been substantial, but independent measurements were not able to be made from the disturbed drill hole samples.

By 6 ka BP (Fig. 12C), the main Hawkesbury estuary upstream of the tidal delta was dominated by fluvial sediments. Sandy marginal shoals had begun to onlap the tidal-delta surface, which had virtually ceased growing by this time (Fig. 6A). Mud basins were mostly confined to slow-

filling tributary valleys such as Pitt Water and Cowan Creek (Roy, 1983) (Fig. 6). At the close of the PMT, barrier building had commenced in the Brisbane Water valley (Figs. 6C, 12C). Leached marine sands encountered in drill holes beneath the Woy Woy beach ridge sequence at about -4 to -10 m (B. G. Thom, pers. commun.) are presumably remnants of an earlier barrier that occupied this site in Pleistocene times (in Figs. 12A and 12B, these old deposits are shown diagrammatically.)

In the main Hawkesbury estuary, fluvial sediments on the channel bed aggraded slowly during the stillstand (about 5 m in the last 2–3 ka, Fig. 6B), and reflect a dramatic retardation of estuarine sedimentation compared with pre-stillstand rates. Following Castaing and Allen (1981), this retardation is attributed to the slow but continuous leakage of fine sediment out of the open estuary mouth under the combined influence of spring tides and river floods. A transitory stage in sediment bypassing is represented by the surficial layer containing fine river sand on the bed of northern Broken Bay (Fig. 12D), a site exposed to reworking by storm waves (Wright and others, 1978). The net sediment flux in the lower part of the main estuary has reversed from landwards during the PMT to seawards during the stillstand, but in its tributary arms, Pittwater and Brisbane Water, the landward movement of sand has continued up until the present.

The present estuary is characterised by moderately high, ambient energy levels during spring-tide cycles and occasional high-energy events due to river floods and storm waves in the estuary mouth. According to Dyson and Druery (1985), a salt wedge persists in the lower estuary during small floods (<7000 m^3 sec^{-1}) with the result that only sediment carried in suspension is discharged to the sea. Sandy-bed sediments are mobilized much less frequently during particularly large flood events. In recent times, the construction of dams in the river's catchment and the extraction of sand and gravel from the channel immediately above the estuarine reach have limited the supply of coarse sediment. How these man-made changes impact on the estuary remain to be documented; however, it is reasonable to assume that a reduction in fluvial sand input will retard the systems' natural evolutionary transition from estuarine (tidal) to fluvial dominance.

Barrier Estuaries

Lake Macquarie.—

The fluvial drainage channels beneath Lake Macquarie were inundated by about 8 ka at which time estuarine muds began slowly accumulating behind a plug of marine sand in the valley mouth (Fig. 13A). This latter deposit includes a relict Pleistocene barrier as well as contemporary (Holocene) tidal inlet deposits, the bulk of which were emplaced by the end of the PMT, 6 ka BP (Fig. 13B). Small storm

FIG. 11.—Reconstructed stages in the evolution of Port Hacking estuary. Stages A and B also cover Bate Bay and Kurnell headland on its northern side. The present-day distribution of rock reefs is indicated in Stage B; these have been uncovered as sand from the protobarrier migrated into the estuary (lithofacies symbols as in Fig. 3).

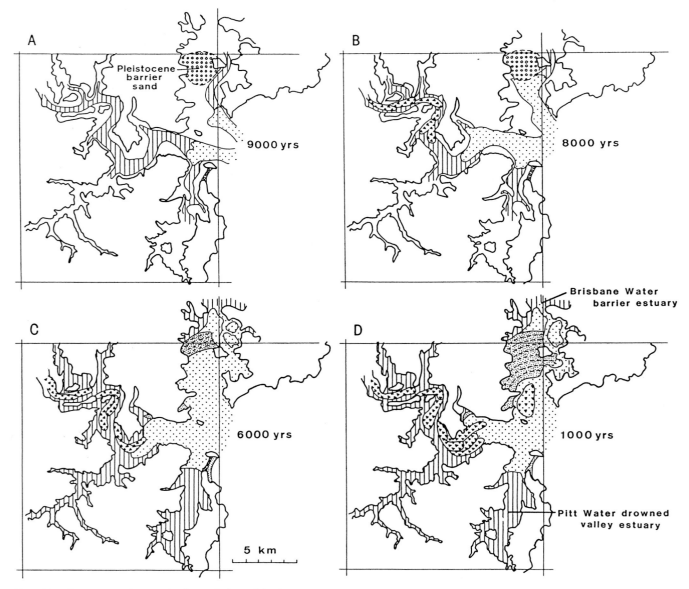

FIG. 12.—Reconstructed stages in the evolution of the lower Hawkesbury estuary, Broken Bay region. Lithofacies distribution in the mouth of Brisbane Water is largely speculative (lithofacies symbols as in Fig. 3).

ridges and dunes, which raise the surface of the Holocene sands above present sea level, possibly formed during a period of slightly higher sea level in the mid Holocene (Flood and Frankel, 1989); now they are covered by urban development. It is hypothesised that the entrance channel was originally located against the southern bedrock ridge and subsequently migrated northwards (Fig. 13B). Although there is no absolute chronology to establish rates of stream delta progradation into Lake Macquarie, drilling in the Dora Creek delta about 3 km upstream of its mouth encountered Holocene muds in the shallow subsurface (Fig. 7C) that suggest the delta has elongated by at least this amount in the last 6 ka BP. However, because of the small stream discharges, fluvial deposits are quite limited in extent, and it

is likely that fluvial-deltaic sedimentation has diminished the estuary water area by less than 10 percent in the late Holocene.

The modern situation is shown in Figure 13C. The estuary-mouth sand deposits are relict and most of their periphery is mantled by estuarine mud (Fig. 7C), the result of slow accretion in the estuary mud basin. Today, active, estuary-mouth sedimentation is restricted to the present entrance channel (mainly tidal reworking) and to recent tidal-delta growth at its inner end (Fig. 7B). Because of the size and depth of the estuary water body, Lake Macquarie has acted as an almost total trap for suspended sediment throughout the Holocene; minor bypassing is only effected during major floods. Thus the resulting 5- to 10-m thick

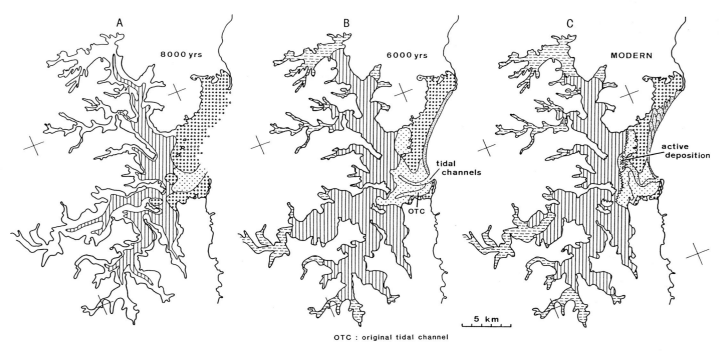

A   8000 yrs

B   6000 yrs

tidal channels

OTC

C   MODERN

active deposition

5 km

OTC : original tidal channel

FIG. 13.—Reconstructed stages in the evolution of Lake Macquarie. The pattern of incised stream channels shown in Stage A is based on detailed seismic profiling (lithofacies symbols as in Fig. 3).

layer of estuarine mud and an unknown but relatively small amount of delta progradation accounts for more than 7 ka of stream erosion of the lakes' catchments. This terrestrial contribution is further reduced by a significant amount (c. 10–20 percent) of biogenic material (shell and organics) produced within the estuary (Roy 1981). Assuming about 640x10⁶ m³ mud in the estuary, this represents an average annual contribution of silt and clay-sized material from the catchment of about 150 g/m². In terms of its maximum capacity, Lake Macquarie is less than half filled with sediment, a phenomenon largely attributable to the small size of the inflowing streams. It also reflects a surprisingly slow influx of marine sand via the entrance channel over most of the stillstand period which suggests that, in the past, sand transport in the estuary mouth was partially blocked by sand bars. Around the end of the last century, this situation was changed by the construction of training walls and breakwaters at the inlet mouth which appear to have had a marked impact on channel morphodynamics not only at the mouth but also at the inlets' inner end (Public Works Department, 1976). In the mouth region, increased tide and wave penetration resulted in bed scouring and shoreline erosion that has led to a gradual increase in tidal discharge (a similar phenomenon has been documented in Wallis Lake, lat. 32.2S by Nielsen and Gordon (1981). Historical records over the last 100 years show that the entrance channel has scoured and its terminus has migrated about 1.0 km northwards (Public Works Department, 1976). Conceivably, the onlapping relationship between tidal-delta sands and estuarine muds shown in Figure 7B is the result of these recent channel changes.

Shoalhaven Estuary

Drilling data are not sufficiently widespread to accurately delineate the planimetric changes of the Shoalhaven Estuary during its Holocene evolution; the infilling patterns shown in Figure 14 are thus highly speculative. Figure 14A depicts an early stage of drowning of the paleo-Shoalhaven valley 9 ka ago when sea level was 15–20 m below its present position, and estuarine muds were accumulating in the axis of the paleo-valley behind a transgressive barrier located seawards of the present coast. Storm breaching and overwash deposition were common features of the retreating coast especially in the Shoalhaven valley mouth. At this time, muds were accumulating rapidly in the estuary basin while upstream of Nowra, fluvial-channel sands and gravels were deposited in the bedrock valley gorge.

By 6 ka BP (Fig. 14B), with the sea at its present level, the estuary had attained the approximate dimensions of the present delta-floodplain (c. 140 km²), and the estuary-mouth sands had spread to their maximum extent (Fig. 10B). Barrier growth during the stillstand constricted the estuary mouth which was presumably located at Crookhaven Heads where incident wave action on the Shoalhaven Bight shoreline is lowest (Wright, 1970). According to the radiocarbon dates, the estuary at this time was less than 10 m deep and was a placid environment in which shelly muds accumulated. Fluvial deltas at the mouths of the Shoalhaven River and Broughton Creek were building into the estuary at this stage, but because of the water depth, their extent was probably not large. Around the estuary sides, a discontinuous fringe of muddy shorelines deposits (the precursors of the present

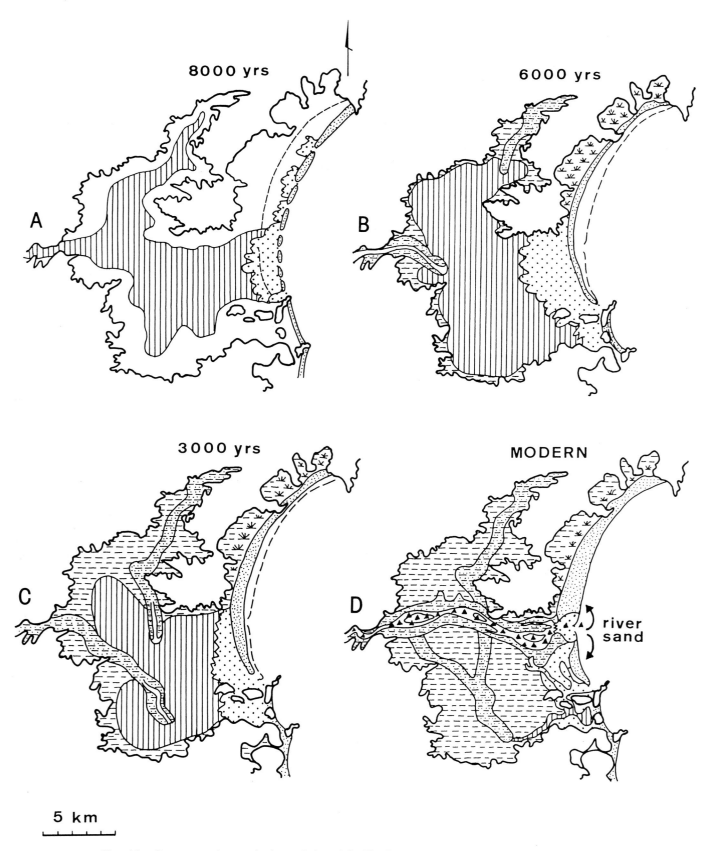

8000 yrs

6000 yrs

A

B

3000 yrs

MODERN

C

D

river sand

5 km

Fig. 14.—Reconstructed stages in the evolution of the Shoalhaven delta (lithofacies symbols as in Fig. 3).

floodplain) were probably beginning to form. Because of restricted entrance conditions, tidal ranges in the large estuary basin were probably small (Roy, 1984), a factor which would have restricted mangrove development. For the Shoalhaven Estuary, the first 3 ka of the stillstand period was a time of slow environmental change despite relatively rapid build-up of mud on the estuary bed. In contrast, the last 3 ka has seen dramatic change culminating in the widespread conversion of estuarine environments to terrestrial floodplains and freshwater swamps.

By 3 ka ago, the estuary basin had shoaled to about 2 m and muds had blanketed much of the backbarrier sand flats (Fig. 14C). From about 4–2 ka BP, the estuary water body shrunk rapidly as levee jetties and floodplains expanded to form restricted sub-embayments with diverse, shallow-water habitats. Wind-wave stirring of the shallow estuary bed undoubtedly produced turbid water conditions and resuspension of sediment that contributed to shoreline accretion (Roy and Peat, 1976; Roy, 1984). It is hypothesised that, as barrier estuaries become more mature, a reduction in water area is accompanied by an increase in tidal range which promotes the spread of mangrove and salt marsh vegetation. This tendency in the Shoalhaven would have been countered to some extent by reduced salinities during large floods, an impact that increased as the water body decreased in volume. Precise rates of change during the final stages of infilling are difficult to document. Although vertical accretion in the estuary was slow, rates of shoreline encroachment were extremely rapid. The present reconstruction suggests that floodplains expanded at an average rate of about 20,000 m^2 yr^{-1} during the last 3–4 ka. In Fullerton Cove, a cut-off embayment in the Hunter delta with an 9 km long shoreline (lat. 32.8°S), a 1 km wide mangrove fringe has encroached into the estuary at between 4 and 8 m yr^{-1} (equivalent to an area of about 50,000 m^2 yr^{-1}) over the last 40 years (Roy, 1980). With the spread of floodplains, river flow increasingly became channelised between levee banks and converged on the Crookhaven entrance. Eventually floods in the main channel breached the earlier levees and cut a more direct course to the sea at Shoalhaven Heads.

Today, infilling is complete except for a remnant of the former estuary at Crookhaven, and the Shoalhaven has become a river estuary confined to a sinuous channel. During floods, its bed is reworked, mid-channel shoals erode and reform, sand banks at the river mouth scour, and sandy sediment is discharged to the sea (Fig. 14D). Sedimentological studies of the coastal sand deposits show that the seaward-most beach ridge contains significant amounts of feldspathic river sand. However, the supply of modern fluvial sand to the coast is a discontinuous process not only because of the erratic nature of flood events but also due to a sediment exchange cycle that they initiate. This cycle involves river mouth scour and offshore sand transport followed by coastal erosion as beach sand migrates alongshore to infill the scoured river mouth. Studies at Tathra (36.7°S latitude: Gordon and others, 1980) suggest that a decade or more may elapse before sand, scoured out of the river channel during a major flood, migrates back onshore to contribute to beach accretion.

DISCUSSION

Two factors control differences in estuary evolution on the NSW coast: river sediment supply and the hydrodynamic conditions operating at the estuary mouth. The latter is intrinsically related to estuary type, which is an inherited characteristic, but the former is not. During youthful stages of evolution, the factors operate largely independently, but as estuaries infill (i.e., become more mature), they increasingly interact. The role of rivers in estuarine sedimentation is preserved in the geological record of fluvial-deltaic and mud-basin lithofacies; that of the marine processes in the estuary mouth is interpreted from the associated marine sand deposits.

The Role of Rivers in Estuary Sedimentation

Comparison between estuaries of different types but with similar river sediment inputs reveals that accumulation trends in river delta and mud basin environments differ radically in degree and change as the estuaries evolve along different pathways. Absolute rates of sedimentation in fluvial deltas are not available for most estuaries, but their development generally parallels that of the basin (prodelta) muds for which more long-term data is available.

The Hawkesbury and Shoalhaven epitomise estuaries with large fluvial sediment supplies. The very high rates at which estuarine muds accumulated in the Hawkesbury River during the PMT (c. 10–15 mm yr^{-1}) reflect its large catchment and high sediment discharge. The duration of mud sedimentation in the lower estuary was, however, quite brief (between c. 10–7 ka BP). Towards the end of the PMT, basin environments were superceded by sandy channel sedimentation, and mud in increasing amounts was expelled from the estuary. The loss of a substantial fraction of the river sediment load reduced rates of accretion to 1–2 mm yr^{-1} on the channel bed and has, presumably, also retarded the spread of subaerial and intertidal deposits along the channel sides. During the latter part of the stillstand, estuarine environments in the Hawkesbury appear to have changed little although tidal energy levels are quite high and sediment through-put is large.

Compared with the Hawkesbury River, mud accumulated less rapidly in the Shoalhaven estuary (c. 4–5 mm yr^{-1}) due in part to its relatively large settling basin, but it accumulated over twice as long a period (from c. 9–3 ka BP). Except for shoaling of the estuary bed, environmental conditions during this interval changed little until the last 3 ka of the Holocene time. At this time, a terrestrial delta plain spread rapidly over the shallow estuary bed and culminated in the Shoalhaven River becoming channelised and cutting a new course through its floodplain to the sea at Shoalhaven Heads. Large, rapid-filling barrier estuaries such as the Shoalhaven show the most dramatic environmental change of any coastal landscape in NSW. The Hawkesbury and the Shoalhaven have now reached mature states of development and both rivers discharge sediment to the sea. However, in drowned-valley estuaries such as the Hawkesbury by-passing is tidally controlled and involves winnowing of fine sand and mud which are transported offshore; there is no evidence that river sand has been added to the ocean beaches in Broken Bay. In contrast, mature barrier estuaries such as the Shoalhaven are more strongly influenced by river flooding, and episodically they discharge a wide range of grain sizes at the coast including a substantial amount of relatively coarse sand that eventually finds its way onto the adjacent beaches. Underlying these different flood behaviours are the configurations of the lower reaches of the two estuary types. Even at mature stages of development, drowned-valley estuaries maintain their funnel shape which acts to reduce flood velocities and sediment loads in a downstream direction. In contrast, the channels of mature barrier estuaries are often constricted at their mouths where they intersect coastal sand barriers. Here flood velocities and sediment carrying capacities are greatest with the result that flooding causes massive scouring in the river mouth.

Port Hacking and Lake Macquarie lie at the other end of the spectrum in terms of river sediment supply. Their fluvial deltas show contrasting growth modes which in some respects reflect differences in estuary type. The fluvial delta at the mouth of the Hacking River is a lobate, subaqueous feature composed of relatively coarse, muddy sands 8–10 m thick. Dora Creek in Lake Macquarie, on the other hand, has built narrow, subaerial levee jetties composed of fine sand and mud only 3 m thick. Subaerial levees in barrier estuaries, also a feature of the Shoalhaven delta, indicate periodically elevated water level when flood waters are impounded behind barriers with constricted outlets to the sea. In contrast, the open mouths of drowned-valley estuaries allow flood waters to escape without significantly raising water levels in the estuary. This is responsible for the subaqueous nature of the Hacking River delta and together with tidal action accounts for the predominance of subaqueous channel environments in the Hawkesbury River.

Rates of mud accumulation in both Lake Macquarie and Port Hacking are slow, about 0.1–1.0 mm yr^{-1} in the former and 1–3 mm yr^{-1} in the latter. The difference is mainly due to estuary basin size, with Lake Macquarie being 10 times larger than Port Hacking. Reasonably, most present day estuaries have rates that lie within this range since faster sedimentation over the stillstand period would have infilled them by now.

The Role of Estuary Mouths on Sedimentation

Net sediment movements in NSW estuary mouths are landward during youthful stages of development and are dominated by marine processes, but at mature stages they are directly seawards mainly under the influence of river floods. This reversal in sediment flux marks a critical stage in estuary evolution; in the Hawkesbury it apparently coincided with the end of the PMT, but in the Shoalhaven it probably took place within the last few millennia. Prior to this critical stage, estuary-mouth sand bodies developed characteristic stratigraphies and age structures in the different estuary types. The open mouths of drowned river valley estuaries promote upstream flood-tide delta growth during both rising and stable sea-level conditions. In the Hawkesbury River mouth and Broken Bay, approximately 2×10^8 m^3 of marine sand had accumulated by about 7 ka BP at which time the tidal delta slip face was overwhelmed

by riverine sediment. Rapid landward growth at the delta front of between 2 and 4 m yr^{-1} was due to the general onshore movement of marine sand accompanying the PMT and the existence of a large sand source on the inner shelf offshore from Broken Bay. In Port Hacking, where slow rates of fluvial sediment input have left central basin environments unfilled, about half of the 1.6×10^8 m^3 of tidal delta sand was emplaced during the stillstand. Average rates of delta-front accretion of 16,000 m^3 yr^{-1} (c. 0.5–1.0 m horizontal growth yr^{-1}) based on radiocarbon dating may be conservative. Certainly in this estuary, there is no evidence that deposition has slowed in late Holocene although a change to more calcareous sand suggests a progressive decline in the supply of clastic quartz sand. In Port Hacking, the question of a primary source for the tidal-delta sand is complicated by the probable existence of a proto-barrier in Bate Bay towards the end of the PMT and a shelf sand body off the adjacent coast. At present, erosion of the seaward ramp of the tidal delta is providing much of the clastic sand for its continuing upstream growth.

As in drowned-valley estuaries, rapid marine sand deposition occurred in barrier estuary mouths during the latter stages of the PMT in association with transgressive barrier development on this coast (Thom, 1984; Roy and others, 1994). Under stillstand conditions, however, estuary-mouth deposition has been less predictable. In some cases, such as those barrier estuaries documented here, deposition virtually ceased 4–5 ka ago, but in others (e.g., Wallis Lake, Roy and others, 1992) it continued into late Holocene time and in a few cases, with engineering help, to the present-day. Growing palaentological evidence from studies of estuarine mud sequences in both SE and SW Australia demonstrates that tidal flushing and salinities in barrier estuaries have decreased significantly in late Holocene time (Pickett, 1983; Hodgkin and Kendrick, 1983; I. Yassini, pers. commun., 1993). There is also evidence that mid Holocene sea levels were 1–2 m higher than today (about 5–3 ka) and have very slowly fallen since (Bryant and others, 1988, 1992; Flood and Frankel, 1989; Chappell and others, 1982). Predictable effects of a slow fall in sea level include shoaling in tidal inlets and beach accretion, both of which would tend to reduce tidal exchange and sand transport in barrier estuaries and thus greatly reduce or stop tidal delta growth (Public Works Department, 1983). Those barrier estuaries with tidal deltas that have continued to grow throughout the stillstand have presumably been able to maintain inlet efficiency by deepending their channels as sea level fell.

As barrier estuaries infill with terrestrial sediment and mud basin environments expand seawards over the estuary-mouth deposits (e.g., Shoalhaven), river flow becomes channelised. The mouth of mature estuaries are increasingly prone to flood scouring, and sediment movements in them increase in magnitude and frequency. The development of subaqueous, crescentic, river mouth bars up to 1 km seawards of the larger river mouths (Floyd and Druery, 1976; Druery and Nielsen, 1980) shows that the locus of sedimentation in mature barrier estuary mouths extends well seawards of the coast. How far sand is transported seawards during major floods is open to speculation (Roy and Stephens, 1981). After a scouring event, sand from the open coast moves back into the river mouth for a limited distance upstream. Roy and Crawford (1977), found that modern marine sands occur in the seaward-most 1–3 km of large rivers in central and northern NSW; this defines the landward limit of sand exchange in mature river estuaries. Dredging of 800,000 m^3 of sand in the Tweed River initiated a massive influx of sand from the updrift beaches (Druery, 1980) and demonstrates the dynamic balance that presently exists between coast and estuary mouth.

CONCLUSIONS

Microtidal estuaries on the high-energy coast of SE Australia attained their primary character at the end of the PMT when deposits of marine sand accumulated in the mouths of coastal valleys and established characteristic tidal regimes. Infilling during sea-level highstands has been with sediments supplied by rivers and exchanged between the estuary and the coast via the estuary mouth. Barrier estuaries occur behind coastal sand barriers and have narrow inlet channels with wave-dominated mouths that restrict tidal ranges in the estuary to less than 10 percent of the ocean tide. Drowned-valley estuaries, on the other hand, occupy deeply incised bedrock valleys and have full tidal ranges. Semi-enclosed bays at their mouths have landward shoaling beds that reduce incident wave action with the result that, despite being on a microtidal coast, drowned-valley estuaries are tide-dominated in their seaward part under all except the most severe storm conditions.

During the PMT, all estuaries trapped large quantities of shelf sand, but only slow-filling drowned valley estuaries, such as Port Hacking, continued to do so after sea level stabilised. Transgressive shelf sands were emplaced quite rapidly as washover lobes in barrier estuaries as the valley mouths were drowned by the rising sea. Under stillstand conditions, however, the growth of flood-tide deltas in these estuaries was retarded due not to an undersupply of shelf sand, but to the low sand transporting capacity of the restricted tidal flows in their inlet channels. In comparison, the influx of shelf sand to form tidal deltas in drowned-valley estuaries during the PMT was considerably larger and continued throughout the stillstand while accommodation space in the central basin lasted. Thus transgressive, onlap relationships between tidal-delta sand bodies and underlying estuarine mud sequences are better developed in drowned-valley estuaries than in barrier estuaries. Because the mobility of inlet channels is constrained by bedrock headlands in the case of barrier estuaries on the embayed coast of NSW, their tidal inlet facies are less dominant than are the associated barrier deposits. On barrier island coasts, in contrast, migrating entrance channels ensure that the barriers are repeatedly reworked, and the dominant sand lithofacies associated with barrier lagoons are tidal-channel deposits (Reinson, 1983).

Mud accumulation rates today in most NSW estuaries range from 0.1 to 3.0 mm yr^{-1}. Faster rates ($\gg$4 mm yr^{-1}) characterized former estuaries at the mouths of large rivers, but their low-energy mud basins rapidly infilled and either converted to flood plains (e.g., Shoalhaven delta), or their channels shoaled and became tide-dominated systems that now bypass fine sediments to the sea (e.g., Hawkesbury estuary). Because of their confined bedrock valleys, much of the sediments filling drowned-valley estuaries are excavated each time sea level falls, only to be redeposited during the following marine transgression and highstand. In contrast, sediments in the broader barrier estuaries seem to experience less erosion during regressions and sea-level lowstands with the result that estuary infilling is a cumulative process during successive glacial/interglacial cycles. Barrier estuaries are thus a model for interpreting composite valley-fill sequences (Boyd and others, 1992).

Compared to barrier estuaries, which only slowly exchange their waters with the sea, the strong tidal flushing characteristics of drowned-valley estuaries, especially during mature stages of development, act as a buffer against the short-term impacts of floods and storms on the estuary. The same buffering effect applies to man-made changes such as land clearing, urbanization, and the construction of dams in the estuary's catchments or dredging aggregate from the channel beds. These activities are responsible for a progressive deterioration of water quality and biological productivity and changes to sedimentation patterns, but their long-term impacts are likely to be less evident in drowned-valley estuaries than in barrier estuaries. Barrier estuaries are also more sensitive to both natural and man-made changes to the estuary mouth. Here flood scouring, the build-up of sand shoals by ocean waves, the construction of training walls and breakwaters, and dredging in the estuary mouth can cause radical and long-lasting changes to tidal regimes, mean water levels, salinity, and water quality in the body of the estuary and to current velocities and sand transport in the entrance channel. Even the adjacent coast may suffer long-term erosion as severely scoured river mouths infill with sand from updrift beaches. Barrier estuaries are thus potentially more vulnerable to human interference than drowned-valley estuaries, but they may also be more amenable to remedial measures.

ACKNOWLEDGMENTS

The data for this study comes from many sources: principally the Geological Survey of NSW with major contributions from B.G. Thom (formerly of the University of New South Wales, Duntroon; now New England University, Armidale) and the Department of Public Works. The latter organisation funded most of the drilling and radiocarbon dating in Port Hacking estuary; the use of this information is greatly appreciated. Bruce Thom, Kelvin Berryman and Ed Clifton reviewed the manuscript and their thoughtful comments have proved invaluable. The work is published with the approval of the Director-General, New South Wales Department of Mineral Resources.

REFERENCES

ALBANI, A. D., AND JOHNSON, B. D., 1974, The bedrock topography and origin of Broken Bay, New South Wales: Journal of Geological Society of Australia, v. 21, p. 209–214.

ALBANI, A. D., RICKWOOD, P. C., JOHNSON, B. D., MCGRATH, C. A., AND TAYLOR, J. W., 1978, A geological investigation of the seaboard area of the Sutherland Shire: Sydney, Unpublished Report for the Sutherland Shire Council prepared by Unisearch, Ltd., 25 p.

BOOTHROYD, J. C., 1978, Mesotidal inlets and estuaries, in Davies, R. A., Jr., ed., Coastal Sedimentary Environments: New York, Springer-Verlag, p. 287–360.

BOYD, R., DALRYMPLE, R., AND ZAITLIN, B. A., 1992, Classification of clastic coastal depositional environments: Sedimentary Geology, v. 80, p. 139–150.

BRYANT, E., 1980, Bathymetric changes in three estuaries of the central New South Wales coast: Australian Journal of Marine and Freshwater Research, v. 31, p. 553–571.

BRYANT, E., ROY, P. S., AND THOM, B. G., 1988, Australia—an unstable platform for tide-gauge measurements of changing sea level: a discussion: Journal of Geology, v. 96, p. 635–640.

BRYANT, E. A., YOUNG, R. W., PRICE, D. M., AND SHORT, S. A., 1992, Evidence of Pleistocene and Holocene raised marine deposits, Sandon Point, New South Wales: Australian Journal of Earth Sciences, v. 39, p. 481–494.

CASTAING, P., AND ALLEN, G. P., 1981, Mechanisms controlling seaward escape of suspended sediment from the Gironde: a macrotidal estuary in France: Marine Geology, v. 40, p. 101–118.

CHAPMAN, D. M., GEARY, M., ROY, P. S., AND THOM, B. G., 1982, Coastal evolution and coastal erosion in New South Wales: Sydney, Report for Coastal Council of New South Wales, 341 p.

CHAPPELL, J., RHODES, E. G., THOM, B. G., AND WALLENSKY, E., 1982, Hydroisostacy and the sea level isobase of 5500 yrs BP in North Queensland, Australia: Marine Geology, v. 49, p. 81–90.

DALRYMPLE, R. W., ZAITLIN, B. A., AND BOYD, R., 1992, Estuarine facies models: conceptual basis and stratigraphic implications: Journal of Sedimentary Petrology, v. 62, p. 1130–1146.

DRUERY, B. M., 1980, Estuarine response to dredging in the Tweed River, Australia: Sydney, Proceedings of the 17th International Coastal Engineering Conference, p. 1599–1618.

DRUERY, B. M., AND NIELSEN, A. F., 1980, Mechanisms operating at a jettied river entrance: Sydney, Proceedings of the 17th International Coastal Engineering Conference, p. 2607–2626.

DYSON, A. R., AND DRUERY, B. M., 1985, The impact of sand extraction on salt intrusion in the Hawkesbury River: Christchurch, Proceedings, Australian Conference on Coastal and Ocean Engineering, p. 557–567.

FLOOD, P. G., AND FRANKEL, E., 1989, Late Holocene higher sea level indicators from eastern Australia: Marine Geology, v. 12, p. 223–242.

FLOYD, C. D., AND DRUERY, B. M., 1976, Results of river mouth training on the Clarence River bar, New South Wales, Australia: Proceedings of the 15th International Conference on Coastal Engineering, p. 194–201.

FIELD, M. E., AND ROY, P. S., 1984, Offshore transport and sand-body formation: evidence from a steep, high-energy shoreface, southeastern Australia: Journal of Sedimentary Petrology, v. 54, p. 1292–1302.

GODFREY, J. S., AND PARSLOW, T., 1976, Description and preliminary theory of circulation in Port Hacking estuary: Report, Australian CSIRO Division of Fisheries and Oceanography, v. 67, 25 p.

GORDON, A. D., LORD, D. B., NOLAN, M. W., ROY, P. S., AND STEPHENS, A. W., 1980, Tathra erosion study: Unpublished Report No. PWD 79015, New South Wales Department of Public Works, 97 p.

HESP, P. A., 1984, Aspects of the geomorphology of southwestern Australian estuaries, in Estuarine Environments of the Southern Hemisphere: Department of Conservation and Environment, Western Australia, Bulletin 161, p. 61–83.

HODGKIN, E. P., 1978, An environmental study of the Blackwood River estuary, Western Australia: Department of Conservation and Environment, Report No. 1, 78 p.

HODGKIN, E. P., AND KENDRICK, G. W., 1983, The changing aquatic environment 7000 BP to 1983 in the estuaries of southwestern Australia, in Estuarine Environments of the Southern Hemisphere: Department of Conservation and Environment, Western Australia, Bulletin 161, p. 85–95.

KRAFT, J. C., 1978, Coastal stratigraphic sequences, in Davis, R. A., Jr., ed., Coastal Sedimentary Environments: New York, Springer-Verlag, p. 361–383.

NEVILLE, M. J., 1976, Sand resources of the Hawkesbury River system between Windsor and Brooklyn: New South Wales Geological Survey, Report GS1976/231, 48 p.

NIELSEN, A. F., AND GORDON, A. D., 1981, Tidal inlet behavioural analysis: Sydney, Proceedings of the 17th International Coastal Engineering Conference, p. 2461–2480.

NIELSEN, A. F., AND ROY, P. S., 1981, Age contamination of radiocarbon dates on shell hash from coastal sand deposits: southeastern Australian examples: Sydney Proceedings of the 5th Australian Conference on Coastal and Ocean Engineering, p. 177–182.

NICHOL, S. L., 1991, Zonation and sedimentology of estuarine facies in an incised valley, wave-dominated micro-tidal setting, in Smith, D. G., Reinson, G. E., Zaitlin, B. A., and Rahmani, R. A., eds., Clastic Tidal Sedimentology: Canadian Society Petroleum Geologists Memoir 16, p. 41–58.

PEAT, C., AND ROY, P. S., 1975, Shell deposits, Port Stephens: New South Wales Geological Quaternary Survey Notes, v. 19, p. 9–19.

PICKETT, J. W., 1983, Geological implications of Pleistocene invertebrates from water bore WRC 39275, near Bulahdelah: Geological Survey of New South Wales, Quarterly Notes, v. 52, p. 8–15.

PUBLIC WORKS DEPARTMENT, 1976, Swansea Channel Waterway Planning Study: New South Wales Department of Public Works, Report 77006, 85 p.

PUBLIC WORKS DEPARTMENT, 1983, Lake Illawarra Entrance Study: New South Wales Department of Public Works, Report 83094, 128 p.

PYE, K., AND BOWMAN, G. M., 1984, The Holocene Marine Transgression as a forcing function in episodic dune activity on the eastern Australian coast, in Thom, B. G., ed., Coastal Geomorphology of Australia: New York, Academic Press, p. 179–196.

REINSON, G. E., 1983, Facies models: 6, barrier island systems, in Walker, G. R., ed., Facies Models: Geoscience Canada, Reprint Series 1, p. 57–74.

RINGIS, J., LEAN, J., AND PALMER, D., 1974, Marine geophysical surveys in Lake Macquarie: city, New South Wales Geological Survey, Unpublished Report GS1974/262, 37 p.

ROY, P. S., 1980, Stratigraphy and depositional environments of Quaternary sediments in the Fullerton Cove area, central New South Wales coast: New South Wales Geological Survey, Records, v. 19, p. 189–219.

ROY, P. S., 1981, Fossil shell assemblages in Lake Macquarie: New South Wales Geological Survey Quaternary Notes, v. 42, p. 12–17.

ROY, P. S., 1983, Quaternary Geology, in Herbert, C., ed., Geology of the Sydney 1:100,000 sheet 9120: Sydney, New South Wales Geological Survey, p. 41–91.

ROY, P. S., 1984, New South Wales estuaries—their origin and evolution, in Thom, B. G., ed., Coastal Geomorphology in Australia: New York, Academic Press, p. 99–121.

ROY, P. S., 1991, Shell hash dating and mixing models for palimpsest marine sediments: Radiocarbon, v. 33, p. 283–289.

ROY, P. S., COWELL, P. J., FORLAND, M. A., AND THOM, B. G., 1994, Wave dominated coasts, in Carter, R. W. G., and Woodroffe, C. D., eds., Coastal Evolution: Cambridge, Cambridge University Press, p. 121–186.

ROY, P. S., AND CRAWFORD, E. A., 1977, Significance of sediment distributions in major coastal rivers, northern New South Wales: Third Australian Conference on Coastal and Ocean Engineering, The Institution of Engineers, 77/2, p. 177–184.

ROY, P. S., AND CRAWFORD, E. A., 1981, Holocene geological evolution of the southern Botany Bay-Kurnell region, central New South Wales coast: New South Wales Geological Survey, Records, v. 20, p. 159–250.

ROY, P. S., AND CRAWFORD, E. A., 1984, Heavy metals in a contaminated Australian estuary-dispersion and accumulation trends: Estuarine, Coastal, and Shelf Science, v. 19, p. 341–358.

ROY, P. S., AND PEAT, C., 1975, Bathymetry and bottom sediments of Lake Macquarie: New South Wales Geological Survey, Records, v. 17, p. 53–64.

ROY, P. S., AND PEAT, C., 1976, Bathymetry and bottom sediments of Tuross estuary and Coila Lake: New South Wales Geological Survey Records, v. 18, p. 103–134.

ROY, P. S., AND STEPHENS, A. W., 1981, Geological controls on process-response, SE Australia: Sydney, Proceedings 17th International Coastal Engineering Conference, p. 913–933.

ROY, P. S., AND THOM, B. G., 1981, Late Quaternary marine deposition in New South Wales and southern Queensland-an evolutionary model: Journal of the Geological Society of Australia, v. 28, p. 471–489.

ROY, P. S., THOM, B. G., AND WRIGHT, L. D., 1980, Holocene sequences on an embayed high-energy coast. An evolutionary model: Sedimentary Geology, v. 26, p. 1–19.

ROY, P. S., ZHUANG, W.-Y., BIRCH, G. F., AND COWELL, P. J., 1992, Quaternary geology and placer mineral potential of the Forster-Tuncurry shelf, southeast Australia: Geological Survey of New South Wales, Report GS 1992/201, 76 p.

THOM, B. G., ROY, P. S., SHORT, A. D., HUDSON, J., AND DAVIS, J., 1986, Modern coastal and estuarine environments of deposition in Southeastern Australia: Canberra, Guide for Excursion 4A, 12th International Sedimentological Congress, 279 p.

THOM, B. G., 1984, Transgressive and regressive stratigraphies of coastal sand barriers in eastern Australia: Marine Geology, v. 56, p. 137–158.

THOM, B. G., BOWMAN, G. M., GILLESPIE, R., TEMPLE, R., AND BARBETTI, M., 1981, Radiocarbon dating of Holocene beach-ridge sequences in southeast Australia: Duntroon, University of New South Wales Faculty of Military Studies, Royal Military College, Monograph 11, 36 p.

THOM, B. G., AND CHAPPELL, J., 1975, Holocene sea levels relative to Australia: Search, v. 6, p. 90–93.

THOM, B. G., POLACH, H. A., AND BOWMAN, G. M., 1978, Holocene age structure of coastal sand barriers in New South Wales, Australia: Duntroon, University of New South Wales, 86 p.

THOM, B. G., AND ROY, P. S., 1983, Sea level change in New South Wales over the past 15,000 years, *in* Hopley, D., ed., Holocene Sea Levels in Australia: IGCP Project 61, James Cook University of North Queensland, Special Monograph, p. 64–84.

THOM, B. G., AND ROY, P. S., 1985, Relative sea levels and coastal sedimentation in southeast Australia in the Holocene: Journal of Sedimentary Petrology, v. 55, p. 257–264.

WRIGHT, L. D., 1970, The influence of sediment availability on patterns of beachridge development in the vicinity of the Shoalhaven River delta, New South Wales: The Australian Geographer, v. 11, p. 336–348.

WRIGHT, L. D., 1977, Morphodynamics of a wave-dominated river mouth: Honolulu, Proceedings of the 15th International Coastal Engineering Conference, p. 1721–1737.

WRIGHT, L. D., BRADSHAW, M., CHAPPELL, J., COWELL, P. J., SHORT, A. D., AND THOM, B. G., 1978, Physical oceanography and morphodynamic processes affecting the nearshore and inshore zones of the Sydney Region with emphasis on the Broken Bay—Palm Beach area: implications for offshore dredging: Sydney, Coastal Studies Unit, The University of Sydney, Report 78/1, 64 p.

WRIGHT, L. D., COLEMAN, J. M., AND THOM, B. G., 1973, Process of channel development in a high-tide range environment: Cambridge Gulf—Ord River delta: Journal of Geology, v. 81, p. 15–41.

STRATIGRAPHIC RESPONSE OF WAVE-DOMINATED ESTUARIES TO DIFFERENT RELATIVE SEA-LEVEL AND SEDIMENT SUPPLY HISTORIES: QUATERNARY CASE STUDIES FROM NOVA SCOTIA, LOUISIANA AND EASTERN AUSTRALIA

SCOTT L. NICHOL
Department of Geography, University of Auckland, Private Bag 92019, Auckland, New Zealand
RON BOYD
Department of Geology, University of Newcastle, Newcastle, NSW 2308, Australia
AND
SHEA PENLAND
Louisiana Geological Survey, University Station, Box G, Baton Rouge, Louisiana 70893

ABSTRACT: The stratigraphic organization of facies within estuarine valley fills for three wave-dominated coasts illustrates the importance of relative sea-level behaviour and sediment supply. The study areas differ primarily in their Holocene sea-level history and relative significance of clastic sediment sources.

Lawrencetown Lake on the eastern shore of Nova Scotia has experienced sea-level rise of 30 to 40 cm/century since early Holocene time and has yet to reach the point of maximum transgression. Sediment is sourced primarily from eroding drumlin headlands, beaches and drowned barriers. Fluvial sediment input is negligible. Valley stratigraphy is characterised by transgressive flood-tidal delta and nearshore-bar facies overlying central basin facies. Bounding surfaces include a lowstand unconformity beneath glacial deposits, a transgressive surface at the base of central basin deposits, an inlet diastem and a shoreface ravinement surface. These surfaces are all stratigraphically separated in the valley fill. Bay-head delta and floodplain facies, and associated bounding surfaces are poorly developed. The maximum flooding surface has yet to form. Locally, abundant supplies of sediment from drumlins and drowned barriers results in periodic shoreline progradation, despite rising sea level.

Shoreline transgression has continued at varying rates along the western sector of the Louisiana coast since about 9 ka, in response to episodic, relative sea-level rise. Sea level is presently at relative stillstand, although the mean water level in Lake Calcasieu is rising at 60 cm/century. Sediment sources include local, low-gradient coastal-plain rivers and distributaries of the Mississippi River that discharge sediment into westward-flowing longshore currents. Subsurface data from Lake Calcasieu reveal a 30- to 55-m deep valley filled predominantly with facies of fluvial origin, including a lowstand wedge, two aggraded fluvial deposits in the transgressive systems tract, transgressive marsh and transgressive to highstand central basin deposits. The contact between lower and upper central basin sediments represents the maximum flooding surface. Modern fluvial channel and bay-head delta facies are incised into aggraded central basin deposits at the head of the estuary. A channel diastem occurs at the contact between bay-head delta and central basin facies. At the seaward end of Lake Calcasieu, the shoreface ravinement surface truncates central basin deposits and extends into the estuary. The presence of a 15 km wide chenier plain indicates that transgression has been punctuated by shoreline progradation.

Sea-level along the New South Wales coast has maintained a stillstand position since about 6.5 ka and estuaries lie close to the highstand position. Marine sediment input was high during the early to mid-Holocene, but inner-shelf supplies of sediment became depleted by 3 ka BP. South-coast streams have relatively steep slopes and drain catchments composed of coarse-grained lithologies. The Wapengo Lagoon and Narrawallee Inlet valley fills display regressive characteristics resulting from bay-head delta progradation across central basin deposits, and in Narrawallee, the river delta interfingers with tidal-inlet facies. The shoreface ravinement surface terminates at the mouths of both estuaries, and inlet diastems appear inactive. Bay-head delta diastems, however, continue to grow seaward. Multiple estuarine sequences are preserved in both valleys due to incomplete scouring during the last sea-level lowstand.

INTRODUCTION

The concept that relative sea level and sediment supply interact to influence depositional style in coastal systems is well established. Previous workers have thoroughly documented the morphology, stratigraphy, facies architecture and evolution of coastal depositional successions in the context of sea-level history and sediment sources (e.g., Curray, 1964; Swift, 1968, 1975; Boyd and Penland, 1984; Elliott, 1986; Davis and Clifton, 1987; Nummedal and Swift, 1987; Boyd and others, 1992). Most studies have provided separate descriptions of modern barriers, lagoons, and coastal-plain rivers (see Leatherman, 1979, 1987; Rampino and Sanders, 1980; Roy and others, 1980; Belknap and Kraft, 1981, 1985; Roy and Thom, 1981; Blum, 1990; Miall, 1992; Reinson, 1992; among others). However, few have considered barriers, lagoons *and* the tide-influenced reaches of rivers in the same context. That is the domain of estuaries. This paper aims to provide a link between coastal and fluvial depositional complexes by examining the stratigraphic organisation of facies in selected wave-dominated estuaries. Here we adopt the approach of Dalrymple and others (1992, Figs. 2, 3), and define wave-dominated estuaries in terms of the relative dominance of wave energy over both tide and river energy.

Estuaries receive clastic sediment from two primary sources: marine and terrestrial. The interplay between these sediment sources and relative sea level affects wave-dominated estuaries in the following manner. When relative sea-level rise exceeds sediment supply, from both terrestrial and marine sources, shoreline transgression is initiated and coastal lithosomes erode (Curray, 1964; Boyd and others, 1992). These conditions are favourable for the creation of estuaries. Sediment liberated from nearshore, inlet, beach, and dune environments by the retreating shoreface is available for re-deposition in these estuaries by wave, tide, and aeolian processes. However, if the rate of sediment input to estuaries is greater than relative sea-level rise, estuaries infill and coastal regression proceeds until a delta or strandplain coast develops, by which point estuaries are destroyed (Boyd and others, 1992; Dalrymple and others, 1992). Thus, for estuaries to form and persist, a delicate balance between relative sea-level change and sediment supply is required. A further influence of the interaction between sea-level change and sediment supply upon estuaries is evident in the behaviour of coastal rivers. Sea-level rise or fall is con-

Incised-valley Systems: Origin and Sedimentary Sequences, SEPM Special Publication No. 51

comitant with a base-level change of rivers. Fisk (1944) was the first to suggest that aggradation of coastal and fluvial environments is a response to eustatic sea-level rise. In estuaries, this may be manifest as a reduction of the capacity of rivers to transport sediment to the coast, thereby enhancing floodplain and channel aggradation in the upper reaches of estuaries (Blum, 1990; Thomas, 1990), and causing a landward shift of the focal point of bay-head delta deposition (Posamentier and Vail, 1988). The three, wave-dominated coasts examined in this study have contrasting sea-level and sediment supply histories. The objective of the study, therefore, is to document the resultant stratigraphic variations among modern incised-valley estuaries that have reached an advanced evolutionary stage.

Study sites for this paper include Lawrencetown Lake on the eastern shore of Nova Scotia, Lake Calcasieu on the western coast of Louisiana, and Wapengo Lagoon and Narrawallee Inlet on the south coast of New South Wales. The eastern shore of Nova Scotia provides a setting characterised by ongoing transgression and a dominantly marine sediment supply. The western coast of Louisiana is currently at stillstand following episodic sea-level rise, with sediment in estuaries derived primarily from fluvial sources. The south-coast of New South Wales is also at sea-level stillstand, but estuaries have received significant input of sediment from both marine and fluvial sources. The stratigraphic expression of sediment supply and sea-level interactions in these case studies is particularly important to understanding incised-valley depositional successions because they encompass the evolutionary path of estuaries, from initial flooding (marine transgression) to complete filling (depositional regression).

METHODS

Data sources for the study sites include:

1. Color aerial photographs of all sites to facilitate facies mapping.
2. A down-valley transect of 19 vibracores (Honig, 1987) in Lawrencetown Lake, from the head of the estuary to the front of the barrier, provided data for the upper 5 to 6 m of the valley fill. Bedrock depths were determined from refraction seismic data collected by Honig (1987) at 16 stations on Lawrencetown beach and the supratidal marsh in lower Lawrencetown Lake.
3. In Lake Calcasieu, a stratigraphic profile along the valley axis has been constructed from 29 vibracores and 80 bridge borehole records (Louisiana Department of Transportation and Development) located along the tidal reaches of the Calcasieu River, and from borehole data (Le Blanc, 1949) from Lake Calcasieu and the chenier plain south of the lake. Vibracores provided a detailed record of the surficial 5 to 6 m, and boreholes provided deeper stratigraphic information that included Pleistocene deposits.
4. In Wapengo Lagoon, 7 vibracores were collected by Nichol (1991a) along the valley axis, from the bay-head delta to the estuary mouth. Vibracores yielded 5- to 6-m samples that in four cores included the Holocene-Pleistocene contact. In Narrawallee Inlet, 6 drill holes,

located on a floodplain that occupies a paleo-estuary, were taken by Nichol (1991a). The drill holes lay along the valley axis and provided continuous core samples to the sandstone floor of the incised valley.

ESTUARINE FACIES ORGANISATION AND BOUNDING SURFACES

Wave-dominated estuaries are characterised by a predictable spatial organisation of facies that exists in response to convergence of fluvial and marine depositional processes (Dalrymple and others, 1992). The resulting, tripartite facies distribution typically comprises (Fig. 1A): (i) an outer zone occupied by sandy sediment of marine provenance, (ii) a central zone of fine-grained sediment derived from suspended river load and autochthonous biological sources, and (iii) a landward tidal-fluvial zone of terrestrially derived deposits. Documented examples include: estuaries along the southeast coast of Australia (Bird, 1967; Reinson, 1977; Roy, 1984a; Nichol, 1991b); the James estuary in Virginia (Nichols and others, 1991); the Gironde estuary (Allen, 1991; Allen and Posamentier, 1993); the Lloydminster member of the lower Cretaceous Manville Group, west-central Canada (Zaitlin and Shultz, 1990); and the Crystal and Sundance/Edson valley-fill deposits of the Viking Formation, Alberta (Reinson and others, 1988; Pattison, 1992).

Figure 1B presents a generalised valley fill for a wave-dominated estuary, showing major facies and bounding surfaces. The model represents an estuary that lies at the point of maximum transgression, and has developed regressive characteristics, notably a beach-ridge plain and bay-head delta. It is presented as a basis for assessing variations and contrasts that may be observed among the case studies. The basal erosion surface in an incised valley is an unconformity formed by fluvial and/or glacial processes during sea-level lowstands. This unconformity represents the basal sequence boundary for an estuarine fill and corresponds with the base of lowstand fluvial sediments (Fig. 1B) (Vail and others, 1984; Galloway, 1989). Transgression generates a surface in estuarine valleys that separates lowstand fluvial deposits from overlying estuarine sediments. This is termed a transgressive surface (Posamentier and others, 1992), and it is shown as lying beneath retrogradational, bay-head delta facies (Fig. 1B) (Dalrymple and others, 1992). This surface is equivalent to the bay ravinement surface of Nummedal and Swift (1987) and the bayline surface described by Thomas (1990) for the Trinity-Sabine incised-valley system, east Texas. The transgressive surface may amalgamate with the lowstand unconformity where erosion of lowstand fluvial deposits has occurred, possibly by river channels as the bay-head delta retrograded (Posamentier and Vail, 1988; Posamentier and others, 1992). Where fully preserved, the transgressive surface extends to the head of the estuary, terminating at the leading edge of the transgression. The apex of transgression is represented by the maximum flooding surface, which is associated with the transition from the transgressive systems tract to the highstand systems tract (Allen and Posamentier, 1993). In some situations, this surface may not be easily identified, particularly where modern channels have scoured into transgressive and lowstand systems tracts.

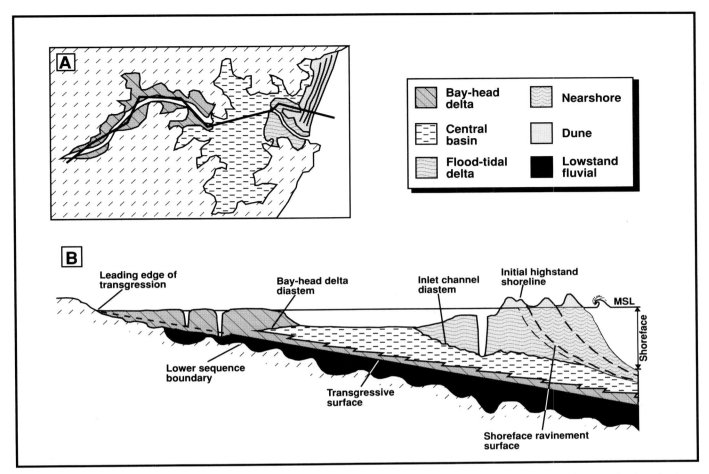

FIG. 1.—(A) Plan view of the tripartite zonation of facies in wave-dominated estuaries. (B) Generalised stratigraphy of a wave-dominated estuary that lies at the point of maximum transgression and has experienced progradation of bay-head delta and beach-ridge facies, showing major bounding surfaces. The lowstand systems tract is represented by lowstand fluvial facies. The transgressive systems tract includes retrograded bay-head delta, lower central basin, and flood-tidal delta facies. The highstand systems tract encompasses prograded bay-head delta, upper central basin and dune facies. The maximum flooding surface lies at the contact between transgressive and highstand systems tracts. The thickness of systems tracts and component facies are controlled by the rate of relative sea-level rise, the relative rate of sediment input, antecedent topography (including valley gradient), and the depth of the shoreface (Belknap and Kraft, 1981). In estuaries with prograded barriers, a shoreface ravinement surface forms with each episode of beach-face retreat. MSL= Mean sea level.

Toward the seaward end of wave-dominated estuaries, the valley fill may display one or more ravinement surfaces produced by shoreface erosion (Fig. 1B). The depth of this surface is controlled by the maximum depth of wave reworking in the nearshore, along with antecedent topography and the rate of sea-level rise (Belknap and Kraft, 1985; Nummedal and Swift, 1987). Typically, the shoreface ravinement surface is situated at the base of nearshore-bar deposits that are in erosional contact with underlying flood-tidal delta or central basin facies. Multiple shoreface ravinement surfaces will exist where the shoreline has prograded to form a beach-ridge plain. The most landward beach ridge represents the initial position of the highstand shoreline and marks the landward limit of shoreface ravinement. Successive ridges and ravinement surfaces record the advance of the shoreline in response to sediment supply exceeding the rate of relative sea-level rise. Each ravinement surface will form during a limited period, because it ceases

to function once the shoreline progrades to a new position. Moreover, beach ridges and associated shoreface ravinement surfaces will be destroyed if transgression is reinitiated.

Channel diastems are an important type of bounding surface in the architecture of incised-valley estuarine sequences. Nummedal and Swift (1987) define a channel diastem to result from lateral migration of a channel floor. In the estuarine context, two types of channel diastem may form (Fig. 1B). The first type, termed tidal-inlet diastem, is associated with tidal-inlet and flood-tidal delta channels in the seaward zone of a wave-dominated estuary. The tidal-inlet diastem is a diachronous surface that becomes younger in a landward direction. The second type of channel diastem is a product of lateral migration of a fluvial channel at the inner part of an estuary. River channels at the head of a wave-dominated estuary are typically flanked by bay-head delta deposits, and the erosion surface is therefore termed a bay-head diastem. This diastem migrates seaward in association with the prograding bay-head delta. Depending on the depth of channel downcutting and valley depths, channel diastems may amalgamate with the transgressive surface and the lowstand unconformity.

In summary, facies organisation in wave-dominated estuaries appears to be predictable, and associated bounding surfaces display geometries that are unique in form and origin to incised-estuary valleys. In particular, the presence of landward- and seaward-migrating channel diastems is a function of tidal-inlet and fluvial processes in action at each end of a wave-dominated estuary. Also, the accommodation space provided by incised valleys can allow for stratigraphic separation of the lowstand unconformity from subsequent bounding surfaces, such as the transgressive surface and shoreface ravinement surface. This contrasts with submerged interfluves on the continental shelf where the lowstand unconformity is commonly amalgamated with the shoreface ravinement surface (Suter and others, 1987). The following examples show that local differences in sediment supply and sea-level history result in departures from the stratal geometries suggested by the model outlined above.

CASE STUDIES

Lawrencetown Lake, Eastern Nova Scotia

Physiography and Coastal Processes.—

The Atlantic coast of Nova Scotia is characterised by numerous embayments formed by fluvial and glacial action during the Late Quaternary. Valleys generally are aligned along southeast-trending lineaments and are incised 40 to 60 m into Ordovician quartzites and slates of the Meguma Group (Boyd and others, 1987). Glacial deposits occur as drumlins 10 to 25 m thick and ground moraine less than 3 m thick (Stea, 1983; Stea and others, 1992a). Drumlins that intersect the coast at headlands are exposed to constant wave attack that forms till cliffs. Cliff faces are retreating as much as 1 m/yr, yielding sand- to cobble-sized sediment for longshore transport into estuaries (Boyd and others, 1987).

Wave and tide action are the primary coastal processes for sediment transport along the eastern shore. Mean annual, ocean wave power is 2.14×10^4 W/m and is classified as high energy (Boyd and others, 1987). Winter storms generate peak wave conditions, with wave heights up to 8 m (Forbes and others, 1991). Average, spring-tidal range is low mesotidal at 2.1 m and is reduced to 0.9 m inside Lawrencetown Lake. Sediment released from drumlins, beaches and barriers is transported alongshore and into estuaries by tidal currents that attain peak velocities exceeding 2 m/s through tidal inlets (Boyd and Honig, 1992). Ice rafting is also a significant agent for sediment transport. Cobbles and small boulders are moved from drumlins by wind-driven ice and deposited in back-barrier and flood-tidal delta environments. Tidal currents are incapable of transporting such material to these sites. Fluvial sediment input to eastern shore estuaries is minor, despite comparatively steep river gradients (Table 1), because bedload sediment is trapped upstream in deep lake basins (Bowen and Boyd, 1983).

Along the Atlantic coast of Nova Scotia, post-glacial fluctuations in relative sea level were influenced by migra-

TABLE 1.—RIVER AND CATCHMENT DIMENSIONS FOR NSW SOUTH COAST, EASTERN SHORE AND WESTERN LOUISIANA COASTAL STREAMS

River	Length (km)	Fall Height (m)	Mean Gradient	Catchment Area (km²)
Wapengo, NSW	11	340	1:32	73
Narrawallee, NSW	15.75	434	1:36	85
Partridge, NS	9.8	76	1:129	14
Chezzetcook, NS	11.25	76	1:148	48
Calcasieu, La	211.75	91	1:2327	9780

tion of the glacial forebulge crest during deglaciation (Quinlan and Beaumont, 1982). As the ice margin retreated, the forebulge caused a fall in relative sea level. Sea-level then rose once the forebulge had crossed the coastal zone. The sea-level curve for the eastern shore shows a 70-m rise since about 11.6 ka at a uniform rate of 30 to 40 cm/century (Fig. 2A) (Scott and others, 1987; Stea and others, 1992b). Modern tide-gauge records for Halifax Harbour indicate continuation of the trend, with mean sea level rising at a rate of 3.6 to 4.0 mm/yr (Carrera and Vanicek, 1989).

Facies Distribution.—

Lawrencetown Lake displays a variety of depositional environments that are recognisable in other eastern shore estuaries (Fig. 3A) (Nichol and Boyd, 1993). The upper reaches of the estuary are characterised by organic mud, typical of a central basin environment (Fig. 3B). The Salmon River flows into the estuary at this point, but the low bedload discharge of the river precludes bay-head delta development. Therefore, fluvial sediments constitute only a minor fraction of the facies in Lawrencetown Lake estuary, and this estuary does not display the full tripartite facies zonation (Boyd and Honig, 1992). The seaward facies zone (marine sand body) in Lawrencetown Lake dominates the estuary. It incorporates beach-ridge plain, foredune, beach, washover fan, nearshore bar, flood-tidal delta, and ebb-tidal delta facies. The continuity of the beach-ridge plain is broken by Lawrencetown Inlet and a small drumlin at Lawrencetown Head (Fig. 3B). The eastern ridge complex includes 25 shore-parallel ridges that range in height from 0.4 m to 1.3 m above mean sea level. Washover deposits are located landward of the western end of Lawrencetown Beach, where the barrier is only 150 m wide. The western beach-ridge system includes eight ridges that have a mean elevation of 2 m above mean sea level.

The greater part of Lawrencetown Lake is occupied by the flood-tidal delta (Fig. 3B). The delta has transgressed 5.6 km from the estuary mouth and interfingers with central basin deposits (Boyd and Honig, 1992). The morphology of the flood-tidal delta is characterised by a flood ramp located immediately landward of the estuary mouth, vegetated intertidal bars alongside the main tidal channel, a network of tidal channels, and a surficial sheet of muddy sand that extends to the upper end of the estuary (Boyd and Honig, 1992). A small ebb-tidal delta has developed outside the estuary entrance. The ebb-tidal delta is defined by sand shoals that flank the inlet channel and a sand bar at the seaward end of the ebb channel. The sedimentological properties of

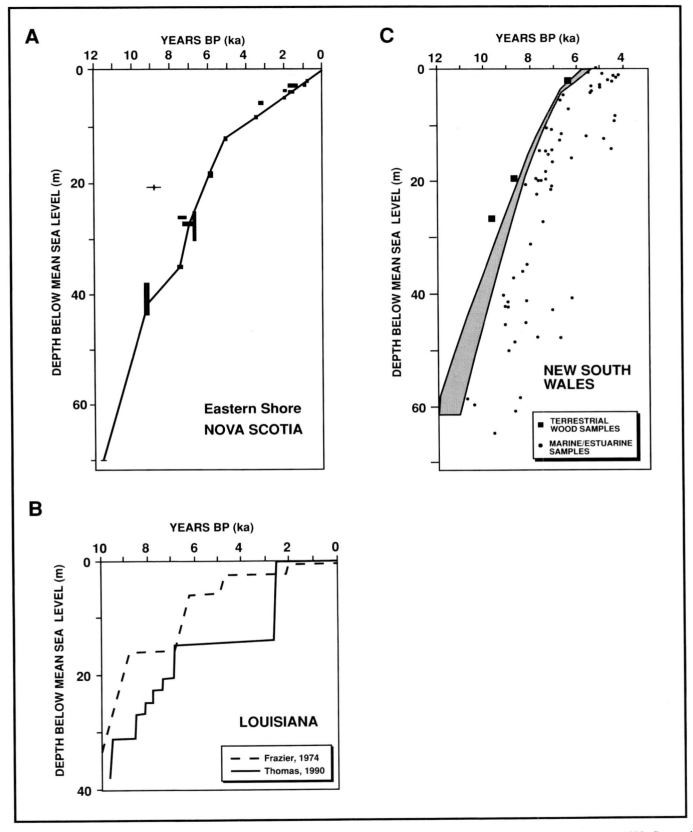

FIG. 2.—Late Pleistocene to Holocene relative sea-level curves for (A) the eastern shore of Nova Scotia (Forbes and others, 1988; Stea and others, 1992b), (B) southwest Louisiana (Thomas, 1990), and (C) New South Wales (Thom and Roy, 1983).

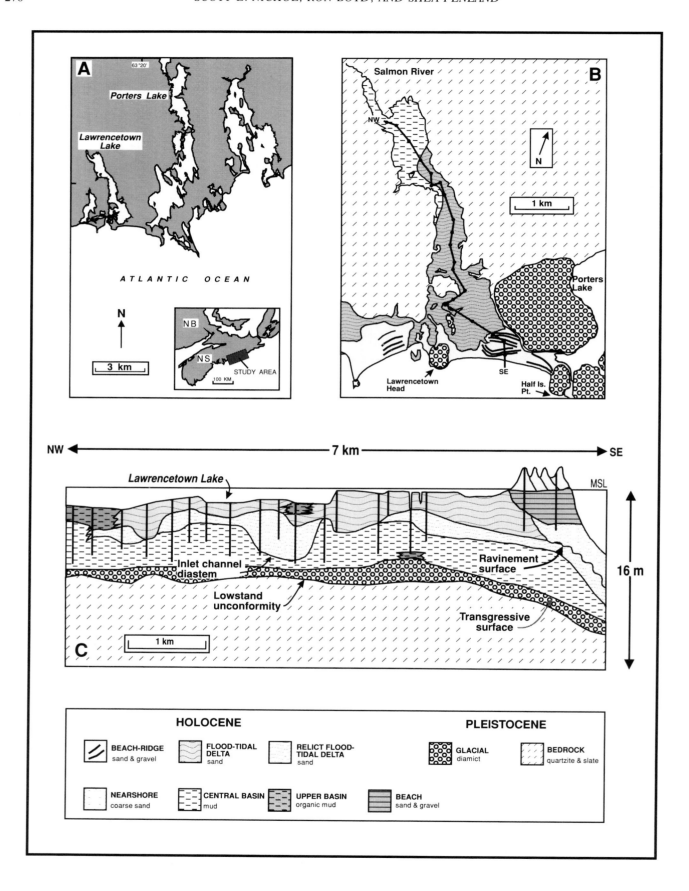

these and other eastern shore barrier deposits are detailed by Nichol and Boyd (1993).

Valley Stratigraphy.—

Lawrencetown Lake has undergone substantial valley filling since the mid-Holocene. Seismic refraction data indicate a mean depth to acoustic basement of 9.75 m beneath the beach-ridge plain (Honig, 1987). At the western end of Lawrencetown beach, however, valley depths of 20 to 24 m were measured by Honig (1987), suggesting a palaeo-drainage line along the valley axis. At present sea level, the 2 m deep central basin offers the greatest remaining accommodation space for further infill. On the basis of seismic reflection and vibracore data collected by Forbes and others (1991) from the Scotian inner shelf, the basal facies in the Lawrencetown fill is interpreted as a glacial diamict. Offshore from Lawrencetown Lake, glacial deposits rest unconformably upon bedrock and in seismic sections have an average thickness of 10 m or less (Forbes and others, 1991). The basal surface of the diamict represents a lower sequence boundary and these deposits belong to the lowstand systems tract. In view of the present, negligible fluvial sediment supply, we assume that fluvial facies are poorly represented in the lowstand systems tract. Figure 3C shows that the Lawrencetown Lake stratigraphic profile is dominated by facies associated with the transgressive systems tract, specifically central basin and flood-tidal delta facies. The contact between glacial deposits and central basin mud is interpreted as a transgressive surface in the sense described by Posamentier and others, (1992). Vibracore data indicate that the central basin facies is at least 3 m thick (Fig. 3C).

The remainder of the transgressive systems tract in Lawrencetown Lake is occupied by a flood-tidal delta that is divided into two units of different age (Boyd and Honig, 1992). The lower flood-tidal delta deposit extends discontinuously from the seaward end almost to the head of the valley, and is incised up to 3.5 m into the central basin facies. Radiocarbon dates indicate that this delta formed between 2 ka and 800 years BP (Boyd and Honig, 1992). The second flood-tidal delta unit extends 5.6 km as a continuous, 0.5- to 3-m thick sand sheet (Fig. 3C). This deposit formed between 800 and 200 years BP (Boyd and Honig, 1992). The tidal-channel diastem associated with the younger unit is generally not as deeply incised as that of the older flood-tidal delta. This is interpreted to be partly a function of a smaller tidal prism and weaker currents during deposition of the second flood-tidal delta.

The beach-ridge plain at the seaward end of Lawrencetown Lake is 800 m wide and characterised by nearshore bar, beach and dune facies (Fig. 3C) (Nichol and Boyd, 1993). Vibracore data from the beach-ridge plain record a 6-m thick succession that is interpreted to represent shoreline progradation from the position of the rear beach ridge, following transgression. The age of the most landward beach ridge is estimated at 700 years BP on the basis of carbon-14 dating and surveys of ridge heights (Hoskin, 1983). Subsequent shoreline regression is recorded by the successive deposition of nearshore bar, beach and foredune facies (Fig. 3C). Map records show the present morphology of the beach-ridge plain was established before 1776 AD (Hoskin, 1983). Progradation at Lawrencetown has been possible, in spite of rising sea level, due to abundant sediment supplies from drumlins at Half Island Point (Fig. 3B) and drowned barriers that had formed in the Lawrencetown embayment at lower sea levels.

The shoreface ravinement surface is located at the contact between nearshore deposits and the underlying flood-tidal delta facies (Fig. 3C). At Lawrencetown, the landward limit of the ravinement surface correlates with the innermost beach ridge. Given continued transgression, the shoreface ravinement surface will remove a significant portion of the flood-tidal delta deposit and possibly some of the central basin facies. Indeed, seismic-reflection data from offshore Lawrencetown Lake show preservation of only a thin (1 to 2 m thick), discontinuous flood-tidal delta unit and 0.5- to 4-m of central basin deposits (Forbes and others, 1991). It is important to emphasise the lack of bay-head delta deposits and an associated bay-head delta diastem in the Lawrencetown estuarine fill. The absence of these elements has allowed the valley fill to be dominated by the transgressive systems tract, notably, central basin mud and flood-tidal delta sand. The maximum flooding surface is also absent from the Lawrencetown succession; ongoing transgression along the eastern shore means that the maximum flooding surface has yet to form in Lawrencetown Lake.

Lake Calcasieu, Western Louisiana

Physiography and Coastal Processes.—

Lake Calcasieu occupies a valley that traverses the chenier plain of the Mississippi River and outcrops of Pleistocene deposits that belong to the Prairie Terrace Formation (Fig. 4A). During the $\delta^{18}O$ Stage 2 lowstand, rivers flowing across the continental shelf of western Louisiana and east Texas incised their valleys to depths ranging between 30 and 55 m below present sea level (Suter, 1986; Anderson and others, 1991). These valleys were flooded when sea level rose after the glacial maximum. At present sea level, Lake Calcasieu is characterised by a central basin that is 24.5 km long and broadens seaward to a maximum width of 19.5 km. Here it is divided from the Gulf of Mexico by a 6.5- to 8.5-km wide chenier-ridge and saltmarsh barrier.

FIG. 3.—(A) Eastern shore, Nova Scotia showing the location of Lawrencetown Lake estuary. (B) Facies distribution in Lawrencetown Lake with vibracore locations and transect for stratigraphic section. (C) Stratigraphic profile of Lawrencetown Lake incised-valley fill. Systems-tract facies are as follows: *Lowstand* = Glacial diamict; *Transgressive* = central basin, flood-tidal delta (relict and modern), nearshore, beach and beach-ridge. Note the absence of highstand bay-head delta deposits and associated diastem. Also, due to ongoing transgression, the maximum flooding surface is yet to form.

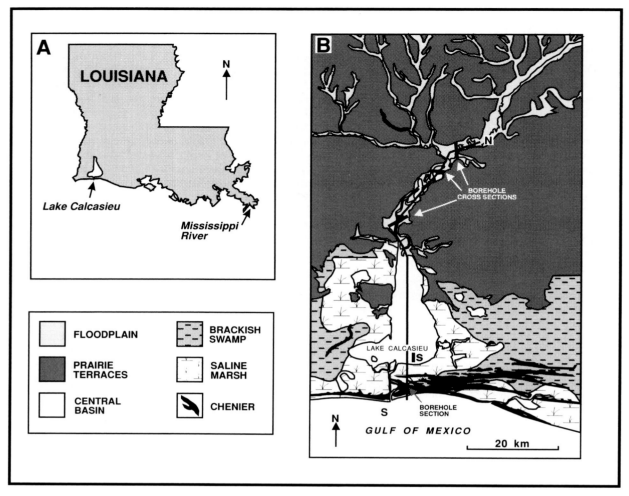

FIG. 4.—(A) Location map for Lake Calcasieu, western Louisiana. (B) Facies distribution in Lake Calcasieu with transects for stratigraphic (borehole) sections.

Upstream of the central basin, Pleistocene outcrop restricts the valley to a mean width of 2.5 km, where tidal and river waters are confined to a tightly meandering channel.

Coastal processes along the chenier plain of southwest Louisiana are characterised by a small tidal range of about 0.6 m and low fairweather wave energy, evident from the statistic that 42 percent of all waves are 1 to 1.5 m high (Becker, 1972). Storm events, principally summer hurricanes and winter cold fronts, generate extremely energetic conditions. Water levels may rise 2 to 7 m above the mean fairweather elevation and, when coupled with increased wave height, cause beach and barrier washover and coastal flooding (Boyd and Penland, 1981). A detailed description of the hydrology of Lake Calcasieu is presented by Nichol and others (1992).

Principal sediment sources for Lake Calcasieu include the Calcasieu River and reworked sediment transported by longshore drift from distributaries of the Mississippi River further east. The Calcasieu River has the largest catchment area but the lowest stream gradient of the study sites (Table 1). The mean annual, suspended sediment load of the Cal-

casieu River, derived from 10 years of sampling, is 85×10^3 m^3 (Water Resources Division, Louisiana Geological Survey). If this rate is assumed to apply to the last 3000 years, the total volume of sediment supplied by the Calcasieu River would be 2.5×10^8 m^3, which is an order of magnitude less than the 2.3×10^9 m^3 volume of Holocene floodplain and bay-head delta deposits. This result suggests that fluvial sediment flux into the Calcasieu estuary has decreased since mid-Holocene times. Subsiding point bars and poorly developed delta-front lobes are additional geomorphic indicators for a recent decrease in fluvial sediment input.

The nearshore zone along the west Louisiana coast has a very high suspended sediment load that is currently derived from the Atchafalaya River (Wells and Roberts, 1980). The annual volume of sediment discharged into the westerly flowing, nearshore mud stream was calculated by Wells and Roberts (1980) as 53×10^6 m^3. An unknown fraction of this load is transported to the seaward face of the chenier-plain barrier at Lake Calcasieu. The Calcasieu chenier plain has therefore prograded in episodes of fairweather mudflat deposition, interrupted by storms that rework mud-flats to concentrate sand and shell in chenier ridges (Penland and Suter, 1989).

The history of relative sea-level change along the Texas-Louisiana coast, shown in Figure 2B, has been reconstructed using radiocarbon-dated deposits (Frazier, 1974) and seismic-stratigraphic methods (Thomas, 1990; Anderson and Thomas, 1991). The curve constructed by Thomas (1990) is derived from stratigraphic data collected in the Trinity-Sabine incised-valley system, located adjacent to Lake Calcasieu. The Trinity-Sabine curve has been calibrated with the Barbados sea-level curve of Fairbanks (1989). It shows several episodes of virtually instantaneous sea-level rise starting from −36 m at about 9 ka BP, with intervening periods of relative stillstand (Fig. 2B) (Thomas, 1990; Anderson and Thomas, 1991). Absolute rates of sea-level rise have not been calculated due to inadequate dating control. The onset of present sea level is uncertain, but Thomas (1990) infers from the Barbados curve that it post-dates 3 ka BP. Modern tide-gauge records indicate continued sea-level rise. In Lake Calcasieu, a mean rise of 0.62 cm/yr has been observed since 1942 (Nichol and others, 1992).

Facies Distribution.—

Lake Calcasieu displays a facies distribution that conforms to the tripartite zonation model (Fig. 4B). The facies zones recognised in Calcasieu estuary are: (i) a tide-influenced fluvial zone that extends 78-km inland along the narrow reaches of Calcasieu River. This zone incorporates meandering channel, floodplain, interdistributary bay (flood basin) and bay-head delta depositional environments; (ii) a central basin zone with fringing saltmarsh. This zone dominates the estuary, presently occupying an area of 246 km^2; and (iii) a low-relief, 6- to 9-km wide, barrier at the seaward end of the estuary composed of cheniers, saltmarsh, mudflats and a tidal inlet. Cheniers range in height from 1 to 3 m above mean sea level, and the maximum width of the chenier system fronting Lake Calcasieu is 4 km. Saltmarsh makes up the remaining 2 to 5 km of the barrier. The geomorphology and stratigraphy of the chenier plain have been described in detail elsewhere (e.g., Howe and others, 1935; Gould and McFarlan, 1959; Penland and Suter, 1989).

Valley Stratigraphy.—

The longitudinal section for the Calcasieu valley fill shows that incision into the Prairie Terrace Formation ranges from 12 m along the narrow upper reaches of the estuary, to a maximum of 55 m beneath the chenier plain (Fig. 5) (Le Blanc, 1949). This surface is interpreted as a lowstand unconformity produced by incision of the Calcasieu River during δ^{18}O Stage 2. It therefore represents the basal sequence boundary. Figure 6 presents a contour map of the depth to the Pleistocene surface, derived from borehole records (Le Blanc, 1949). The contours highlight a pronounced trench beneath the present Lake Calcasieu that extends offshore, to the east of the modern inlet. A shallower (30 m, 80–100 ft) tributary valley lies to the west of the main valley.

The basal unit in the depositional succession is interpreted from borehole data (Le Blanc, 1949) as a regressive fluvial facies that represents the lowstand wedge of the lowstand systems tract (Van Wagoner and others, 1988). In the deepest portion of the incised valley, this facies is 16 m thick and is characterised by medium sand that is interpreted as a braided-river deposit (Le Blanc, 1949). Toward the upper reaches of the valley, the lowstand deposit is shallower and much thinner (<5 m; Fig. 5). Aggradation of the braided-river bed is interpreted as a response to rising base level during the early stages of sea-level rise. Beneath the chenier plain, the upper surface of the braided lowstand deposit varies between 36 m and 40 m below sea level, and is recognised as the transgressive surface that marks the transition from fluvial to estuarine conditions in the Calcasieu valley. This surface is correlated here with the -36 m intermediate flooding surface recognised by Anderson and others (1991) within the inner-shelf continuation of the Trinity-Sabine River valley. This flooding surface is defined on the basis of seismic records of the Trinity-Sabine offshore valley fill that show four, bay-head delta units buried at progressively shallower depths updip along the valley (Anderson and others, 1991). The upper surface of each bay-head delta is taken to represent relative sea-level stillstands, at −36, −29, −20 and −14 m. Assuming the Calcasieu River has a similar evolutionary history to the Trinity-Sabine River system, aggradation of the lowstand wedge was followed by stillstand at −36 m. This presumably allowed the Calcasieu River to prograde a bay-head delta downdip of the aggraded fluvial deposit documented by Le Blanc (1949).

The lowstand deposit is overlain by a 10-m thick bed of silty clay, also of fluvial origin. The lithological change is attributed by Le Blanc (1949) to a shift from braided to meandering-channel conditions in response to a reduced river gradient. Suter (1986) also interprets a meandering-channel style for this unit, on the basis of inner-shelf seismic and vibracore data collected southwest of Lake Calcasieu. Seismic sections display high-angle clinoform reflectors, indicating point-bar deposition, and vibracores contain fine-grained sediments typical of a meandering river (Suter, 1986). The change to a meandering river presumably took place during sea-level stillstand or slow rise, and conditions similar to the present tidal reaches of the Calcasieu river are envisaged. The meandering channel form was maintained during the next episode of sea-level rise as the river aggraded a 10-m thick deposit. Given that the meandering fluvial facies was deposited during sea-level rise, it is part of the transgressive systems tract (Van Wagoner and others, 1988).

An 8-m thick deposit of fine fluvial sand overlying the meandering facies at −30 m is interpreted to result from a second phase of regressive, braided-channel conditions (Fig. 5) (Le Blanc, 1949). The upper surface of this braided-channel sand can be correlated with a regional intermediate flooding surface. In the Trinity-Sabine valley, a stillstand surface is mapped at −20 m by Anderson and others (1991). In the Calcasieu valley, the depth of the top of the braided-fluvial sand varies between −17 m and −21.5 m and is taken as the equivalent of the −20-m stillstand. This still-

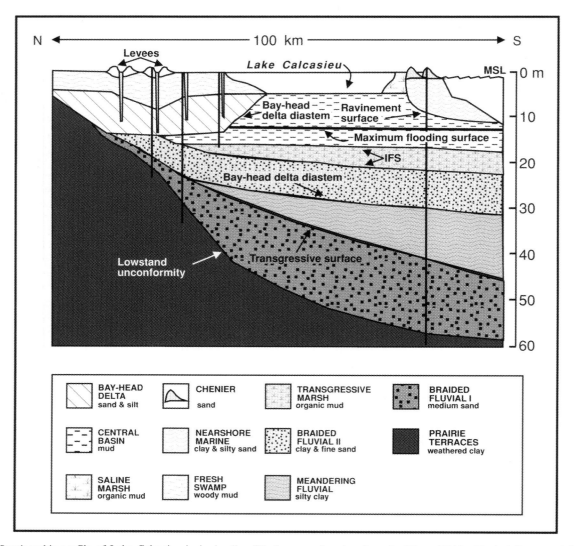

FIG. 5.—Stratigraphic profile of Lake Calcasieu incised-valley fill, incorporating data from Le Blanc (1949). Vertical lines are drillhole sites. Systems-tract facies are as follows: *Lowstand* = braided fluvial I; *Transgressive* = meandering fluvial, braided fluvial II, transgressive marsh and lower part of the central basin; *Highstand* = upper part of the central basin, bay-head delta, levees, freshwater swamp, saline marsh, nearshore marine and chenier ridge. The transgressive surface lies at the contact between braided fluvial I and meandering fluvial. The contact between meandering fluvial and braided fluvial II is a bay-head delta diastem formed during the −20 m stillstand. Intermediate flooding surfaces (IFS) bound the transgressive marsh facies. The maximum flooding surface is represented by the contact between lower (transgressive) and upper (highstand) central basin mud at −12 m.

stand presumably provided conditions suitable for a temporary shift of channel form, from meandering to braided. In this situation, channel braiding indicates a regressive depositional style. The base of the braided unit may therefore represent a bay-head delta diastem, not the −29-m flooding surface of Anderson and others (1991).

An organic clay overlies the braided-fluvial facies; it is interpreted as a transgressive marsh facies deposited as the river valley was flooded by brackish waters. The transgressive marsh is in turn overlain by a soft clay that is interpreted as a central basin facies. The surface separating these facies is abrupt and varies in depth between 15 and 17 m below sea level. It is recognised as a flooding surface that correlates with the −14-m stillstand surface in the Trin-

ity-Sabine valley (Anderson and others, 1991). This flooding surface is significant because it represents the onset of open bay (marine) conditions in the area of the modern Lake Calcasieu lagoon (Le Blanc, 1949). Following this, estuarine conditions were established as sea level reached its present position and the chenier plain developed after about 3 ka BP (Gould and McFarlan, 1959). Beneath the chenier plain, the maximum thickness of the central basin facies is 10.5 m. Here, the lower 7 m of central basin deposits are characterised by a soft clay with brackish-water fauna (Le Blanc, 1949) that is interpreted as part of the transgressive systems tract. A unit of firm clay, up to 3.5 m thick, characterises central basin deposits of the highstand systems tract. The contact between soft and firm clay lies 12-m below the

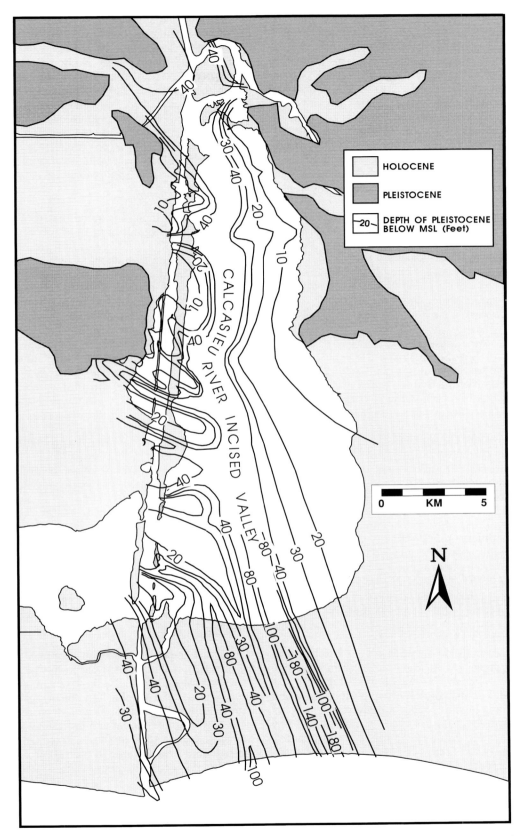

FIG. 6.—Contour map showing the depth (feet) of the Pleistocene surface below mean sea level in Lake Calcasieu. Reproduced from Le Blanc (1949).

surface of the chenier plain and is recognised as the maximum flooding surface (Fig. 5). The chenier plain itself is 5 to 7 m thick and consists of nearshore marine, beach-ridge and marsh facies of the highstand systems tract (Fig. 5). Within the succession, beach-ridge facies are 2- to 4-m thick sand bodies that rest upon 1 to 4 m of marsh and nearshore mud (Penland and Suter, 1989). Modern nearshore-marine deposits overlie central basin facies, both beneath the modern chenier plain and offshore.

Toward the head of the estuary central basin deposits are preserved beneath the bay-head delta as discontinuous, 5- to 10-m thick beds. Fluvial channel and delta facies have incised up to 10 m into, and prograded across, the central basin facies. The basal contact represents the bay-head delta diastem that has replaced the maximum flooding surface in the upper part of the incised-valley fill. A 5-m thick, aggradational, fresh-water swamp facies forms the surficial facies in the upper reaches, except where levees occur alongside channels.

Wapengo Lagoon and Narrawallee Inlet, Southern New South Wales

Physiography and Coastal Processes.—

The south coast of New South Wales (NSW) extends for 250 km between the southern limit of the Lachlan Fold Belt and the southern extent of the Sydney Basin structural province (Fig. 7A). A total of 68 coastal valleys are incised into the Ordovician metasediments that dominate the Lachlan Fold Belt, and the Permian sandstones of the Sydney Basin. These valleys are solely fluvial in origin since the region did not experience glaciation during Late Quaternary time (Nakada and Lambeck, 1989). Bedrock depths in embayments range from 10 to 30 m, but some valleys have less than 10 m available for Holocene deposits due to partial preservation of Pleistocene (last interglacial) fill (Roy and others, 1980; Nichol and Murray-Wallace, 1992).

Depositional conditions in NSW south-coast estuaries are controlled by a highly energetic wave climate and microtidal regime. Mean annual wave power for southerly ocean-swell waves is 4.2×10^4 W/m (Kidd, 1978). Storm-wave heights exceeding 9-m have been recorded (Foster and others, 1975). Spring-tidal range is 1.6 m, but this is attenuated to less than 1-m within estuaries due to frictional dissipation across inlet shoals (Nichol, 1991b).

The Late Pleistocene to Holocene history of relative sea-level change is represented in Figure 2C by an envelope derived from comprehensive radiocarbon dating of back-barrier, lagoon, tidal-delta and offshore deposits (Thom and Roy, 1983). The envelope describes a rapid rise of 1.3 m/century from −60 m at 12 ka, to −5 m by 7.7 ka BP. The rate of sea-level rise decelerated to 0.4 m/century between 7.7 ka and 6.4 ka. Since then, sea level has maintained a (stillstand) position within 1 m of the present level (Thom and Roy, 1983).

NSW south-coast estuarine sediments are sourced from discrete marine and fluvial provenances. Supplies of marine sediment were abundant during early to mid-Holocene time, but appear to have dwindled since the onset of sea-level stillstand at 6.5 ka BP, becoming negligible by 3 ka BP

(Thom and others, 1978; Roy and others, 1980). Limited radiocarbon dating of flood-tidal delta deposits suggests that deposition in estuary mouths was rapid and terminated shortly after stillstand (Roy, 1984b; Hudson, 1989; Nichol, 1991a). In view of the lack of river-borne sediment on NSW beaches and in the nearshore, fluvial-sediment flux to the coast has been described as low (Roy and Crawford, 1977; Roy and others, 1980). However, south-coast streams have comparatively small catchment areas and steep gradients (Table 1) that drain coarse-grained source rocks. Consequently, relatively large bay-head delta and floodplain deposits have accumulated in the upper reaches of estuaries.

Facies Distribution.—

Previous investigations along the NSW south coast have recognised the organisation of estuarine facies into three distinct zones (e.g., Bird, 1967; Reinson, 1977; Roy, 1984a). Wapengo Lagoon also displays three clearly defined zones (Fig. 7B). The landward, tide-influenced fluvial zone is 4 km² in area and includes floodplain, channel and bay-head delta facies. The central basin zone comprises lagoon and fringing shoreline facies that together occupy an area of 1.4 km². The seaward zone is dominated by a series of flood-tidal delta shoals and tidal channels that together cover an area of 1.5 km², and extend 3 km landward from the estuary mouth. The estuary does not possess an ebb-tidal delta due to high wave energy in the nearshore zone. A small barrier is recessed into the embayment and saltmarsh facies fringe the western side of the flood-tidal delta (Fig. 7B).

The surficial geology of Narrawallee Inlet contrasts with Wapengo Lagoon (Fig 8B). At present sea level, the estuary has almost no accommodation space for further deposition. The former site of the central basin is now occupied by a floodplain and associated network of tide-influenced fluvial channels. The total area of the infilled valley is 10.8 km² and, of this, 9.5 km² is taken up by the floodplain. Floodplain deposits lie adjacent to flood-tidal delta sands less than 1 km from the estuary mouth. The Narrawallee barrier consists of a series of ten, 1 to 2 m high, beach ridges located behind a 5- to 6-m high foredune that is bisected by a tidal inlet. The sedimentological properties of Wapengo Lagoon and Narrawallee Inlet deposits are summarised by Nichol (1991a, b).

Valley Stratigraphy.—

The stratigraphy of Wapengo Lagoon demonstrates clearly the effects of sediment focusing from two sources (Fig. 7C). The seaward end of the valley fill is occupied by a transgressive flood-tidal delta unit that is in erosional contact with oxidised, Pleistocene fluvial deposits. The contact lies 2- to 3-m below sea level and defines the inlet-channel diastem. Here, the diastem has amalgamated with the low-stand unconformity. Limited core control prevents accurate reconstruction of the diastem profile. A carbon-14 date from the landward limit of the flood-tidal delta suggests that the delta ceased transgressing 6230 ± 200 years BP (SUA-2759) and indicates that the diastem has not extended further landward since the onset of sea-level stillstand. The shoreface ravinement surface in the Wapengo valley fill is located at the mouth of the estuary and is shown as a steep surface

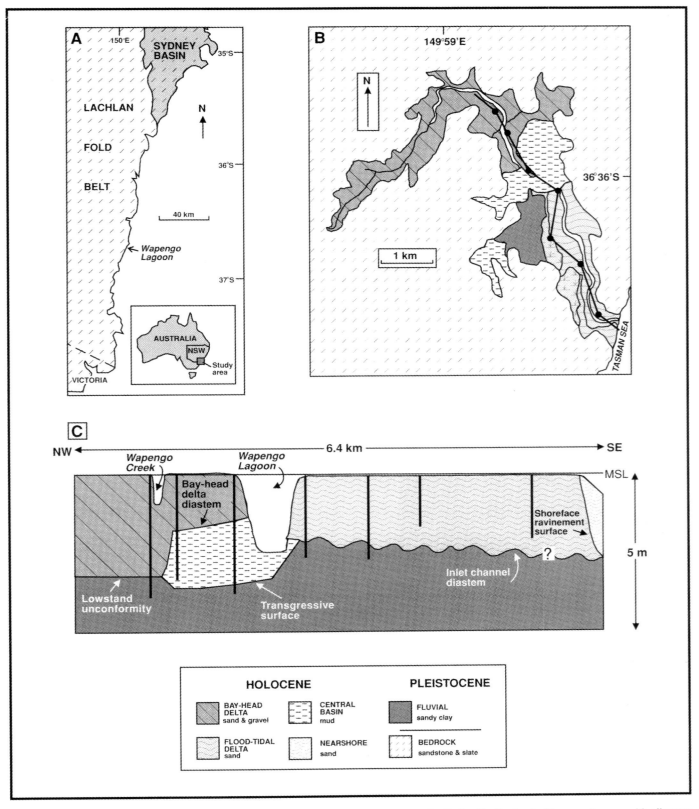

FIG. 7.—(A) New South Wales south coast showing the location of Wapengo Lagoon. (B) Facies distribution in Wapengo Lagoon with vibracore locations and transect for stratigraphic section. (C) Stratigraphic profile of Wapengo Lagoon incised-valley fill. Pleistocene deposits are interpreted as a fluvial facies. The apparent rise of the Pleistocene surface below Wapengo Lagoon is an artefact of the core transect, which at this point is close to the valley side.

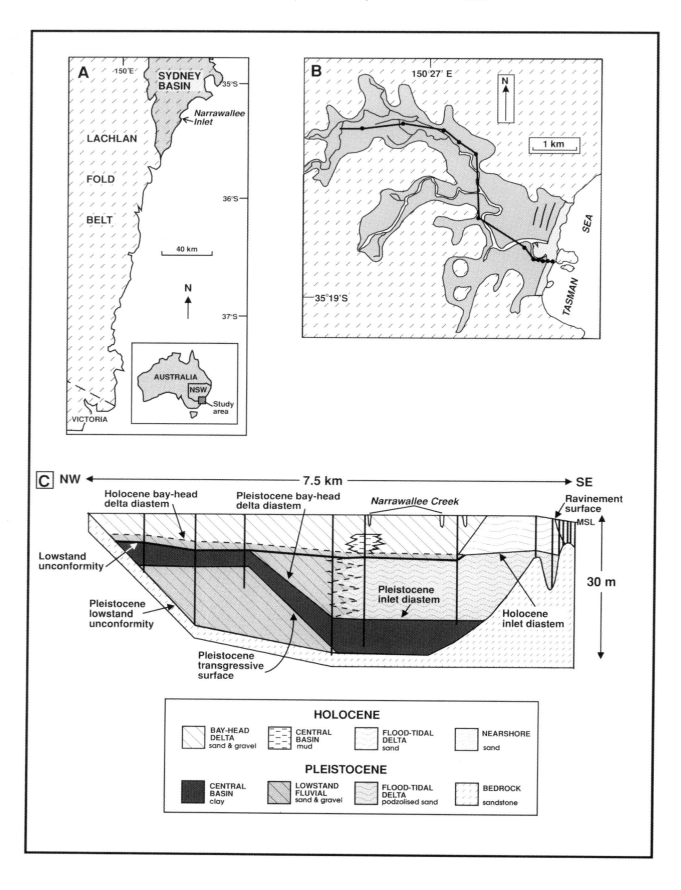

that terminates at the beach face (Fig. 7C). In cases where the estuary is fronted by a beach-ridge plain, the shoreface ravinement surface will extend further into the estuary, to the position of the innermost ridge.

At the landward end of Wapengo Lagoon, a bay-head delta is prograding into the central basin (Fig. 7C). Fluvial sand and gravel are deposited on the floor of Wapengo Creek, which has incised into central basin muds to a depth of 1.5- to 1.8-m below sea level. During flood events, fluvial sediments are deposited overbank, on the supratidal surface of delta lobes. Toward the landward end of Wapengo valley, fluvial deposits disconformably overlie oxidised Pleistocene fluvial sediments at a depth of 3.2 to 3.5 m. The thickness of these Pleistocene deposits is not known. The base of the overlying fluvial facies is interpreted as a channel diastem formed during bay-head delta progradation. It represents the sequence boundary. From the available data, it is not possible to differentiate between lowstand fluvial and modern bay-head delta deposits. A vibracore from the seaward limit of the bay-head delta shows central basin deposits directly overlying weathered Pleistocene deposits at 3.6-m below sea level. Here, the lowstand unconformity is amalgamated with the transgressive surface. The lack of a clear lithologic change within the central basin unit prevents separation of transgressive from highstand systems tracts, hence the maximum flooding surface is not identified in this instance.

The Narrawallee Inlet incised-valley fill has Pleistocene and Holocene components that record two, successive sea-level highstands. The basal Pleistocene unit contains a wedge of fluvial sand and gravel that is thickest at the landward end of the valley (Fig. 8C). The deposit displays maximum thickness of 12 m and thins abruptly both landward and seaward to <0.5 m. The basal contact with bedrock defines the lowstand unconformity for the Pleistocene sequence. A Pleistocene central basin facies overlies the fluvial deposit along the length of the Narrawallee valley, and the contact between these facies represents a Pleistocene transgressive surface. At the head of the valley, the central basin facies is 3 to 4 m thick; downdip it is deeper, 6.5 to 8 m thick and separated from bedrock by a thin deposit of fluvial sand. Amino acid racemization dates of shell from the central basin deposit, calibrated with radiocarbon dates, indicate a last interglacial age for the unit (Nichol and Murray-Wallace, 1992). The basal fluvial facies is assumed, therefore, to be older than 120,000 years. Fluvial sand and gravel disconformably overlie the Pleistocene central basin clay midway along the valley. The contact dips seaward from -7.5 m to -17 m and is interpreted as a Pleistocene bay-head delta diastem formed during the latter stages of last interglacial estuarine deposition. The Pleistocene fluvial facies interfingers seaward with a 4- to 15-m thick deposit of

well oxidised sand (Hann, 1985). The podzolised condition of the deposit suggests subaerial exposure, and it is interpreted as a remnant of a last interglacial, tidal-inlet fill that survived lowstand and transgressive scouring (Fig. 8C).

The Holocene portion of the Narrawallee fill is characterised by three facies that record the progression from an estuary with a tripartite facies distribution to an infilled valley dominated at the surface by prograded bay-head delta deposits (Fig. 8C). A lowstand unconformity lies at the base of a thin bed of Pleistocene lowstand fluvial deposits. An Holocene bay-head delta channel diastem is inferred to separate Pleistocene from Holocene prograded fluvial facies, but core disturbance prevents its clear identification. The fluvial deposit has prograded approximately 7 km, and modern channel fills are incised into tidal inlet and flood-tidal delta sands toward the estuary mouth, marking the present limit of the bay-head delta diastem (Fig. 8C). Holocene-age central basin deposits appear restricted to the middle section of the valley fill, where a 3- to 4-m thick lagoon clay, containing wood with a carbon-14 age of 6320 ± 100 years BP (SUA-2907), is encased within the bay-head delta facies. This unit displays limited areal extent indicating significant erosion of Holocene central basin deposits by laterally migrating fluvial channels during bay-head delta progradation.

At the seaward end of the valley, the Pleistocene tidal-delta sand is overlain by unweathered tidal-inlet sand of Holocene age; the contact between these deposits is recognised as a tidal-inlet diastem (Fig. 8C). A radiocarbon age of 7070 ± 75 years BP (SUA-2477) was reported by Hann (1985) for a shell hash recovered between -4 and -5 m at the landward end of the flood-tidal delta in the active inlet channel. This result provides further support for the contention that the marine-derived facies in NSW estuaries is relict. Finally, a 6-m deep shoreface ravinement surface is located at the base of the nearshore/beach facies.

DISCUSSION

The four, estuarine depositional successions presented here illustrate some of the variability that may result from differences in the balance between relative sea-level changes and sediment supply in wave-dominated estuaries. Specifically, relative sea-level changes and sediment supply interact to control the organization of facies and geometry of regional bounding surfaces such as sequence boundaries and flooding surfaces in stratigraphic successions. Depositional processes (waves, tides, rivers) control the character of individual facies and local surfaces such as diastems. The idealised sequence stratigraphy for a modern wave-dominated estuary presented in Figure 1 represents an estuary that lies at the point of maximum transgression and has

FIG. 8.—(A) New South Wales south coast showing the location of Narrawallee Inlet. (B) Facies distribution in Narrawallee Inlet with drillhole locations and transect for stratigraphic section. (C) Stratigraphic profile of Narrawallee Inlet incised-valley fill. The separation of Pleistocene lowstand (δ^{18}O stage 2) fluvial deposits from modern bay-head delta deposits is tentative, and the bay-head delta diastem is shown to pass below the Holocene age central basin deposits. The drill hole that recovered these deposits was located near the valley margin, where diastem incision was presumably shallower than along the valley axis.

abundant sediment input from terrestrial and marine sources. The case studies illustrate departures from this model in estuaries at an advanced stage of infill.

The Lawrencetown Lake case differs from the model because it does not lie at the point of maximum transgression and the rate of relative sea-level rise exceeds that of sediment supply, especially from rivers. Deposits that lie within the path of shoreface ravinement have been remobilised and transported into the estuary mouth by wave, tide and aeolian processes. The estuary is at an advanced infill stage due to efficient recycling of sediment from drowned barriers and drumlins. The valley fill is therefore dominated by facies of the transgressive systems tract, and the maximum flooding surface has yet to form. Regressive fluvial facies are poorly developed and bay-head delta channel diastems are absent from eastern shore estuaries. This represents a major departure from the stratigraphy suggested by the model. Bounding surfaces also record estuary flooding and ongoing transgression. This process is exemplified by the landward-migrating inlet-channel diastem, that extends far into the estuary. However, this surface is being removed by shoreface ravinement as relative sea-level rise continues. Moreover, under present conditions of 30 to 40 cm/century, sea-level rise and shoreface reworking to depths of -15 m, the preservation potential of all but the deepest estuarine deposits is low. The presence of thin and discontinuous deposits of central basin and flood-tidal delta facies on the Scotian inner shelf supports this prediction.

Lake Calcasieu represents a situation in which sea level has risen in a series of discrete steps, with intervening stillstands, and is now relatively stable (Anderson and Thomas, 1991). Rising lake levels, induced by regional subsidence, indicate continued sea-level rise, but the presence of a maximum flooding surface and the development of highstand regressive facies imply transgression has finished. In the Calcasieu valley fill, sea-level rise episodes are correlated with phases of river-channel aggradation, and as a result the transgressive and highstand systems tracts are dominated by fluvial facies. Accommodation space has been sufficiently reduced that a bay-head delta has now prograded into the northern part of Lake Calcasieu, where central basin and marsh aggradation occurs in response to subsidence of the coastal plain. Also, abundant supplies of sediment from fluvial sources alongshore has allowed the chenier plain to resist transgression and locally prograde. The large volume of fluvial deposits in this case suggests that the model stratigraphy may understate the significance of such facies in incised valleys. Further, a comparatively complex set of bounding surfaces are recognised in the Calcasieu estuarine succession. In the context of the model (Fig. 1B), the available data for Lake Calcasieu indicate differences in the form of multiple (intermediate) flooding surfaces within the transgressive systems tract and the apparent absence of a tidal-inlet diastem.

The estuaries of southern NSW differ from those on the other two coasts studied, because they have experienced protracted relative sea-level stillstand and are at a more advanced stage of infilling. Indeed, Narrawallee Inlet estuary has almost reached the point of extinction, due to extensive bay-head delta progradation. Marine sediment input along the south coast was initially high during the mid-Holocene, but is now relatively insignificant. Consequently, flood-tidal delta deposits are largely relict and inlet diastems moribund. River input is low to moderate from high-gradient rivers with coarse sediment loads. A seaward-migrating channel diastem develops in association with bay-head delta growth. In this sense, the NSW estuaries closely resemble the model stratigraphy (Fig. 1B). Examples of prograded barriers dominating valley fills do exist along the NSW coast (Thom and others, 1978) but these deposits are also relict. Eventually, central basin, flood-tidal delta and barrier facies may be partly destroyed by prograding bay-head deltas and laterally migrating fluvial channels.

Both Wapengo Lagoon and Narrawallee Inlet possess multiple estuarine sequences that are interpreted as the product of two, successive sea-level highstands. The lower sequence in Narrawallee records a period of at least partial valley filling during the last interglacial (Nichol and Murray-Wallace, 1992). Similar stratigraphic relationships and diagenetic properties were observed in the Wapengo lower sequence, and a last interglacial age is inferred. The preservation of older, estuarine valley deposits reduces the accommodation space during preceding highstands; hence, Narrawallee Inlet is now filled with sediment. The depositional succession in Narrawallee is characterised by a complex array of bounding surfaces, not predicted by the model. This complexity is a direct result of stacked estuarine sequences occupying an incised valley, and is an example of a compound valley fill (cf. Dalrymple and others, this volume).

Preservation of last interglacial deposits in NSW estuaries is attributed to three factors. First, the NSW coast was not glaciated during late Pleistocene exposure; therefore, one mechanism for valley scouring was not operative. Second, south-coast streams appear to have a low capacity to completely remove valley fills, even during sea-level lowstand. Third, NSW estuaries lie at the point of maximum transgression, hence they remain largely unaffected by shoreface ravinement processes. In contrast, Lawrencetown Lake does not display multiple estuarine sequences and is an example of a simple valley fill (cf. Dalrymple and others, this volume). Clearly, glaciation of eastern shore valleys would have removed any pre-existing estuarine deposits. Lake Calcasieu was not glaciated, but it occupies a large ancestral river valley that extended across the inner shelf and attained its present dimensions during the Stage 2 lowstand (Suter, 1986; Suter and others, 1987). The ancestral Calcasieu River presumably removed the majority of last interglacial estuarine deposits. Preservation of these deposits is likely to be restricted to the margins of the valley (cf. Thomas and Anderson, this volume). The estuary valley is now at an advanced stage of infill due to significant fluvial aggradation during the recent sea-level rise.

The significance of the interaction between relative sea-level changes and sediment supply in terms of estuarine stratigraphy is well highlighted by these four examples. However, it is apparent that the model introduced at the outset must be modified to account for factors such as multiple estuarine successions (compound valley fills) or major episodes of fluvial deposition in the transgressive systems tract. We await further documentation of wave-dominated estuarine successions in coastal settings different to those considered here.

SUMMARY

The relationship between relative sea-level changes and sediment supply as recorded by four, wave-dominated estuarine depositional successions may be summarised as follows.

1. Where estuary filling occurs within a framework of ongoing relative sea-level rise and the dominant sediment supply is from marine sources, the resulting stratigraphy is composed largely of transgressive facies (i.e., central basin, flood-tidal delta, and tidal-inlet). Bay-head delta and floodplain facies are poorly developed under these conditions. Bounding surfaces include a sequence boundary at the base of pre-modern deposits, a transgressive surface that separates estuarine (central basin) facies from non-estuarine deposits, a shoreface-ravinement surface at the base of nearshore facies, and a tidal-channel diastem that incises far landward into central basin sediments. The maximum flooding surface has yet to form. The succession may also display regressive character when marine sediment supply is very high and a beach-ridge plain develops. Given continued transgression, the preservation potential of all but the deepest part of the transgressive systems tract is low.

2. In conditions of very rapid, episodic, relative sea-level rise followed by stillstand, moderate to high, fluvial sediment input and moderate delivery of sediment from the inner shelf and nearshore, estuarine stratigraphy is dominated by aggraded fluvial facies of the transgressive systems tract. A lowstand unconformity and fluvial sediments of the lowstand systems tract underlie these deposits. Multiple (intermediate) flooding surfaces record the stepped rise of sea level. During relative sea-level stillstand and continued sediment input, the estuary develops regressive characteristics in the form of chenier plain and bay-head delta progradation, and aggradation of the central basin. A diastem associated with the bay-head delta extends seaward into the central basin, possibly replacing pre-existing surfaces such as the maximum flooding surface. Deeper deposits of the transgressive systems tract should, however, be preserved.

3. Infilling of wave-dominated estuaries during a protracted period of relative sea-level stillstand, low to moderate fluvial input, and low marine sediment supply produces a stratigraphy with strongly regressive character. Transgressive systems tract deposits are present but may be largely replaced by highstand deposits. In shallow valleys, channel diastems associated with the bay-head delta and tidal inlet may amalgamate with the lowstand unconformity. Channel diastems and the lowstand unconformity are separated, however, in deeper valleys. In these situations, conditions of non-glaciation, small stream power and limited shoreface ravinement allow for preservation of multiple (compound) estuarine successions.

ACKNOWLEDGMENTS

The data and ideas presented in this paper derive from almost a decade of work in estuarine environments by the authors. Support from several institutions and granting agencies is acknowledged: University of Sydney, Dalhousie University, Louisiana State University, Louisiana Geological Survey and the Natural Science and Engineering Research Council of Canada, Imperial Oil Canada, and Husky Oil Canada. Thanks go to Rufus Le Blanc for providing stratigraphic information for Lake Calcasieu. We also thank John Anderson, Bob Dalrymple, Lee Krystinik, and Fernando Siringan for helpful comments on the draft version of this paper.

REFERENCES

ALLEN, G. P., 1991, Sedimentary processes and facies in the Gironde estuary: a recent model for macrotidal systems, *in* Smith, D. G., Reinson, G. E., Zaitlin, B. A. and Rahmani, R. A., eds., Clastic Tidal Sedimentology: Calgary, Canadian Society of Petroleum Geologists Memoir 16, p. 29–40.

ALLEN, G. P., AND POSAMENTIER, H. W., 1993, Sequence stratigraphy and facies model of an incised valley fill: the Gironde estuary, France: Journal of Sedimentary Petrology, v. 63, p. 378–391.

ANDERSON, J. B., AND THOMAS, M. A., 1991, Marine ice-sheet decoupling as a mechanism for rapid, episodic sea-level change: the record of such events and their influence on sedimentation, *in* Biddle, K. T., and Schlager, W., eds., The Record of Sea Level Fluctuations: Sedimentary Geology, v. 70, p. 87–104.

ANDERSON, J. B., SIRINGAN, F. P., SMYTH, W. C., AND THOMAS, M. A., 1991, Episodic nature of Holocene sea-level rise and the evolution of Galveston Bay (abs.): Gulf Coast Section, Society of Economic Paleontologists and Mineralogists Foundation, Twelfth Annual Research Conference, Program and Abstracts, p. 8–14.

BECKER, R. E., 1972, Wave Energy Studies along the Louisiana Coast: Coastal Resources Unit, Center for Wetland Resources, Louisiana State University, Report No. 12, 22 p.

BELKNAP, D. F., AND KRAFT, J. C., 1981, Preservation potential of transgressive coastal lithosomes on the U.S. Atlantic shelf: Marine Geology, v. 42, p. 429–442.

BELKNAP, D. F., AND KRAFT, J. C., 1985, Influence of antecedent geology on stratigraphic preservation potential and evolution of Delaware's barrier systems: Marine Geology, v. 63, p. 235–262.

BIRD, E. C. F., 1967, Depositional features in estuaries and lagoons on the south coast of New South Wales: Australian Geographical Studies, v. 5, p. 113–125.

BLUM, M. D., 1990, Climatic and eustatic controls on Gulf Coastal Plain fluvial sedimentation: an example from the late Quaternary of the Colorado River, Texas, *in* Armentrout, J. M., and Perkins, B. F., eds., Sequence Stratigraphy as an Exploration Tool: Concepts and Practices in the Gulf Coast: Houston, Eleventh Annual Research Conference, Gulf Coast Section, Society of Economic Paleontologists and Mineralogists Foundation, p. 71–84.

BOWEN, A. J., AND BOYD, R., 1983, The eastern shore Beaches: Halifax, Final Report to Nova Scotia Department of Lands and Forests, 71 p.

BOYD, R., BOWEN, A. J., AND HALL, R. K., 1987, An evolutionary model for transgressive sedimentation on the eastern shore of Nova Scotia, *in* Fitzgerald, D. M., and Rosen, P. S., eds., Glaciated Coasts: New York, Academic Press, p. 87–115.

BOYD, R., DALRYMPLE, R. W., AND ZAITLIN, B. A., 1992, Classification of coastal sedimentary environments: Sedimentary Geology, v. 80, p. 139–150.

BOYD, R., AND HONIG, C. A., 1992, Estuarine sedimentation on the eastern shore of Nova Scotia: Journal of Sedimentary Petrology, v. 62, p. 569–583.

BOYD, R., AND PENLAND, S., 1981, Washover of deltaic barriers on the Louisiana coast: Transactions, Gulf Coast Association of Geological Societies, v. 31, p. 243–248.

BOYD, R., AND PENLAND, S., 1984, Shoreface translation and the Holocene stratigraphic record: examples from Nova Scotia, the Mississippi delta and eastern Australia: Marine Geology, v. 60, p. 391–412.

CARRERA, G., AND VANICEK, P., 1989, A comparison of present sea-level linear trends from the tide gauge data and radiocarbon curves in eastern Canada: Palaeogeography, Palaeoclimatology, Palaeoecology, v. 68, p. 127–134.

CURRAY, J. R., 1964, Transgressions and regressions, in Miller, R. L., ed., Papers in Marine Geology-Shephard Commemorative Volume: New York, MacMillan, p. 175–203.

DALRYMPLE, R. W., ZAITLIN, B. A., AND BOYD, R., 1992, Estuarine facies models: Conceptual basis and stratigraphic implications: Journal of Sedimentary Petrology, v. 62, p. 1030–1146.

DAVIS, R. A., JR., AND CLIFTON, H. E., 1987, Sea-level change and the preservation potential of wave-dominated and tide-dominated coastal sequences, in Nummedal, D., Pilkey, O. H., and Howard, J. D., eds., Sea Level Fluctuation and Coastal Evolution: Tulsa, Society of Economic Paleontologists and Mineralogists Special Publication 41, p. 167–178.

ELLIOTT, T., 1986, Siliciclastic shorelines, in Reading, H. G., ed., Sedimentary Environments and Facies: Oxford, Blackwell, p. 155–188.

FAIRBANKS, R. G., 1989, A 17,000 year glacio-eustatic sea-level record: influence of glacial melting rates on the Younger Dryas event and deep-ocean circulation: Nature, v. 342, p. 637–642.

FISK, H. N., 1944, Geological investigations of the alluvial valley of the lower Mississippi River: Vicksburg, Mississippi River Commission, United States Army Corps of Engineers, 78 p.

FORBES, D. L., BOYD, R., SHAW, J., JOHNSTON, L., HEFFLER, D. E., AND MCLAREN, S., 1988, Cruise Report 87042-CSS Dawson Operations on the Inner Scotian Shelf and Sable Island Bank: Dartmouth, Geological Survey of Canada Open File, Bedford Institute of Oceanography, 51 p.

FORBES, D. L., TAYLOR, R. B., ORFORD, J. D., CARTER, R. W. G., AND SHAW, J., 1991, Gravel-barrier migration and overstepping: Marine Geology, v. 97, p. 305–313.

FOSTER, D., GORDON, A. D., AND LAWSON, N. Y., 1975, The storms of May-June 1974, Sydney, N.S.W.: Gold Coast, Proceedings Second Australian Conference on Coastal and Ocean Engineering, Institution of Engineers, p. 1–11.

FRAZIER, D. E., 1974, Depositional Episodes: Their Relationship to the Quaternary Stratigraphic Framework in the Northwestern Portion of the Gulf Basin: Austin, Texas Bureau of Economic Geology, Geologic Circular, 74–1, 28 p.

GALLOWAY, W. E., 1989, Genetic stratigraphic sequences in basin analysis I: architecture and genesis of flooding-surface bounded depositional units: American Association of Petroleum Geologists Bulletin, v. 73, p. 125–142.

GOULD, H. R., AND MCFARLAN, E., 1959, Geologic history of the chenier plain, southwestern Louisiana: Transactions, Gulf Coast Association of Geological Societies, v. 9, p. 261–272.

HANN, J. M., 1985, Coastal and Offshore Quaternary Geology of the Ulladulla Region, NSW: Geological Survey of New South Wales, Unpublished Report No. GS1985/27, 42 p.

HONIG, C. A., 1987, Estuarine Sedimentation on a Glaciated Coast: Lawrencetown Lake, eastern shore, Nova Scotia: Halifax, Dalhousie University, Centre for Marine Geology, Technical Report No. 9, 132 p.

HOSKIN, S., 1983, Coastal Sedimentation at Lawrencetown Beach, eastern shore, Nova Scotia: Halifax, Dalhousie University, Centre for Marine Geology, Technical Report No. 5, 46 p.

HOWE, H. V., RUSSELL, R. J., AND MCGUIRT, J. H., 1935, Physiography of coastal southwest Louisiana: Department of Conservation, Louisiana Geological Survey, Geological Bulletin No. 6, p. 1–72.

HUDSON, J. P., 1989, The Heavy Mineral Resource within an Estuarine Tidal Delta Deposit: Narrabeen Lagoon, Sydney: Unpublished report prepared for Patterson, Britton and Partners, 30 p.

KIDD, R. W., 1978, Estuarine sediment regimes, far south coast, New South Wales: Unpublished Ph.D. Thesis, Macquarie University, Sydney.

LEATHERMAN, S. P., ed., 1979, Barrier Islands from the Gulf of St. Lawrence to the Gulf of Mexico: New York, Academic Press, 325 p.

LEATHERMAN, S. P., 1987, Annotated chronological bibliography of barrier island migration: Journal of Coastal Research, v. 3, p. 1–14.

LE BLANC, R. J., 1949, Recent and Pleistocene geology of the Calcasieu entrenched valley system of southwest Louisiana: Unpublished Shell Oil Company Report 128, 27 p.

MIALL, A. D., 1992, Alluvial deposits, in Walker, R. G., and James, N. P., eds., Facies Models: Response to Sea Level Change: St. Johns, Geological Association of Canada, p. 119–142.

NAKADA, M., AND LAMBECK, K., 1989, Late Pleistocene and Holocene sea-level change in the Australian region and mantle rheology: Geophysical Journal, v. 96, p. 497–517.

NICHOL, S. L., 1991a, Sedimentology of two wave-dominated, incised valley estuaries: New South Wales south coast: Unpublished Ph.D. Thesis, University of Sydney, Sydney, 501 p.

NICHOL, S. L., 1991b, Zonation and sedimentology of estuarine facies in an incised valley, wave-dominated, microtidal setting, New South Wales, Australia, in Smith, D. G., Reinson, G. E., Zaitlin, B. A., and Rahmani, R. A., eds., Clastic Tidal Sedimentology: Calgary, Canadian Society of Petroleum Geologists Memoir 16, p. 41–58.

NICHOL, S. L. AND BOYD, R., 1993, Morphostratigraphy and facies architecture of sandy barriers along the eastern shore of Nova Scotia: Marine Geology, v. 114, p. 59–80.

NICHOL, S. L., BOYD, R., AND PENLAND, S., 1992, Hydrology of a wave-dominated estuary: Lake Calcasieu, southwest Louisiana: Transactions, Gulf Coast Association of Geological Societies, v. 42, p. 627–636.

NICHOL, S. L., AND MURRAY-WALLACE, C. V., 1992, A partially preserved last interglacial estuarine fill: Narrawallee Inlet, New South Wales: Australian Journal of Earth Sciences, v. 39, p. 545–553.

NICHOLS, M. M., JOHNSON, G. H., AND PEEBLES, P. C., 1991, Modern sediments and facies model for a microtidal coastal plain estuary, the James estuary, Virginia: Journal of Sedimentary Petrology, v. 61, p. 883–899.

NUMMEDAL, D., AND SWIFT, D. J. P., 1987, Transgressive stratigraphy at sequence-bounding unconformities: some principles derived from Holocene and Cretaceous examples, in Nummedal, D., Pilkey, O. H., and Howard, J. D., eds., Sea Level Fluctuation and Coastal Evolution: Tulsa, Society of Economic Paleontologists and Mineralogists Special Publication 41, p. 241–260.

PATTISON, S. A. J., 1992, Recognition and interpretation of estuarine mudstones (central basin mudstones) in the tripartite valley-fill deposits of the Viking Formation, central Alberta, in Pemberton, S. G., ed., Applications of Ichnology to Petroleum Exploration: SEPM (Society for Sedimentary Geology), Core Workshop 17, p. 223–250.

PENLAND, S., AND SUTER, J. R., 1989, The geomorphology of the Mississippi River chenier plain: Marine Geology, v. 90, p. 231–258.

POSAMENTIER, H. W., AND VAIL, P. R., 1988, Eustatic controls on clastic deposition II- sequence and systems tract models, in Wilgus, C. K., Hastings, B. S., Kendall, C. G. St. C., Posamentier, H. W., Ross, C. A., and Van Wagoner, J. C., eds., Sea-level Changes: An Integrated Approach: Tulsa, Society of Economic Paleontologists and Mineralogists Special Publication 42, p. 125–154.

POSAMENTIER, H. W., ALLEN, G. P., AND JAMES, D. P., 1992, High resolution sequence stratigraphy—The East Coulee delta, Alberta: Journal of Sedimentary Petrology, v. 62, p. 310–317.

QUINLAN, G., AND BEAUMONT, C., 1982, The deglaciation of Atlantic Canada as reconstructed from the post-glacial relative sea-level record: Canadian Journal of Earth Sciences, v. 18, p. 2232–2246.

RAMPINO, M. R., AND SANDERS, J. E., 1980, Holocene transgression in south-central Long Island, New York: Journal of Sedimentary Petrology, v. 50, p. 1063–1080.

REINSON, G. E., 1977, Hydrology and sediments of a temperate estuary-Mallacoota Inlet, Victoria: Australian Bureau of Mineral Resources, Geology and Geophysics, Bulletin 178, 91 p.

REINSON, G. E., 1992, Transgressive barrier island and estuarine systems, in Walker, R. G., and James, N. P., eds., Facies Models: Response to Sea-level Change: St. Johns, Geological Association of Canada, p. 179–194.

REINSON, G. E., CLARK, J. E., AND FOSCOLOS, A. E., 1988, Reservoir geology of Crystal Viking field, Lower Cretaceous estuarine tidal channel-bay complex, south-central Alberta: American Association of Petroleum Geologists Bulletin, v. 72, p. 1270–1294.

ROY, P. S., 1984a, New South Wales estuaries: their origin and evolution, in Thom, B. G., ed., Coastal Geomorphology in Australia: Sydney, Academic Press, p. 99–122.

ROY, P. S., 1984b, Holocene sedimentation histories of estuaries in southeastern Australia, in Hodgkin, E. P., ed., Estuarine Environments of the Southern Hemisphere: Perth, Western Australian Department of Conservation and Environment, Bulletin 161, p. 23–59.

Roy, P. S., and Crawford, E. A., 1977, Significance of sediment distribution in major coastal rivers, northern New South Wales: Melbourne, Third Australian Conference on Coastal and Ocean Engineering Institution of Engineers, p. 177–184.

Roy, P. S., and Thom, B. G., 1981, Late Quaternary marine deposition in New South Wales and southern Queensland- an evolutionary model: Journal of the Geological Society of Australia, v. 28, p. 471–489.

Roy, P. S., Thom, B. G., and Wright, L. D., 1980, Holocene sequences on an embayed high-energy coast: an evolutionary model: Sedimentary Geology, v. 26, p. 1–19.

Scott, D. B., Boyd, R., and Medioli, F. S., 1987, Relative sea-level changes in Atlantic Canada: observed level and sedimentological changes vs. theoretical models, *in* Nummedal, D., Pilkey, O. H., and Howard, J. D., eds., Sea Level Fluctuation and Coastal Evolution: Tulsa, Society of Economic Paleontologists and Mineralogists Special Publication 41, p. 87–96.

Stea, R. R., 1983, Surficial geology of the western part of Cumberland County, Nova Scotia: Nova Scotia Department of Mines and Energy, Report 83–1, p. 357–368.

Stea, R. R., Conley, H., and Brown, Y., compilers, 1992a, Surficial geology of the province of Nova Scotia: Nova Scotia Department of Natural Resources, Map 92–3, Scale 1:500 000.

Stea, R. R., Fader, G. B. J., and Boyd, R., 1992b, Quaternary seismic stratigraphy of the inner shelf region, Nova Scotia (abs.): Geological Association of Canada, Program with Abstracts, v. 17, p. 104–105.

Suter, J. R., 1986, Ancient fluvial systems and Holocene deposits, southwestern Louisiana continental shelf, *in* Berryhill, H. L. Jr., Suter, J. R., and Hardin, N. S., eds., Late Quaternary Facies and Structure, Northern Gulf of Mexico: Interpretations from Seismic Data: Tulsa, American Association of Petroleum Geologists, Studies in Geology 23, p. 81–129.

Suter, J. R., Berryhill, H. L., and Penland, S., 1987, Late Quaternary sea-level fluctuations and depositional sequences, southwest Louisiana continental shelf, *in* Nummedal, D., Pilkey, O. H., and Howard, J. D., eds., Sea Level Fluctuation and Coastal Evolution: Tulsa, Society of Economic Paleontologists and Mineralogists Special Publication 41, p. 199–220.

Swift, D. J. P., 1968, Coastal erosion and transgressive stratigraphy: Journal of Geology, v. 76, p. 444–456.

Swift, D. J. P., 1975, Barrier island genesis: evidence from the central Atlantic east shelf, eastern U.S.A.: Sedimentary Geology, v. 14, p. 1–43.

Thom, B. G., Polach, H. A., and Bowman, G. M., 1978, Holocene age structure of coastal sand barriers in New South Wales, Australia: University of New South Wales, Department of Geography, Faculty of Military Studies, Unpublished Report, 86 p.

Thom, B. G., and Roy, P. S., 1983, Sea-level change in New South Wales over the past 15 000 years, *in* Hopley, D., ed., Australian Sea Levels in the last 15,000 Years: A Review: Townsville, James Cook University, Monograph Series Occasional Paper No. 3, p. 64–85.

Thomas, M. A., 1990, The impact of long-term and short-term sea-level changes on the evolution of the Wisconsin-Holocene Trinity/Sabine incised valley system, Texas continental shelf: Unpublished Ph.D. Thesis, Rice University, Houston, 247 p.

Vail, P. R., Hardenbohl, J., and Todd, R. G., 1984, Jurassic unconformities, chronostratigraphy, and sea-level changes from seismic stratigraphy and biostratigraphy, *in* Schlee, J. S., ed., Interregional Unconformities and Hydrocarbon Accumulation: Tulsa, American Association of Petroleum Geologists Memoir 36, p. 129–144.

Van Wagoner, J. C., Posamentier, H. W., Mitchum, R. M., Vail, P. R., Sarg, J. F., Loutit, T. S., and Hardenbol, J., 1988, An overview of the fundamentals of sequence stratigraphy and key definitions, *in* Wilgus, C. K., Hastings, B. S., Kendall, C. G. St. C., Posamentier, H. W., Ross, C. A., and Van Wagoner, J. C., eds., Sea-level Changes: An Integrated Approach: Tulsa, Society of Economic Paleontologists and Mineralogists Special Publication 42, p. 39–45.

Wells, J. T., and Roberts, H. H., 1980, Fluid mud dynamics and shoreline stabilization: Louisiana chenier plain: Proceedings 17th International Coastal Engineering Conference, p. 1382–1401.

Zaitlin, B. A., and Shultz, B. C., 1990, Wave-influenced estuarine sand body, Senlac heavy oil pool, Saskatchewan, Canada, *in* Barwis, J. H., McPherson, J. G., and Studlick, R. J., eds., Sandstone Petroleum Reservoirs: New York, Casebooks in Earth Science, Springer-Verlag, p. 363–387.

DEPOSITIONAL MODEL FOR VALLEY FILLS ON A PASSIVE CONTINENTAL MARGIN

GAIL M. ASHLEY AND ROBERT E. SHERIDAN

Department of Geological Sciences, Rutgers-The State University of New Jersey, New Brunswick, New Jersey 08903

ABSTRACT: High-resolution seismic-reflection profiles and Vibracore information from unpublished and published studies of the U. S. Coastal Plain are used to develop depositional models for valley-fill sequences formed on a passive continental margin. The lower bounding unconformity (SB1) is produced by fluvial incision during sea-level lowstands. Valleys are both shore-parallel controlled by Coastal Plain cuestas and shore-normal. Depressions are cut by both fluvial and tidal erosion. Some small valleys, tidal inlet throats, are infilled with cross-bedded sands, whereas small river channels are likely to be backfilled with mud as the base level changes during a transgression. Intermediate-sized valleys represent deposition in major tributaries to Coastal Plain rivers, and the fill is a fining-upward package generally truncated by a ravinement and overlain with inner shelf sands. Large "drowned-river" valleys are characterized by a sediment sandwich of sand-mud-sand which may contain several marine erosion surfaces and have a high proportion of sand. Subsidence rates of the Atlantic margin are 1–2 mm/yr, topographic relief is <40 m, sediment influx is low, and present shoreline migration rates are 3 m/yr. During transgressions, depth of erosion is estimated at 5–10 m, and thus preservation potential for the lower portion of the valley fill is excellent for the large valleys, good for the intermediate valleys, and poor for the small valleys. Topography is an important factor in valley-fill preservation on passive margins. Depressions created from fluvial or shoreface erosion often provide the only "accommodation space" on continental shelves of passive margins that will shield TST deposits from erosion and ensure preservation of the geological record.

INTRODUCTION

Continental margins are at the interface between land and sea and thus alternate between being sites of erosion during low sea level and sites of deposition during high sea level. Seismic records and cores from trailing edge (passive) continental margins typically reveal a layered stratigraphy consisting of sedimentary sequences. These sequences are the depositional record of sea-level change separated by prominent, laterally persistent unconformities. An ideal sequence retains the sedimentary record of the lowstand, transgressive, and highstand phases (Haq and others, 1988; Boyd and others, 1989; Walker, 1990, 1992) (Fig. 1). The regional unconformities are thought to reflect subaerial exposure and erosion by surficial processes during sea-level lows. They have been used to correlate sequences within a single continental margin and between margins based on the assumption that global (i.e., eustatic) sea-level fluctuations are the primary cause of the unconformities (Haq and others, 1987). This assumption can be supported for some time intervals and for some continental margins (Olsson and others, 1987; Miller and others, 1990; Aubrey, 1991). The record left by sea-level cycles, however, will vary with tectonic setting (continuous uplift or continuous subsidence versus episodic uplift or episodic subsidence), the relative amount of sediment supply compared to the level of energy available to entrain and transport the sediment, the antecedent topography of the coastal plain (i.e., continental shelf), and the relative rate of sea-level rise (including tectonics, compaction, and eustasy).

During falling sea level, fluvial degradation erodes channels into the substrate (Kraft and others, 1974; Knebel and others, 1979; Swift and others, 1980; Hine and Snyder, 1985; Demarest and Kraft, 1987; Nummedal and Swift, 1987; Suter and others, 1987; Colman and Mixon, 1988; Chen and others, 1992). Extensive dendritic fluvial-channel systems evolve in response to the change in base level. The incised channels convey water and sediment to the new coastline creating deltas at the river mouth. During the subsequent sea-level rise, the surficial sediment on the fluvial plain is reworked by waves and tides. Rates of shoreline translation due to sea-level rise across the shelf may range from 1 to 3 m/yr given estimated shelf slopes of 0.006–0.00016 and rates of sea-level rise from 1 to 10 mm/yr. Walker (1992) argues that up to 5–15 m (typical depth to wave base) may be removed by marine erosion during sea-level rise, and thus only the deepest portions of the incised channels are likely to be preserved in the geologic record. Hine and Snyder (1985) found that on the North Carolina shelf, shoreface erosion during recent sea-level fluctuations had stripped all of the Holocene and much of the Pleistocene record; however, an extensive network of incised channels retains a sedimentary record of past events. Pilkey and others (1981) concluded in a study on the Georgia continental shelf that shelf-sediment cover is thin (5 m), and extensive in-place mixing (reworking) of the surficial sediments occurred during the most recent flooding of the shelf (late Pleistocene and Holocene). They found no early- or mid-Pleistocene fossils despite numerous Pleistocene sea-level cycles, indicating either complete stripping occurs during transgressions or leaching of carbonates during regressions or both.

As the sea transgresses over the shelf and coastal plain, topographic lows are backfilled by sediments deposited in a myriad of coastal environments. Environments of deposition that produce valley fills range from shore-parallel, wave-dominated barrier island and lagoonal complexes to shore-normal environments such as rivers and tidal channels. Coastal deposits characteristically include intertidal peat, an abundance of mud, a faunal record reflecting less-than-normal salinity, interbedded sand and mud, and cross-bedded sands with both landward and seaward paleocurrent indicators. The exact nature of the record, though, is strongly influenced by the size of the incised valley. For example, the records of a valley fill from a relatively narrow (500–1000 m), shallow (5–10 m) drainage basin tributary or tidal-inlet (throat) channel are expected to be significantly different from valley fills originating in wide (several km), deep (>30 m) drowned-river estuarine valleys. Although the fluvial incision is created during lowering of the sea, infilling occurs during rising water, and thus most of the valley fills are part of the transgressive systems tract, not the lowstand systems tract (Fig. 1). The lower portions of

Incised-valley Systems: Origin and Sedimentary Sequences, SEPM Special Publication No. 51

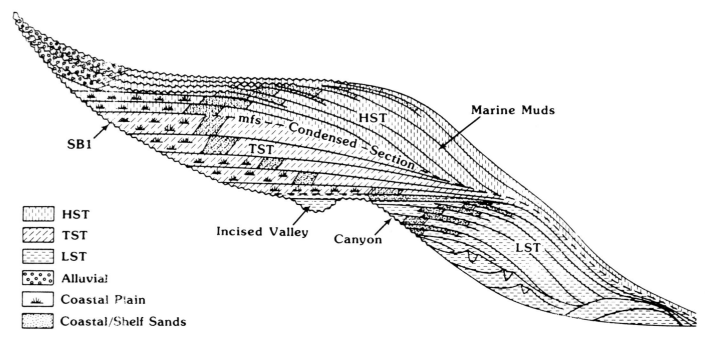

Fig. 1.—Major features of sequence and associated systems tracts: Incised valleys and canyons; LST = lowstand systems tract; TST = transgressive systems tract; HST = highstand systems tract; SB1 = Type 1 sequence boundary; mfs = maximum flooding surface (from Boyd and others, 1989, Fig. 1).

incised valley-fill successions are sheltered from erosion during subsequent transgressions and regressions and consequently may hold the only record of some sea-level events that would normally be completely stripped from interfluve areas (Hine and Snyder, 1985). Although valley fills comprise a small portion of continental margin deposits, they are extremely important particularly on passive margins where subsidence rates and sedimentation rates may be very low compared to the frequency of sea-level cycles and depth of shoreface erosion.

The U. S. Atlantic Coastal Plain is part of a passive continental margin that has been subsiding at decreasing rates since Triassic time as a result of thermal cooling (Grow and Sheridan, 1981). It consists of a seaward-thickening mass of stratified sediment which overlies a deeply faulted and subsided basement. However, a lack of substantial Pliocene-Pleistocene deposition suggests that portions of the shelf may actually be rising rather than sinking. This paper will focus on passive continental margin settings that typically have a low (1–2 mm/yr) continuous rate of subsidence, low sediment supply, mixed wave and tidal energy, and low (0–40 m) topographic relief. Our objectives are to present depositional models for various kinds of valley fills preserved on a passive continental margin during a transgression. These models are based on a synthesis of high-resolution seismic data "ground-truthed" with Vibracores from several sites on the U. S. Atlantic continental shelf (Fig. 2). We compare and contrast the variation in valley-fill records resulting from differences in scale (size of the valley), depositional environment, and sedimentary processes.

GEOMORPHIC AND HYDROGRAPHIC SETTING

Fenneman (1938) divided the U. S. Atlantic coastline into two geomorphic sections (Fig. 2). South of Cape Lookout, North Carolina (sea-island section) the coast is characterized by barrier islands protecting small, closely-spaced estuaries that are nearly filled in. The northern portion (embayed section) contains several large drowned-river estuaries. The coastlines between these broad estuaries have barrier islands and tidally-influenced lagoons which trap both marine and terrestrial sediment. Sedimentation rates in the lagoons are apparently keeping pace with the present relative rate of sea-level rise (1–3 mm/yr)(Nichols, 1989). The hydrographic regime is mixed energy; tidal range is 1–2 m and significant wave height 1 m. The continental shelf is generally wide (120 km) and gently sloping (0.0001) except in the central portion at Cape Hatteras where it is narrower (23 km) with a steeper slope (0.0073). The shelf is dominated by storms (tropical and nor'easters), and littoral drift is generally to the south (Bumpus, 1965). The shelf contains well-defined, shelf-transverse, shelf-valley complexes (Hudson, Great Egg, Delaware, Chesapeake, Susquehanna, Virginia Beach, Albemarle and Altamaha) separated by broad interfluves (Swift and Sears, 1974). These shelf-valley complexes mark the retreat paths of major estuary mouths during the Holocene transgression (Freeland and others, 1981) although many of the buried ancestral river valleys are offset from the shelf valley or not reflected at all in the modern shelf topography (Swift and others, 1972; Twichell and others, 1977; Swift and others, 1980). Large accumulations of sand are common on the northern flank

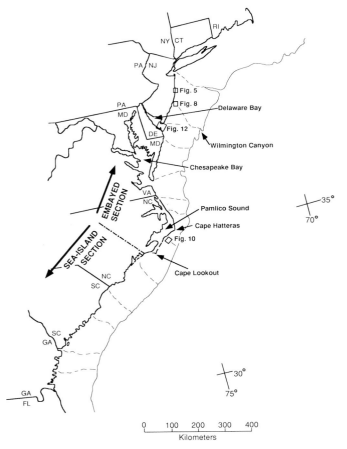

FIG. 2.—U. S. Atlantic continental margin regional location map. Shelf edge is indicated by the 200 m bathymetric contour. Approximate position of major paleochannels that were known to exist during the most recent (Holocene) sea-level rise are indicated with dashed lines. Area covered by regional maps (Figs. 5A, 8, 10A and 12) are outlined by boxes.

Cross-sectional profiles may range from symmetric to asymmetric, and the width is likely to vary along the valley.

Depressions incised into older shelf deposits by tidal flow exclusively tend to be about 1000 m in length and spoon-shaped compared to the longer and narrower, fluvially-eroded valleys. The relatively short, tidally-eroded depressions are developed under periodically reversing currents that are concentrated in the narrow zone of the barrier systems fringing the coast. The deepest tidal erosion (15–20 m) occurs at estuarine mouths with more shallow incisions occurring in inlet throats (10–15 m) and back-barrier tidal channels (5–12 m). The back-barrier tidal-channel erosion can extend 1 to 2 km landward of the inlet. Some of the amalgamated deposits of the tidal valleys may be very wide (1–4 km shore-parallel dimension) because of the tendency for inlets in particular to shift laterally driven by the long-shore drift. Migrating inlets will, in turn, affect all hydraulically connected tidal drainage channels landward of the barrier island causing them to migrate as well.

The range of sedimentary environments that typically exists during a transgression (although not necessarily simultaneously) is depicted in a schematic of a passive-margin coastal plain (Fig. 3). The infilling process, for the most part, takes place during sea-level rise, and the deposit may be partially or completely cannibalized during the transgression. Figure 3 illustrates three valley groups based on size: Small-sized valleys, Intermediate-sized valleys, and Large-sized valleys, in various stages of formation. In the following section, we present representative examples of these depositional settings from studies conducted on the Atlantic continental shelf (Fig. 2) and summarize the deposits and preservational potential of fills from a wide spectrum of natural settings.

REPRESENTATIVE EXAMPLES OF VALLEY FILLS

Small Valleys-First Order Tributaries

Relatively small streams that drain into the tributary system of large rivers will create narrow (50–100 m) and shallow (~5 m) incisions (Fig. 3A, A1). Examples from the well-studied Delaware paleodrainage system indicate a simple fining-upward infill similar to the sedimentary infill of the tributaries (see the detailed model for Intermediate-sized Valleys).

Small Valleys-Barrier Inlet Throats

Barrier islands are common features on sandy micro- and meso-tidal coastlines. Inlets (200–500 m wide and 5–15 m deep) are breaches in the barrier that are maintained by tidal forcing. The geometry of both the inlet throat (channel) and the associated sand bodies (flood- and ebb-tidal deltas) reflect a balance between the amount of sediment delivered to the inlet by the wave-generated drift system and the relative strength of the tidal currents to redistribute the sediment. Figure 4A shows a shore-perpendicular section of A2 (Fig. 3A) obliquely through an active inlet. Beneath the modern inlet sediments are older back-barrier lagoon and tidal-flat sediments that have been truncated by wave and tidal currents during the ongoing transgression. Tidal ra-

of shelf valleys. Called "estuary-shoal-retreat massifs," these sand bodies build as estuary-mouth shoals and then are abandoned and reworked as sea level rises and the shoreline moves landward (Swift and Sears, 1974).

DEPOSITIONAL SETTINGS OF VALLEY FILLS

The coastal zone is the focus of sediment transported seaward by rivers and landward by waves, flood tides, and storm surges (Meade, 1969; Nichols, 1989; Reinson, 1991; Dalrymple and others, 1992). Most of the elongate depressions (valleys) that become infilled by the sediment are initially cut by through-flowing streams and perhaps, only later, modified by tidal currents. Because these depressions were formed as an integral part of a drainage system, they have continuity and occur in a dendritic branching pattern with progressively ordered, cross-sectional areas that increase in a seaward direction. Along the strike of the valley, the bounding erosion surface may vary 5–20 meters in elevation due to the alongstream spatial variation in fluvial processes that produce pools and riffles in channelized flow.

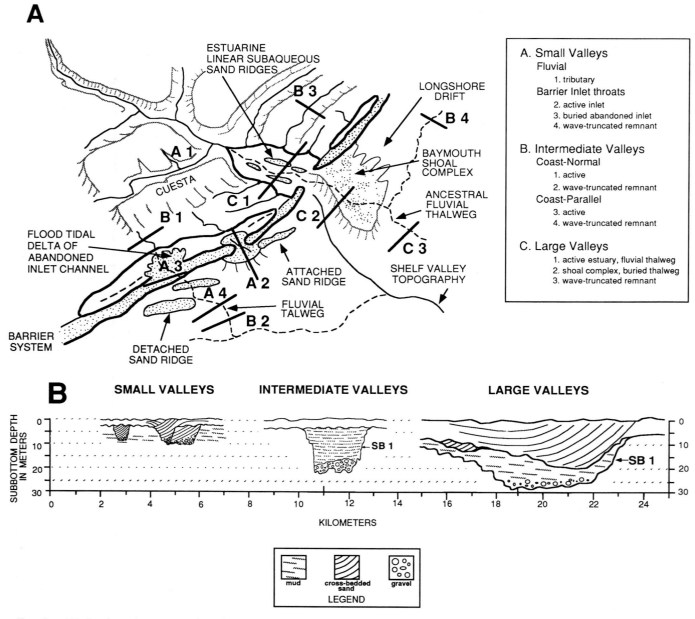

FIG. 3.—(A) A schematic representation of an Atlantic type, passive margin Coastal Plain depicting the physical settings in which Small (A) (Fig. 4), Intermediate (B) (Fig. 7), and Large (C) (Fig. 11) valley fills might originate. (B) A composite shore-parallel cross section comparing the three sizes of incised valleys.

vinement occurs in the inlet throat and in the back-barrier tidal channels that extend 1–2 km landward of the inlet. The tidal-channel system may move laterally in the direction of net littoral drift creating a wide (1–4 km), tidal-cut incision in the shore-parallel direction (Figs. 4B, C). The resulting erosion surface (ravinement #1) has relief of up to 10 meters and slopes gently seaward (0.0001) (Ashley and others, 1991). Tidal processes keep the inlet open (by erosion) and maintain the deltas (by deposition). The barrier island will respond to rising sea level by becoming

smaller or migrating landward by removing of sediment from the shoreface and transporting it through the barrier, over the barrier, or offshore into deeper water.

The tidal-delta deposits and the infill of the throat contain little or no mud and are well-sorted sands composed of medium-scaled cross-beds with landward directed paleocurrent indicators (Barwis and Makurath, 1978; Moslow and Tye, 1985; Reinson, 1991). The cross-bedding is produced by bedforms driven onshore by waves on the ebb-tidal delta and by flood-oriented currents in the inlet throat and on the

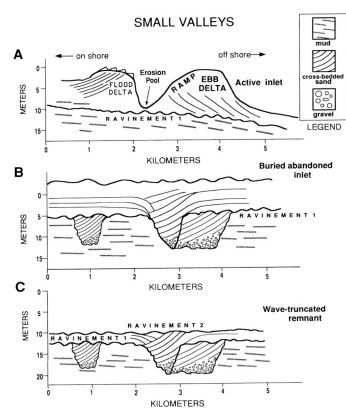

FIG. 4.—Valley-fill model for Small Valleys, barrier inlet throats (A) Active inlet (shore normal section), (B) Buried abandoned inlet (shore parallel section), and (C) Wave-truncated remnant (shore parallel section). Note that the migration of the tidal inlet results in the creation of a tidal cut ravinement (#1) under the barrier (4B) and the broader (1–2 km) amalgamated deposit of channel sands (4C).

flood-tidal delta (Fig. 4A). Shallowly seaward-dipping clinoforms reflecting episodic deposition from suspension are typical of the distal portion of the ebb-tidal delta.

Figure 4B is a shore-parallel section revealing examples of inlet channels incised into the older intertidal deposits (Fig. 3A, A3). The wide amalgamated deposit of channel sands and gravels was produced by a progressively migrating inlet throat. Each channel was sealed off by longshore drift and ultimately abandoned. The basal deposit of an abandoned channel will be coarse gravel (1–2 m thick) with broken shell hash reflecting a high-energy event just before abandonment. A series of storms or a single severe storm is commonly associated with the sealing of the channel and the eventual permanent closing of the inlet.

Figure 4C is a section through older inlets which have been truncated by erosion (Fig. 3A, A4). Only the "root" of the barrier island remains. The remainder has been removed by waves during the formation of ravinement #2. No surface expression remains of the former inlet. The valley-fill record consists of a gravel lag or shell hash at the base overlain with well sorted, cross-bedded sands.

Barnegat Inlet, New Jersey.—

Barnegat is a modern inlet in which the main tidal channel is 500 m wide and 15 m deep in the deepest pools in the throat (Fig. 5A). Peak mean flood velocities in the channel are >1 m/sec and peak mean ebb velocities are <1 m/sec. The mean grain size is 0.25 mm (Fields and Ashley, 1987.) High-resolution seismic profiles reveal 3 prominent reflectors (R1, R2, and R3) (Fig. 5B). Cores 1, 3, and 7 through the uppermost reflector, R3, exposed a tidal-cut ravinement (marine erosion surface) which occurs less than 1 meter below the modern inlet channel (Ashley and others, 1991). The sediments beneath the ravinement are Holocene (5–8 ka BP) intertidal sediments. Incision into these older sediments probably has occurred by channel erosion but is not revealed in this shore-normal section. The lateral shift in the tidal channel leaves 1 m of sand as an ephemeral cover overlying the tidal-cut ravinement (R3).

A seismic record from the modern Barnegat ebb-tidal delta detecting a former position of the main tidal channel (width = 200 m, depth = 6.5 m) is shown in Figure 6. The R3 wave-cut ravinement was buried by the migratory Barnegat Inlet ebb-tidal delta. The Inlet channel then eroded through the delta lobe, the channel was abandoned, truncated by further wave erosion, and a new lobe of the delta is now burying the truncated channel. This valley fill will be preserved intact only if the barrier is preserved at its present high stand limit. However, barrier deposits are generally truncated during transgressions leaving only the deepest portion of the record. The root of a former barrier island system between unconformities R1 and R2 was interpreted from seismic records that showed a tripartite shore-parallel sedimentary package (Fig. 5B) that could be traced for 15 km along shore (Wellner and others, 1993). The interpreted barrier is thought to be a remnant of a former relative "highstand" of sea level at 1–2 km offshore and −20 m depth. The sedimentary package consists of a central core of structureless sand with shallowly seaward-dipping sands interpreted as shoreface deposits. Seaward of the ancient barrier is a seismically transparent unit (probably bioturbated? mud). Landward is a highly variable, discontinuous lithofacies interpreted as a complex of intertidal lagoon, marsh, creek, and tidal-flat deposits. This sedimentary package demonstrates that evidence for a former barrier can be preserved in the geologic record on passive margins. Within these preserved barriers, tidal-inlet deposits will also be preserved.

Although the presence of a barrier-inlet-lagoon system is critical for creating a setting that focuses strong currents long enough to incise older sediment, only a small portion, if any, of the barrier system is likely to be preserved during transgression (Fig. 4C). The lower portion of the valley fill may be retained while the upper portion is stripped by wave and tidal currents. The sediment between the two ravinements is a parasequence (Haq and others, 1987) and represents a fluctuation of relative sea level with no subaerial exposure.

Intermediate Valleys-Second Order Tributaries to Major Coastal Plain Rivers

The Atlantic Coastal Plain has been the site of cyclic sea-level fluctuations since Cretaceous time. The dip direction

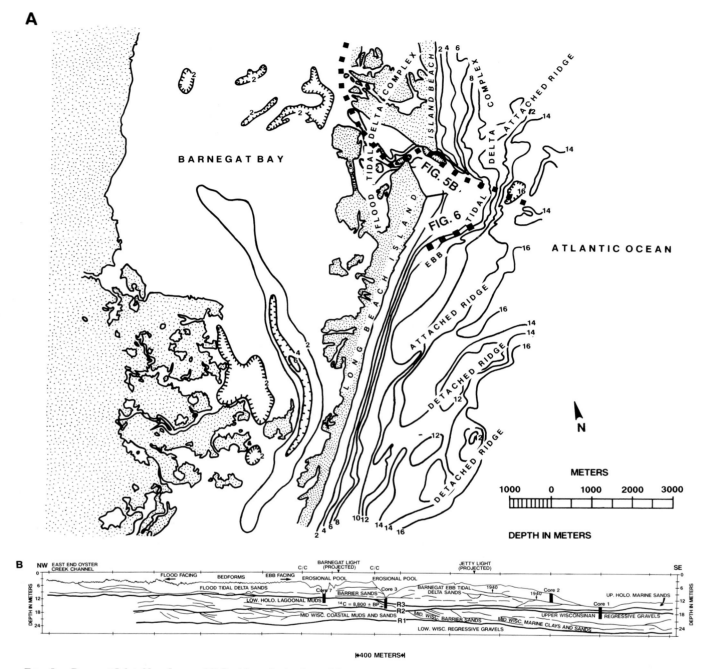

FIG. 5.—Barnegat Inlet, New Jersey. (A) Position of seismic tracklines indicated by dashed lines. (B) Interpreted shore-normal seismic-reflection profile taken through the modern inlet channel showing location of Vibracores used for ground truthing and dating (from Ashley and others, 1991). Erosional pools are the hachured depressions shown in A. Note that the tidal cut ravinement surface (R3) is covered by 1m of emphemeral sand and gravel in the erosion pools. Also, the tidal channels landward of the inlet have migrated with the inlet and have created R3 in this location under the flood-tidal deltas. See Figure 2 for location.

of the beds ranges from NE to E to SE, and the strike is approximately parallel to the present shoreline. Consequently, during lowered sea level, coastal-plain fluvial drainage patterns are controlled by the underlying structure. The main trunk streams cut across strike and the tributaries flow along strike between the cuestas of seaward dipping strata. These strike-valley tributaries incise into older sed-

iments during sea-level lowstands and then are filled during transgressions. Figures 7A and 7B summarize the valley-fill record for intermediate-sized valleys of coastal-plain streams shown on Figure 3A as B1, B2, B3, and B4.

Fluvial dissection and creation of the elongate channel form occurs during subaerial exposure during major regressions. The lower bounding surface is an archetypical sequence boundary (Haq and others, 1987). Presumably each channel is part of an integrated drainage network carrying run-off to the sea, and thus the elevation of the basal erosional contact decreases seaward reflecting the general direction of paleodrainage. The channels range in size from 1–2 km wide and 10–20 m in depth. The bottom of the channel typically has 1–2 m of gravels (Fig. 7A). As sea level rises, coarse alluvial sediments are trapped in the drainage basins because of a decrease in gradient and/or a decrease in flow capacity resulting in a gradually fining upward sequence. Eventually salt water penetrates the freshwater system and the depositional regime changes to fine-grained estuarine sedimentation with a characteristic increase in proportion of mud (Rahmani, 1988; Reinson and others, 1988).

This backing-up of the rivers and the passive infilling of the valleys with fines is the dominant process until the shoreline encroaches on the site (Wood and Hopkins, 1989). As the inner shelf and near shore environments transgress landward, the grain size increases as estuarine and marine sands are added to the mainly muddy valley fill (Fig. 7A). As the transgression proceeds, waves and tides truncate the upper valley fill creating a ravinement surface. Nearshore marine sands and ridge sands are consequently juxtaposed directly over the estuarine fines in the valley-fill sequence of small or intermediate-sized rivers.

Beach Haven Tributary.—

An unpublished, comprehensive high-resolution seismic and Vibracore study off central New Jersey near modern Little Egg tidal inlet describes a portion of a fluvial drainage system that was infilled and covered during the Holocene transgression (Miller and Dill, 1973). The main channel is oriented north-south and follows a shore-parallel strike valley similar to B3 (Fig. 3A). The channel can be traced for at least 5 km, ranges from 335–670 m wide, and is 8 m deep (Fig. 8). The elevation of the channel bottom is 23 m below present sea level. The southern section widens and appears to lead into a fan-shaped deposit. Two smaller tributaries (150 m wide, 1–2 m deep) feed the main channel.

The valley fill consists of 1-m thick pebbly sand (clasts > 1 cm) overlain by 3- to 4-m thick organic clay (Fig. 9). A radiometric date near the base of the clay indicates the clay began accumulating in early Holocene time (8,400 BP). A sandy clay, probably estuarine in origin, completely fills the valley and spills over and becomes widespread. The sandy clay is cut by a ravinement surface. The sediments overlying the unconformity are relatively thin marine sands and a prominent sand ridge (Miller and Dill, 1973). The valley system was cut during the most recent sea-level lowstand (oxygen isotope stage 2), and the pebbly sand was fluviallly deposited when the coastline was on the outer shelf. The fan-shaped deposit could be a delta formed as the shoreline encroached on the area. As sea level continued to rise, the valley became a drowned river estuary accumulating organic clay and later sandy clay as tidal currents and waves became more effective. A marine-erosion ravinement surface clearly separates the sandy clay from the nearshore marine sands and likely marks the development

of a barrier-lagoon-ridge system seaward of the site. The system migrated landward and is continuing to migrate at present. Tide and wave erosion created the ravinement, a regional unconformity (R3) that can be traced over 50 km to Barnegat Inlet (Fig. 5B).

Pamlico Sound and Shelf.—

The coastline between Cape Hatteras and Cape Lookout is deeply embayed with two drowned rivers, the Nuese and Pamlico, that join and form broad, shallow (4 m) Pamlico Sound, the largest lagoon on the Atlantic seaboard (Fig. 10A). A barrier island chain separates the estuary from the narrow continental shelf that ranges from 23 km wide (slope = 0.0073) at Cape Hatteras to 53 km (slope = 0.0031) at Cape Lookout. The head of Hatteras Submarine Canyon lies southeast off Cape Hatteras. Veatch and Smith (1939) concluded that submarine canyon heads such as this one were subaerially eroded during lowered sea level. Early seismic-reflection studies of Quaternary stratigraphy detected at least three superposed channel patterns on the shelf that likely represent three periods of erosion and infilling (Brown and Welby, 1970; Welby, 1974). The complex of buried channels is probably related to the ancestral Nuese-Pamlico drainage system that connected the upland to the head of Hatteras Canyon during a lowered sea level.

A recent high-resolution seismic and Vibracore study of the valley fills suggests that most of the sediment was deposited during the most recent sea-level rise (Foley, 1984; Decker, 1985). The interpretation of a seismic-reflection profile of a representative paleochannel is shown in Figure 10B (Decker, 1985). The feature is 2–3 km wide and 8 m deep. The seismic profile may have been taken oblique to the valley trend so that the exact width is not known with certainty. A 6-m core (Fig. 10C) reveals four sedimentary units all separated by sharp contacts. The sharp contacts are seismically traceable across the valley. At the base of the channel is a meter of compact, mottled medium-grained sand which is probably fluvial in origin. Above the sand is a 0.4-m thick peat dated at 13,112 BP ± 196 years and is thought to be an intertidal-marsh sediment (Lipp and others, 1975). Above the peat is a 0.75-m muddy unit which grades upward from a gravelly, medium-to-fine sand to a very fine sand. This "coarse" mud has rip-up clasts at the base and was interpreted to be a shallow (nearshore) estuarine deposit (Decker, 1985). The uppermost unit which is exposed on the modern sea floor is a 3.75-m thick muddy, very fine sand that began accumulating at 11,031 BP based on radiocarbon dating. The muddy sand was interpreted to be estuarine sediment.

Large Valleys-Major River Channels and Estuaries

The U. S. Atlantic continental margin is a mature passive margin with well developed large-scale river drainages that have persisted for most of the late Cenozoic (several million years). The Hudson, Delaware, and Susquehanna are examples of such fluvial systems that penetrate deep into the Appalachian hinterland. The valley fills of these major rivers are the most sedimentologically complex of the incised valleys because of the enormous scale of incision into

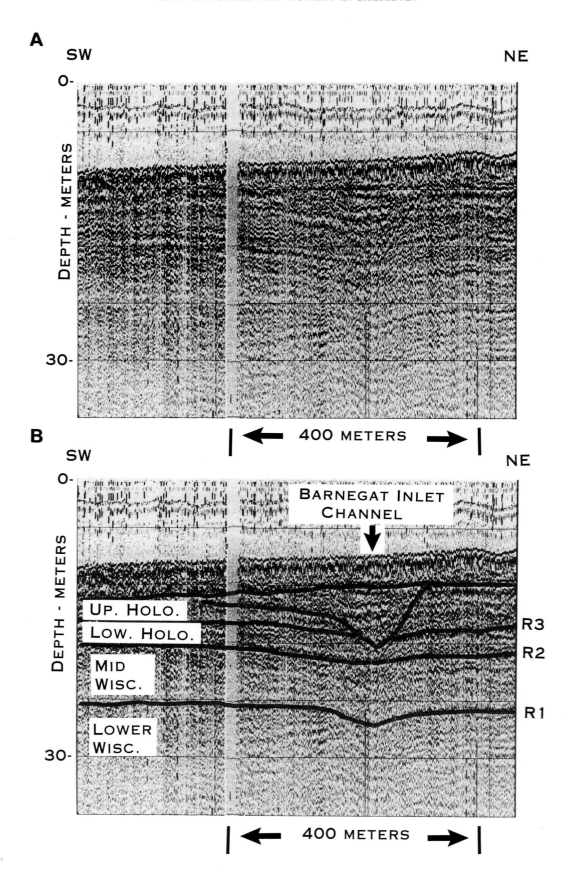

INTERMEDIATE VALLEYS

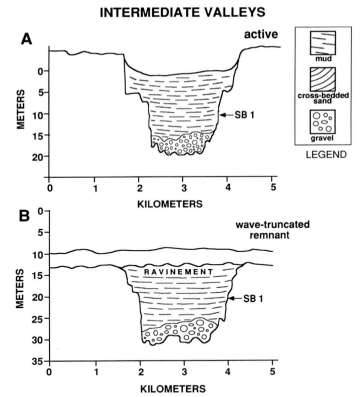

FIG. 7.—Valley-fill model for Intermediate Valleys. (A) Coast-normal and coast-parallel, active. The deposits are fining-upward estuarine or lagoonal mud. (B) Coast-normal and coast-parallel, wave-truncated remnants. A ravinement surface separates the mud from overlying shallow marine sand.

the continental shelf (thalwegs of 10–20 km widths and 50–60 m depths) and because of the influence of the large estuaries that inevitably develop during transgressions.

The sketch of a coastal plain (Fig. 3A) shows the location of three typical Large Valley cross sections: C1 — the active estuary (Fig. 11A), C2 — the active bay-mouth shelf valley (Fig. 11B), and C3 — the wave- and tide-truncated remnant (Fig. 11C). Figure 11 depicts the sedimentary facies, the type 1 sequence boundary (SB1), and several marine-cut ravinement surfaces (stacked ravinements) that characterize the evolution of an incised valley-fill sequence that is likely to be preserved in the geologic record.

During the early stages of transgression, the major estuary thalwegs are first filled in with channel lag gravels covered by muddy sands and later by a broad blanket of subtidal-flat muds (Fig. 11A). These muds are eventually dissected by strong tidal currents as the bay mouth trans-

gresses. A major tidally-cut ravinement surface which contains channels is formed (ravinement #1). Above this, strong flood currents rework subaqueous levee sand that comes from overbank flow. The linear tidal sand ridges are oriented parallel to tidal flow and consist of fine sand with some intercalated mud.

Eventually the bay mouth transgresses the area and even stronger tidal currents erode into the subaqueous linear sand ridge deposits (ravinement #2). The finer-grained sands of the linear ridges are overlain by medium-to-coarse sands of the coarser-grained bay-mouth shoal complex (Fig. 11B). Longshore inner shelf sand drift creates an extensive (100 km^2) and thick (10 m) sand deposit (Fig. 3A) containing well-developed oblique progradational clinoforms. This actively prograding sand of the bay-mouth shoal complex (Fig. 11B) forms the steeper slope of the asymmetric shelf valley. With further transgression, the bay-mouth shoal complex is itself truncated by storm waves and shelf currents, and only the deeper portions of the prograding shoal complex are preserved (Fig. 11C). Given this scenario, there are likely to be 10–20 m of well-sorted marine sands and smaller remnants (5 m) of muddier linear ridge sands preserved in the incised valleys of major estuaries.

Delaware River and Bay.—

This major embayment (Fig. 2) consists of an estuary about 200 km in length. The upper 60 km is a tidal river, the middle portion a partially mixed tidal river (80 km), and the lower tide-dominated estuary is 75 km (Fletcher and others, 1992).

Extensive, high-resolution seismic-reflection surveys and Vibracoring have been done in Delaware Bay and its bay-mouth region (Fig. 12) as well as on the inner continental shelf and Delaware Shelf Valley (Sheridan and others, 1974; Kraft and others, 1974; Belknap and others, 1976; Weil, 1976; Twichell and others, 1977; Knebel and Circe, 1988; Knebel and others, 1988). Profiles across the Delaware shelf valley and bay-mouth shoal complex (Figs. 13A, B) indicate that a large proportion of the valley fill is sand. In addition, side-scan studies in the bay-mouth region of 1- to 7-m high flood-oriented dunes and current meter measurements (nearly 1 m/sec at the surface) document the dominance of tidal processes in the estuary (Weil, 1976). This sand movement into the bay from the ocean eventually sources the linear tidal-built sand ridges that border the deeply eroded channels (Weil, 1976). Weil (1976) summarized the evolution of Delaware Bay during the Holocene transgression (e.g., Fig. 13C), and notes that during this complex evolution, because of the larger size (width and depth) of the incisement, multiple unconformities occur in the section above the subaerially cut (SB1) sequence boundary. Wave

FIG. 6.—High resolution seismic-reflection profile of an infilled paleochannel of Barnegat Inlet. Location indicated on Figure 5A. (A) Uninterrupted seismic record. (B) Preserved channel form is asymmetric and approximately 200 m wide and 6.5 m deep. Infill consists of sands deposited as oblique progradational clinoforms suggesting high-energy environment. Note that the channel cut into the lower Holocene muds and through what was the pre-existing terminal lobe of the ebb-tidal delta (above R3). The channel migrated and the channel fill was truncated by wave erosion and later buried by a new lobe of the delta.

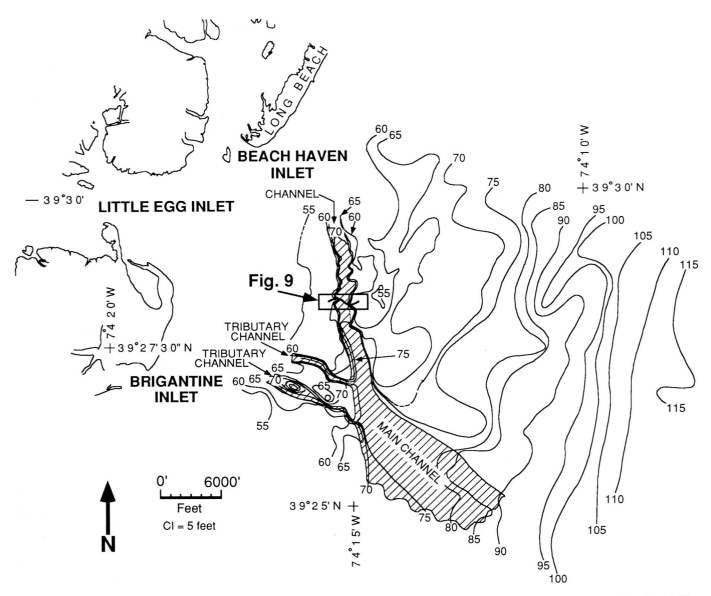

FIG. 8.—Beach Haven inner shelf, New Jersey. Contoured depth (in feet) to pre-Holocene reflection showing incised river valley (from Miller and Dill, 1973). Note the north-south nearly shore-parallel orientation of this tributary stream valley. See Figure 2 for location.

erosion and washover truncate the marshes fringing the estuary. Later strong tidal currents truncate the subtidal mud-flat deposits. Subsequently, bay-mouth tidal currents truncate the tidal-current sand ridge deposits resulting in a sequence with stacked sediments separated by multiple marine-cut ravinements (Fig. 11C).

Oblique progradational clinoforms on seismic-reflection profiles document the migration of the Delaware bay-mouth shoal complex to the southwest (Fig. 13A). Using the regional knowledge of the rate of transgression and sea-level rise, the mapping of the sand thickness yields a calculated migration rate of 0.23 m/year (Belknap and others, 1976). Over several thousands of years of transgression, the northeast Delaware shelf valley wall has migrated 2–3 km southwest over the thalweg of the ancestral Delaware River

drainage. Sheridan and others (1974) also noted the "detachment" of the shelf valley topography from that of the ancestral Delaware River thalweg. Twichell and others (1977) followed the incised Delaware River thalweg in seismic-reflection profiles toward the head of Wilmington Canyon (Fig. 2), indicating an easterly trend quite distinct from the southeast trend of the Delaware shelf valley topography. A similar southward migration path has been noted for the Hudson (Knebel and others, 1979) and the Chesapeake (Colman and Mixon, 1988).

DISCUSSION

The U. S. Atlantic margin is an archetypal, trailing-edge continental platform that is characterized by low subsidence

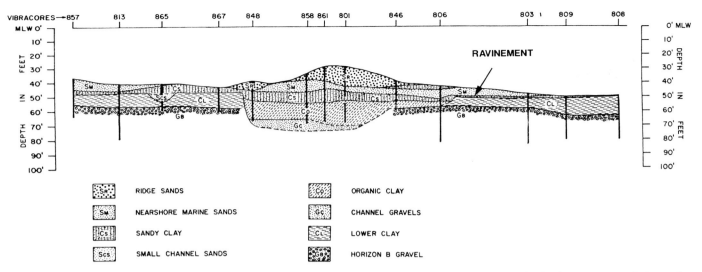

FIG. 9.—Interpreted geologic cross section of paleochannel shown in Figure 8 (from Miller and Dill, 1973). Ravinement occurs between the sandy clay (Cs) and nearshore marine sands (Sm).

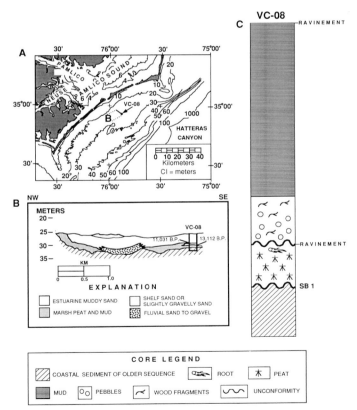

FIG. 10.—Pamlico Sound and Shelf, North Carolina. (A) Location map. (B) Interpreted section through the valley fill based on high-resolution seismic-reflection profile. (C) Stratigraphic section of Vibracore, VC-08 (modified from Decker, 1985). Ravinement surface is directly at the sea floor at core site VC-08. See Figure 2 for location.

rates and low alluvial sediment influx. When sea-level fluctuations occur at widely spaced intervals (0.5–1.0 million years), the sedimentary record produced should be a layer-cake of sequences separated by major regional unconformities (Fig. 1). However, when sea-level fluctuations occur at closely spaced intervals (<0.1 million years), a large portion of the transgressive systems tract (TST) is reworked by fluvial processes during lowering of sea level and may be completely stripped from interfluve areas (Hine and Snyder, 1985). However, during transgressions sediments deposited into depressions created by shoreface and tidal current erosion or by fluvial incision may survive the rigors of wave processes as the area passes through the surf zone, as well as fluvial degradation during subaerial exposure. A study of large sand ridges in the Upper Cretaceous Cardium Formation indicates the ridges represent TST sediments protected in shore-parallel, wave-cut benches which were covered by subsequent HST deposits (Leggitt and others, 1990). Incised-valley fills of the U. S. Atlantic passive margin serve a similar function on the shelf by preserving fragments of previous sea-level events which would otherwise be lost to erosion and transported seaward to become part of the lowstand systems tract (LST) deposits.

Atlantic Coastal Plain stratigraphy consists of eastward dipping beds which have been etched into shore-parallel cuesta and valley topography. Drainage networks range from dendritic to trellis depending on the extent of geologic structural control. Many of the smaller tributaries flow shore-parallel creating depressions at right angles to the orientation of the major trunk streams that become "drowned-river estuaries" during transgressions.

A second type of coastal-plain setting (tidal inlets) creates a shore-normal incised valley even though they may

LARGE VALLEYS

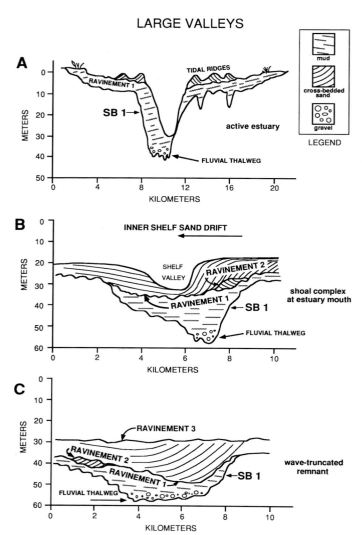

FIG. 11.—Valley-fill model for Large Valleys. (A) Active estuary and fluvial thalweg. (B) Shoal complex, buried thalweg, and estuary. Note that the longshore sediment transport results in shifting the shelf valley topography down current from the buried fluvial thalweg. (C) Wave-truncated remnant, shoal complex, fluvial thalweg, and estuary. The youngest ravinement is at the sea floor.

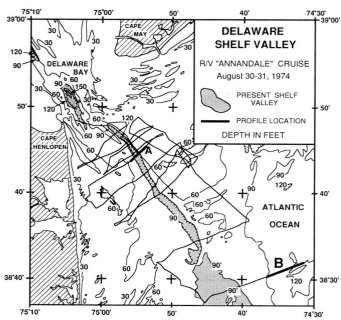

FIG. 12.—Delaware Estuary. Bathymetric map shows location of seismic-reflection profiles shown in Figure 13 (A and B) (modified from Belknap and others, 1976). See Figure 2 for location.

be short and discontinuous. Flow is faster in the confines of the inlet throat and fans out on the seaward side during ebb and the landward side during the flood. Erosion by tidal currents creates deep scour holes in the inlet throat which are later infilled. The incision into coastal-plain sediments, then, can occur by both fluvial or tidal processes. Valleys cut by rivers are either shore-parallel or shore-normal and are likely to have a greater continuity than those cut within tidal inlets that are exclusively shore-normal.

The lithofacies that infill incised valleys varies with the sedimentary environment and may range from all well-sorted sand and gravel to nearly all mud to a "sediment sandwich" of sand-mud-sand to stacked sequences separated by unconformities with no obvious vertical trends.

Small valleys (<200 m wide) incised and filled by either tidal or fluvial processes will be shallow (<10 m) after

truncation of the valley during transgression. The small river channels are backfilled and likely have a muddy, fining-upward fluvial sedimentary sequence (Schumm, 1977). The tidal-inlet fills are gravel and/or shell hash overlying an erosional base, with sandy cross-bedded sediments completing the sequence (Cheel and Leckie, 1990). Cross-beds may be large-scale (meters high) clinoforms built by sediment deposited on the channel margin similar to point-bar, lateral accretion deposits or small-scale (0.5–2.0 m thick) formed by migrating subaqueous dunes.

Intermediate-sized valleys are 1–2 km wide and 10–20 m deep and represent infilling of tributaries of major drainage networks. Because topography of the coastal plain has a predominate shore-parallel fabric, many of the 2nd order streams are oriented shore-parallel (Fig. 3A). The infills are generally fining-upward packages truncated at the top by marine erosion (the ravinement surface) and capped with marine, inner shelf or coastal sand (Figs. 7B, 9, 14A). The large-scale fining-upward sequence results from backfilling associated with a rising base level (Wood and Hopkins 1989; Howard and Whittaker, 1990; Dalrymple and others, 1992). Although our studies of intermediate-sized valleys did not find any multiple (stacked) sequences, they have been noted elsewhere (Wood and Hopkins, 1989). Marine submergence of the lower portion of the river alters the depositional environment by trapping coarse alluvium in the drainage basins and increasing deposition of mud. The biota change from freshwater to a brackish water fauna. The increase in sand content of the estuarine mud near the top (Fig. 9) signals the contribution from bay-mouth barriers. As the transgression progresses, a marine erosion surface truncates the mud. A resulting ravinement separates the es-

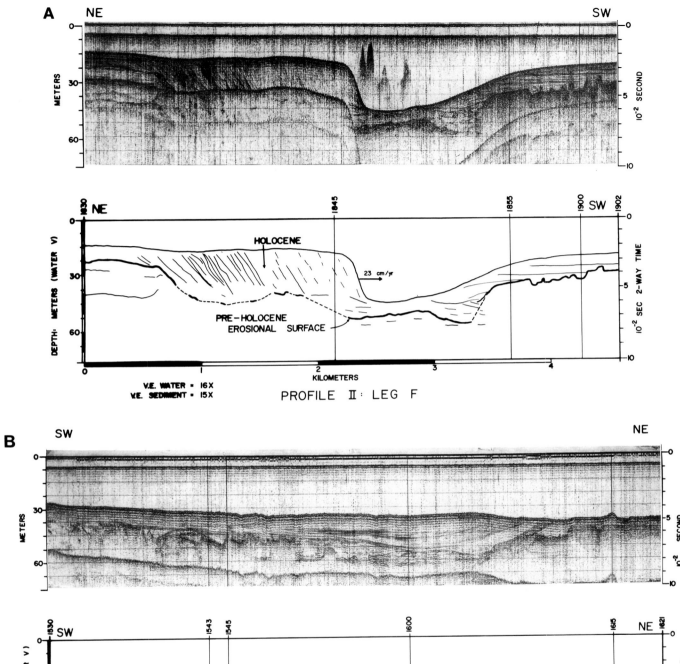

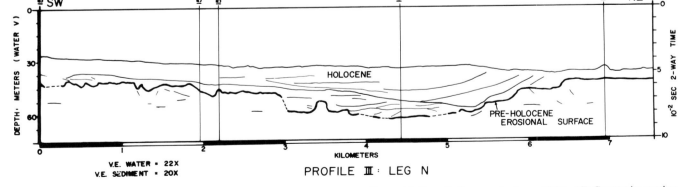

FIG. 13.—(A and B) Interpreted high-resolution reflection profiles located on Figure 12 (from Belknap and others, 1976). (C) Composite section of Delaware Bay incised valley interpreted from Vibracores and seismic-reflection profiles (from Weil, 1976). Note multiple stacked ravinement surfaces above the basal subaerially-cut sequence boundary unconformity.

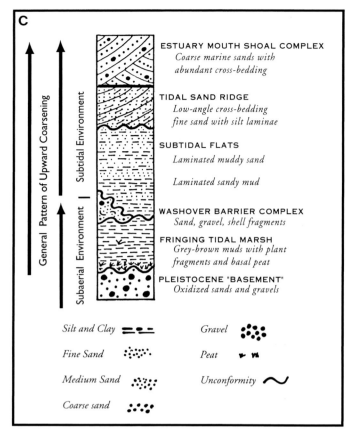

FIG. 13.—Continued.

tuarine mud from overlying sands deposited in shallow water and higher energy conditions (core C; Dalrymple and others, 1992) (Fig. 14A).

Large incised-valley fills (10–20 km wide, 20–40 m thick) develop through a complex history of repeated "cut-and-fills" even during one uninterrupted transgression. The large estuary, similar to the smaller tidal inlet, locally constrains tidal currents so that they can both erode and focus deposition of sand. Fairweather and storm waves rework the shallow water sediments, commonly shifting the thalweg of the estuary in the direction of longshore drift (Fig. 11B). High-resolution seismic profiles through Quaternary-age coastal-plain deposits dispel the widely-held myth that all valley fills are mud and concur with findings from the Western Canada Sedimentary Basin (Rahmani, 1988; Reinson and others, 1988; Wood and Hopkins, 1988; Cheel and Leckie, 1990; Leggitt and others, 1990). Sand and gravel are likely to be immediately above the SB1 unconformity, and sand occurs at the top of the sequence with an intervening mud unit. This "sedimentary sandwich" is characteristic of Large Valley fills. The high-energy bay-mouth environment can be both an area of tidal scour creating marine erosion surfaces with meters of relief and an area of deposition of thick units of sand. The estuary-shoal-retreat massifs on the modern shelf that mark the retreat paths of major estuary mouths during the Holocene are the visible

record of a former, high-energy estuary-mouth environment (Swift and Sears, 1974). The buried paleochannels, however, retain an even greater portion of the estuary-mouth sand trapped within the valley fills (Swift and others, 1972).

Preservation potential of valley fills on trailing-edge margins remains a key question (Fig. 14B). Dalrymple and others (1992) propose a scheme of lithofacies that would result from a wave-dominated estuary during a transgression (Fig. 14A). The portion of the record preserved is dependent on net depth of erosion which in turn is dependent on relative rates of sea-level rise, tectonic change, sediment influx, and topography (Fig. 14B). Topography includes relief generated by fluvial incision during sea-level low stands and by wave and tidal processes during transgressions. Topography is a particularly important factor on passive margins when subsidence rates and sedimentation rates may be low compared to the frequency of sea-level fluctuations. Estimates exist of 5–10 m of erosion on the inner continental shelf during transgressions (Pilkey and others, 1981; Hine and Snyder, 1985). Erosion depth might have been greater (15-m?) on the outer shelf where wave energy was probably higher. Consequently, only the lower portions of the fills proposed by Dalrymple and others (1992) are likely to be preserved on passive margins (i.e., about half of the sections C1, C2, C3, and C4 in Figure 14A).

CONCLUSIONS

1. Although valley fills comprise a small portion of continental margin deposits, they are extremely important on trailing-edge margins where subsidence rates and sedimentation rates may be low compared to the frequency of sea-level cycles and net depth of erosion. The incised valleys may retain the only geological record of some sea-level events.

2. Quaternary-age valley fills on the Atlantic margin range in size from a few tens of meters wide to 10–20 kms wide. The valleys may be oriented perpendicular or parallel to the paleoshoreline. Deposition does not always represent a passive infilling of a depression with estuarine muds. In particular, the large, drowned-river valleys show a highly varied record that may include several episodes of erosion and deposition during one uninterrupted transgression. The estuary mouth is a high-energy, dynamic environment in which both erosion and sand deposition take place.

3. Valley fills may contain a large proportion of sand. Small valleys formed in tidal inlet throats and large drowned-river estuaries commonly contain a high proportion of well-sorted, highly cross-bedded sands.

4. Preservation potential is excellent for the large incised valleys, good for intermediate-sized valleys, and poor for small valleys although tidal inlet fills can be preserved in highstand barriers. On the storm-dominated Atlantic shelf that has about 40 m relief, a low sediment influx, low subsidence rate, and a shoreline progradation of 3 m/yr, it appears that about ~5 m of shelf sediment is removed by shoreface erosion (and perhaps as much as 10 m) during a transgression. Only the lower to middle portion of the wave-dominated valley-fill se-

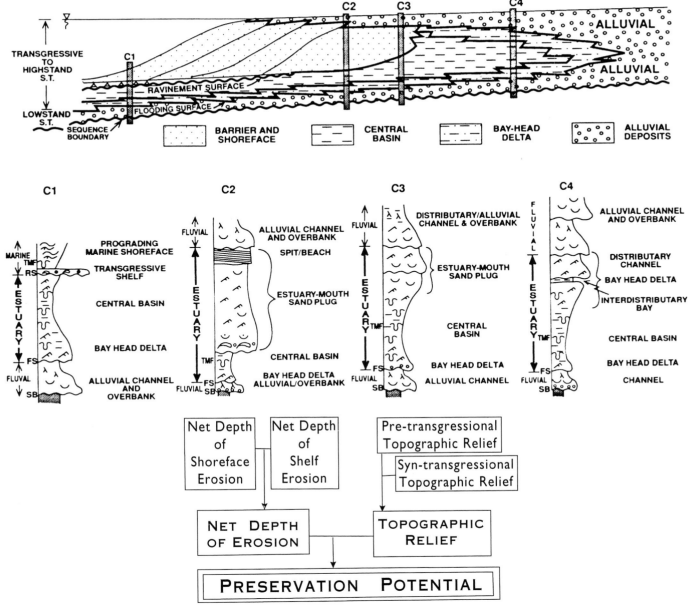

FIG. 14.—Preservation potential of valley fills. A Schematic interpretation of a typical transgressive sequence expected during the drowning of a coastal-plain river (from Dalrymple and others, 1992). Based on studies of Atlantic shelf late Quaternary, only the lowermost section appears to be preserved whereas the upper section is not. B. Conceptual model of the factors controlling the preservation of coastal facies during the infilling of an incised valley (from Decker, 1985).

quence proposed by Dalrymple and others (1992) is likely to be preserved on a passive margin.

ACKNOWLEDGMENTS

The authors gratefully acknowledge the use of unpublished data and interpretations from former students D. F. Belknap, C. B. Weil, Jr., and S. M. Decker, University of Delaware and R. W. Wellner, Rutgers University. The research was partially funded by NOAA Sea Grant Program—New Jersey Marine Sciences Consortium; NA 89AA-D-S6057 (Proj. No. RS-14). ShayMaria Silvestri helped with many of the illustrations.

REFERENCES

ASHLEY, G. M., WELLNER, R. W., ESKER, D., AND SHERIDAN, R. E., 1991, Clastic sequences developed during late Quaternary glacio-eustatic sea-level fluctuations on a passive margin: Example from the inner continental shelf near Barnegat Inlet, New Jersey: Geological Society of America Bulletin, v. 103, p. 1607–1621.
AUBREY, M.-P., 1991, Sequence stratigraphy: Eustasy or tectonic imprint?: Journal of Geophysical Research, v. 96, p. 6641–6680.

BARWIS, J. H., AND MARKURATH, J. H., 1978, Recognition of ancient tidal inlet sequences: an example from the Upper Silurian Keyser Limestone in Virginia: Sedimentology, v. 25, p. 61–82.

BELKNAP, D. F., SHERIDAN, R. E., SWIFT, D. J. P., AND LAPIENE, G., 1976, Geophysical investigations of the Delaware Shelf Valley (abs.): Geological Society of America Abstracts/Programs, v. 8, p. 131–132.

BOYD, R., SUTER, J., AND PENLAND, S., 1989, Relation of sequence stratigraphy to modern sedimentary environments: Geology, v. 17, p. 926–929.

BROWN, L. H., AND WELBY, C. W., 1970, Subsurface channels in the Pamlico-Pungo River area: Journal Elisha Mitchell Scientific Society, v. 86, p. 177.

BUMPUS, D. F., 1965, Residual drift along the bottom on the continental shelf in the Middle Atlantic shelf areas: Limnology and Oceanography, Supplement 3, p. 48–53.

CHEEL, R. J., AND LECKIE, D. A., 1990, A tidal-inlet complex in the Cretaceous epeiric sea of North America: Virgelle Member, Milk River Formation, southern Alberta, Canada: Sedimentology, v. 37, p. 67–81.

CHEN, Z. Q., HOBBS, C. H., III, AND KIMBALL, S., 1992, An investigation of Late Pleistocene paleochannel systems in the shelf, south of Chesapeake Bay mouth: EOS Transactions, American Geophysical Union, v. 72, p. 68.

COLMAN, S. M., AND MIXON, R. B., 1988, The record of major Quaternary sea-level changes in a large coastal plain estuary, Chesapeake Bay, eastern United States: Palaeogeography, Palaeoclimatology, Palaeocology, v. 68, p. 99–116.

DALRYMPLE, R. W., ZAITLIN, B. A., AND BOYD, R., 1992, Estuarine facies models: conceptual basis and stratigraphic implications: Journal of Sedimentary Petrology, v. 62, p. 1130–1146.

DECKER, S. M., 1985, Geological and geophysical reconnaissance of the shallow subbottom in Raleigh Bay, North Carolina: Unpublished M.S. Thesis, University of Delaware, Newark, 152 p.

DEMAREST, J. M., II, AND KRAFT, J. C., 1987, Stratigraphic record of Quaternary sea levels: implication for more ancient strata, in Nummedal D., Pilkey, O. H., and Howard, J.D., eds., Sea-level Fluctuation and Coastal Evolution: Tulsa, Society of Economic Paleontologists and Mineralogists Special Publication 41, p. 223–237.

FENNEMAN, N. M., 1938, Physiography of the eastern United States: New York, McGraw Hill Co., 714 p.

FIELDS, M. L., AND ASHLEY, G. M., 1987, Barnegat Inlet, New Jersey—A stabilized inlet: New Orleans, Coastal Sediments '87, American Society of Civil Engineers, p. 2006–2021.

FLETCHER, C. H., III, KNEBEL, H. J., AND KRAFT, J. C., 1992, Holocene depocenter migration and sediment accumulation in Delaware Bay: a submerging marginal marine sedimentary basin: Marine Geology, v. 103, p. 165–183.

FOLEY, F. D., 1984, Neogene seismic stratigraphy and depositional history of the lower Georgia coast and continental shelf: Unpublished M.S. Thesis, University of Georgia, Atlanta, 80 p.

FREELAND, G. L., STANLEY, D. J., SWIFT, D. J. P., AND LAMBERT, D. N., 1981, The Hudson Shelf Valley: Its role in shelf sediment transport: Marine Geology, v. 42, p. 399–427.

GROW, J. A., AND SHERIDAN, R. E., 1981, Deep structure and evolution of the continental margin off the eastern United States, in Oceanological, Acta Supplement v. 4: Paris, 26 International Geological Congress, Colloque C 3, Geology of Continental Margins, p. 11–19.

HAQ, B. U., HARDENBOL, J., AND VAIL, P. R., 1987, The chronology of fluctuating sea level since the Triassic: Science, v. 235, p. 1156–1167.

HAQ, B. U., HARDENBOL, J., AND VAIL, P. R., 1988, Mesozoic and Cenozoic chronostratigraphy and eustatic cycles in Wilgus, C. K., Hastings, B. S., Kendall, C. G., Posamentier, H. W., Ross, C. A., and Van Wagoner, J. C., eds., Sea-level changes: An Integrated Approach: Tulsa, Society of Economic Paleontologists and Mineralogists Special Publication 42, p. 71–108.

HINE, A. C., AND SNYDER, S. W., 1985, Coastal lithosome preservation: Evidence from the shoreface and inner continental shelf off Bogue Banks, North Carolina: Marine Geology, v. 63, p. 307–330.

HOWARD, R. H., AND WHITAKER, S. T., 1990, Fluvial-estuarine valley fill at the Mississippian-Pennsylvanian unconformity, Main Consolidated field, Illinois, in Barwis, J. H., McPherson, J. G., and Studlick, R.

J., eds., Sandstone Petroleum Reservoirs: New York, Springer-Verlag, p. 319–341.

KNEBEL, H. J., AND CIRCE, R. C., 1988, Late Pleistocene drainage systems beneath Delaware Bay: Marine Geology, v. 78, p. 285–302.

KNEBEL, H. J., FLETCHER, C. H., AND KRAFT, J. C., 1988, Late Wisconsinan-Holocene paleogeography of Delaware Bay: a large Coastal Plain estuary: Marine Geology, v. 83, p. 115–133.

KNEBEL, H. J., WOOD, S. A., AND SPIKER, E. C., 1979, Hudson River: Evidence for extensive migration on the exposed continental shelf during Pleistocene time: Geology, v. 7, p. 254–258.

KRAFT, J. C., SHERIDAN, R. E., MOOSE, R. D., STROM, R. N., AND WEIL, C. B., 1974, Middle-late Holocene evolution of the morphology of a drowned estuary system-the Delaware Bay: Memoires de l'Institute de Geologie de Bassin d'Aquitaine, v. 7, p. 297–305.

LEGGITT, S. M., WALKER, R. G., AND EYLES, C. H., 1990, Control of reservoir geometry and stratigraphic trapping by erosion surface E5 in the Pembina-Carrot Creek area, Upper Cretaceous Cardium Formation, Alberta, Canada: American Association of Petroleum Geologists Bulletin, v. 74, p. 1165—1182.

LIPP, M. S., SHERIDAN, R. E., NEWTON, J. G., AND EDGERTON, H. E., 1975, Seismic reflection profiles and morphologic development of a ridge and swale topography on the Atlantic continental shelf off Ocracoke Inlet, North Carolina (abs.): Geological Society of America Abstracts/Program, v. 7, p. 540.

MEADE, R. H., 1969, Landward transport of bottom sediments in estuaries of the Atlantic Coastal Plain: Journal of Sedimentary Petrology, v. 39, p. 222–234.

MILLER, H. J., AND DILL, C., 1973, Geophysical investigation Atlantic Generating site and region: Norwood, Alpine Geophysical Association Technical Report, 56 p.

MILLER, K. G., KENT, D. V., BROWER, A. N., BYBELL, L. M., FEIGENSON, M. D., OLSSON, R. K., AND POORE, R. Z., 1990, Eocene-Oligocene sea-level changes on the New Jersey coastal plain linked to the deep-sea record: Geological Society of America Bulletin, v. 102, p. 331–339.

MOSLOW, T. F., AND TYE, R. S., 1985, Recognition and characterization of Holocene tidal inlet sequences: Marine Geology, v. 63, p. 129–151.

NICHOLS, M. M., 1989, Sediment accumulation rates and relative sea-level rise in lagoons, in Ward, L., and Ashley, G. M., eds., Physical Processes and Sedimentology of Siliciclastic-Dominated Lagoonal Systems: Marine Geology, v. 88, p. 201–209.

NUMMEDAL, D., AND SWIFT, D. J. P., 1987, Transgressive stratigraphy at sequence-bounding unconformities: some principles derived from Holocene and Cretaceous examples, in Nummedal, D., Pilkey, O. H., and Howard, J. D., eds., Sea-level Fluctuation and Coastal Evolution: Tulsa, Society of Economic Paleontologists and Mineralogists Special Publication 41, p. 241–260.

OLSSON, R. K., MELILLO, A. J., AND SCHREIBER, B. L., 1987, Miocene sea level events in the Maryland coastal plain and the offshore Baltimore Canyon Trough, in Ross, C. A., and Haman, D., eds., Timing and Depositional History of Eustatic Sequences: Constraints on Seismic Stratigraphy: Hanover, Cushman Foundation for Foraminiferal Research Special Publication 24, p. 85–97.

PILKEY, O. H., JR., BLACKWELDER, B. W., KNEBEL, H. J., AND AYERS, M. W., 1981, The Georgia Embayment continental shelf: Stratigraphy of a submergence: Geological Society of America Bulletin, v. 92, p. 52–63.

RAHMANI, R. A., 1988, Estuarine tidal channel and nearshore sedimentation of late Cretaceous epicontinental sea, Drumheller, Alberta, Canada, in de Boer, P. L., Van Gelder, A., and Nio, S. D., eds., Tide-influenced Sedimentary Environments and Facies: Dordrecht, D. Riedel Publishing Company, p. 433–471.

REINSON, G. E., 1991, Transgressive barrier island and estuarine systems, in Walker, R. G., and James, N. P., eds., Facies Models: Response to Sea Level Change: St. Johns, Geological Association of Canada, p. 179–194.

REINSON, G. E., CLARK, J. E., AND FOSCOLOS, A. E., 1988, Reservoir geology of Crystal Viking field, Lower Cretaceous estuarine tidal channel-bay complex, south-central Alberta: American Association of Petroleum Geologists Bulletin, v. 72, p. 1270–1294.

SCHUMM, S. A., 1977, The Fluvial System: New York, Wiley-Interscience, 338 p.

SHERIDAN, R. E., DILL, C. E., AND KRAFT, J. C., 1974, Holocene sedimentary environment of the Atlantic inner shelf off Delaware: Geological Society of America Bulletin, v. 85, p. 1319–1328.

SUTER, J. R., BERRYHILL, H. L., AND PENLAND, S., 1987, Late Quaternary sea-level fluctuations and depositional sequences, southwest Louisiana continental shelf, in Nummedal, D., Pilkey, D. H., and Howard, J. D., eds., Sea-level Fluctuation and Coastal Evolution: Tulsa, Society of Economic Paleontologists and Mineralogists Special Publication 41, p. 199–222.

SWIFT, D. J. P., KOFOED, J. W., SAULSBURY, F. P., AND SEARS, P., 1972, Holocene evolution of the shelf surface, in Swift, D. J. P., Duane, D. B., and Pilkey, O. H., eds., Shelf Sediment Transport: Stroudsburg, Dowden, Hutchison and Ross, Inc., p. 499–574.

SWIFT, D. J. P., MOIR, R., AND FREELAND, G. L., 1980, Quaternary rivers on the New Jersey shelf: Relation of seafloor to buried valleys: Geology, v. 8, p. 276–280.

SWIFT, D. J. P., AND SEARS, P., 1974, Estuarine and littoral deposition patterns in the surficial sand sheet, central and southern Atlantic shelf of North America: Memoires de l'Institute de Geologie de Bassin d'Aquitaine, v. 7, p. 171–189.

TWICHELL, D. C., KNEBEL, H. J., AND FOLGER, D. W., 1977, Delaware River: Evidence for its former extension to Wilmington submarine canyon: Science, v. 195, p. 483–485.

VEATCH, A. C., AND SMITH, P. A., 1939, Atlantic submarine valleys of the United States and the Congo Submarine Valley: New York, Geological Society of America Special Paper 7, 101 p.

WALKER, R. G., 1990, Facies modeling and sequence stratigraphy: Journal of Sedimentary Petrology, v. 60, p. 777–786.

WALKER, R. G., 1992, Facies, facies models, and modern stratigraphic concepts, in Walker, R. G. and James, N. P., eds., Facies Models: Response to Sea Level Change: St. Johns, Geological Association of Canada, p. 1–14.

WEIL, C. B., JR., 1976, A model for the distribution, dynamics, and evolution of Holocene sediments and morphologic features of Delaware Bay: Unpublished Ph.D. Dissertation, University of Delaware, Newark, 407 p.

WELBY, C. W., 1974, North Carolina estuarine-shelf complex, Pleistocene to Recent history: Memoires de l'Institute de Geologie de Bassin d'Aquitaine, v. 7, p. 331–335.

WELLNER, R. W., ASHLEY, G. M., AND SHERIDAN, R. E., 1993, Seismic stratigraphic evidence for a submerged Mid-Wisconsin barrier: Implications for sea-level history: Geology, v. 21, p. 109–112.

WOOD, J. M., AND HOPKINS, J. C., 1989, Reservoir sandstone bodies in estuarine valley fill: Lower Cretaceous Glauconitic member, Little Bow Field, Alberta, Canada: American Association of Petroleum Geologists Bulletin, v. 37, p. 1361–1382.

TRANSGRESSIVE VALLEY-FILL LITHOSOMES: DELAWARE AND MAINE

DANIEL F. BELKNAP
Department of Geological Sciences, University of Maine, Orono, Maine 04469-5711
JOHN C. KRAFT
Department of Geology, University of Delaware, Newark, Delaware 19716
AND
RICHARD K. DUNN
Department of Geology, University of Delaware, Newark, Delaware 19716

ABSTRACT: Incised-valley fills provide the greatest potential for preservation of sediments in a transgressive system. We compare examples from the coastal plain of Delaware and the glaciated bedrock terrain of Maine. Facies models developed in these areas suggest that 1/2 to 2/3 of the initial phases of transgression may be preserved below the shoreface ravinement surface in coastal-plain settings, recording initial fluvial, estuarine, lagoon, and some flood-tidal delta deposits. Coastal-plain systems are controlled by processes of open-ocean wave energy and back-barrier tidal systems. Lithosomes are irregular and may be disconnected lenses, 10–30 m maximum thickness, 1–5 km normal to the shoreline, and 10's of kilometers alongshore extent. Shoreface incision to a wave base of 10 m creates a ravinement unconformity. Incised-valley fills along the margins of a major estuary, Delaware Bay, record a similar sequence, but shoreface incision is smaller, approximately 1 m. In Maine, embayments are framed by bedrock, and cut into glaciomarine sediments. The tide-dominated system accumulates sediment in the inner reaches but becomes progressively truncated by tidal-channel erosion at mid-embayment, creating an estuarine, tidal-ravinement surface. The outer, less geographically sheltered reaches are dominated by wave erosion, which removes the majority of the sequence. Lithosomes are disjunct lenticular pods of a few meters to 10 m thickness and kilometer scale in lateral and longitudinal extent. In both cases, maximum preservation may occur as sea level reaches highstand, producing a prograding sequence that caps the earlier transgressive units.

INTRODUCTION

Incised valley-fill deposits, in the sequence-stratigraphy model of Posamentier and others (1988), are an important identifying feature overlying unconformity surfaces at Type 1 sequence boundaries. Type 1 sequence boundaries are characterized by subaerial exposure and erosion during stream rejuvenation, basinward shift of facies and downward shift in coastal onlap, followed by onlap of overlying strata (Van Wagoner and others, 1988, p. 41). As sea level falls, fluvial systems incise valleys into a prior highstand systems tract. These valleys may at first receive fluvial sediments and may then later fill with transgressive estuarine and other coastal sediments. We describe here two systems of contrasting geologic setting that are dominated by transgressive coastal lithosomes (bodies of similar lithology bounded by interfingering facies relationships). These lithosomes are part of an as-yet-incomplete depositional sequence (in the sense of Mitchum and others, 1977) that includes the marine and coastal deposits of the Holocene transgression.

This paper develops a facies model for transgressive valley-fill lithosomes using these examples. Common methods of data collection, sequence analysis, and comparison to models are used in three distinct settings. First, we examine the Delaware outer coast, an example of a coastal-plain barrier system. Second, we examine a valley-fill succession on the flank of a major coastal-plain estuary, Delaware Bay. Third, we examine a rock-framed system in Maine. Synthesis of the similarities in and differences among these settings allows formation of general models with applications to settings elsewhere.

The Delaware coast formed on a coastal plain over a paleotopography of trellis-dendritic drainage systems cut during Wisconsinan lowstand and filled during Holocene rising sea level with estuarine, lagoon, and barrier sediments (Kraft, 1971; Kraft and others, 1979; Belknap and Kraft, 1985). A complete succession of infill is found behind the present

Atlantic barrier, while only portions of the infill lithosomes are preserved in paleovalleys offshore below the shoreface ravinement surface. The Maine coast consists of predominantly rock-framed embayments, modified by glacial erosion and draped with glacial and glaciomarine sediments. Valleys were incised into this Wisconsinan cover during relative sea-level fall from about 14,000 to 10,500 BP, caused by isostatic uplift during deglaciation (Belknap and others, 1989; Kelley and others, 1992). Holocene transgression has produced estuarine valley fills that become progressively reworked at the higher-energy mouths of rocky embayments (Belknap and others, 1986). An incomplete record is preserved in deep channels offshore.

METHODS

A variety of methods were used to construct geological cross sections at upper valley, mid-valley, and offshore settings. High-resolution seismic reflection systems included Uniboom and Geopulse boomers, and auxiliary Raytheon 3.5 kHz profiles. In Delaware, seismic systems penetrated 30–50 m to the base of nearshore late Wisconsinan paleovalleys, resolving several internal seismic facies (Sheridan and others, 1974). These data were compiled into isopach and structure contour maps (Belknap and Kraft, 1985) and compared with onshore coring data (Chrzastowski, 1986; Kraft and others, 1987). In Maine, seismic profiles penetrated to bedrock, often through more than 50 m of glaciomarine and post-glacial sediments, except where obscured by seismically impenetrable zones caused by natural gas (Belknap and Shipp, 1991; Belknap and others, 1989; Shipp, 1989; Kelley and others, 1986).

Cores up to 12 m length were obtained offshore in Delaware using barge-mounted pneumatic vibracoring (Belknap and Kraft, 1985; Kraft and others, 1987). Shell Development Company drilled numerous continuous rotary cores in 1962, that were used by Kraft (1971) and in later studies to develop the basic barrier stratigraphy. Truck-mounted auger, vibracore, and a variety of hand coring techniques completed the extensive terrestrial core sampling. In the 1970's, the Delaware group developed a catamaran-mounted vibracoring system (Hoyt and Demarest, 1981) used in numerous thesis projects to sample the back-barrier and estuarine margins. In Maine, numerous vibracores have been taken using the Lanesky and others (1979) concrete vibrator technique, with aluminum tubes 7.6-cm diameter and up to 14-m length, on land and in shallow water. Underwater cores were taken in up to 10-m water depth from a lobster-boat research vessel assisted by SCUBA divers.

Sediments were described using standard textural-analytical techniques, and shelly and peaty samples were identified by fossil type. The term "peat" used here and in related previous publications is a field term referring to fibrous sediments rich in organics but which usually contain a majority of inorganic material by dry weight. Radiocarbon dates were obtained from shell, peat, and wood samples, and dated using conventional methods. Dates (Table 1) are given as conventional radiocarbon results (5568 year half-life) and "corrected" by the Stuiver and Reimer (1986, 1987) calibration for dates younger than 8100 BP. For dates older than this, only correction to the 5730 year half-life is used. Sedimentology, paleoecology, and dating methods have been described in previous publications, cited in discussions below.

GEOLOGIC SETTING

Delaware

Delaware (Fig. 1) sits on the interior margin of the Atlantic coastal plain-continental shelf province. It is situated on the northwestern margin of the Baltimore Canyon Trough. Holocene sea level has risen at a decreasing rate from −26 m at 11 ka, to −10 m at 5 ka and to within 1 m of present

in the past 0.5 ka (Belknap and Kraft, 1977) (Fig. 2). This sea-level record was reconstructed from more than 100 dated peats and other materials found in coastal lithosomes and valley-fill deposits. The rate of rise is more rapid than those found in stable areas (e.g., Florida: Scholl and others, 1969) and more rapid than the Fairbanks (1989) Barbados curve over the past 7 ka. The increased rate may be due to basin subsidence, hydroisostatic shelf tilt, and/or subsidence of a glacioisostatic marginal bulge (Belknap and Kraft, 1977).

The southeastern margin of Delaware is a microtidal barrier-lagoon system facing the open Atlantic ocean. The remainder of the eastern shore of Delaware faces on Delaware Bay, a major coastal-plain estuary, and consists of estuarine washover barriers protecting marshes, as well as complex tributary estuaries, pre-Holocene headlands, and, farther north, marshes exposed along the shoreline. The pre-Holocene surface underlying Holocene coastal lithosomes is a trellis-dendritic drainage system of tributaries to the ancestral Delaware River (Fletcher and others, 1990). Major valleys rising at headwaters such as Indian River can be directly traced under the Atlantic barrier and offshore. Tributaries draining into Delaware Bay, such as the Murderkill River, can be traced into similar, major Wisconsinan paleovalleys under Delaware Bay (Knebel and others, 1988). These valleys are filled with up to 30 m of Holocene sediments. The gently sloping coastal plain provides a substrate for relatively uniform coastal migration, excepting areas where pre-Holocene stream drainage strongly influenced later coastal evolution ("nexus" of Halsey, 1979). Major valleys have influenced the location of open-Atlantic coast inlets in spite of vigorous longshore transport, while lower wave energy in the Delaware Bay estuarine systems ensures that valleys and the exchange of their tidal prisms with the open bay completely control location of present inlets.

Maine

Maine's widely known "rock-bound coast" reflects drowning of a complex topography of eroded crystalline

TABLE 1.—RADIOCARBON DATES

Sample	Depth: m MHW	Material	¹⁴C-5568 Years BP	Corrected* Years BP
Delaware Atlantic Coast: Kraft (1976)				
Drillhole R-4115				
Shell Dev.	−12.3	*Crassostrea virginica*	3430 ± 170	3469–3909
Shell Dev.	−27.2	Peat and wood (Detrital?)	10,800 ± 300	11,124
Delaware Bay Coast: Kraft (1976)				
Core JCK-7–69				
I-4624	−6.0	Salt marsh	2550 ± 100	2479–2762
Drillhole DH-2–71				
I-5950	−11.6	Salt marsh	3360 ± 95	3473–3705
I-5927	−16.7	Salt marsh	5205 ± 110	5899–6099
I-5994	−22.2	Salt marsh	7730 ± 125	8389–8629
I-5928	−25.6	Salt marsh	9435 ± 155	9710
Maine Coast: Belknap and others (1989); Davies (1992)				
Vibracore DR-VC-18				
PITT-0757	−8.8	*Mya arenaria* + *C. virginica*	3755 ± 50	3997–4230
PITT-0758	−10.2	*Mya arenaria* + *C. virginica*	4835 ± 60	5480–5646
Vibracore DR-VC-6				
SI-6617	−15.0	Brackish peat	6295 ± 55	7184–7292

*Following Stuiver and Reimer (1986, 1987) for dates younger than 8100 B.P. and using the 5730 year half-life for older dates.

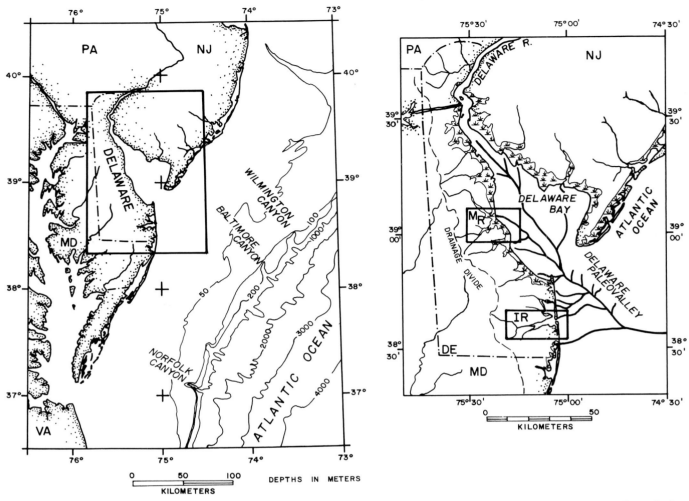

Fig. 1.—Location map for Delaware showing study areas, Indian River (IR) and Murderkill River (MR). Paleodrainage from Fletcher and others (1990).

rocks of variable resistance (Fig. 3). Pre-Quaternary fluvial erosion (Denney, 1982) was modified by glacial erosion to produce streamlined forms and deepened valleys (Johnson, 1925; Belknap and others, 1987; Kelley, 1987). The peninsulas and valleys of the west-central coast strongly reflect the structure of the isoclinally folded, high-grade metamorphic rocks, while the central coastal zone of broad bays and islands is controlled by igneous plutons. This bedrock framework is overlain by variable thicknesses of glacial till and outwash and glaciomarine mud. The Laurentide ice sheet retreated through the coastal zone between 13.8 and 13.2 ka (Stuiver and Borns, 1975; Smith, 1985) in contact with marine waters. The glaciomarine Presumpscot Formation (Bloom, 1963) was deposited as a drape over the coastal lowlands at present elevations of 60–70 m. Inland, this drape extends up to elevations of +132 m, 100 km north of the present coast (along a surface tilted by differential isostatic rebound). The local, relative sea-level curve is a reflection of rapidly changing isostatic conditions (Fig. 2). Sea level fell to a lowstand at −60 m by 10.5 ka as the rate of re-

bound became equal to the rate of eustatic rise (Belknap and others, 1987; Kelley and others, 1992). After that time, sea level rose to −20 m by 9.2 ka (Kelley and others, 1992), −15 m by 6.2 ka and at a decreasing rate until reaching within 1 m of present sea level 2.0 to 1.5 ka (Belknap and others, 1989).

Sediments within Maine's embayments and estuaries reflect a source at eroding glacial and glaciomarine bluffs, migration of environments during rising sea level, and long-term export of material seaward. Belknap and others (1986), Kelley (1987), and Shipp and others (1985, 1987) produced a model of embayment evolution that demonstrates: (1) an inner zone of sediment storage, in tidal flats and marshes, (2) a middle zone of eroding bluffs and tidal channels, and (3) an outer eroded zone of rocky headlands and coarse pocket beaches. These zones have migrated inland during sea-level rise. This transgressive stratigraphic model was built on the energy-regime model developed by Kellogg (1982) to explain archaeological site distribution. Most narrow embayments of the central coast are muddy with coarse

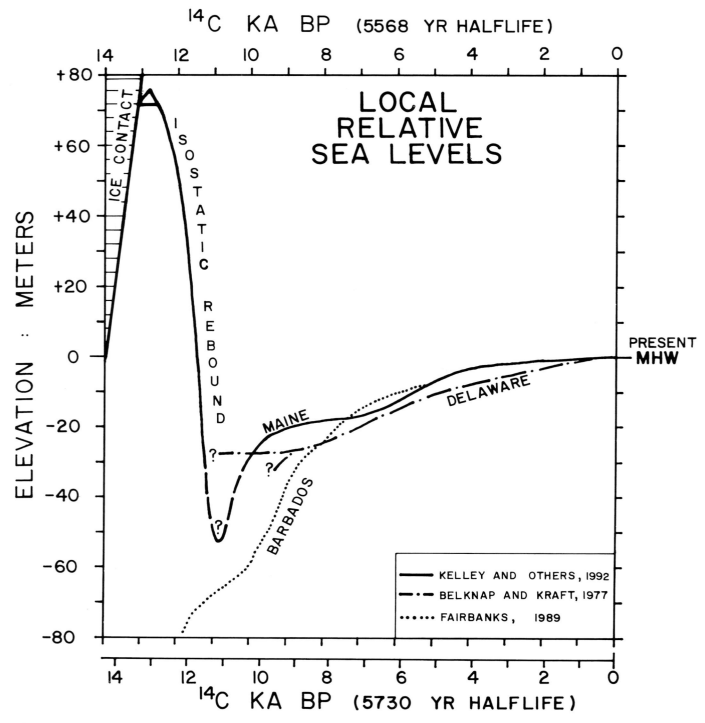

FIG. 2.—Late Quaternary local relative sea-level curves for Delaware and Maine, compared to Barbados. After Belknap and Kraft (1977), Belknap and others (1987), Kelley and others (1992), and Fairbanks (1989).

gravel fringing and pocket beaches. Maine has several types of embayments and estuaries. First are "neutral embayments" (Kelley, 1987), which receive little or no freshwater input (e.g., Booth Bay). The second type comprises estuaries that are tidally dominated with minimal freshwater input, such as the Damariscotta River (1.4–2.8 m³/sec freshwater input versus 2000 m³/sec tidal flux in mid-estuary; water flushing times of 1–5 weeks). Damariscotta River is a tide-dominated, well-mixed to partially mixed estuary (McAlice, 1977; Fefer and Schettig, 1980). The third

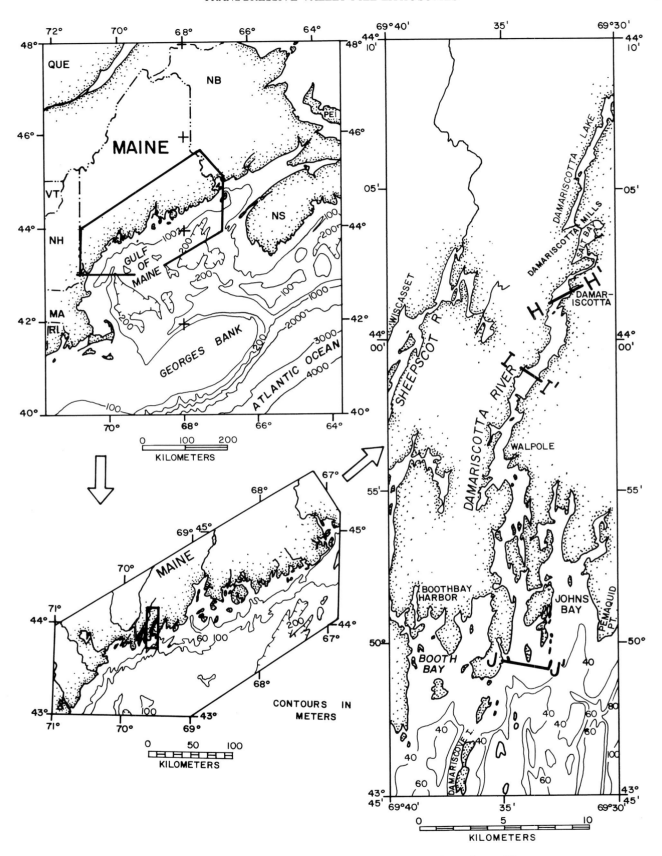

Fig. 3.—Location map for coastal Maine showing study area, Damariscotta River.

type comprises larger, fluvial-dominated systems with flows of 350 m³/sec average flow (e.g., Kennebec River), in which the saline influence may be completely flushed out by spring runoff flooding.

Within the muddy embayments with glacial and glacio-marine bluffs, Smith (1990) and Kelley and Hay (1986) have documented a cycle of bluff erosion and stability related to: (1) mass wasting, (2) colonization by marsh plants, (3) protection of the bluff by continued marsh upgrowth, until (4) later erosion exposes the bluff to renewed instability. This cycle may be decades to centuries in length in different locations.

Sandy barrier systems are found in southwestern Maine near outwash and other sources of coarse glaciogenic materials. Sandy environments are minor constituents elsewhere in Maine near localized pockets of glacial and glaciomarine sediments.

RESULTS AND DISCUSSION

Delaware

The Delaware Atlantic coast contains several filled incised valleys. The largest and best studied is Indian River (Fig. 4). Indian River rises at the drainage divide of the Delmarva Peninsula at an elevation of 20 m and reaches tidal influence at Millsboro. The valley continues under Indian River Lagoon to the Atlantic barrier system under Indian River Inlet. It is confined between pre-Holocene headlands at Cotton Patch Hill and Long Neck/Burton Island. Offshore, the valley was traced as a tributary to the ancestral Delaware River valley (Belknap and Kraft, 1985), which in turn was traced across the shelf to Wilmington Canyon (Twichell and others, 1977). Recent work suggests that offshore relationships are more complex with several paleovalley systems of different ages (Knebel and Circé, 1988; D. Krantz and S. McGeary, pers. commun., 1992).

Cross-sections of the Indian River paleovalley (Fig. 5) have been constructed using seismic reflection profiles offshore, vibracores both offshore and behind the barrier, along with drillholes, and push cores. The paleofluvial valley was cut into pre-Holocene sediments, including middle to upper Pleistocene barrier and back-barrier facies (Demarest and others, 1981). This erosional surface is a major unconformity, which we refer to as the basal unconformity (Belknap and Kraft, 1985). The incised valley contains a transgressive series of sedimentary facies arrayed in accord with Walther's Law (Middleton, 1973), such that the environments found adjacent to one another along the trend of the present Indian River system are also repeated in the vertical succession. A woody organic mud is the basal unit in the transgressive succession. No major fluvial deposits have been identified in Delaware's tributary valley systems. Under Indian River Inlet there are sands, containing marine shells, most likely attributable to a tidal channel (John, 1976, Fig. 79). Under the present Indian River Inlet, the oldest date recovered in the Delaware marine transgressive succession records sea level at −27 m 11 ka (corrected; refer to Table 1) within this basal unit. This date may be 1000 years or more too old due to incorporation of transported wood (Belknap and Kraft, 1977) as suggested by comparison to the Barbados curve. The next unit is brackish to salt-marsh organic mud, reflecting the onlapping succession in the estuarine to back-barrier lagoon. Definition of the transition from estuary to broad lagoon is uncertain, and in this paper refers primarily to paleogeography. Modern trends of decreasing salinity westward into Indian River may be recorded by foraminifers (Kraft, 1971), but detailed downcore work has not been performed. For a working model, to interpret older core logs with no microfaunal data, muds with abundant plant fragments are interpreted as narrow, Atlantic coastal estuarine (tidal river) sediments. These sediments interfinger with and are overlain by mud containing mollusk shells such as *Mercenaria* and *Ensis*, interpreted here as back-barrier lagoonal sediments.

The innermost section, A-A′ (Fig. 5), records the progress of the transgression to this point. In section B-B′, flood-tidal delta sands overlap lagoonal mud, demonstrating increasing tidal inlet proximity during coastal retreat, and thus increasing tidal-current energy. Tidal-delta facies are also evident in section C-C′, while two cores penetrated the fill of a former inlet channel. The tidal delta overlapped the lagoon here at some time after 3.5 ka. The top of this section is barrier and dune facies, reflecting the present coastline and a relatively complete stratigraphic succession from fluvial-estuarine, to back barrier, to barrier facies. Offshore, in 6-m water depth, section D-D′ reflects the later evolution of the system as shoreface erosion produces a ravinement unconformity over the valley-fill deposits. This ravinement surface intersects the basal unconformity and pre-Holocene sediments to either side of the valley. In the Belknap and Kraft (1981, 1985) model of preservation potential, maximum preservation occurs in the incised valley with up to 24 m of section preserved, while there is no preservation on the interfluves. Offshore sampling is incomplete, but most of the barrier lithosome has been removed (more than 10-m thickness) with the exception of distal flood-tidal delta deposits. Over the ravinement unconformity lies a variable cover of inner-shelf sands, varying from exposed pre-Holocene, to centimeters to meters of shoreface sand, to more than 5 m of sand in shoreface-connected sand ridges (Sheridan and others, 1974).

Thus, the Delaware Atlantic coast sequence records a transgressive succession of estuarine-backbarrier-barrier sediments that thickens until intersected by the retrograding coastline. Preservation potential in the present setting is totally dependent on depth of paleovalley incision. Ashley and others (1991) have described a similar, lower transgressive systems tract from the inner shelf of New Jersey. The succession is truncated by the ravinement surface (marine erosion unconformity of Ashley and others, 1991), which is overlain in turn by shoreface sands. The ravinement surface migrates landward up the incised-valley axis during sea-level rise, removing the upper portions of the back-barrier succession.

In incised-valley fills, an important distinction must be made between the basal unconformity (Type I sequence boundary) and the ravinement unconformity. An ideal succession of facies in the Delaware Atlantic coast (Fig. 6) rests on the basal unconformity over pre-Holocene sediments, and is interrupted by the ravinement unconformity. However, the basal unconformity, representing an hiatus of

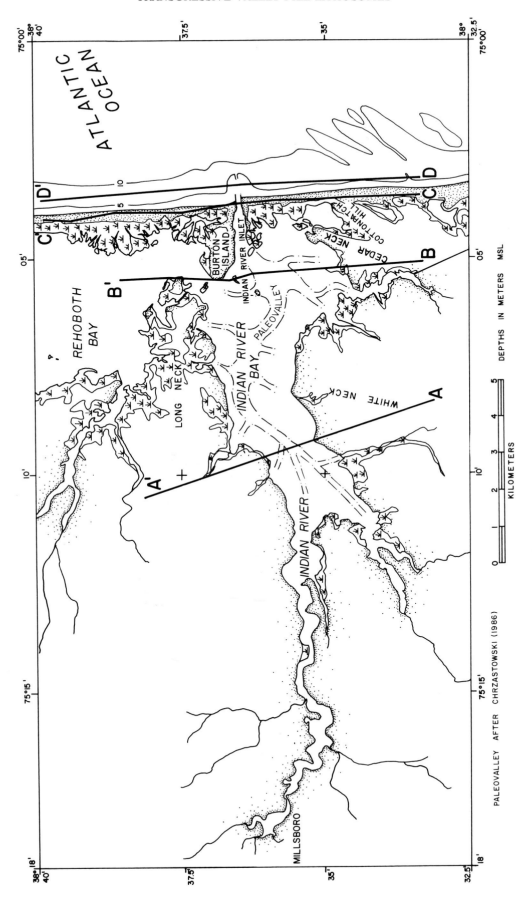

PALEOVALLEY AFTER CHRZASTOWSKI (1986)

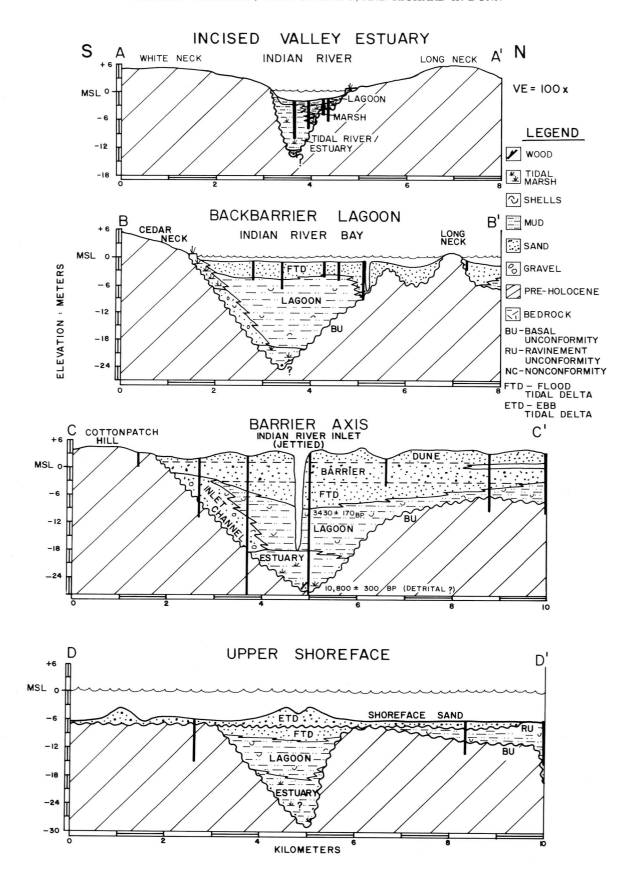

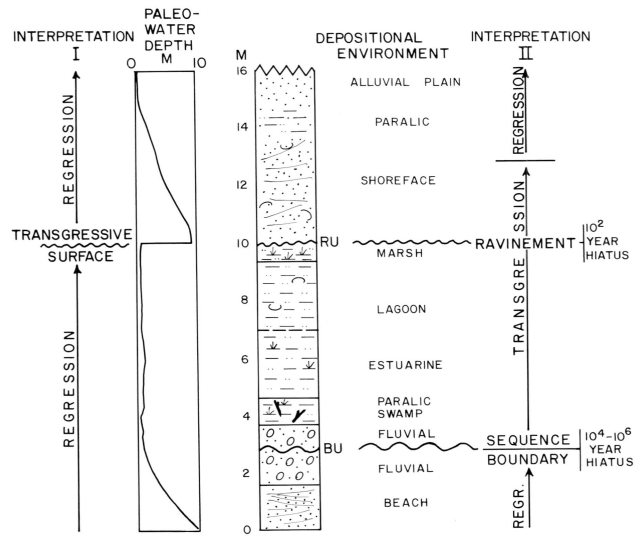

FIG. 6.—Idealized succession of facies in Atlantic coastal Delaware. Note basal unconformity (BU) and ravinement unconformity (RU) (Belknap and Kraft, 1985). Changes in paleo-water depth and lithologic contrasts may lead to misinterpretation of the sequence of events in a rock section if the significance of the hiatuses is not recognized, after Demarest and Kraft (1987, Fig. 15).

10^4–10^6 years may juxtapose fluvial sand over pre-Holocene sand and gravel or Holocene lagoonal mud over pre-Holocene lagoonal mud. The ravinement unconformity, representing a hiatus of only 10^2 years, often juxtaposes shoreface sand over back-barrier mud and peat. Thus, on the basis of acoustic contrast, change in paleowater depth, or lithologic character, the ravinement unconformity presents the more obvious break in the succession, and may lead to misinterpretation (Fig. 6-I). However, the proper interpretation (Fig. 6-II) shows the sequence boundary at

the basal unconformity and a depositional sequence including a transgressive facies succession with the included shoreface ravinement surface, followed by a regressive succession. The regressive part of the sequence is hypothetical for the present Delaware coast but is well represented in Pleistocene littoral systems inland in the Omar Formation (Demarest and Kraft, 1987). This interpretation allows prediction of expected preserved sequences in ancient rocks (Demarest and Kraft, 1987; Belknap and Kraft, 1985).

FIG. 5.—Sequential cross sections at Indian River Bay, Delaware, within the tidal estuary (A-A'), in the lagoon (B-B'), at the barrier (C-C'), and 0.5 km offshore (D-D') on a shore-parallel crossing. RU—ravinement unconformity, BU—basal unconformity. Location in Figure 4. Sources of data: Kraft (1971), John (1977), Belknap and Kraft (1985), and Chrzastowski (1986).

To the north, along the western shore of Delaware Bay, the Murderkill River valley (Fig. 7) displays a complementary stratigraphy but is representative of an estuarine margin system. Three cross sections (Fig. 8) were constructed from highway borings, hand-cores and vibracores at the head of the broad salt marsh in Frederica (E-E'), the back-barrier marsh at Bowers (F-F'), and offshore of the estuarine washover barrier at 3 m depth in Delaware Bay (G-G'). In E-E', bridge borings record 14 m of organic mud and brackish peaty mud overlying pre-Holocene gravelly sands. Although environmental information is limited, this record appears to represent continuous accumulation of tidal sediments throughout the middle to late Holocene. A more complete section is available at the present barrier, where the paleo-Murderkill River valley is incised to −30 m (Belknap and Kraft, 1977, Fig. 12). A 1.6-m thick basal gravel, representing fluvial channel deposits overlies pre-Holocene sediments at the base of the transgressive succession. This thin, narrow fluvial lithosome is typical of Delaware tributary valleys. Organic-rich muds of a tidal river and marsh were deposited prior to 9.7 ka, creating a tidal marsh system by 8.4–8.6 ka, and continuing until at least 5.9–6.1 ka, when open-bay or lagoonal muds containing

mollusks transgressed over the marsh. Between 6.0 and 3.7 ka, the rate of sea-level rise slowed and sediment input was sufficient to cause local progradation (Belknap and Kraft, 1977, Fig. 12). The early stages of evolution of the estuary may resemble more headward reaches of Delaware Bay today with limited fetch, mud and marsh-dominated open shorelines (Fletcher and others, 1990). After 3.7 ka, tidal marsh again occupied this site, possibly as a result of formation of sandy barriers as increasing fetch in Delaware Bay increased available wave energy. Transgression prevailed some time after 2.7 ka, resulting in the passage of the present estuarine washover barrier over section F-F'.

Offshore (G-G'), shallow estuarine shoreface erosion has removed only a thin portion of the stratigraphic section (only 1 m removed 1 km offshore), and the majority of the lower units are preserved in the paleovalley. Depth and infill of the valley in this section are speculative, based on extrapolation from the onshore drill holes and seismic data collected 3 km to the southeast by Weil (1977). Farther offshore the shoreface ravinement surface is covered by 1 m or less of estuarine mud. Still farther toward the center of the estuary, a series of tidal sand shoals and channels (Weil,

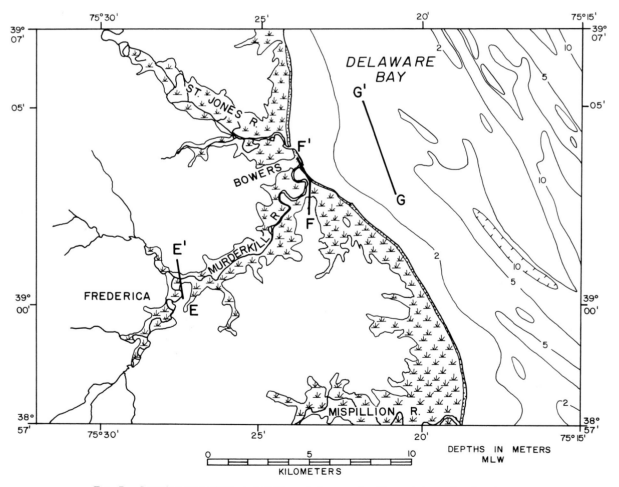

FIG. 7.—Location map of Murderkill River study area. See Figure 1 for regional setting.

1977) provide another facies in the transgressive stratigraphic succession.

Recent seismic work in Delaware Bay has identified two main paleochannels of the Delaware River (Fig. 1) (Fletcher and others, 1990; Knebel and Circé, 1988; Knebel and others, 1988). The Murderkill is a tributary paleovalley that may connect to the southwestern channel, the major cross-shelf valley of the region at lowstand. The Murderkill valley system extends from the head of tide where tidal-river deposits onlap the pre-Holocene deposits, to the present Delaware Bay estuarine wave and tide ravinement surface (RU in Fig. 8). The valley contains a transgressive valley-fill succession similar to that of the Atlantic coast. It differs in details of facies, and in the shallow depth of erosion at the estuarine ravinement unconformity.

Maine

The geomorphology of the Maine coast is dominated by bedrock structure, eroded by glaciers and drowned during the Holocene transgression. The Damariscotta River (Fig. 3) is a deep estuary/embayment in the west-central Maine coast. It has received considerable study, partly because it is the location of the University of Maine Darling Marine Center at Walpole, but also because it is typical of this part of the coast and is a location of important archaeological sites (Sanger and Belknap, 1987; Shipp, 1989; Davies, 1992).

The Damariscotta River rises in Damariscotta Lake and enters tidal influence below a set of falls at Damariscotta Mills. Above the towns of Newcastle and Damariscotta, a 1-km stretch of rapids and reversing tidal falls, known as Johnny Orr, separate a broad estuarine embayment, Salt Bay, with a tidal range of less than 1 m, from the more open estuary with a spring tidal range of nearly 3 m. At this junction, a series of huge (9-m thick) *Crassostrea virginica* oyster shell middens record human harvesting at a unique period between 2.2 ka and 0.8 ka, when Johnny Orr was first overtopped by rising sea level. Besides the geoarchaeological significance (Sanger and Belknap, 1987), this locality provides a relatively precise sea-level indicator at −1 m roughly 2.2 ka. The lower estuary is sinuous and extends 13 km south through a series of constrictions controlled by pegmatite dikes intruding the high-grade, metasedimentary country rock, the Bucksport Formation. These dikes also form ledges, that divide the estuary into seven separate basins, which were sequentially flooded during the Holocene transgression (Shipp, 1989). Johnny Orr is the most recently overtopped ledge (2 ka), while Damariscotta Mills would be overtopped with a future rise in sea level of 16 m. At the outer coast, the bedrock structural trend continues seaward confining the paleovalley in a geometry similar to that of the present embayment.

Cross sections of the Damariscotta River were constructed from high-resolution seismic profiles and underwater vibracores (Fig. 9). Section H-H′ demonstrates the initial accumulation phase of the succession. Bedrock is overlain by discontinuous till as seen in outcrop along the shorelines. The thickest facies is Presumpscot Formation glaciomarine mud, which drapes over the bedrock and till topography. This blanket subdued the initial topography,

thickening in the valley and thinning over the ridges. The Presumpscot Formation was eroded by littoral processes during falling sea level between 12.5 and 11 ka, forming coarse beach deposits in many locations (Thompson, 1980) and by fluvial channel incision around the time of lowstand (11–10 ka) and early transgression. This lowstand incision created a valley with 20- to 30-m local relief, nearly centered over the deeper bedrock valley. Bridge borings and seismic profiles in the Sheepscot River (10 km west) record the deepest portions of a similar paleovalley with a possible coarse sand and gravel lag at the base of estuarine muds (Belknap and others, 1986), but seismic records in the Damariscotta River show no fluvial deposits (Shipp, 1989). Fluvial deposits are found in larger river systems, such as the Penobscot River (Knebel and Scanlon, 1985) and the Kennebec River. At the mouth of the Kennebec River a paleodelta was produced near lowstand at 11 to 9 ka (Belknap and others, 1986). Overlying the Presumpscot Formation is a gray estuarine mud, containing ubiquitous *Mya arenaria* (soft-shell clams) at the base. The *Mya* burrowed into the blue-gray Pleistocene mud at the unconformity and are preserved *in situ*. The estuarine muds interfinger with fringing salt marsh laterally and with tidal-channel sands in the estuary axis. This transgressive systems tract is the sole contributor to the sequence in this valley; no highstand systems tract has yet begun to form.

At Section I-I′, there is less complete preservation of the section. At Lower Dodge Point, a basal, higher-high-marsh peat lies on the erosional unconformity cutting the Presumpscot Formation. This peat provides a precise sea-level marker at −15 m, 6295 ± 55 BP (7.1–7.3 ka corrected). This level corresponds to the level of Glidden Ledge, 1.6 km downstream, that controlled the flooding of the Glidden Basin in which the peat lies (Shipp, 1989). Overlying the peat is an estuarine mud containing *in situ Mya arenaria* and *Crassostrea virginica* dating to 4 ka at −8.8 m and 5.5 ka at −10.2 m respectively. Oysters disappear from the upper 3 m of the section as environments changed to saltier and cooler conditions (Sanger and Belknap, 1987). The subtidal-flat environment laps up laterally onto intertidal flats dominated by *Mya arenaria* and fringed by coarse beaches at the toe of eroding bluffs of Pleistocene glaciomarine mud and till. The thalweg of the estuary contains a 20-m deep tidal channel with eroding margins exposing Pleistocene and Holocene sediments. This tidal channel is encroaching on the mid- to upper Holocene sediments, producing a tidal ravinement surface (e.g., Allen and Posamentier, 1993) within the estuarine sequence, capped by little or no sediment in most locations.

The outer coast section is known only through seismic profiles. Section J-J′ near Damariscove Island demonstrates almost total removal of Quaternary sediments down to bedrock, above depths of 25 m. Angular unconformities that truncate stratified glaciomarine sediments here and in similar settings along the coast attest to this removal (Belknap and Shipp, 1991). Only the deep channels of the bedrock valley maintain abbreviated stratigraphic successions. Early Holocene estuarine sediments are inferred but are generally masked in seismic data by natural gas. This gas may be produced by methanogenic bacteria from buried marsh or

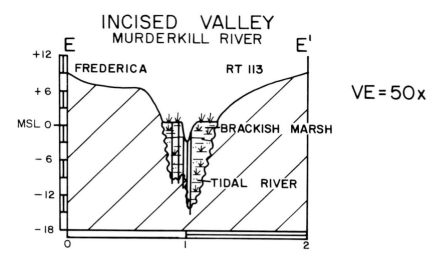

INCISED VALLEY
MURDERKILL RIVER

VE = 50x

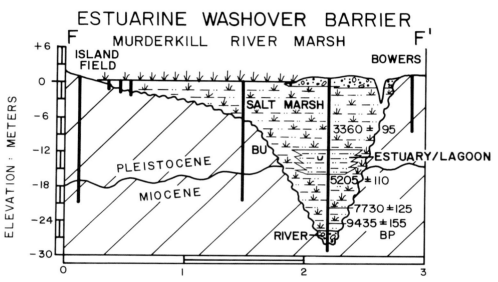

ESTUARINE WASHOVER BARRIER
MURDERKILL RIVER MARSH

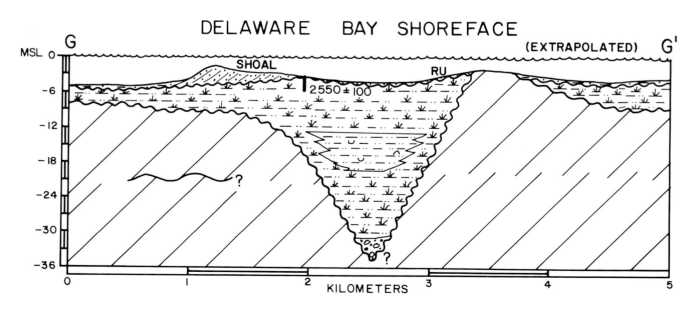

DELAWARE BAY SHOREFACE
(EXTRAPOLATED)

KILOMETERS

organic-rich estuarine mud in the paleovalley axis (Belknap and others, 1986; Kelley and others, 1986; Shipp, 1989).

Comparisons

There are obvious differences between the Delaware and Maine transgressive systems tracts. The geometry of Delaware's paleovalleys is controlled by a trellis-dendritic drainage pattern tributary to the ancestral Delaware River, while Maine's paleovalleys are controlled by underlying bedrock structure, despite fluvial incision into overlying Pleistocene glacial and glaciomarine deposits. Also, the sea-level histories are radically different (Fig. 2), because of differences in isostatic response. Nevertheless, the transgressive valley fills demonstrate striking similarities. The basal units represent fluvial erosional lags followed by initial onlap of the leading edge of the transgressive facies succession. Note that in each case this onlap occurs in sheltered environments dominated by deposition and relatively continuous successions. In Delaware, the deposition continues without interruption until intersection by the transgressing barrier. Later erosion at the shoreface removes the upper 50% or more of the succession, preserving only the earliest, most sheltered, and most landward facies of the transgressive systems tract from erosion. In Maine, the process is more gradual, with increasing exposure of the estuarine succession to migrating tidal channels, and in many cases the embayment widens, exposing it to higher-energy wave conditions. By the time the succession is exposed on the outer coast, only the paleovalley below storm wave base (40 m or greater) is preserved.

In a recent synthesis of estuarine facies, Dalrymple and others (1992) discuss a generalized three-zone model influenced by marine, tidal, and river processes. Allen and Posamentier (1993) show a specific example that relates to this model in the Gironde Estuary. This model compares directly to the evolutionary model for Maine's estuaries and embayments developed by Shipp and others (1985; 1987), Belknap and others (1986), and Kelley (1987), as well as to the Fletcher and others (1990) study of Delaware Bay, and can clearly be used to evaluate well-established facies relationships in Delaware's Atlantic coast (Kraft, 1971 and subsequent work). Incised-valley geometry and processes can be understood in a spectrum of relative influences, in which the Maine and Delaware systems fall as end members. Maine embayments occur in narrow incised valleys, and are tide dominated. Delaware has broader valleys and varying wave energies that influence the mouths of the incised-valley systems, from high-energy conditions that produce barriers on the open Atlantic coast, to lower energy settings in Delaware Bay.

Facies relationships of the Maine and Delaware transgressive valley fill deposits are summarized in axial sections (Fig. 10) that emphasize onlap and transgressive stratigraphic succession. An axial section through the Indian River paleovalley demonstrates the simple transgressive stratigraphy typical of the Delaware Atlantic coast. Onlap of progressively thickening back-barrier and barrier systems is abruptly truncated by the ravinement surface. Ultimately, the leading edge of the transgression, the incised-valley fill representing 1/2 to 2/3 of the stratigraphic succession, is preserved below marine sands. In the Murderkill River paleovalley, a somewhat more complex history is recorded by transgressive-regressive-transgressive reversals in accumulation, related to rate of sediment influx, wave-energy levels in a progressively broadening Delaware Bay, and rates of sea-level change (Belknap and Kraft, 1977). Erosion of the estuarine shoreface is shallower than on the Atlantic coast. Eventual arrival of tidal channels and shoal environments now found in central Delaware Bay could remove more of the littoral and incised-valley successions, should sea-level rise continue and allow these environments to migrate to this position. Ultimately, highstand deposits may preserve more of the sequence (Demarest and Kraft, 1987).

The axial section through Damariscotta River, Maine, demonstrates a transgressive systems tract lacking a barrier, and with a higher degree of reworking by tidal currents within the estuarine embayment. The schematic (lower) section removes the bedrock topography, to emphasize changes in sediment thicknesses. Accumulation occurs in the inner zone in flats and marshes. The tidal ravinement surface, as well as slumping and minor wave erosion at the shoreline, erodes sediments in the middle zone. Only the deepest sediments in the axis of the incised valley are preserved.

CONCLUSIONS

Maine and Delaware have experienced different sea-level histories and sedimentary environments over the past 15 ka, yet similarities in transgressive fill of incised valleys suggest that they may fit into an integrated facies model. Their differences emphasize the importance of process-response models in reconstructing evolutionary histories. The evolutionary pathways of each of these systems are reconstructed in facies models (Fig. 11). Conceptually, these diagrams can be considered either as relative-energy relationships among modern environments (modified from Dalrymple and others, 1992), if they are considered as lateral relationships at any single **time**, or the history of changes among energy relationships and sedimentary environments at any one **location** during transgression. This is simply another way of stating Walther's Law. Another factor, marsh growth, should be added to the energy-based model, reflecting the importance of this facies in modern systems. Fluvial energy, prominent in the Dalrymple and others (1992) model, is unimportant in these systems. Fluvial sedimen-

FIG. 8.—Sequential cross sections at Murderkill River valley, Delaware. See Figure 7 for location. E-E′: Bridge borings at Delaware Route 113; F-F′: Rotary auger and hand cores; G-G′: hand cores and extrapolated from seismic reflection data by Weil (1977). Legend in Figure 5. Sources of data: Kraft (1971), Kraft and others (1976), and Belknap and Kraft (1977).

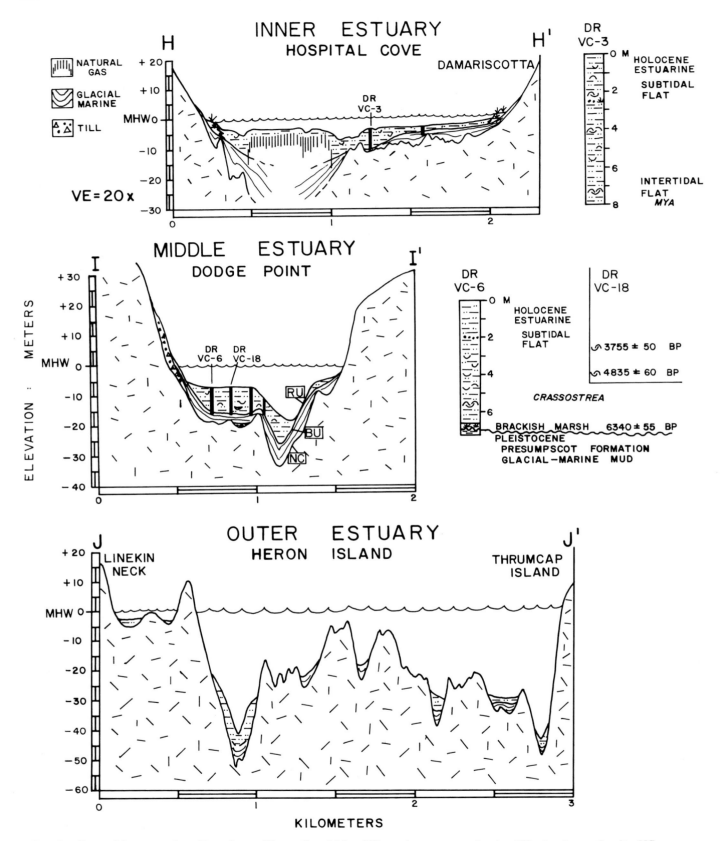

FIG. 9.—Sequential cross sections, Damariscotta River valley, Maine. RU—ravinement unconformity, BU—basal unconformity, NC—nonconformity. DR-VC-3, 6, 18 are vibracores. Legend in Figure 5. See Figure 3 for location. Sources of data: Shipp (1989) and Davies (1992).

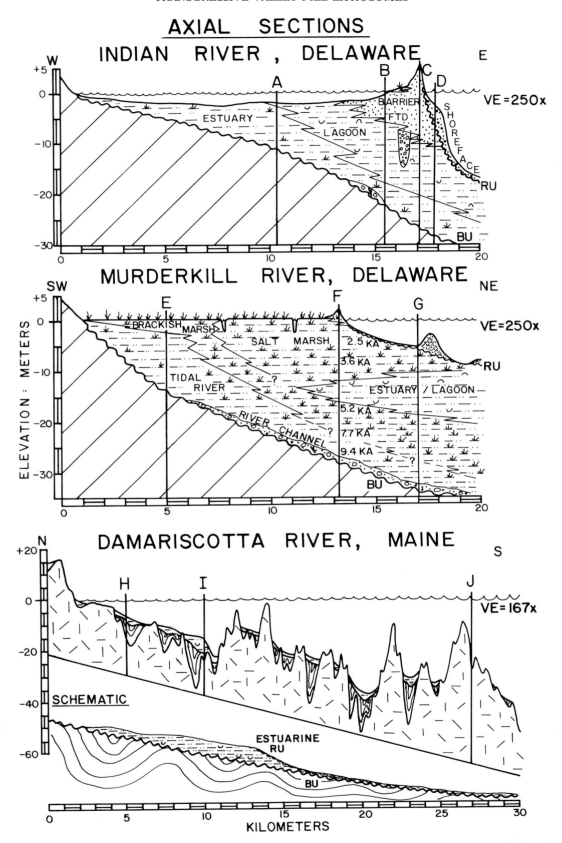

FIG. 10.—Schematic axial cross-sections, Delaware and Maine. RU—ravinement unconformity, BU—basal unconformity. Schematic section under Damariscotta River removes bedrock topography to emphasize changes in thickness of the transgressive systems tract.

FACIES MODELS
TRANSGRESSIVE VALLEY FILLS

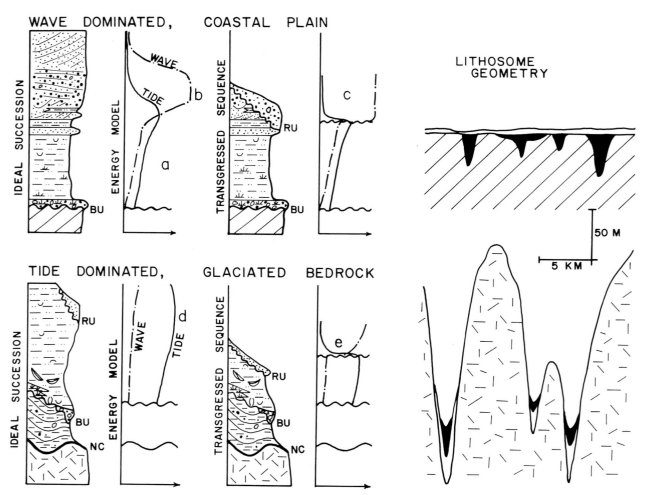

Fig. 11.—Facies models and conceptual energy models for evolution of incised-valley systems. Legend in Figure 5. RU—ravinement unconformity, BU—basal unconformity, NC—nonconformity. Ideal successions refer to complete preservation of transgressive systems tract. In the lithosome geometry summary, black units are the incised valley-fill deposits.

tary processes are only important in the major trunk stream, the Delaware River, on the coastal plain, and in large Maine drainage systems such as the Kennebec River.

In the Delaware transgressive valley-fill deposits, a wave-dominated coastal-plain system, river influence is primarily important during incision. As the incised valley is drowned, it gradually changes from confined estuary to open backbarrier lagoon. The wave energy gradually rises as the fetch increases (Fig. 11A). Tidal influence increases dramatically at the flood tidal delta to a maximum at the tidal inlet (Fig. 11B), then declines dramatically at the wave-dominated shoreline and shoreface (Fig. 11C). Marshes dominate fringing estuarine and lagoon environments and are common on the lagoon side of the barrier on former washover and flood-tidal deltas. The evolutionary pathway of the Murderkill River is similar, with lower absolute wave en-

ergy and depth of shoreface scour in Delaware Bay, and greater continuing tidal influence offshore of the estuarine washover barrier. Marsh dominates the backbarrier system during recent slow rates of sea-level rise but may give way to open estuarine conditions at times of higher rates of rise and/or lower rates of sediment supply. As identified by Belknap and Kraft (1985) and Demarest and Kraft (1987), the major discontinuities in the section occur at the basal fluvial incision (basal unconformity) and at the shoreface ravinement surface. Tidal ravinement surfaces may also occur near major channels such as at the Indian River flood-tidal delta system. The separation of the basal and ravinement surfaces determines the preservation potential. This separation is most strongly governed by the paleotopography of the fluvial system created by fluvial incision at sea-level lowstand.

In Maine, a glaciated, bedrock-framed coast, river influence is generally low. Tidal influence peaks within the central reaches of the estuary or embayment (Fig. 11D). Maximum tidal- current speeds are commonly 50 cm/sec, and can reach 150 cm/sec in constrictions at ledges and narrows (NOAA-NOS, 1993). Tidal flats initially accumulate sediments and later are modified by intense tidal currents that actively scour the channels. Wave influence gradually increases until the coast opens onto the exposed shoreline with some offshore islands (Fig. 11E). Waves act in conjunction with mass wasting to erode bluffs of glacial and glaciomarine sediment. Minor influences include fringing marshes and ice effects. The major erosional unconformities (Figs. 10, 11) occur at the basal fluvial incision and the shoreface ravinement surface, as on a coastal-plain setting, but there are also estuarine ravinement surfaces caused by tidal-channel scour. Preservation occurs in isolated lenses depending on: (1) the irregular bedrock surface and thickness of Pleistocene glacial and glaciomarine cover, (2) integration of erosional effects of littoral and fluvial processes during falling sea level, lowstand, and early rise, and (3) modification by later estuarine tidal processes and open Gulf of Maine wave and tide energy.

The ultimate result of coastal evolution in these two settings would be a lithosome geometry (Fig. 11) consisting of isolated lenses of incised-valley fill deposits. In the glaciated bedrock terrain, the profound unconformity between rock and sediment occurs at the base of the glacial sequence, yet the rock structure continues to influence geomorphology and processes in the later transgressive infill. In the coastal-plain setting, separation of one transgressive interglacial succession from another is more difficult (Demarest and others, 1981) as lagoon sediments may fill a valley incised into older lagoonal sediments, and unless a complete sequence including the fluvial basal units is found, the interpretation may be difficult. During continued evolution, the Delaware system will reach a highstand and transform to a regressive strandplain at highstand with complete infill of the incised valley in the hinterlands. This would complete the depositional sequence with a highstand systems tract and an overlying unconformity as sea level began to fall. The Maine system may stabilize in the three-zone conditions seen today, but limited sediment input is likely to preclude major infill, and the sediments from the eroding bluff will eventually be depleted and reworked into intertidal and subtidal flats. Throughout the transgression, there has been net export seaward, but at highstand, infill would be expected as no new accommodation space would be created.

ACKNOWLEDGEMENTS

This work is the result of numerous student theses and funded research projects at the University of Delaware (UD) and University of Maine (UM), with funding by NOAA Sea Grant projects at UM and UD and NSF-EPSCoR projects at UM. We would like to thank Michael J. Chrzastowski, R. Craig Shipp, and Joseph T. Kelley for long-term collaboration in this work. We also thank W. Roland Gehrels, reviewers Duncan M. FitzGerald and Anthony P. Belperis, and editors Ron Boyd and Robert W. Dalrymple for helpful suggestions.

REFERENCES

ALLEN, G. P., AND POSAMENTIER, H. W., 1993, Sequence stratigraphy and facies model of an incised valley fill: the Gironde Estuary, France: Journal of Sedimentary Petrology, v. 63, p. 378–391.

ASHLEY, G. M., WELLNER, R. W., ESKER, D., AND SHERIDAN, R. E., 1991, Clastic sequences developed during late Quaternary glacio-eustatic sea-level fluctuations on a passive margin: example from the inner continental shelf near Barnegat Inlet, New Jersey: Geological Society of America Bulletin, v. 103, p. 1607–1621.

BELKNAP, D. F., ANDERSEN, B. G., ANDERSON, R. S., ANDERSON, W. A., BORNS, H. W., JR., JACOBSON, G. L., KELLEY, J. T., SHIPP, R. C., SMITH, D. C., STUCKENRATH, R., JR., THOMPSON, W. B., AND TYLER, D. A., 1987, Late Quaternary sea-level fluctuations in Maine: in Nummedal, D., Pilkey, O. H., and Howard, J. D., eds., Sea-Level Fluctuation and Coastal Evolution: Tulsa, Society of Economic Paleontologists and Mineralogists Special Publication 41, p. 71–85.

BELKNAP, D. F., AND KRAFT, J. C., 1977, Holocene relative sea-level changes and coastal stratigraphic units on the northwest flank of the Baltimore Canyon Trough geosyncline: Journal of Sedimentary Petrology, v. 47, p. 610–629.

BELKNAP, D. F., AND KRAFT, J. C., 1981, Preservation potential of transgressive coastal lithosomes on the U. S. Atlantic shelf: Marine Geology, v. 42, p. 429–442.

BELKNAP, D. F., AND KRAFT, J. C., 1985, Influence of antecedent geology on stratigraphic preservation potential and evolution of Delaware's barrier systems: Marine Geology, v. 63, p. 235–262.

BELKNAP, D. F., AND SHIPP, R. C., 1991, Seismic stratigraphy of glacial-marine units, Maine inner shelf, in Anderson, J. B., and Ashley, G. M., eds., Glacial-Marine Sedimentation: Paleoclimatic Significance: Boulder, Geological Society of America Special Paper 261, p. 137–157.

BELKNAP, D. F., SHIPP, R. C., AND KELLEY, J. T., 1986, Depositional setting and Quaternary stratigraphy of the Sheepscot Estuary, Maine: a preliminary report: Géographie physique et Quaternaire, v. 40, p. 55–69.

BELKNAP, D. F., SHIPP, R. C., KELLEY, J. T., AND SCHNITKER, D., 1989, Depositional sequence modeling of late Quaternary geologic history, west-central Maine, in Tucker, R. D., and Marvinney, R. G., eds., Studies in Maine Geology, Vol. 5: Quaternary Geology: Augusta, Maine Geological Survey, p. 11–28.

BLOOM, A. L., 1963, Late Pleistocene fluctuations of sea level and postglacial crustal rebound in coastal Maine: American Journal of Science, v. 261, p. 862–879.

CHRZASTOWSKI, M. J., 1986, Stratigraphy and geologic history of a Holocene lagoon: Rehoboth Bay and Indian River Bay, Delaware: Unpublished Ph.D. Dissertation, University of Delaware, Newark, 337 p.

DALRYMPLE, R. W., ZAITLIN, B. A., AND BOYD, R., 1992, Estuarine facies models: conceptual basis and stratigraphic implications: Journal of Sedimentary Petrology, v. 62, p. 1130–1146.

DAVIES, C. P., 1992, Estuarine preservation potential model for archaeological sites in coastal Maine: Unpubublished M.Sc. Thesis, Institute for Quaternary Studies, University of Maine, Orono, 195 p.

DEMAREST, J. M., II, BIGGS, R. B., AND KRAFT, J. C., 1981, Time-stratigraphic concepts of a formation: interpretation of surficial Pleistocene deposits by analogy with Holocene paralic deposits, southeastern Delaware: Geology, v. 9, p. 360–365.

DEMAREST, J. M., II, AND KRAFT, J. C., 1987, Stratigraphic record of Quaternary sea levels: implications for more ancient strata, in Nummedal, D., Pilkey, O. H., and Howard, J. D., eds., Sea-level Fluctuation and Coastal Evolution: Tulsa, Society of Economic Paleontologists and Mineralogists Special Publication 41, p. 223–229.

DENNEY, C. S., 1982, The geomorphology of New England: Washington, D. C., United States Geological Survey Professional Paper 1208, 18 p.

FAIRBANKS, R. G., 1989, A 17,000-year glacio-eustatic sea level record: influence of glacial melting rates on the Younger Dryas event and deep-ocean circulation: Nature, v. 342, p. 637–642.

FEFER, S. I., AND SCHETTIG, P. A., 1980, An ecological characterization of coastal Maine: Newton Corner, United States Fish and Wildlife Service Report, FWS/OBS-80/29, 4 Vols. and 9 Atlases.

FLETCHER, C. H., III, KNEBEL, H. J., AND KRAFT, J. C., 1990, Holocene evolution of an estuarine coast and tidal wetlands: Geological Society of America Bulletin, v. 102, p. 283–297.

HALSEY, S. D., 1979, Nexus, a new model of barrier island development, *in* Leatherman, S. P., ed., Barrier Islands from the Gulf of St. Lawrence to the Gulf of Mexico: New York, Academic Press, p. 185–210.

HOYT, W. H., AND DEMAREST, J. D., 1981, A versatile twin-hull barge for shallow-water vibracoring: Journal of Sedimentary Petrology, v. 51, p. 656–657.

JOHN, C. J., 1977, Internal sedimentary structures, vertical stratigraphic sequences, and grain-size parameter variations in a transgressive coastal barrier complex: the Atlantic coast of Delaware: Newark, Delaware Sea Grant Technical Report 10–77, Delaware Sea Grant College Program, University of Delaware, 287 p.

JOHNSON, D., 1925, The New England—Acadian Shoreline, Facsimile Edition (1967): New York, Hafner Publishing Company, 608 p.

KELLEY, J. T., 1987, An inventory of coastal environments and classification of Maine's glaciated shoreline, *in* FitzGerald, D. M., and Rosen, P. S., eds., Glaciated Coasts: San Diego, Academic Press, p. 151–175.

KELLEY, J. T., DICKSON, S. M., BELKNAP, D. F., AND STUCKENRATH, R., JR., 1992, Sea-level change and the introduction of late Quaternary sediment to the southwestern Maine inner continental shelf, *in* Fletcher, C. H., III, and Wehmiller, J. F., eds., Quaternary Coastal Systems of the United States: Tulsa, SEPM (Society for Sedimentary Geology) Special Paper 48, p. 23–34.

KELLEY, J. T., AND HAY, B. W. B., 1986, Bunganuc Bluffs, Day 3, Stop 6, *in* Kelley, J. T., and Kelley, A. R., eds., Coastal Processes and Quaternary Stratigraphy Northern and Central Coastal Maine: Orono, Society of Economic Paleontologists and Mineralogists Eastern Section Field Trip Guidebook, p. 66–74.

KELLEY, J. T., KELLEY, A. R., BELKNAP, D. F., AND SHIPP, R. C., 1986, Variability in the evolution of two adjacent bedrock-framed estuaries in Maine, *in* Wolfe, D. A., ed., Estuarine Variability: Orlando, Academic Press, p. 21–42.

KELLOGG, D. C., 1982, Environmental factors in archaeological site location for the Boothbay, Maine region with an assessment of the impact of coastal erosion on the archaeological record: Unpubublished M.Sc. Thesis, University of Maine, Orono, 230 p.

KNEBEL, H. J., AND CIRCÉ, R. C., 1988, Late Pleistocene drainage systems beneath Delaware Bay: Marine Geology, v. 78, p. 285–302.

KNEBEL, H. J., FLETCHER, C. H., III, AND KRAFT, J. C., 1988, Late Wisconsinan—Holocene paleogeography of Delaware Bay; a large coastal plain estuary: Marine Geology, v. 83, p. 115–133.

KNEBEL, H. J., AND SCANLON, K. M., 1985, Sedimentary framework of Penobscot Bay, Maine: Marine Geology, v. 65, p. 305–324.

KRAFT, J. C., 1971, Sedimentary facies patterns and geologic history of a Holocene marine transgression: Geological Society of America Bulletin, v. 82, p. 2131–2158.

KRAFT, J. C., 1976, Radiocarbon dates in the Delaware coastal zone: Delaware Sea Grant Technical Report DEL-SG-19–76, 20 p.

KRAFT, J. C., ALLEN, E. A., BELKNAP, D. F., JOHN, C. J., AND MAURMEYER, E. M., 1976, Delaware's Changing Shoreline: Dover, Delaware Coastal Zone Management Program Technical Report No. 1, 319 p.

KRAFT, J. C., ALLEN, E. A., BELKNAP, D. F., JOHN, C. J., AND MAURMEYER, E. M., 1979, Processes and morphologic evolution of an estuarine and coastal barrier system, *in* Leatherman, S. P., ed., Barrier Islands from the Gulf of St. Lawrence to the Gulf of Mexico: New York, Academic Press, p. 149–183.

KRAFT, J. C., CHRZASTOWSKI, M. J., BELKNAP, D. F., TOSCANO, M. A., AND FLETCHER, C. H., III, 1987, The transgressive barrier-lagoon coast of Delaware: morphostratigraphy, sedimentary sequences and responses to relative rise in sea level, *in* Nummedal, D., Pilkey, O. H., and Howard, J. D., eds., Sea-level Fluctuation and Coastal Evolution: Tulsa, Society of Economic Paleontologists and Mineralogists Special Publication 41, p. 129–143.

LANESKY, D. E., LOGAN, B. W., BROWN, R. G., AND HINE, A. C., 1979, A new approach to portable vibracoring underwater and on land: Journal of Sedimentary Petrology, v. 49, p. 654–657.

MCALICE, B. J., 1977, A preliminary oceanographic survey of the Damariscotta River estuary, Lincoln County, Maine: Orono, Maine Sea Grant Technical Report TR-13–77, 27 p.

MIDDLETON, G. V., 1973, Johannes Walther's law of the correlation of facies: Geological Society of America Bulletin, v. 84, p. 979–988.

MITCHUM, R. M., JR., VAIL, P. R., AND THOMPSON, S., III, 1977, Seismic stratigraphy and global changes of sea level, part 2: the depositional sequence as a basic unit for stratigraphic analysis: *in* Payton, C. E., ed., Seismic Stratigraphy—Applications to Hydrocarbon Exploration: Tulsa, American Association of Petroleum Geologists Memoir 26, p. 53–62.

NOAA-NOS, 1993, Tidal Current Tables 1993, Atlantic Coast of North America: Riverdale, National Oceanic and Atmospheric Administration, National Ocean Service, 243 p.

POSAMENTIER, H. W., JERVEY, M. T., AND VAIL, P. R., 1988, Eustatic controls on clastic deposition II—sequence and systems tract models: *in* Wilgus, C. K., Hastings, B. S., Kendall, C. G. St. C., Posamentier, H. W., Ross, C. A., and Van Wagoner, J. C., eds., Sea-level Changes-An Integrated Approach: Tulsa, Society of Economic Paleontologists and Mineralogists Special Publication 42, p. 125–154.

SANGER, D., AND BELKNAP, D. F., 1987, Human responses to changing marine environments in the Gulf of Maine: *in* McKinnon, N. A., and Stewart, G. S. L., eds., Man and the Mid-Holocene Climatic Optimum: Calgary, Proceedings 17th Annual Chacmool Conference, Nov. 10–12, 1984, Department of Archaeology, University of Calgary, p. 245–261.

SCHOLL, D. W., CRAIGHEAD, F. C., SR., AND STUIVER, M., 1969, Florida submergence curve revisited: its relation to coastal sedimentation rates: Science, v. 163, p. 562–564.

SHERIDAN, R. E., DILL, C. E., JR., AND KRAFT, J. C., 1974, Holocene sedimentary environments of the Atlantic inner shelf off Delaware: Geological Society of America Bulletin, v. 85, p. 1319–1328.

SHIPP, R. C., 1989, Late Quaternary geologic evolution and sea-level fluctuations of the northwestern Gulf of Maine: four examples from the Maine coast, Unpublished Ph.D. Dissertation, University of Maine, Orono, 832 p.

SHIPP, R. C., STAPLES, S. A., AND ADEY, W. H., 1985, Geomorphic trends in a glaciated coastal bay: a model for the Maine coast: Washington, D. C., Smithsonian Institution Press, Smithsonian Contributions to the Marine Sciences No. 25, 76 p.

SHIPP, R. C., STAPLES, S. A., AND WARD, L. G., 1987, Controls and zonation along a glaciated coast, Gouldsboro Bay, Maine, *in* FitzGerald, D.M., and Rosen, P.S., eds., Glaciated Coasts, San Diego, Academic Press, p. 209–231.

SMITH, G. W., 1985, Chronology of late Wisconsinan deglaciation of coastal Maine: *in* Borns, H. W., Jr., LaSalle, P. and Thompson, W. D., eds., Late Pleistocene History of Northeastern New England and Adjacent Quebec: Boulder, Geological Society of America Special Paper 197, p. 29–44.

SMITH, R. V., 1990, Geomorphic trends and shoreline dynamics in three Maine embayments: Unpubublished M.Sc. Thesis, University of Maine, Orono, 200 p.

STUIVER, M., AND BORNS, H. W., JR., 1975, Late Quaternary marine invasion in Maine: its chronology and associated crustal movement: Geological Society of America Bulletin, v. 86, p. 99–104.

STUIVER, M., AND REIMER, P. J., 1986, A computer program for radiocarbon age calibration: Radiocarbon, v. 28, p. 1022–1030.

STUIVER, M., AND REIMER, P. J., 1987, User's guide to the programs CALIB & DISPLAY 2.1: Seattle, Quaternary Isotope Lab, University of Washington, 13 p.

THOMPSON, W. B., 1980, Recession of the late Wisconsin ice sheet in coastal Maine, *in* Larson, G. H. and Stone, B. D., eds., Late Wisconsinan glaciation of New England: Dubuque, Kendall/Hunt Publishing Company, p. 211–228.

TWITCHELL, D. C., KNEBEL, H. J., AND FOLGER, D. W., 1977, Delaware River, evidence for its former extension to Wilmington Submarine Canyon: Science, v. 195, p. 483–484.

VAN WAGONER, J. C., POSAMENTIER, H. W., MITCHUM, R. M., JR., VAIL, P. R., SARG, J. F., LOUTIT, T. S., AND HARDENBOL, J., 1988, An overview of the fundamentals of sequence stratigraphy and key definitions: *in* Wilgus, C. K., Hastings, B. S., Kendall, C. G. St. C., Posamentier, H. W., Ross, C. A., and Van Wagoner, J. C., eds., Sea-level Changes—An Integrated Approach: Tulsa, Society of Economic Paleontologists and Mineralogists Special Publication 42, p. 39–45.

WEIL, C. B., 1977, Sediments, structural framework and evolution of Delaware Bay, a transgressive estuarine delta: Newark, Delaware Sea Grant Technical Report DEL-SG-4–77, College of Marine Studies, University of Delaware, 199 p.

PRESERVATION OF TRANSGRESSIVE AND HIGHSTAND LATE PLEISTOCENE VALLEY-FILL/ESTUARY DEPOSITS, WILLAPA BAY, WASHINGTON

H. EDWARD CLIFTON
Conoco, Incorporated, Houston, Texas 77252

ABSTRACT: Pleistocene terrace deposits exposed along the margins of Willapa Bay, Washington, illustrate the nature of preservation of transgressive and highstand valley-fill/estuary deposits that accumulated in a setting where fluvial influences are minor relative to tidal processes. Five depositional units can be delineated beneath a relatively young terrace surface on the basis of paleobathymetry and internal stratigraphic relations. The oldest unit (I) represents upper subtidal to intertidal deposition in a muddy, fluvial-tidal-channel/ flat environment. It is succeeded by a sandy, subtidal sediment (Unit II) that accumulated in the central part of an ancient bay. Dating using amino acid racemization techniques indicates that both units formed during or just prior to the sea-level highstand associated with marine oxygen isotope stage 7, possibly as transgressive and highstand estuarine systems respectively. A fall in relative sea level, probably associated with oxygen isotope stage 6, led to incision of small gullies and ravines that were subsequently filled by nonmarine mud with abundant woody material and rhizoliths (Unit III). The fourth unit (IV) is the most widespread and heterolithic. It represents deposition in a bay first characterized by trough-filling, then by lateral migration of tidal channels and banks. Racemization dates place its deposition during the marine highstand of oxygen isotope stage 5. Dissection and filling of valleys under predominantly fluvial conditions (Unit V), possibly during smaller sea-level fluctuations in stage 5, completes the succession.

The preservation of these different accumulations depends on a combination of their location within the bay, their lithology as it relates to resistance to erosion, and the subsequent history of relative sea-level change. Interchanneling of the units (and therefore stratigraphic complexity within the set) increases dramatically in an up-bay direction over a distance of about 10 km. Erosion by migrating tidal channels during accumulation of Unit IV appears to have eliminated much of the older units in the central bay area. These units become increasingly preserved in an up-bay direction, probably as a consequence of the erosional capacity of tidal currents in the upper bay. Intertidal facies in Unit I are remarkably well-preserved, even in the central bay setting, because the cohesive mud has resisted erosion. The contact between the transgressive valley fill of Unit III and the overlying highstand deposits of Unit IV is erosional, except in the upper reaches of the paleo-bay, where it is transitional, again probably a function of reduced erosion by tidal flow in this setting. Although Unit IV, the last highstand accumulation, is well preserved in the terraces today, fluvial and tidal erosion during a subsequent cycle of sea-level change would probably erase much of this unit, even in a subsiding setting. The currently active tectonic uplift in this area will probably cause most or all of these terrace deposits to be removed from the stratigraphic record.

The only unequivocal sequence boundary in the succession lies at the base of the valley-fill deposits of Unit III. This boundary is present only locally; mostly it has been eroded by tidal-channel migration during the accumulation of Unit IV. Such erosion can produce a prominent and laterally extensive erosional surface, particularly in the central portions of paleo-bays in which tidal influences exceed fluvial influences. Such surfaces are analogous to transgressive surfaces of erosion in their potential to modify sequence boundaries, but they are best developed during conditions of stillstand. In the Willapa terraces, these surfaces developed during late Pleistocene highstands.

INTRODUCTION

Much of our understanding of transgressive valley-fill deposits derives from the study of modern coastal systems developed during the marine transgression of the past 18,000 years (c.f. Peterson and Sheidegger, 1984; Nichols and others, 1991; Allen, 1991; Amos and others, 1991; Nichol, 1991; Peterson and Phipps, 1991). Although these studies document the preservation of the valley fill deposited during the rapid sea-level rise, the description of depositional facies typically has focused on the modern deposits that accumulated during the Holocene stillstand that began about 4,000 years ago (Fairbanks, 1989). The preservation of these facies depends on a combination of subsequent relative sea-level change, their position within future estuaries, and their lithologic competence. A renewed significant eustatic rise would drown the current deposits, incorporating them into a valley-fill complex that includes the older transgressive units. Their preservation would depend on the extent and depth of tidal current (or shoreface) erosion as the estuary shifted landward. A eustatic fall would strand the current deposits as a highstand assemblage. Preservation in this case becomes dependent upon the extent and depth of fluvial erosion and on local tectonism. In a subsiding setting, these highstand deposits could be extensively preserved, buried beneath subsequent estuarine accumulations.

The nature of preservation of transgressive and highstand estuary deposits is documented in Pleistocene terrace deposits exposed in sea cliffs around the margins of Willapa Bay, Washington. A variety of depositional facies reflect relative sea-level fluctuations over the past 200–250 ka. Analysis of these facies and their degree of preservation provides insights into the combination of factors that contribute to the preservation of valley-fill/estuary deposits.

SETTING

The Pleistocene estuary deposits probably formed in an environmental setting similar to that of the present Willapa Bay, which occupies the confluence of several relatively small rivers on the coast of southwestern Washington (Fig. 1). The bay has two distinct arms; one extends east of the inlet into the North and Willapa Rivers; the other extends south into the Palix, Nemah, and Naselle Rivers (Fig. 1). These arms flood valleys cut by the merged rivers during the Wisconsin lowstand. In addition, a large barrier spit protects the main body of the bay from the open Pacific Ocean. Willapa Bay thus results from a combination of valley-drowning and barrier development.

The barrier spit, the North Beach Peninsula, is the longest barrier on the conterminous U. S. West Coast. The inlet to the bay lies at the north end of the spit. The inlet area is about 8 km wide and contains broad, shallow subtidal and intertidal flats dissected by two channels less than a kilometer across and 10–20 m deep. A large ebb-tidal delta encroaches into the ocean at the bay's mouth. The flood-

Incised-valley Systems: Origin and Sedimentary Sequences, SEPM Special Publication No. 51

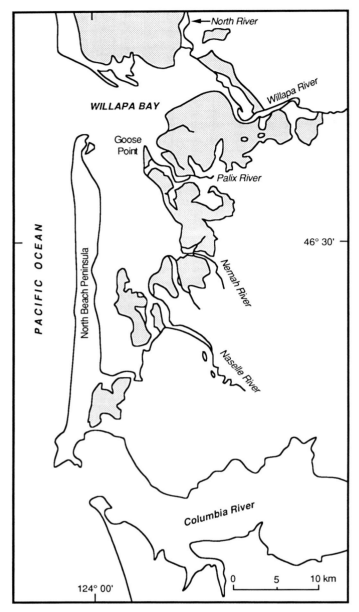

FIG. 1.—Distribution of Pleistocene terraces (stippled pattern) around Willapa Bay, Washington (modified from Clifton and others, 1989; Walsh and others, 1987).

occupy most of the bay. Channels as much as 25 m deep in the central bay and 5–10 m deep in its upper reaches dissect these flats. Tidal currents within the larger channels reach velocities of 2–3 m/s. In contrast to many other modern estuaries, fluvial influences are relatively minor. River discharge is low except during flood stages when stream discharge significantly increases the ebb flow at the entrance (Hedgepeth and Obrebski, 1981), and tidal influences predominate most of the time well into the uppermost reaches of the estuary.

Unlike many other modern estuaries, Willapa Bay is not dominated by a single river. Instead, five different drainage systems feed into the bay from the north and west. The upper extent of tidal deposition in these streams occurs in relatively narrow valleys mostly incised into volcanic bedrock where deposition can clearly be characterized as "valley filling." Within the main body of the bay, however, it is not clear to what extent the primary channel system follows pre-existing topography as opposed to active incision by the tidal currents. Erosion by tidal currents is evident along the bayward side of the North Beach Peninsula where tidal channels locally erode into eolian beach ridges and elsewhere in the bay where high-resolution seismic profiles and historical data (particularly in the inlet area) document lateral shifting of the larger tidal channels. In places, the floors or walls of the channels expose older mud deposits, further evidence of the erosional capacity of the tides. It is likely that some of the physiography of the central bay reflects tidal enlargement of valley systems cut by rivers en route to a distant Wisconsin lowstand shoreline.

The bay displays the tripartite (coarse-fine-coarse) zonation characteristic of wave/tide-dominated estuaries (Dalrymple and others, 1992) although the zonation seems to be displaced landward within Willapa Bay. The North Beach Peninsula derives from sand discharged at the Columbia River mouth and carried north by longshore transport. The peninsula appears to have originated early in the history of the Holocene bay. At least twelve, nearly parallel sand ridges on the barrier document its seaward progradation since sea level reached its current level several thousand years ago. The third-oldest of these extends nearly to the northern end of the spit, indicating that the inlet has existed on the northwestern margin of the bay almost since its inception. Well-sorted, fine sand underlies the flats and channels in most of the central body of the bay, whereas the upper reaches contain muddy sand and mud. Most of the sand in the bay has an oceanic origin. Heavy mineral analysis indicates that rivers contribute sand only to the upper reaches of the bay (Luepke and Clifton, 1983), a situation common to high-gradient Pacific Northwest estuaries with low fluvial input (Peterson and others, 1984). The relatively high coastal gradient imposes a fairly abrupt transition between fluvial and tidal processes. Gravel extends as channel floor lag only a short distance bayward from this interface.

Prominent marine terraces around the margins of the bay imply recent tectonic uplift. The assemblage of stacked estuary deposits beneath the terrace surfaces, as described in the following section, indicates a complex tectonic history

tidal delta, truncated by a large tidal-channel system extending north from the south-trending arm of the bay, is less pronounced.

Willapa Bay is probably best classified as intermediate between a wave-dominated estuary (high wave energies at the mouth and a large barrier spit) and a tide-dominated estuary (high tidal energies at the mouth and elongate tidal sand bars within the larger channels) (Dalrymple and others, 1992). The bay encompasses about 260 km^2 at mean high tide (Sayce, 1976), and a tidal range of 2–3 m generates a tidal prism that exceeds 700,000 m^3 (U. S. Army Corps of Engineers, 1975). Broad, mostly intertidal flats with long intervals of continued subsidence between the episodes of uplift.

TERRACE STRATIGRAPHY

The location occupied by the modern bay seems to have served repeatedly as a site for estuary development during late Cenozoic time. Pleistocene terrace deposits, consisting of a stacked succession of bay and valley-fill sediments, mantle the area proximal to Willapa Bay (Fig. 1). The predominance of bay deposits here probably reflects a combination of the steep coastal gradient and the fixed position for the Columbia River mouth within a large bedrock valley just south of the bay. The volcanic uplands east of the bay impose a barrier to further encroachment of the sea, and the large volume of sand discharged by the Columbia River into a prevailing northward, littoral transport system serves as a mechanism for generating barrier spits that would promote repeated bay development at the Willapa site.

Two distinct sets of terrace deposits are recognizable: an older set that extends to elevations of at least 150 m (Wells, 1979) and a younger set that laps onto the older set beneath a well-developed terrace surface about 13 m above present sea level (Fig. 2). The older deposits underlie dissected terrace surfaces, are slightly tilted tectonically, and are cut by faults. The ages of these deposits are poorly constrained; some contain an extinct clam, *Mytilus condoni* Dall that is restricted to late Pliocene or early Pleistocene units. Deposits in the younger set range in age from 200–100 ka (Kvenvolden and others, 1979). This set crops out in nearly continuous sea cliff exposure in the 10 km between Goose Point and Pickernell Creek (Fig. 3). The deposits are probably also exposed in sea cliffs to the north and south, but the outcrops are limited and discontinuous. The younger set is the primary focus of this paper because its stratigraphic continuity, better preservation, and lack of tectonic com-

plication allow for delineation and correlation of internal units.

Delineation of stratigraphic units within a predominantly estuarine succession is inherently difficult. Lateral lithologic variation can be pronounced as a consequence of textural change within the same depositional environment. Studies using SCUBA in the modern bay, for example, documented marked lithologic change over short distances (in some cases, a few hundred meters along an isobath on an accretionary bank of a tidal channel). Tidal channels rapidly migrate laterally—major channels at the inlet have shifted laterally about 5 km in the past 100 years—producing pronounced and, in some cases, laterally extensive surfaces. Such surfaces can be very difficult to distinguish from those separating deposits of very different ages. These major breaks can also be quite cryptic where they separate sediment of similar textural and depositional origin.

The approach I used to delineate stratigraphic units within these exposures is premised on the concept that embayments typically fill rapidly to an equilibrium platform corresponding approximately to the upper intertidal level. Accordingly, a bay/valley-fill complex is likely to consist of a succession of "stillstand units," each reflecting a specific relative stand of the sea (Clifton, 1982). Interpreting this succession requires a recognition of paleobathymetric change (which may be restricted to discriminating between intertidal and subtidal facies) and the reconstruction of relative sea-level curves.

An inherent drawback in this approach lies in the potential difficulty of distinguishing between deposits of different age that accumulated at similar water depths. Five stillstand units have been identified in the younger terrace set (Fig. 3), but the possible existence of additional, unrecognized units cannot be eliminated. It is particularly difficult to establish whether lithologic units of subtidal origin reflect deposition during different stands of the sea or represent separate facies that accumulated during the filling of a particular bay. The five stillstand units described here represent the simplest interpretation that is consistent with the observations; the actual depositional history may be substantially more complex.

LITHOLOGIC CHARACTER OF THE LATE PLEISTOCENE UNITS

Unit I

The oldest stillstand unit crops out intermittently between Goose Point and Pickernell Creek (Fig. 3). This unit consists mostly of laminated, slightly bluish-gray mud. Unit I mostly straddles the modern upper intertidal-flat surface. Its top lies a few meters above present sea level (Fig. 3), and except for an exposure in the sea cliffs just north of Pickernell Creek, its base lies below the level of the modern tidal flat. The unit contains numerous scattered remains of marine (or estuarine) mollusks.

The nature of lamination in Unit I varies in part with stratigraphic levels within the unit. In most exposures, the interval 1–2 m above the modern intertidal flat consists of apparently horizontal to gently inclined stratification (Fig. 4). Close examination shows that this stratification comprises rhythmic alternations of laminated clay and burrowed

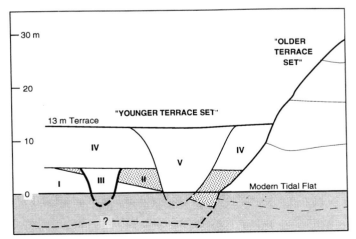

FIG. 2.—Schematic illustration of the stratigraphic relationships of Late Pleistocene Terrace deposits at Willapa Bay relative to one another and to older terrace deposits (modified from Clifton and Leithold, 1991). Heavy line at base of Unit III indicates sequence boundary. Basal contacts of Units II and IV are highstand surfaces of tidal erosion. Basal contact of Unit V is potentially a sequence boundary, but the sequence involved consists only of a single valley filling late in an episode of overall highstand.

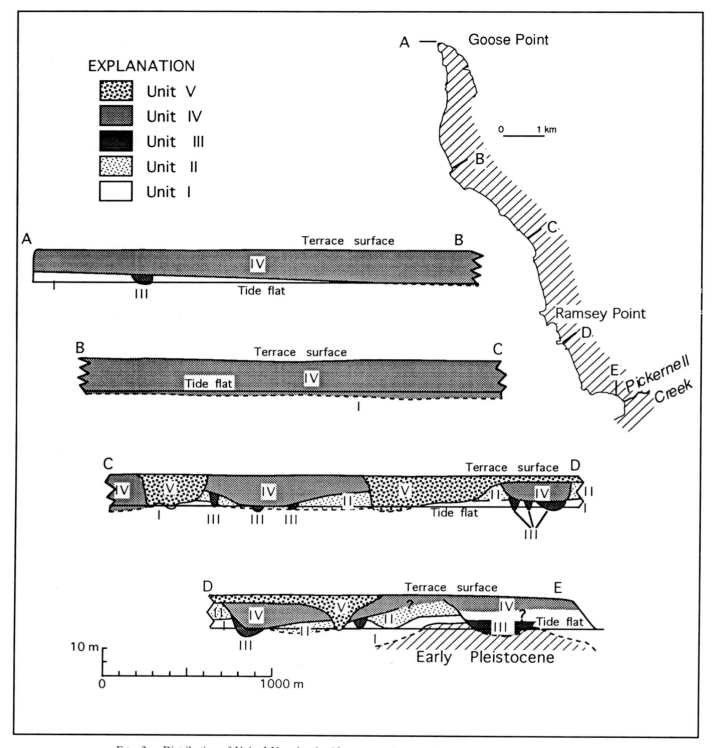

FIG. 3.—Distribution of Units I-V under the 13-m terrace between Goose Point and Pickernell Creek.

fine sand, each about 0.5 cm thick. Similar stratification is present on the accretionary banks of muddy, fluvial-tidal channels in the modern bay (Fig. 5). Higher in the unit, particularly in the exposures south of Goose Point, lenticular sets, decimeters to 1.5 m thick, of more steeply in-clined, mud-dominated strata locally occupy the section (Fig. 4). Stratification in these sets consists of finely interlaminated lenses and layers of mud, fine sand, and concentrations of organic detritus. Similar lamination occurs on the accretionary banks of runoff channels on the modern muddy

FIG. 4.—Laminated mud of Unit I beneath a shell bed at the base of Unit IV about 900 m south of Goose Point, Willapa Bay. Note very gently-inclined stratification beneath the 40-cm-long machete and steeper inclination of the strata above. Note also borings into the upper surface of Unit I just below the shell bed. Erosional contact at the base of the shell bed is a highstand surface of tidal erosion.

intertidal flats. Lateral migration of the channels produces inclined mud strata (Fig. 6) comparable to that in Unit I. Horizontal lamination in the upper part of Unit I takes the form of alternations of fine sand and mud several millimeters to a centimeter thick. Such lamination is produced today on the tidally-exposed, muddy banks of tidal rivers in the bay by seasonal fluctuations in energy level. At several localities (for example just south of Goose Point), an interval several decimeters thick, dominated by thin slightly wavy laminae marked by concentrations of organic matter and the yellow alteration mineral, jarosite, occupies the upper part of the lower laminated section. Bedding plane exposures indicate an abundance of blades of the marine grass *Zostera* and occasionally some rhizomes, suggesting that these intervals represent zones of intense *Zostera* growth. Such zones occur in the modern bay on intertidal flats as well as just below the intertidal area along river banks.

In the exposures north of Pickernell Creek, where Unit I directly overlies earlier Pleistocene deposits of the older terrace set, it is sandier and contains locally-derived pebbles of basalt. The section here lacks the internal stratigraphic organization of the more northerly exposures, but narrow, relatively deep, filled channels like those on modern flats provide evidence of intertidal deposition.

In summary, Unit I appears to be deposited in an muddy, fluvial/tidal environment, and the exposures in the sea cliffs represent the transition from upper subtidal to intertidal deposition. The channel-floor facies that should be associated with such a system lies below the present intertidal flat and is nowhere exposed.

Unit II

Unit II is a predominantly sandy deposit of limited extent that overlies Unit I in a few exposures between Goose Point and Pickernell Creek (Fig. 3 C-D, D-E). The similarity of this sandy sediment to local facies in Unit IV complicates its delineation; the two units can be distinguished with confidence only where they can be traced laterally to locations where Unit III separates them (as in Fig. 3 C-D). The sand in Unit II is well-sorted and fine grained, and mud drapes and layers are common. In some exposures, the sand is well-stratified and exhibits abundant crossbedding and ripple lamination. In others, it is intensely burrowed and shows only remnants of bedding. Where the unit is muddier (particularly in exposures farther south in the bay), it contains molds of the oyster *Ostrea lurida*.

The abundant crossbedding and beds of *Ostrea lurida* indicate that Unit II accumulated in a subtidal environment

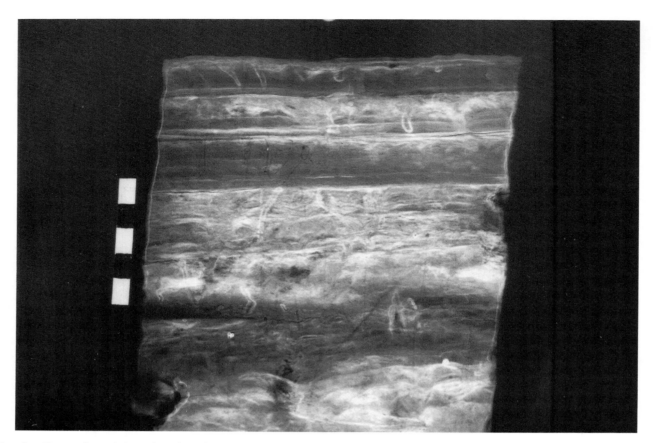

Fig. 5.—X-ray radiograph (negative print) of modern muddy fluvial/tidal bank sediment showing alternating mud (dark) and sand (light) laminae. Sample taken in a water depth of about 5 m in the upper Palix River. Centimeter scale.

of uncertain water depth (Clifton, 1983). Similar sandy deposits exist in the central channel of the modern bay, particularly in the northern reaches toward the inlet (Clifton and Phillips, 1980).

Unit III

Unit III is the most localized of the terrace units. As seen in the seacliffs, this unit occupies narrow valleys, typically no more than a few tens of meters across, incised into units I and II (Figs. 3, 7). The sediment that fills these incisions is muddy and rich in organic detritus. Fossil roots and rhizomes (including those of the marsh grass *Triglochin*) are common in the mud. Logs and tree branches occur in many exposures. Except for a crude stratification resulting from differences in the abundance of organic detritus, this unit is generally devoid of sedimentary structures.

Unit III clearly represents the filling of relatively small gullies and valleys and may be entirely nonmarine. Although thriving stands of *Triglochin* in the modern bay are daily inundated by the tides, the grass can also grow solely in the presence of fresh water. No other marine biota were found in Unit III.

Unit IV

Unit IV is the most widespread and lithologically variable of the younger terrace sequences. Except where cut

out by Unit V, this unit crops out almost continuously between Goose Point and Pickernell Creek (Fig. 3). For most of its extent, Unit IV rests erosionally on the underlying units (Fig. 4). Near Pickernell Creek, however, fossiliferous muds that appear to be part of Unit IV grade downsection into *Triglochin*-bearing mud of Unit III. The interval that should contain the contact is marked by several layers of pebbles, but none of these are associated with a clearly defined erosional surface. The top of Unit IV coincides in most places with the 13-m terrace surface.

Two general facies types characterize Unit IV: unstratified fossiliferous mud and stratified mud and/or sand. Where present, the unstratified deposits typically occupy the lower part of the unit. In the vicinity of Goose Point, the basal part of Unit IV consists of a bed, locally more than a meter thick, composed of mostly disarticulated and broken mollusk shells (Fig. 4). Some of the bivalves (particularly *Ostrea lurida*) are in growth position. In addition to shells, the bed also contains scattered pebbles and fragments of wood. The shell bed rests directly on the mud of Unit I; the contact is sharp but broken by numerous tubular borings (up to 2 to 3 cm in diameter and filled with fine shell debris) that penetrate the topmost meter of Unit I. At its top, the shell bed passes upward into a meter or so of structureless sand or mud that in turn underlies an interval of stratified sediment (Fig. 8). Similar shell concentrations re-

FIG. 6.—Mud cross-strata (far bank) produced by lateral migration of tidal runoff channel (tidal creek) on muddy intertidal flats of the Palix River. Forty-cm-long machete and footprints for scale.

side today on the floors of tidal channels within the bay, and the shell bed south of Goose Point is assigned to this environment. It is gently inclined toward the south and passes beneath the tidal flat about 2 km south of Goose Point (Fig. 3).

Farther south, about 5 km south of Goose Point, the basal contact of Unit IV lies below the current tidal-flat surface, and the lower part of Unit IV consists of massive mud that contains thick, lenticular concentrations of *Ostrea lurida* in growth position (Fig. 9). This thin-valved oyster is susceptible to temperature changes associated with intertidal exposure and presently thrives only in the subtidal environment (Hopkins, 1937). The muddy deposits in the lower part of Unit IV are therefore considered subtidal in origin, probably accumulating on the floor of broad trough of an ancient bay (as opposed to an active tidal channel).

The stratified deposits, which constitute the upper part of Unit IV in most places, are highly variable due primarily to differences in the relative proportions of sand and mud. Where sand is a very minor constituent, the deposits consist of mud laminae separated by thin partings of sand. Starved ripples are fairly common in this facies. In some exposures, rhythmic alternations some centimeters thick of laminated and bioturbated sandy mud predominate (Fig. 10). With increased sand content, flaser bedding becomes progressively more abundant. Where the proportion of sand exceeds that

of mud, cross-bedding and ripple lamination separated by drapes and layers of mud predominate. The lateral transition between sand-rich and sand-poor facies can occur within a hundred meters.

This facies contains abundant evidence of tidal influence in the form of mud couplets, reversed ripple lamination, and rhythmically-repeated mud drapes on crossbed foresets. In many exposures, the strata in this facies of Unit IV are broadly inclined (Fig. 10). Such inclination indicates deposition on the accretionary banks of tidal channels. In the modern bay, abrupt lateral transitions in the proportion of sand to mud occur at the same scale as those in these deposits.

All of the evidence in the strata of Unit IV indicates deposition in a subtidal environment (Clifton, 1983). The fact that the unit is capped by the 13-m terrace surface suggests the possibility that the top of Unit IV conforms with an intertidal platform. Intense weathering, however, within the soil profile beneath the terrace surface has destroyed any existing evidence of intertidal deposition.

Unit V

Unit V is, like Unit III, clearly confined to discrete channels, but the valleys filled by Unit V are larger (Fig. 3 C-D, D-E) and can be reconstructed into a relatively well-

FIG. 7.—Mud-filled channel of Unit III about 750 m south of Goose Point. Note lateral continuity of Unit IV shell bed across and beyond the channel-fill. Forty-cm-long machete for scale at the base of the outcrop, just below base of the central part of the channel. Contact at the base of the channel is a sequence boundary.

defined, interconnected system (Fig. 11). Among the facies that can be distinguished in Unit V are sand/gravel deposits that probably accumulated in channel thalwegs, inclined and locally deformed stratified mud attributable to accretionary bank deposition, and structureless clay that probably represents deposition in abandoned channels. The sand/gravel deposits contain numerous aligned logs that appear to define the direction of the channel axis. No clear evidence of tidal conditions such as reversal of cross-bedding could be found in these deposits. The stratified muds are characterized by numerous, regularly-spaced partings of fine sand. The rhythmic nature of the stratification suggests tidal influence, but the absence of burrowing in this facies suggests deposition upstream from marine salinities. The structureless clay facies is best developed at the north end of the Unit V valley fill exposed slightly more than a kilometer north of Ramsey point (Figs. 3, 12). Its occurrence in the upper part of the Unit above inferred channel bank and thalweg facies suggests abandonment here late in the filling of the valley.

Like Unit IV, Unit V seems to be graded to the 13-m terrace surface. Both units are therefore inferred to have formed at a similar stand of the sea.

AGE OF THE TERRACE UNITS

Clifton (1983) describes the inferred ages of the terrace units and their relationship to eustatic sea level. To summarize briefly here, the degree of amino acid racemization in shells of the bivalve *Saxidomus* provides an indication not only of relative but, assuming that we have adequately reconstructed temperature history, absolute ages of the terrace units (Kvenvolden and others, 1979). Units I and II have ages that are nearly equivalent, about 200 ky, whereas Unit IV has an age of approximately 100 ky. These age designations indicate that Units I and II and Unit IV accumulated during the sea-level highstands respectively associated with marine oxygen isotope stages 7 (I and II) and 5 (IV) of Shackelton and Opdyke (1973). By inference, the valleys filled by Unit III are presumed to have been incised during the lowstand of the sea associated with marine oxygen isotope stage 6. The coincidence of the top of Units IV and V, like Unit IV, originated during the series of highstands in stage 5.

In terms of transgressive and highstand successions, units I and II may be grouped separately from Units III, IV, and V. The transition from shallowest subtidal and intertidal de-

FIG. 8.—Lower part of Unit IV south of Goose Point. Note basal shell bed overlying bored top surface of Unit I. Shell bed grades up into structureless sand, which in turn is sharply overlain by interlaminated sand and mud of Unit IV. Contact at the base of the shell bed is the highstand surface of tidal erosion shown in Figure 4.

posits (Unit I) to subtidal deposits (Unit II) requires a rise in relative sea level. The muddy deposits of Unit I resemble those found in the upper estuary today whereas the sands of Unit II are like those presently accumulating in the central estuary. Both units are of the same age within the resolution of amino acid dating. It seems likely that Units I and II, respectively, represent the transgressive and highstand associated with marine oxygen isotope stage 7, Unit I reflecting upper estuary channels/flats deposits that were transgressed and covered by central bay sands (Unit II) as have occurred in the Gironde Estuary sequence (Allen and Posamentier, 1993)

Units III and IV can fit into a similar transgressive-highstand succession associated with the sea-level rise culminating in the highstand of marine oxygen isotope stage 5. Unit II represents a true valley filling, and its basal erosional surface is a sequence boundary formed during the lowstand of oxygen isotope stage 6. The complex facies association of Unit IV reflects a complicated highstand assemblage formed during stage 5. The origins of Unit V are less clear. The unit clearly fills valleys cut into the underlying units and either represents a late, predominantly fluvial, phase in the filling of the 100 ky estuary or results from the incision and backfilling of valleys in response to

a fluctuation of relative sea level during the latter part of the stage 5 highstand.

PALEOGEOGRAPHY

Each of these Pleistocene units reflects accumulation in a system where both valleys and tidal channels trended generally toward the northwest. Although the Units I, II and IV formed in different settings in bays of possibly dissimilar sizes, they share a common trend to increasingly up-bay facies toward the south-southeast (an up-bay direction in the modern bay). Unit I becomes sandier and contains more basaltic pebbles in its presumed upper reaches just north of Pickernell Creek where greater fluvial influence could be expected. Similarly, Units II and IV become muddier in an up-bay direction. Cross-bedding and ripple foreset measurements in both units indicate northwesterly and southeasterly flow, presumably following tidal-channel trends. The larger valleys filled by Unit III seem to trend to the north or north-northwest (Clifton and others, 1989) as do the fluvial incisions of Unit V (Fig. 11).

EROSION AND PRESERVATION

Each of the units delineated within the younger terrace set overlies a basal erosional surface. Of these, only that

FIG. 9.—Lenticular concentrations of *Ostrea lurida* in structureless mud of Unit IV about halfway between Goose and Ramsey Points. Entrenching tool for scale.

at the base of Unit III clearly qualifies as a sequence boundary. The basal contact of Unit I is only locally exposed where this unit overlies topographic highs atop the older terrace set; elsewhere the contact and the nature of any underlying deposits associated with the sea-level cycle of stage 7 lie beneath the present tidal flat. The highstand deposits (Units II and IV) rest on extensive erosional surfaces, the lowest parts of which lie unexposed beneath the present tidal-flat surface. Where exposed, the surface appears to be cut by migrating tidal channels as at the base of Unit IV in section A-B, Figure 3. The erosional surface at the base of Unit IV, which has a gentle gradient in the seacliffs south of Goose Point (Fig. 3A-B), increases in steepness and relief toward Pickernell Creek (Fig. 3C-D, D-E). This change may reflect more localized incision owing to a reduced rate of tidal-channel migration caused by a combination of smaller tidal flux and more cohesive banks in the upper reaches of the paleo-bay. The Unit IV/Unit III contact is abrupt for most of the exposure, probably as a consequence of erosion caused by shifting tidal channels in Unit IV. Just north of Pickernell Creek, however, the contact is gradational perhaps again because tidal channels of Unit IV migrated to a lesser extent.

The basal contact of Unit II does not show a similar increase in complexity toward Pickernell Creek for several possible reasons. First, the base of Unit II nowhere lies topographically higher than the intertidal deposits of Unit I possibly because Unit II accumulated directly on these deposits as part of a transgressive succession. Second, the extent of tidal-channel migration in Unit II may not have significantly declined over the exposure interval. The unit becomes muddy only in isolated exposures farther south.

The basal contact of Unit V resembles a sequence boundary; it reflects an abrupt seaward shift in facies and may represent erosion during a sea-level lowstand (albeit after a minor fall). This unit, however, seems to be part of a highstand assemblage in its relation to the terrace surface at its top and the absence of an overlying transgressive systems tract. If subsequent erosion and deposition obscured the upper contact relations of this unit (particularly in its near coincidence with the top of Unit IV), it would be almost unequivocally considered to be a sequence boundary. In reality, the sequence represented consists only of the channel fill itself, formed at an overall highstand of the sea.

The stratigraphic complexity of the preserved deposits increases in an up-bay direction. The northern half of the Goose Point to Pickernell Creek exposure is dominated by Unit IV, whereas much interchanneling characterizes the southern half and the older units are preserved to a greater degree (Fig. 3). I attribute this change to reduced tidal erosion in the upper paleo-bays. Presumably, the shifting of tidal

FIG. 10.—Inclined alternating laminated and bioturbated intervals in Unit IV north of Ramsey Point. Stratified section is about 7 m thick. Note massive, modern soil interval at top of section.

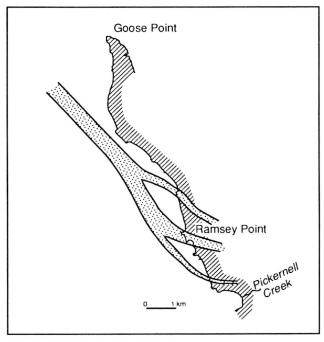

FIG. 11.— Reconstructed channel system of Unit V (stippled pattern) between Goose Point and Pickernell Creek.

channels in the central bay area during deposition of Unit IV was sufficient to form an extensive erosional surface.

The extensive preservation of intertidal facies in Unit I is remarkable given the erosional setting and the limited potential for preservation of intertidal deposits which cap simple estuarine sequences and thus are particularly susceptible to erosion. The preservation here probably relates to the cohesive mud lithology of Unit I. Near Ramsey Point, where Unit V directly overlies Unit I, borings into the top of Unit I are filled by well-sorted, fine sand unlike that in Unit V but characteristic of the sand in Units II and IV. These borings imply that the incision associated with Unit V removed the friable sand of Units II and/or IV but was checked by the more resistant mud of Unit I.

Unit II is preserved only in the southern part of the exposure (Fig. 3C, D-E). This unit is so friable and subject to erosion that its presence probably implies an absence of channeling by any of the younger units.

No upper bay facies comparable to Unit I lie between Units III and IV. Intertidal facies almost certainly accumulated at this interval during the transgression but are nowhere preserved. Possibly they were sandy and more susceptible to erosion than the mud of Unit I. In addition, Unit I seems to represent an intermediate stillstand during a transgression in which a relatively thick upper bay succes-

Fig. 12.— Structureless clay in Unit V (upper part of photograph) above contact that cuts downward across sandy facies of Unit IV about 200 m south of location C in Figure 3. Note soil development at top of photograph. Contact at the base of the clay is an erosional contact formed by fluvial incision, probably as part of a relatively minor fall in relative sea level during the overall highstand of marine oxygen isotope stage 5.

sion could accumulate. If the transgression leading to Unit IV was continuous or more rapid, any upper bay deposits could be thin and more subject to complete removal. It is also possible that some upper bay deposits are preserved below Unit IV where its base lies beneath the modern tidal flat.

Unit IV is presently very well preserved, but much of it is likely to be lost to erosion in the future. Even in a subsiding basin, the continuance of fluctuating sea level would cause Unit IV to be eroded by the same processes that removed much of Unit II. In the present regime of tectonic uplift, Unit IV and the other terrace deposits as well have a very limited potential for survival in the stratigraphic record.

CONCLUSIONS

Repeated rise and fall of the sea can produce a very complicated succession of transgressive and highstand estuary/valley-fill deposits. The stratigraphic complexity is likely to decrease in an up-bay direction owing to less laterally extensive erosion as the tidal flux diminishes and the bank sediments become finer and more cohesive.

The preservation of transgressive, upper bay deposits may depend on a combination of their thickness and their lithology, as it relates to erosional resistance. Deposits ac-

cumulating during intermediate stillstands may be more preservable than those accumulating under conditions of continuous or rapid sea-level rise.

Highstand estuary deposits may initially be thick and laterally extensive. Much of these deposits may be lost to erosion if sea level continues to fluctuate.

Erosion caused by the lateral shifting of tidal channels is a powerful mechanism for erosion during stillstands of the sea. This erosion is likely to be more effective in the central bay regions than in the upper bay. In a setting like that at Willapa Bay, where tidal influences greatly exceed fluvial influences, tidal erosion may produce laterally extensive erosional surfaces capable of replacing sequence boundaries as a ravinement surface commonly does in transgressive successions. The tidal erosion surface can be unrelated to transgression; in the Willapa terrace deposits, it is best developed at the base of highstand accumulations.

A complex of estuary/valley-fill deposits is likely to include stacked sets of transgressive and highstand accumulations. Separating these sets into individual transgressive-regressive episodes requires careful bathymetric analysis and excellent exposure. There are few (if any) locations in the Willapa terrace exposures described here where a single well would penetrate all five of the units described here.

ACKNOWLEDGMENTS

This paper is based on field work done by the U. S. Geological Survey to which many persons contributed. I particularly must acknowledge the field participation of R. L. Phillips and R. J. Anima. The report has benefitted greatly from thoughtful, constructive comment by Bruce Thom, Trevor Elliot, and Robert Dalrymple.

REFERENCES

ALLEN, G. P., 1991, Sedimentary processes and facies in the Gironde Estuary: a recent model for macrotidal estuarine systems, *in* Smith, D. G., Reinson, G. E., Zaitlin, B. A., and Rahmani, R. A., eds., Clastic Tidal Sedimentology: Calgary, Canadian Society of Petroleum Geologists Memoir 16, p. 29–40.

ALLEN, G. P., AND POSAMENTIER, H. W., 1993, Sequence stratigraphy and facies model of an incised valley fill: the Gironde estuary, France: Journal of Sedimentary Petrology, v. 63, p. 378–391.

AMOS, C. L., TEE, K. T., AND ZAITLIN, B. A., 1991, The post-glacial evolution of Chignecto Bay, Bay of Fundy, and its modern environment of deposition, *in* Smith, D. G., Reinson, G. E., Zaitlin, B. A., and Rahmani, R. A., eds., Calgary, Clastic Tidal Sedimentology: Canadian Society of Petroleum Geologists Memoir 16, p. 59–90.

CLIFTON, H. E., 1982, Estuarine deposits, *in* Scholle, P. A., and Spearing, D., eds., Sandstone Depositional Environments: Tulsa, American Association of Petroleum Geologists Memoir 31, p 179–189.

CLIFTON, H. E., 1983, Discrimination of subtidal and intertidal facies in Pleistocene deposits, Willapa Bay, Washington: Journal of Sedimentary Petrology, v. 53, p. 353–369.

CLIFTON, H. E., AND PHILLIPS, R. L., 1980, Lateral trends and vertical sequences in estuarine sediments, Willapa Bay, Washington, *in* Field M. E., Bouma, A. H., Colburn, I. P., Douglas, R. G, and Ingle, J. C., eds., Quaternary Depositional Environments of the Pacific Coast: Bakersfield, Pacific Section Society of Economic Paleontologists and Mineralogists Pacific Coast Paleogeography Symposium No. 4, p. 55–71.

CLIFTON, H. E., PHILLIPS, R. L., AND ANIMA, R. J., 1989, Sedimentary Facies of Willapa Bay, Washington—A Field Guide: Calgary, Canadian Society of Petroleum Geologists Field Trip Guidebook, Second International Research Symposium on Clastic Tidal Deposits, 64 p.

DALRYMPLE, R. W., ZAITLIN, B. A., AND BOYD, R., 1992, Estuarine facies models: conceptual basis and stratigraphic implications: Journal of Sedimentary Petrology, v. 62, p. 1130–1146.

FAIRBANKS, R. G., 1989, A 17,000-year glacio-eustatic sea-level record: influence of glacial melting rates on the younger Dryas event and deep-ocean circulation: Nature, v. 342, p. 637–642.

HEDGEPETH, J. W., AND OBREBSKI, S., 1981, Willapa Bay: A historical perspective and a rationale for research: Washington, D. C., Office of Biological Services, United States Fish and Wildlife, FWS/OBS-81/03, 52 p.

HOPKINS, A. E., 1937, Experimental observations on spawning, larval development, and setting in the olympic oyster, *Ostrea lurida*: Fisheries Bureau Bulletin No. 23, p. 439–502

KVENVOLDEN, K. A., BLUNT, D. J., AND CLIFTON, H. E., 1979, Amino acid racemization in Quaternary shell deposits at Willapa Bay, Washington: Geochimica Cosmochimica Acta, v. 43, p. 1505–1520.

LUEPKE, G., AND CLIFTON, H. E., 1983, Heavy-mineral distribution in modern and ancient bay deposits, Willapa Bay, Washington: Sedimentary Geology, v. 35, p. 233–247.

NICHOL, S. L., 1991, Zonation and sedimentology of estuarine facies in an incised valley, wave-dominated, microtidal setting, *in* Smith, D.G., Reinson, G. E., Zaitlin, B. A., and Rahmani, R. A., eds., Clastic Tidal Sedimentology: Calgary, Canadian Society of Petroleum Geologists Memoir 16, p. 41–58.

NICHOLS, M. M., JOHNSON, G. H., AND PEEBLES, P. C., 1991, Modern sediments and facies model for a microtidal coastal plain estuary, the James estuary, Virginia: Journal of Sedimentary Petrology, v. 61, p. 883–899.

PETERSON, C. D., AND PHIPPS, J. B., 1991, Holocene sedimentary framework of Grays Harbor Basin, Washington, U. S. A., *in* Fletcher, C. H., and Wehmiller, J. F., eds., Quaternary Coastal Systems of the United States, Marine and Lacustrine Systems: Tulsa, SEPM (Society for Sedimentary Geology) Special Publication 48, p. 273–285.

PETERSON, C. D., AND SCHEIDEGGER, K. F., 1984, Holocene depositional evolution in a small active-margin estuary of the northwestern United States: Marine Geology, v. 59, p. 51–83.

PETERSON, C., SCHEIDEGGER, K., KOMAR, P., AND NIEM, W., 1984, Sediment composition and hydrogeography in six high-gradient estuaries of the northwestern United States: Journal of Sedimentary Petrology, v. 54, p. 87–97.

SAYCE, C. S., 1976, The oyster industry of Willapa Bay: Cheney, Proceedings of the Symposium on Terrestrial and Aquatic Ecological Studies of the Northwest, Eastern Washington State College, p. 347–356.

SHACKELTON, N. J., AND OPDYKE, N. D., 1973, Oxygen isotope and palaeomagnetic stratigraphy of equatorial Pacific core V28–238: Oxygen isotope temperatures and ice volumes on a 10^5 and 10^6 year scale: Quaternary Research, v. 3, p. 39–55.

UNITED STATES ARMY CORPS OF ENGINEERS, SEATTLE DISTRICT, 1975, Willapa River and Harbor navigation project, Washington: Environmental Impact Statement Review Draft, July, 99 p.

WELLS, R. E., 1979, Geologic map of the Cape Disappointment Naselle-River Area, Pacific County, Washington: United States Geological Survey Open-File Report 79–389.

SEGMENT 3—TERRESTRIAL SYSTEMS

SEQUENCES AND SEQUENCE BOUNDARIES IN GLACIAL SLUICEWAYS BEYOND GLACIAL MARGINS

GORDON S. FRASER

Indiana Geological Survey, Bloomington, Indiana 47405

ABSTRACT: The Pleistocene and Holocene alluvial sediments filling incised valleys beyond glacial margins share a number of characteristics, despite variations in magnitude and timing of events in their respective drainage basins. In a gross sense, the alluvial fills are composed of a two-part stratigraphy consisting of a lower, coarse-grained interval deposited in response to glaciation of the drainage basin and an upper fine-grained interval deposited by Holocene rivers.

In detail, however, both lower and upper intervals commonly consist of multiple sequences deposited in response to variations in discharge and imposed sediment load. Sequences were deposited during periods of aggradation, and sequence boundaries formed during erosional episodes. The resultant architecture is characterized by inset stratigraphic relationships and abrupt lateral facies changes.

Investigations in the Ohio, White, Whitewater, and Wabash Rivers in Indiana reveal that as much as 50 meters of alluvium fill bedrock valleys. The valleys normally are steep-sided with broad, flat floors incised by a narrow, deep trough (called the Deep Stage). These valleys were eroded in step-wise fashion during late Tertiary time and earliest Quaternary time. The basal alluvium in these valleys consists of consolidated gravel and sand deposited during pre-Wisconsin ice advances, probably by braided stream systems. These earliest outwash sediments are capped by a boulder-cobble lag or by channel and overbank deposits that accumulated during interstadials. Pre-Wisconsin sediments were eroded in response to increased flow during the initial stages of the Wisconsin glaciation, and valley floor aggradation occurred when outwash arrived somewhat later.

Stacked sequences, that accumulated in response to multiple glacial events in their drainage basins, can be recognized in Wisconsin fluvial deposits in these valleys. Sequences, in turn, are composed of stacked depositional units that accumulated in response to the annual meltwater cycle and the passage of storms. Diurnal variations in the glacial meltwater regime are not reflected in these deposits because their large drainage basins served to buffer short-term events.

Braided-stream deposits may be interbedded at valley margins with lacustrine deposits where rapid aggradation of valley floors dammed tributary valleys and formed small lakes. Other associated deposits include windblown silt and sand that was stripped from exposed channels during low-flow stages and deposited at valley margins.

Rivers readjusted to new conditions of sediment and water discharge toward the end of Wisconsin time and the beginning of Holocene time by incising their valley floors and changing their channel patterns. The Holocene rivers are meandering, single-channel streams. Migration of channels across valley bottoms produces parasequences, consisting of sandy channel deposits and thick, fine-grained floodplain deposits, separated by erosional surfaces produced during rapid changes in channel position.

Tributary streams draining large basins adjusted to these new conditions by eroding new channels across these alluviated plains and often rejoining trunk streams at different places than their precursor channels. Smaller tributary streams deposited fine-grained alluvial fans at valley margins. In places, these are large enough to modify migration patterns of trunk streams. The sedimentary response in the trunk valley to these readjustments resulted in complex architecture consisting of multiple facies within single-cycle fluvial deposits.

INTRODUCTION

Most rivers experienced considerable change in sediment and water discharge with the onset of Quaternary glaciations. In regions not directly affected by glaciation, this was prompted by changes in precipitation, vegetative cover, and concomitant runoff in drainage basins that produced changes in channel pattern and rates of erosion and deposition. In northern Eurasia and North America, on the other hand, changes in sediment and water discharge were directly caused by glaciation. In some cases, water courses were covered by glacial ice or they were diverted during glacial advances (e.g., Wayne, 1952, 1963; Gray, 1991). Valley fills of such rivers commonly display complex architectures, with multiple levels of glacial, glaciofluvial, glaciolacustrine, and interglacial deposits in a variety of lateral and vertical stratigraphic relationships (e.g., Melhorn and Kempton, 1991; Bleuer 1991). The alluvial architecture reflects the succession of events that occurred when these valleys experienced multiple ice advances and withdrawals during glacial periods and the pronounced change in hydraulic regime that occurred during subsequent interstades (Bleuer, 1991).

In other cases, the valleys themselves were not glaciated, but they were sluiceways that drained glaciers, and their deposits are dominated by glaciofluvial sediments. The stratigraphic successions deposited in these valleys during glacial events commonly display a high degree of complexity related to rapid and extreme changes in sediment load and discharge which also triggered changes in sedimentation in their tributaries. Periods of aggradation were punctuated by erosional episodes that occurred when ice had largely withdrawn from drainage basins. Sedimentary response to alternating periods of aggradation and erosion produced abrupt lateral and vertical facies changes and inset stratigraphic relationships wherein younger units occupy channels eroded into older ones.

The sedimentological, geomorphological, and stratigraphic characteristics of the surface and near-surface sediments of these sluiceways have been studied in detail, especially where they are exposed in terraces, in terms of their sedimentological, geomorphological, and stratigraphic characteristics. Sediments at depth are considerably less well described. Even though the sediment fills in these valleys have been intensely explored for water and mineral resources, such studies normally provide only generalized notions of the gross aspects of their stratigraphy in terms of the hydrologic or economic aspects.

The lower reaches of the Wabash, White, Whitewater, and Ohio river valleys in Indiana (Fig. 1) are typical of glacial sluiceways. The Wabash and Ohio Rivers are among the twenty largest rivers, in terms of discharge, in the United States, and the White River is the largest tributary of the Wabash. During times of glacial advance, these three valleys, as well as the Whitewater valley, carried a substantially greater discharge of both water and sediment. Large

Incised-valley Systems: Origin and Sedimentary Sequences, SEPM Special Publication No. 51

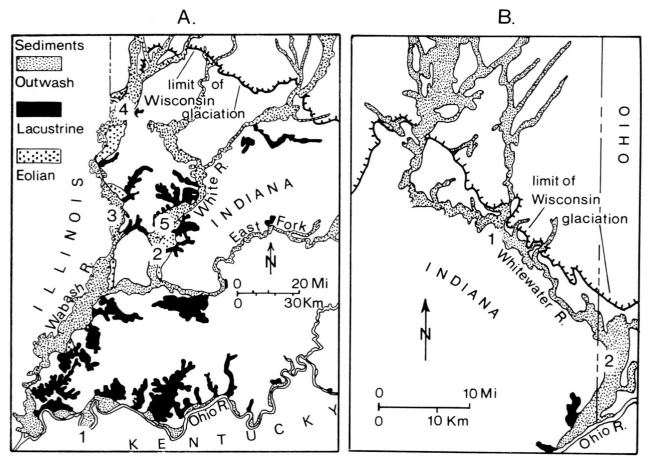

FIG. 1.—Maps of southern Indiana showing locations of the various study sites and the relationship of outwash, eolian sand plains, and lacustrine sediments to: (A) the valleys of the Wabash, Ohio, and White (both main channel and East Fork) Rivers (modified from Gray and others, 1970), and (B) the valley of the Whitewater River (modified from Gray and others, 1972).

parts of their drainage basins were covered by ice at times, but even those parts that were not glaciated were subject to abrupt and extreme hydrographic variations imposed on them by melting ice.

A general understanding of the stratigraphy and physical character of the sediments filling the Wabash, Ohio, Whitewater, and White river valleys has been gained through numerous studies of their water and mineral resources (Harvey, 1956; Walker, 1957; Price, 1964; Ray, 1965, 1966; Straw, 1968a, b; Gallaher and Price, 1966; Webb, 1970; Straw and others, 1977). Detailed studies of their architecture have been also been made (Gruver, 1983; Hartke and others, 1983; Gray, 1984; Fraser, 1986; Fraser and Fishbaugh, 1986; Fraser and Gray, 1992), and reconnaissance studies made by the author in the Miami River in Ohio and the Illinois and Embarass river valleys in Illinois indicate that these valleys are probably representative of most glacial sluiceways. This report synthesizes this information into a model of the origin and character of the Quaternary sediments filling incised valleys in reaches just beyond glacial margins.

AGE AND CHARACTER OF INCISION

The bedrock surface of the valleys of the Wabash, Ohio, and White Rivers appears to have been shaped by at least

two and perhaps three erosional episodes. The eastern and central parts of the midcontinent were apparently once occupied by an extensive peneplain variously named the Lexington, Highland Rim, or Cumberland Plain (for a review of this feature, see Ray, 1966). Remnants of this surface form the uplands along the Ohio River. Intermittent stream rejuvenation initiated by uplift during the latter part of the Tertiary Period dissected the plain (Ray, 1965) and created a series of gravel-capped steps and accordant hill crests in the bedrock leading down to the present Ohio and Wabash Rivers. Paired and unpaired bedrock terraces under the alluvial fill are also evidence of intermittent erosional episodes that formed the valleys (Theiss, 1922; Ray, 1966; Fraser and Fishbaugh, 1986).

A notable feature of these valleys is the presence of a deep, v-shaped trough incised into broad, relatively flat valley floors. This deep channel, informally referred to as "the Deep Stage," has been noted in other major pre-Pleistocene drainage systems (Fisk, 1944; Horberg, 1945; Wayne, 1952). The age and cause of this deep incision are open to speculation. The erosional episode obviously postdates the development of the Lexington Peneplain and predates the age of the oldest alluvium in the valleys which can only be confidently dated as Pleistocene age. L. L. Ray (1966) believed that the rapid downcutting of the deep valley was the last in a series of erosional episodes caused by uplift during the late Tertiary. Wayne (1952) believed that the deep stage formed during the Pleistocene (after the so-called "Nebraskan" Age) when diversion of the upper reaches of the Teays-Mahomet drainage system into the Ohio River caused static rejuvenation. It may also have formed with the inception of through-flowing drainage in the Wabash and Ohio Rivers. Bleuer (1991) believes that this may have occurred about 0.7 to 0.8 Ma (marine isotope stage 22) with blockage by ice of the Teays River valley in east-central Indiana.

LITHOFACIES DESCRIPTION AND INTERPRETATION

Holocene Lithofacies

Holocene sediments of the valley fill include a variety of fluvial and alluvial fan lithofacies. Fluvial-channel lithofacies consist dominantly of deposits of single channel systems. These channels tend to meander where valley floors are sufficiently wide, but they are straight in narrow reaches. The fluvial-channel deposits of Holocene rivers in general and glacial sluiceways in particular have been studied in detail, for example; the Vermillion River (Jackson, 1980), the Wabash River (Jackson, 1975, 1976), and the Mississippi River (Daviess, 1966; Potter and others, 1988; Autin and others, 1991; Jordan and Pryor, 1992), and it is not the purpose of this paper to duplicate these studies. The details of overbank sediments are less well known because sedimentologists in general have emphasized studies of channel belt sediments (Farrell, 1987).

The characteristics and internal architecture of the overbank deposits of some glacial sluiceways, including the Ohio River (Gray and others, 1983; Gray, 1984; Fraser, 1986), and the Mississippi River (Fisk, 1944; Ray, 1976; Farrel, 1987), however, have been described in some detail. They consist of deposits of the floodplain and of the alluvial ridge, including levee and crevasse splay sediments.

Floodplain Facies.—

In their simplest form, floodplain sediments deposited away from the alluvial ridge by a laterally migrating channel occur in upward-fining sequences consisting of interlaminated silty clay, clayey silt, and sand (Fig. 2). Sand is most abundant in the lower meter of most overbank sequences where it occurs in thin laminae and ripple-laminated beds a few centimeters thick. Sand declines rapidly in abundance upward, and the remainder of most overbank sequences consists of alternating beds with variable proportions of silt and clay. These sediments tend to be finely laminated near the base of sequences, but bedding becomes indistinct and finally absent upward where bioturbation has destroyed primary structures. Soil horizons are generally absent except at the top in these simple sequences.

Considerable lateral variation, however, can occur even in the most simply organized floodplains. The surface of the floodplain is marked by a regular series of concentric ridges and swales in both highly sinuous streams and streams with low sinuosity. Sediments in swales differ from those over ridges by: (1) having almost no sand in the lower part

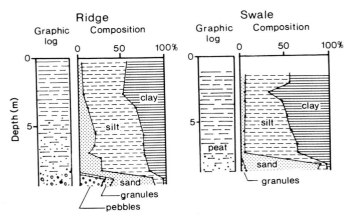

FIG. 2.—Vertical sequences in the alluvium of the Ohio River near Evansville, Indiana showing the difference in the composition of the overbank sediments accumulating over scroll bar ridges and in interbar swales (see Fig. 1A, site 1 for location) (after Fraser and Fishbaugh, 1986).

of overbank sequences; (2) containing considerably more clay upward in sequences (Fig. 2); and (3) having abundant organic material, especially at the base of overbank sequences where they overlie point-bar sands, and also occurring as macerated debris throughout sequences.

Variation in this simple sequence can occur near alluvial ridges where levee and crevasse splay deposits are considerably coarser than floodplain deposits (Fig. 3). Appreciable amounts of sand are found throughout levee sequences, and occasional layers of sand and granules are also intercalated with the sandy muds and muddy sands that make

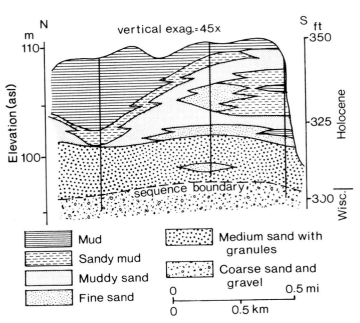

FIG. 3.—Cross-section through the late Wisconsinan and Holocene alluvium in the Ohio River Valley near Evansville, Indiana showing the internal arrangement of levee sediments (see Fig. 1A, site 1 for location).

up the bulk of the sequences. Levee sequences fine irregularly upward by a reduction in the amount of sand, but unlike floodplain sequences, sand is abundant throughout, and the proportion of clay is relatively small.

The pattern of sedimentation displayed by floodplain facies suggests that aggradation of the floodplain surface occurred rapidly. Modern long-term rates of vertical accretion averaged over periods of several thousand years have been documented in excess of 0.2 m per year (Fraser, 1986), and deposition in places on the floodplain of the Ohio River during a single flood of as much as 0.5 m has occurred (Mansfield, 1938). Initial rates of accumulation were probably very high because sedimentation on point-bar surfaces occurred during annual floods. As accretion proceeded, however, floodplain surfaces became less susceptible to flooding and accretion rates slowed, allowing bioturbation by plants to destroy primary sedimentary structures. In some cases, channel downcutting has resulted in floodplain abandonment with the same resultant change in floodplain sedimentation and soil formation.

The ridges probably formed as scroll bars on point-bar surfaces, but the ridge and swale pattern is visible on the floodplain surface even though ridges are mantled by overbank sequences as much as 10 m thick. The sediment distribution indicates that sedimentary processes differed markedly over ridges and swales. During overbank flooding, water depths were shallower over ridges where higher flow velocities and shear-induced turbulence kept clays in suspension. Deeper water and reduced turbulence, however, allowed clays and organic debris to accumulate in troughs. Following floods, exceptionally deep troughs may also have remained as shallow ponds where peat was able to accumulate.

These simple sequences can be complicated when channels avulse or change their direction of migration (Grissinger and Murphey, 1983; Bridge, 1984; Farrel, 1987) or change their rate of aggradation or degradation under the influence of climatic changes or in response to neotectonism (Autin, 1985, 1992; Brakenridge, 1981, 1984; Burnett and Schumm, 1983; Schumm, 1987; Bettis, 1990). Multiple soil horizons, changes in grain-size trends, development of cross-cutting relationships, amalgamation of alloformations (Autin, 1992), and expansion of crevasse splays and levees into floodplains depositing upward coarsening sequences (Farrel, 1987) can produce considerable complexity in floodplain stratigraphy.

Wisconsin Lithofacies

Wisconsin components of the valley fill include a variety of braided stream lithofacies in the trunk valley and some tributaries, loess and eolian sand along the margins of the main valley, and lacustrine sediments in the tributaries. Braided-stream lithofacies include deposits of both deep and shallow multi-thread channels.

Deep Channel Facies.—

Deposits of deep channels are found at the base of Wisconsin fluvial sequences. They consist of sand in sequences of bedding structures that thin and change character upward

(see Fig. 3, Fraser, 1993). The base of the sequence consists of planar cross-beds, as much as 2 m thick, with tangential basal contacts. Cross-set thickness decreases upward although grain size remains relatively constant.

The lack of an upward increase in grain size concomitant with the upward decrease in set thickness suggests that the change in bedding style in these sequences was probably caused by a change in water depth rather than flow velocity. This interpretation is supported by the similarity of these sequences to those deposited on aggrading sandflats in the Saskatchewan River, a relatively deep multichannel stream described by Cant and Walker (1978). The sequences were probably deposited during the initial phase of Wisconsin alluviation in the valleys when increased discharge from melting ice at the outer reaches of drainage basins deepened trunk streams and the lower reaches of tributaries but before significant amounts of coarse-grained outwash was added to their sediment load.

Shallow Channel Facies.—

Deposits of shallow braided streams include massive or crudely-bedded gravels and sands, planar-bedded sand and fine gravel, trough cross-bedded sand with minor gravel, and ripple-bedded and plane-bedded fine sand and silt (Fig. 4). Mud is conspicuous by its near absence in these deposits. These sediments are typical of those deposited in braided glaciofluvial channels (e.g., Smith, 1985), and need not be further described here. However, features characteristic of glaciofluvial sediments deposited in small glacial meltwater streams in response to the diurnal melt cycle, such as reactivation surfaces, infiltrated matrix, and mud drapes (Smith, 1985), are uncommon in the braided stream deposits of these large streams.

Facies of shallow braided streams occur in upward fining units (Type A) 1–2 m thick. Bedding becomes more prominent and clast size decreases, and lenticular beds of ripple-bedded and planar laminated sand and silt occur at the top of gravel-rich massive or crudely bedded Type A units. Grain size and set thickness decrease upward, and lenticular beds of sand and silt also occur at the top of finer-grained, planar cross-bedded Type A units.

Type A sedimentation units are, in turn, grouped into Type B units 3–5 m thick. In some cases, Type B units consist of alternating deposits of massive or crudely-bedded, gravel-rich sediment, and deposits of planar cross-bedded sand and gravel. In other Type B units, such deposits alternate with sand-rich sediments in a variety of bedding structures (Fraser, 1993).

Type A units were probably deposited in response to flood events. The massive or crudely-bedded gravel and sand were deposited on longitudinal bars, and the planar cross-bedded sand and fine gravel were deposited on 2-dimensional dunes during flood stage (Fraser, 1993). Sand in medium-scale trough cross-beds accumulated in interbar and interdune channels during falling stage, and ripple-bedded and plane-bedded sand and silt accumulated in channels that formed on bar-top and dune-top channels during waning flow (Fraser, 1993).

Proglacial streams at glacial margins commonly display abundant evidence of their deposition under conditions of

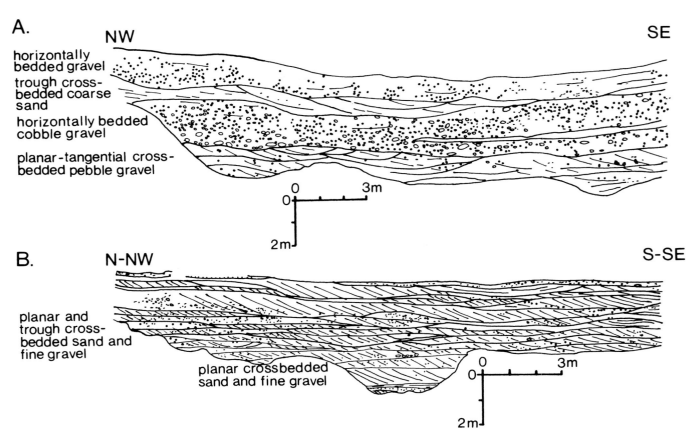

FIG. 4.—Cross-sections traced from photomosaics showing the change in grain size and bedding style of outwash in the valley of the Whitewater River, a tributary of the Ohio River, deposited: (A) at the limit of Wisconsin glaciation near Brookville, Indiana (see Fig. 1B, site 1 for location); and (B) 50 km downstream from boundary at Harrison, Ohio (see Fig. 1B, site 2 for location) (after Gruver, 1983).

extreme diurnal flow fluctuations (Smith, 1985). The absence of evidence of diurnal flow fluctuations in glacial sluiceways far from glacial margins may be due to the fact that the river systems were too large and too well-integrated to respond to events of such short duration.

Deposition during relatively short duration events, however, is probably represented by Type A units. Their thinness and relative simplicity suggest that they may be the result of storm-forced flow variation. Longer term flow variation, on the other hand, is indicated where Type B units are composed of amalgamated Type A units. The thickness and complexity of Type B units suggest that they were deposited in response to longer-term cyclic flow variations, such as an annual meltwater cycle, on which the shorter term events which deposited Type A units were superimposed (Fraser, 1993).

Muddy sediments are rare in these deposits because those deposited during slow flow were eroded during succeeding flood events, or flow in the sluiceways was never slow enough to allow deposition of mud. The presence of ripple-bedded and laminated fine sand and silt in the sediments indicates that the latter is more probably the case, suggesting that Type A sedimentation units did not form in response to daily flow fluctuations.

Lacustrine Facies.—

Lacustrine deposits, consisting dominantly of well-laminated to poorly-laminated and occasionally ripple-bedded mud, occur in many of the tributaries of glacial sluiceways (Fig. 1). Finely-laminated mud consists of horizontal, mm-scale silt-, clay-, and occasional sand-rich laminae (Fig. 5). These laminae are, in turn, grouped into cm-scale beds in which silt- or clay-rich laminae dominate. The color of the lacustrine mud lithofacies ranges from medium gray to black depending on the amount of admixed, finely macerated organic material. Peat layers and beds containing abundant shell material also occur within this facies, and there is local bioturbation (T. A. Thompson, pers. comm., 1992). The lacustrine mud facies generally forms the lower part of upward-coarsening sequences, as much as 10 m thick, that culminate in deposits of sand or sand with gravel (Fraser and Gray, 1992).

Outcrop exposures of lacustrine deposits are rare, and our understanding of them comes mainly from subsurface data. The few diagnostic features that have been identified, such as climbing ripples and thin graded beds, suggest deposition from low velocity density flows. The thickness and lateral extent of the mud lithofacies, its occurrence in up-

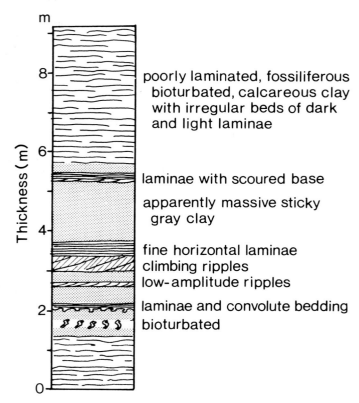

FIG. 5.—Vertical sequence through tributary lake deposits in the Prairie Creek lacustrine basin, a tributary of the White River near Washington, Indiana (see Fig. 1A, site 2 for location) (unpublished data from T. A. Thompson).

ward-coarsening vertical sequences, its occurrence in basins blocked by valley-train sediments and its lateral facies relationship with those sediments, and the occurrence of climbing ripples and graded beds suggest that the mud lithofacies represents the basinal deposits of deltas prograding into tributary basins from the trunk valley.

Wisconsin/Holocene Lithofacies

Several lithofacies developed initially during the latter Wisconsin and continued their development into the Holocene. These lithofacies accumulated in a position marginal to the alluvial fill in the valley and include eolian sand, loess, alluvial fan deposits, and paludal deposits.

Eolian Facies.—

Loess blankets the rolling uplands of southern Illinois and Indiana. Loess reaches a maximum thickness of about 15 m adjacent to the Wabash Valley but thins to a maximum uneroded thickness of about 1 m away from major drainages (Ruhe and Olson, 1978). True loess is nonstratified, oxidized, and calcareous only at depth. It is commonly mottled and crossed by root casts and iron oxide tubules. It may occur in upward-fining sequences with an upper silty zone and a lower sandy zone (Hall, 1973), or it may occur in crude cycles that exhibit variable grain size (S. Brown, written comm., 1993). It is differentiated from wind-trans-

ported silt that accumulated in lacustrine and paludal environments which is stratified, calcareous, commonly highly fossiliferous, and unoxidized with abundant disseminated organic material.

Eolian sand occurs predominantly in dune fields on the leeward sides of valleys. Dunes can be as much as 10 m high and are composed of medium fine-grained, very well-sorted sand with a very slight upward-coarsening trend. Shallow trenches in dunes reveal no stratification; the sand is massive and mottled. Rare deep exposures suggest that primary structures in dunes consist mainly of subhorizontal laminae grouped into bundles of parallel laminae a few 10's of cm thick.

Loess accumulated most rapidly during periods of glacial advance when outwash in the Wabash, White and Ohio valleys was stripped of its fine sediment by the dominant westerly winds. Eolian sand and loess accumulated concomitantly to form a continuum of sediments that thin and become finer grained away from their valley sources (Franzmeier, 1970; Frazee and others, 1970).

Paludal Facies.—

Paludal deposits consist of gray to black, laminated, clay-rich mud that is locally fossiliferous with both aquatic and non-aquatic species. Organic material is normally abundant, and layers of peat are common. Sand rarely exceeds 10 percent of paludal sediment and silt is the dominant component except near the top where sediments may consist of as much as 70 percent clay-sized material.

Swamps in the tributary valleys began to form during the latest Wisconsin, but in some cases they continued to exist until modern times when they were drained for agricultural purposes. Swamps apparently represent the final stage in the evolution of lakes in tributary valleys. They formed when tributary lakes were filled or when migrating dunes blocked drainage into trunk streams (Fraser and Gray, 1992). The lakes were filled primarily by glacially-derived sediments washing in from the trunk stream, but the swamps were filled by clastic debris derived from local sources and by wind-blown silt from the trunk stream (Fraser and Gray, 1992).

Alluvial Fan Facies.—

Alluvial fans occur at the mouths of tributaries along the margins of the Wabash Valley (Fig. 6). Sediments are coarsest grained near valley margins and along fan axes, but they fine rapidly into the valley where they become indistinguishable from floodplain sediments (Hoge, 1982). Upward-fining sequences, consisting of sandy sediments at the base that grade upward into muddy sediments, are common in fan deposits (Fig. 7).

The fans formed along the margins of the Wabash Valley after water from ancestral Lake Erie drained catastrophically down the valley during the late Wisconsin and eroded a trough in the outwash (Fraser and Bleuer, 1988; Fraser and Fleming, 1992). Floods of similar magnitude have also been identified in other glacial sluiceways, and they may be common components of the hydrographic regimens of midcontinent glaciation (Fraser and Bleuer, 1988).

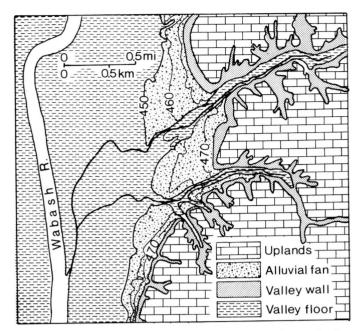

FIG. 6.—Map of a small alluvial fan extending from the mouth of an unnamed tributary onto the floodplain of the Wabash River south of Terre Haute, Indiana (see Fig. 1A, site 3 for location).

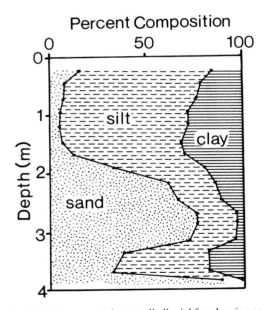

FIG. 7.—Vertical sequence in a small alluvial fan showing an upward-fininng sequence developed in response to channel establishment and abandonment on the alluvial fan extending from Sugar Creek into the valley of the Wabash River (unpublished data of R. A. Hoge).

Incision of the valley floor steepened tributary profiles and caused erosion of their valley fills. Increased sediment flux from the tributaries, along with the abrupt reduction in gradient between the valley floor of the trunk stream and its tributaries, resulted in deposition of alluvial fans at tributary mouths. Upward-fining sequences common in allu-

vial fan deposits may represent establishment and gradual abandonment of channels, or they may have been deposited during a time of channel incision when active sedimentation on fan surfaces slowed.

STRATIGRAPHIC RELATIONSHIPS

Glacial Facies

Characteristics of the glacially-derived lithofacies in the valleys suggest that valleys began to aggrade in response to increased sediment and water discharge as glaciers advanced into their drainage basins. Discharge was controlled by the seasonal meltwater cycle and storm events, and flow variations were extreme. Rivers were dominantly multi-channeled with longitudinal bars, 2-dimensional sand-waves, and associated channels. The preponderance of upward-fining sequences in Type A sedimentation units suggests that they formed in response to short-term flood events.

Bars and sandwaves were most active during flood flow. The abundance of erosional contacts between bar deposits and laterally equivalent, finer-grained channel deposits suggests that bars were modified during waning flow and were mostly inactive during low flow when active sedimentation was confined to the channels. Type A units are normally amalgamated into Type B units that were a response to longer-term flow variations. At first glance, these deposits appear as a bewildering display of remnants of depositional units and erosional surfaces. Careful discrimination of grain-size distributions, bedding characteristics, and paleoflow directions, however, has revealed that these deposits are organized into consistent facies patterns.

Lateral Relationships.—

Beyond glacial boundaries, sluiceways show systematic changes in grain size and bedding. Sediments are normally poorly sorted and very coarse near glacial boundaries with boulders common and cobbles abundant. Coarse sediments occur as crudely bedded deposits of longitudinal bars and sheet floods and as lags at the bases of channel deposits (Fig. 4A). Finer-grained sediments occur as deposits of bar-top and interbar channels. Valley-train deposits further downstream consist of sand and relatively fine gravel in planar cross-beds, trough cross-beds, and planar beds (Fig. 4B). These are the deposits of the 2-dimensional dunes and associated channel deposits that are the downstream equivalents of the longitudinal bars and channels farther upstream.

Similar lateral facies change occurs in a direction transverse to the flow. Deposits tend to be coarser grained in the center of the valley than along the margins, and bedding characteristics also suggest that sedimentation in the central part of the valley was dominated by conditions of higher basal shear. For example, valley margin equivalents of crudely-bedded, cobble-rich longitudinal bar deposits in the central part of the valley can consist of well-bedded deposits of longitudinal bars or planar cross-bedded, 2-dimensional dune deposits.

It is almost axiomatic that alluvial sediments fine downstream, and studies of glacial and non-glacial braided streams show that a concomitant change in bedding style also occurs (e.g., Smith, 1970; Boothroyd and Ashley, 1975). These changes, however, are not manifest in glacial sluiceways within glacial margins due to the multiplicity and variability of their lateral sources and to variations in channel gradient and valley width that result in random changes in flow velocity. The fact that such downstream changes do occur once sluiceways exit glaciated terrains indicates that, even though they were proglacial streams, they responded like any other large rivers to seasonal changes in sediment flux and water discharge, storm flood events, and downstream changes in valley gradient.

Preferential accumulation of coarse-grained deposits in the central part of valleys has produced a cross-valley facies distribution consisting of coarse mid-valley facies flanked by relatively finer-grained lateral facies (Figs. 8, 9). This facies differentiation of valley-train sediments may be the result of the positioning of the main anabranches of the multi-channeled streams in the center of the valleys for significantly longer periods of time than the sides.

Vertical Relationships.—

Valley-train deposits may also be arranged in upward-coarsening sequences in response to repeated advances of ice into drainage basins. Sequences are bounded by sequence boundaries consisting of erosional surfaces often marked by very coarse-grained lags. They display an upward change in the mid-valley facies from deposits domi-

nated by relatively fine-grained, cross-bedded to horizontally-bedded or massive deposits. The most obvious of these sequences begins at the base of the Wisconsin deposits where sand-rich sediments overlie boulder-rich, heavily oxidized lag deposits, but other such sequences occur within the Wisconsin deposits (Fig. 9).

Valley-train sequences formed by a process of valley downfilling as described by Schumm (1993). Sluiceways began to aggrade as ice sheets advanced into their drainage basins. Initial deposits were relatively fine-grained because of the lag time involved in arrival of coarser-grained sediments at a given position downstream, but sediment caliber coarsened rapidly as ice advanced farther into the basin and gravel-rich sediments were transported farther downvalley.

Valley Margin Relationships.—

Valley-floor aggradation dammed tributaries forming lakes in their valleys (Fraser and Gray, 1992). The resultant valley-fill architecture in those tributaries consists of tributary mouth facies, basin axis facies, and basin margin facies. The coarsest-grained valley-fill facies in tributaries occur near mouths of tributary valleys and consist of fluvial and lacustro-deltaic sand and gravel in stacked, upward-fining sequences that are overlain gradationally by upward-coarsening, lacustro-deltaic and fluvial sequences (Fig. 10). Sequences are bounded by erosional surfaces.

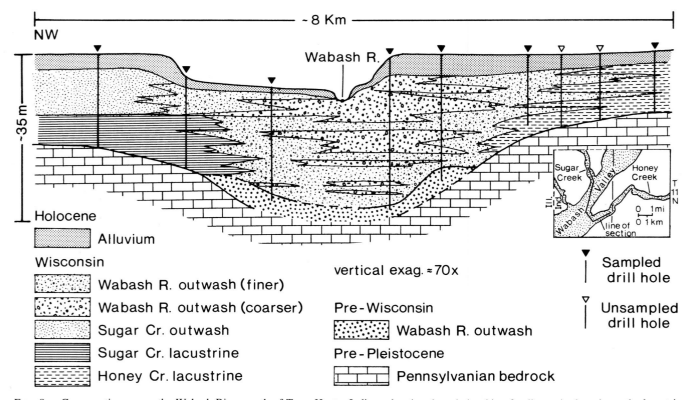

FIG. 8.—Cross-section across the Wabash River south of Terre Haute, Indiana showing the relationship of valley-train deposits to the lacustrine sediments in the Sugar Creek and Honey Creek valleys, the dominance of coarse outwash in the axis of the Wabash valley, and the relative thickness of the Holocene alluvium in the tributary valleys (see Fig. 1A, site 4 for location) (after Fraser, 1993).

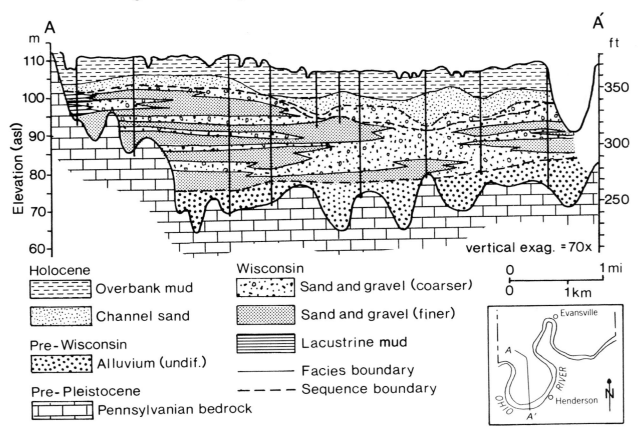

FIG. 9.—North-south cross-section across the Ohio River valley at Evansville, Indiana showing three depositional sequences separated by erosional sequence boundaries, and the occurrence of coarsest sediments along the valley axis (see Fig. 1A, site 1 for location) (after Fraser and Fishbaugh, 1986).

Lacustrine basin axes, where underflows were concentrated, are dominated by lacustrine sand. Basin axis facies consist of upward-coarsening sequences consisting of lacustrine mud at the base grading upward into silt-rich, commonly highly organic sand. These sequences may or may not be bounded by erosional surfaces (Fig. 11).

Silt-rich lacustrine muds dominate basin margin facies (Fig. 11). Sequences fine very slightly upward by an increase in clay content at the expense of the small amount of sand present except at the top where a large, abrupt increase in the amount of clay occurs at the expense of silt (Fig. 4, Fraser and Gray, 1992). Sequence boundaries are not erosional but are, instead, marked by an abrupt increase in silt content and amount of organic material.

Multiple stacked sequences formed in tributary basins as they were alternately filled and/or drained and then reoccupied by lakes (Gray, 1971; Heinrich 1982; Fraser and Gray, 1992). Initially, upward-fining fluvial sequences were deposited in response to rising local base level (Fig. 10). Upward fining continued as water levels rose, and as the lakes expanded, onlap sequences were deposited. Eventually, however, the lakes were fully established and a pattern of offlapping, upward-coarsening lacustrine sedimentation prevailed. This pattern consisted of sandy deltaic wedges deposited into the basin primarily from the trunk stream and

secondarily from upstream reaches (Fig. 10). Underflows at the prodelta slope deposited sandy muds along basin axes, and laminated muds settled from suspension along lake margins.

Lakes formed during periods of ice advance and drained during intervening periods of ice retreat when outwash in the trunk valleys was eroded and outlets were established in tributary mouth dams. Each sequence was deposited on an erosional sequence boundary that formed as streams were reestablished on exposed lake surfaces. The most obvious of these sequence boundaries is at the base of the Wisconsin deposits. For example, pre-Wisconsin deposits are deeply eroded in the Prairie Creek lake basin, and fluvial deposits occur at the base of the eroded trough (Fig. 11). The fluvial deposits fine upward into the first of the subsequent lacustrine sequences. These sequences are also separated by erosional sequence boundaries although they are not nearly as well developed as that at the base of the Wisconsin.

The final sequence in the Prairie Creek lake basin did not develop as a direct result of alluviation of the trunk stream. The basin drained following final withdrawal of ice from the White River drainage basin about 13 ka, and a channel system was established on the exposed lake plain. However, the outlet was later blocked by migrating dunes about 10 ka and a shallow lake was reestablished that quickly

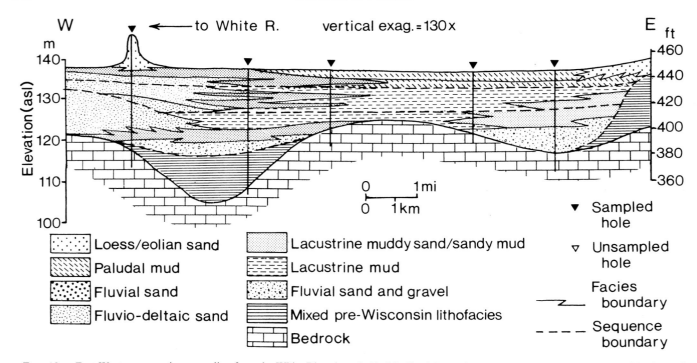

FIG. 10.—East-West cross-section extending from the White River into the Prairie Creek lacustrine basin showing the relationship of the lacustrine deposits in the basin to the valley-train alluvium in the White River, the internal arrangement of the lithofacies in the lacustrine and paludal deposits, and their relationship to erosional sequence boundaries (see Fig. 1A, site 5 for location) (after Fraser and Gray, 1992).

evolved into an extensive marsh (Figs. 10, 11) that existed until an outlet was reestablished about 4 ka.

Nonglacial Facies

The principal nonglacial facies are channel and overbank deposits of single channel, sinuous streams. The genetic and stratigraphic relationships between these two components have been described at length in the literature and need not be further explored here. There are, however, some aspects of the architecture of the nonglacial alluvium and its relationship to the underlying Wisconsin deposits that are specific to its post-glacial origin.

Basal Contact.—

Perhaps the most notable of these aspects is the inset stratigraphic relationship that Holocene alluvium normally has with the Pleistocene valley train (Figs. 8, 9). Shallow troughs were cut into the outwash in the central parts of valleys leaving valley-train terraces along the valley sides. The resulting erosional surface may consist of a relatively flat-based trough cut into the coarse outwash, or the base of the trough may be a highly irregular surface. In either case, the surface is normally marked by a gravel lag and/or an abrupt change in grain size.

Holocene channel and overbank alluvium, as much as 10 m thick, fill these troughs whereas only overbank muds mantle the terraces. Because they are raised above the level of the floodplain, these terraces are flooded only occasionally, and long-term depositional rates are very slow (Fraser and Fishbaugh, 1986).

Erosion of the underlying Pleistocene fluvial deposits began during the transition into the Holocene hydraulic regime. Erosion may reflect a change from proximal to distal channel system types associated with ice recession or climatically-induced changes in magnitude and variabilty of water discharge, a change in the quantity and caliber of the sediment load or a combination of all of these factors (Maizells, 1983; Autin and others, 1991). In some places, the erosion continues today as channels migrate across valley floors.

Occasionally, Pleistocene gravel bars are exposed during lateral migration of channels. Because of the coarseness of their sediments, channels tend to migrate around these gravel bars leaving them as palimpsest features of channel floors and, in the process, producing an irregular base to the Holocene sequence. These bars tend to localize subsequent deposition of Holocene sands as the channel migrates around them (Fig. 12), and eventually they are incorporated into laterally accreting floodplains (Fraser, 1986). There they are expressed as ridges that are appreciably wider and lenticular in shape, unlike the narrow and elongate scroll bar ridges. Like scroll bar ridges, however, they served to localize deposition of silt-rich overbank alluvium in contrast to the clay-rich organic muds that occur in the swales.

Lateral Relationships.—

There is a significant difference between the degree of development of relatively fine-grained alluvium in trunk valleys and those tributaries entering downstream reaches of the trunk streams which typically have thicker deposits

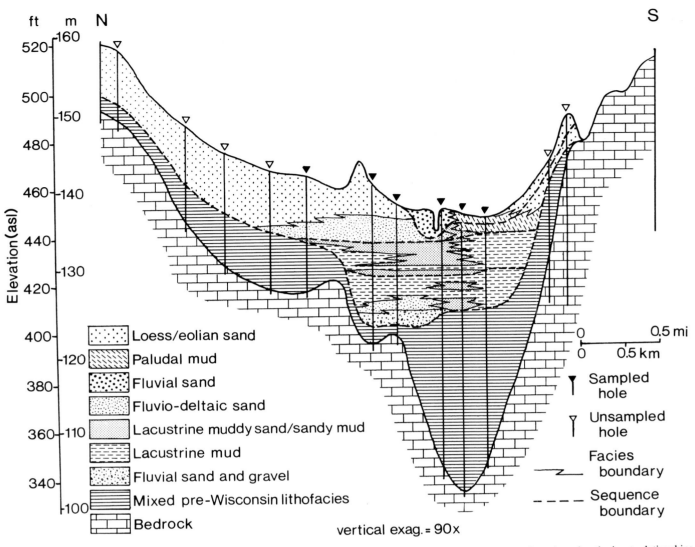

FIG. 11.—Cross-section across the Prairie Creek lacustrine basin showing the deep incision of the pre-Wisconsinan deposits, the inset relationships with the succeeding Wisconsinan deposits and their arrangement into sequences separated by erosional sequence boundaries, the upward-fining sequence at the base of the Wisconsinan deposits, the facies relationship between eolian and paludal deposits at the top of the valley fill, and the fractionation of the lacustrine deposits into axial and lateral facies (see Fig. 1A, site 5 for location) (after Fraser and Gray, 1992).

of Holocene alluvium, especially overbank muds, than the trunk stream (Fig. 8).

Alluvial fans occur at mouths of tributaries where they enter the valleys of trunk streams. Alluvial fan deposits of the larger tributaries tend to have erosional contacts with the underlying valley-train sediments. Fan deposits of smaller tributaries tend not to have erosional basal contacts although the change in grain size between alluvial fan deposits and the underlying valley-train sediments is typically abrupt. Fan deposits of both large and small tributaries have lateral gradational contacts with Holocene overbank alluvium in the floodplain. In addition, these fans tend to show a gross upward-fining sequence although in detail the sequences may be quite variable.

Thickest deposits of eolian sand and loess occur on the lee side of valleys. Somewhat thinner deposits of loess oc-

cur in the uplands immediately adjacent to the valley, and thin loess deposits may extend 100's of kilometers away from their sources. They rest with a hiatal contact on soils developed on bedrock and earlier glacially-derived sediments, but they may have facies relationships with Holocene overbank alluvium in the trunk valley and paludal deposits in tributary valleys. Dunes are currently inactive and covered with vegetation, and artifacts from prehistoric Native Americans found on dune surfaces are estimated to be 10,000 to 11,000 years old (Fraser and Gray, 1992).

Tributaries entering downstream reaches of trunk streams tend to have thicker deposits of Recent alluvium because they ceased to carry outwash before valley-train sedimentation ceased in the main channel. The transition to Holocene conditions of sediment and water discharge in tributary streams, thus, predated that in the trunk stream, but

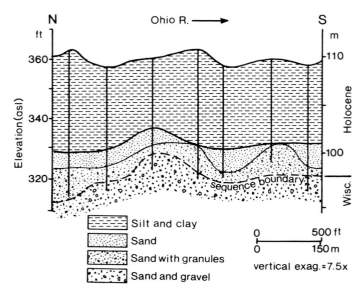

FIG. 12.—Cross-section through the upper part of the alluvial fill in the Ohio River valley near Evansville, Indiana showing the relationship of the Holocene channel and overbank alluvium to the underlying Pleistocene gravel ridge (see Fig. 1A, site 1 for location) (after Fraser, 1986).

the shallow gradients that existed in these tributaries due to alluviation of the trunk stream remained shallow, and their rates of alluviation remained high.

Alluvial fans formed at margins of valleys during the latest Wisconsin and Holocene when valley-train outwash was incised and steep gradients were formed where tributaries entered the valleys. The increased gradient probably allowed large tributaries to develop sufficient shear to initially erode channels through coarse-grained outwash, but it also caused rejuvenation of these streams and the delivery of large volumes of sediment that were deposited as fans at valley mouths. The upward-fining sequences may be the result of any one of several mechanisms that operate during the evolution of a fan and its source area (Fraser and Suttner, 1986). Initial rejuvenation of the source area may have eventually given way to renewed storage and the delivery of progressively smaller amounts of finer-grained material. Incision of feeder channels into fan surfaces may have allowed coarse sediment to bypass fans, and avulsion or lateral migration of fan head channels may also have resulted in the deposition of upward-fining sequences.

The bulk of the loess and eolian sand in glacial sluiceways were probably deposited during glacial advances. Thickest accumulations were deposited during the late Wisconsin, but these commonly overlie earlier Wisconsin and pre-Wisconsin deposits (Hall, 1973; Ruhe and Olson, 1978). Johnson (1965) suggests that loess deposition ceased about 14 ka when ice withdrew from the Wabash River basin. McKay (1979), however, gave a date of 10 ka for cessation of loess deposition, and Fraser and Gray (1992) believe that windblown silt was still accumulating in tributary basins during the early Holocene, and that dunes were active until about 10,000 years ago on the basis of the age of cultural remains on the eolian dunes on the east side of the White

River valley. Therefore, it is likely that sand and silt continued to be eroded from valley floors and deposited at valley margins during the early Holocene before a complete vegetative cover was established on flood-plain surfaces.

SUMMARY AND CONCLUSIONS

Broad, flat-floored bedrock valleys were incised during the late Tertiary in the north-central U. S. Narrow, v-shaped valleys were later eroded into these valley floors, possibly in response to climatically-induced changes in hydrography during the early Pleistocene or to diversion of drainage patterns by advancing glaciers. The lithofacies that filled these valleys during the Quaternary were deposited and post-depositionally modified in response to widely varying conditions of water and sediment discharge, climate, and vegetation. The resultant valley-fill architecture reflects the complex interaction of all these variables.

Pre-Pleistocene deposits have not yet been encountered in the glacial sluiceways of Indiana. The oldest deposits that have been identified are pre-Wisconsin, possibly Illinoian in age. In most places these consist of consolidated valley-train outwash capped by an oxidized boulder-cobble lag. In at least one place in the Ohio River Valley, the pre-Wisconsin outwash is overlain by an upward-fining sequence that may have been deposited by a single-channel stream during an interstadial period (Fig. 13A). Pre-Wisconsin deposits in tributary valleys consist of locally-derived alluvium and/or lacustrine deposits (Fig. 13B, C).

Sand and gravel outwash of Wisconsin age comprises the bulk of the sediments in the valleys. Downvalley changes from coarse-grained outwash deposits of longitudinal bars to finer-grained deposits of 2-dimensional dunes are reflected in the upward-coarsening, valley downfilling sequences. Similar cross-valley variations produced a transverse fractionation of the outwash into coarse-grained mid-valley and finer-grained valley margin facies (Fig. 13A). Sequences were deposited during episodes of glacial advance into the drainage basins, and they are separated by erosional sequence boundaries that formed during periods when ice had retreated from drainage basins.

Lakes, formed in tributary valleys as trunk valleys aggraded during glacial events, were filled primarily by sediments washing in from the trunk valley and secondarily by sediments derived from the local drainage (Fig. 13C). Successive periods of aggradation and erosion in the trunk valley correspond to periods of lake expansion and draining, leading to stacked lake-filling sequences separated by erosional sequence boundaries. The most prominent sequence boundary occurs at the Wisconsin/pre-Wisconsin boundary where Wisconsin lacustrine sediments are inset deeply within the trough eroded in the pre-Wisconsin sediments (Fig. 13C).

Deltaic deposits at tributary mouths pass upvalley into muddy sands deposited by density currents and then into muds that settled from suspension. Coarser-grained sediments were confined to basin axes, and finer-grained muds accumulated in areas lateral to the axes producing a fractionation of the incoming sediments into axial and lateral facies (Fig. 13C). Lakeward progradation of tributary mouth deltas resulted in upward-coarsening sequences except where

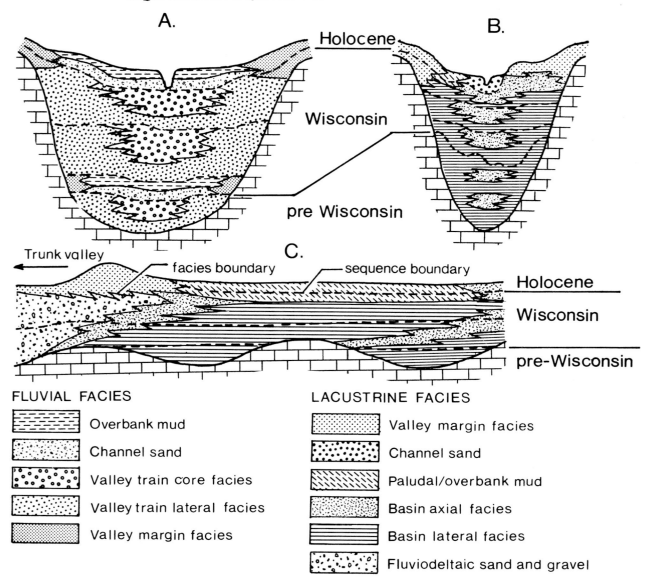

FIG. 13.—Diagrammatic representations of the Quaternary sediments filling incised valleys beyond glacial margins showing: (A) a transverse cross-section through alluvial fill showing concentration of coarse outwash in the valley axis and finer ouwash toward valley margins, coarsening upward sequences separated be erosional sequences boundaries, inset relationship between interstadial stream deposits and glacial outwash, and lateral facies relationships of interstadial and late stage glacial sediments with valley-margin facies; (B) transverse cross-section through lacustrine fill showing the deeply inset relationship between Wisconsinan and pre-Wisconsinan deposits, relationship between axial and lateral lacustrine facies, upward-coarsening sequences separated by erosional sequence boundaries, and the facies relationship between eolian, and fluvio-deltaic and paludal sediments capping the fill; (C) longitudinal cross-section showing the relationship between lacustrine deposits in the tributary valley ith outwash in the trunk stream, upward-fining sequence of fluvial deposits formed during lacustrine onlap, and upward-coarsening sequences formed by lacustrine offlap.

locally-derived sediments accumulated in upward-fining, onlap sequences during episodes of lake expansion (Fig. 13C).

Highly fossiliferous, laminated muds rich in organic debris accumulated in swamps in tributary valleys as lakes filled. The most notable of these cap the Wisconsin sequences in these valleys, but paludal deposits, in the form of dark gray and black fossiliferous muds with occasional peat layers, were also deposited during earlier periods of lake-shallowing at sequence boundaries.

Lithofacies that developed along margins of trunk valleys include loess, eolian sand, and alluvial fan sand and mud. Loess forms thick deposits along valley margins, but thinner deposits blanket upland hills. Eolian sand accumulated in dune fields at valley margins. Maximum rates of accumulation occurred during the various glacial events of the Wisconsin and pre-Wisconsin, but deposition at a reduced rate probably also took place during interstadials.

Fluvial deposits as much as 50 m thick occur in the incised valleys beyond glacial margins, and they consist of stacked sequences separated by sequence boundaries that developed in response to changes in water discharge and sediment caliber and discharge. Conditions in the trunk streams in turn influenced sedimentation in tributaries where other types of sequences evolved concurrently. It is perhaps instructive that such thick and areally widespread successions can develop without regard to variations in base level.

It might be argued that inferences derived from such successions cannot be widely applied because the differences between glacial meltwater processes and fluvial processes during interglacials or interstadials were so extreme. However, these rivers were simply responding to hydrographic variations; such changes might also be expected in response to tectonic events or during less dramatic changes in climate. Care must be taken to discriminate between these possible influences and the effects of base-level changes when using stratigraphic successions in river valleys to document eustatic changes in sea level.

REFERENCES

AUTIN, W. J., 1985, Alluvial morphology and stratigraphy of a meandering segment of the Amite River, southeastern Louisiana: Southeastern Geology, v. 26, p. 95–110.

AUTIN, W. J., 1992, Use of alloformations for deposition of Holocene meander belts in the middle Amite River, southeastern Louisiana: Geological Society of America Bulletin, v. 104, p. 233–241.

AUTIN, W. J., BURNS, S. F., MILLER, B. J., SAUCIER, R. T., AND SNEAD, J. I., 1991, Quaternary geology of the lower Mississippi Valley, in Morrison, R. B., ed., Quaternary Nonglacial Geology: Conterminous United States: Boulder, Geological Society of America, p. 547–582.

BETTIS, E. A., III, 1990, Holocene alluvial stratigraphy in western Iowa, in Bettis, E. A., III, ed, Holocene Alluvial Stratigraphy and Selected Aspects of the Quaternary History of Western Iowa: Iowa City, Midwest Friends of the Pleistocene, 37th Field Conference, Iowa Quaternary Studies Group Contribution No. 36, p. 1–16.

BLEUER, N. K., 1991, The Lafayette Bedrock System of Indiana: concept, form, and till stratigraphy, in Melhorn, W. N., and Kempton, J. P., eds., Geology and Hydrology of the Teays-Mahomet Bedrock Valley System: Boulder, Geological Society of America Special Paper 258, p. 51–77.

BOOTHROYD, J. C., AND ASHLEY, G. M., 1975, Process, bar morphology, and sedimentary structures on braided outwash fans, northeastern Gulf of Alaska, in Jopling, A. V., and McDonald, B. C., eds., Glaciofluvial and Glaciolacustrine Sedimentation: Tulsa, Society of Economic Paleolontologists and Mineralogists Special Publication 23, p. 193–222.

BRAKENRIDGE, G. R., 1981, Late Quaternary floodplain sedimentation along the Pomme de Terre River, southern Missouri: Quaternary Research, v. 15, p. 62–76.

BRAKENRIDGE, G. R., 1984, Alluvial stratigraphy and radiocarbon dating along the Duck River, Tennessee: Implications regarding floodplain origin: Geological Society of America Bulletin, v. 95, p. 9–25.

BRIDGE, J. S., 1984, Large-scale facies sequences in alluvial overbank environments: Journal of Sedimentary Petrology, v. 54, p. 583–588.

BURNETT, A. W., AND SCHUMM, S. A., 1983, Active tectonics and river response in Louisiana and Mississippi: Science, v. 22, p. 49–50.

CANT, D. J., AND WALKER, R. G., 1978, Fluvial processes and facies sequences in the sandy, braided South Saskatchewan River: Sedimentology, v. 25, p. 625–648.

DAVIESS, D. K., 1966, Sedimentary structures and subfacies of a Mississippi River point bar: Journal of Geology, v. 74, p. 234–239.

FARREL, K. M., 1987, Sedimentology and facies architecture of overbank deposits of the Mississippi River, False River region, Louisiana, in Etheridge, F. G., Flores, R. M., and Harvey, M. D., eds., Recent developments in fluvial sedimentology: Tulsa, Society of Economic Paleontologists and Mineralogists Special Publication 39, p. 111–120.

FISK, H. N., 1944, Geological investigations of the alluvial valley of the lower Mississippi River: Vicksburg, United States Army Corps of Engineers, Mississippi River Commission, 78 p.

FRANZMEIER, D. P., 1970, Particle size sorting of proglacial eolian materials: Soil Science Society of America Proceedings, v. 34, p. 920–924.

FRASER, G. S., 1993, Sedimentation in an interlobate outwash stream: Sedimentary Geology, v. 83, p. 53–70.

FRASER, G. S., 1993, Sedimentology and history of the late Wisconsinan alluviation of the Wabash Valley: Bloomington, Indiana Geological Survey Special Report 56, 18 p.

FRASER, G. S., 1986, Origin of mid-channel islands in the Ohio River near Evansville, Indiana: Bloomington, Indiana Geological Survey Special Report 38, 15 p.

FRASER, G. S., AND BLEUER, N. K., 1988, Sedimentological consequences of two floods of extreme magnitude in the late Wisconsin Wabash Valley, in Clifton, H. E., ed. Sedimentological Consequences of Convulsive Events: Boulder, Geological Society of America Special Paper 229, p. 111–125.

FRASER, G. S. AND FISHBAUGH, D. A., 1986, Alluviation of the Ohio River Valley near Evansville, and its effect on the distribution of sand and gravel in the area: Bloomington, Indiana Geological Survey Special Report 36, 26 p.

FRASER, G. S., AND FLEMING, A. H., 1992, History of late Wisconsinan runoff from the Laurentide ice sheet (abs.): Geological Society of America, Abstracts with Programs, v. 24, p. A 274.

FRASER, G. S., AND GRAY, H. H., 1992, Quaternary evolution of the Prairie Creek lake basin, Daviess County, Indiana: Bloomington, Indiana Geological Survey Special Report 53, 20 p.

FRASER, G. S., AND SUTTNER, L. J., 1986, Alluvial fans and fan deltas: Boston, International Human Resources Development Corporation, 199 p.

FRAZEE, C. J., FEHRENBACHER, J. B., AND KRUMBEIN, W. C., 1970, Loess distribution from a source: Soil Science Society of America Proceedings, v. 34, p. 296–301.

GALLAHER, J. T., AND PRICE, W. E., 1966, Hydrology of the alluvial deposits in the Ohio River valley in Kentucky: United States Geological Survey Water-Supply Paper 1818, 80 p.

GRAY, H. H., 1971, Glacial lake deposits in southern Indiana; Engineering problems and land-use: Bloomington, Indiana Geological Survey Report of Progress 30, 15 p.

GRAY, H. H., 1984, Archeological sedimentology of overbank silt deposits on the floodplain of the Ohio River near Louisville, Kentucky: Journal of Archeological Science, v. 11, p. 421–432.

GRAY, H. H., 1991, Origin and history of the Teays drainage system, in Melhorn, W. N., and Kempton, J. P., eds., Geology and Hydrogeology of the Teays-Mahomet Bedrock Valley System: Boulder, Geological Society of America Special Paper 258, p. 43–50.

GRAY, H. H., WAYNE, W. J., WIER, C. E., KLEGG, K. E., AND WILLMAN, H. B., 1970, Geologic Map of the 1° × 2° Vincennes Quadrangle and parts of adjoining quadrangles, Indiana and Illinois, showing bedrock and unconsolidated deposits: Bloomington, Indiana Geological Survey Regional Geologic Map 3.

GRAY, H. H., FORSYTH, J. L., SCHNEIDER, A. F., AND GOODING, A. M., 1972, Geologic map of the 1° × 2° Cincinnati Quadrangle, Indiana and Ohio, showing bedrock and unconsolidated deposits: Bloomington, Indiana Geological Survey Regional Geologic Map 7.

GRAY, H. H., FRASER, G. S., MUNSON, C. A., 1983, Evolution of the ridged floodplain of the Ohio River: Archeological implications, in Shaver, R. H., and Sunderman J. A., eds., Field Trips in Midwestern Geology: Boulder, Geological Society of America, Indiana Geological Survey, Department of Geology, Indiana University, p. 198–213.

GRISSINGER, E. H., AND MURPHEY, J. B., 1983, Present channel stability and late Quaternary valley deposits in northern Mississippi, in Collinson, J. D., and Lewin, J., eds., Modern and Ancient Fluvial Systems: Oxford, International Association of Sedimentologists Special Publication 6, p. 241–250.

GRUVER, B. L., 1983, Pleistocene valley train deposition, Whitewater River, southeastern Indiana: Unpublished M.S. Thesis, Indiana University, Bloomington, 145 p.

HALL, R. D., 1973, Stratigraphy of the Wisconsinan loess and the Sangamon paleosol in southwestern Indiana (abs.): Geological Society of America Abstracts with Programs, v. 5, p. 649.

HARTKE, E. J., HAILER, J. G., AND FRASER, G. S., 1983, Environmental geology of Vigo County, Indiana—An aid to planning: Bloomington, Indiana Geological Survey Special Report 31, 58 p.

HARVEY, E. J., 1956, Geology and groundwater resources of the Henderson area, Kentucky: Washington, D, C., United States Geological Survey Water-Supply Paper 1356, 227 p.

HEINRICH, P. V., 1982, Geomorphology and sedimentology of Pleistocene Lake Saline, southern Illinois: Unpublished Ph.D. Thesis, University of Illinois, Urbana, 145 p.

HOGE, R. J., 1982, Fluvial sedimentation around the Wabash River and Sugar Creek: Unpublished B.S. Thesis, DePauw University, Greencastle, 22 p.

HORBERG, C. L., 1945, A major buried valley in east-central Illinois and its regional relationships: Journal of Geology, v. 53, p. 349–359.

JACKSON, R. G., II, 1975, Velocity-bedform-texture patterns of meander bends in the lower Wabash River of Illinois and Indiana: Geological Society of America Bulletin, v. 86, p. 1511–1522.

JACKSON, R. G., II, 1976, Depositional model of point bars in the lower Wabash River: Journal of Sedimentary Petrology, v. 46, p. 579–594.

JACKSON, R. G. II, 1980, Sedimentology of the modern meander belt of the Vermilion River (Illinois and Indiana, U.S.A.) and its significance for lithofacies models of meandering alluvial streams, *in* Fraser, G. S., ed., Sediments of the modern meander belt of the Vermilion River near Eugene, Indiana and Sedimentology of the late Wisconsinan terrace deposits along the bend area of the Wabash River: Field Trip Guidebook, 10th Annual Meeting, Great Lakes Section-SEPM, p. 17–44.

JOHNSON, G. H., 1965, The stratigraphy, paleontology, and paleoecology of the Peoria Loess (Upper Pleistocene) of southwestern Indiana: Unpublished Ph.D. Thesis, Indiana University, Bloomington, 229p.

JORDAN, D. W., AND PRYOR, W. A., 1992, Hierarchical levels of heterogeneity in a Mississippi River meander belt and application to reservoir systems: American Association of Petroleum Geologists Bulletin, v. 76, p. 1601–1624.

MAIZELLS, J. K., 1983, Proglacial channel systems: change and thresholds for change over long, intermediate, and short time-scales: *in* Collinson, J. D., and Lewin, J., eds., Modern and ancient fluvial systems, International Association of Sedimentologists Special Publication 6, p. 251–265.

MANSFIELD, G. R., 1938, Flood deposits of the Ohio River, January-February 1937: Washington, D. C., United States Geological Survey Water-Supply Paper 838, p. 693–736.

MCKAY, E. D., 1979, Wisconsinan loess stratigraphy of Illinois: Urbana, Illinois State Geological Survey Guidebook 13, p. 95–108

MELHORN, W. N., AND KEMPTON, J. P., eds., 1991, Geology and hydrogeology of the Teays-Mahomet bedrock valley system: Boulder, Geological Society of America Special Paper 258, 128 p.

POTTER, P. E., PRYOR, W. A., SMITH, L. M., AND RICH, D., 1988, Teaching and field guide to alluvial processes and sedimentation of the Mississippi River, Fulton County, Kentucky, and Lake County, Tennessee: Lexington, Kentucky Geological Survey, 46 p.

PRICE, W. E., JR., 1964, Geology and hydrology of alluvial deposits along the Ohio River between southwestern Louisville and West Point, Kentucky: Washington, D. C., United States Geological Survey Hydrologic Investigation Atlas HA-111.

RAY, L. L., 1965, Geomorphology and Quaternary geology of the Owensboro Quadrangle, Indiana and Kentucky: Washington, D. C., United States Geological Survey Professional Paper 488, 72 p.

RAY, L. L., 1966, Pre-Wisconsin glacial deposits in northern Kentucky: Washington, D. C., United States Geological Survey Professional Paper 550-B, p. B91-B94.

RAY, P., 1976, Structure and sedimentological history of the overbank deposits of a Mississippi River point bar: Journal of Sedimentary Petrology, v. 46, p. 788–801.

RUHE, R. V., AND OLSON, C. G., 1978, Loess stratigraphy and paleosols in southwestern Indiana: Bloomington, Midwest Friends of the Pleistocene Guidebook, 25th Field Conference, Indiana University, 72 p.

SCHUMM, S. A., 1987, The effect of active tectonics on alluvial rivers, *in* Studies in Geophysics, Active Tectonics: Washington, D.C., National Academy Press, p. 80–94.

SCHUMM, S. A., 1993, River response to baselevel change: Implications for sequence stratigraphy: Journal of Geology, v. 101, p. 279–294.

SMITH, N. D., 1970, The braided stream depositional environment: Comparison of the Platte River with some Silurian clastic rocks, north central Appalachians: Geological Society of America Bulletin, v. 81, p. 2993–3014

SMITH, N. D., 1985, Proglacial fluvial environments, *in* Ashley, G. M., Shaw, J., and Smith, N. D., eds., Glacial Sedimentary Environments: Tulsa, Society of Economic Paleontologists and Mineralogists Short Course 16, p. 135–238.

STRAW, W. T., 1968a, Geomorphology, hydrogeology and economic geology of the Ohio River valley, Mauckport to Cannelton, Indiana: Unpublished Ph.D. Dissertation, Indiana University, Bloomington, 182 p.

STRAW, W. T., 1968b, The upper alluvial terrace along the Ohio River in south central Indiana: Indiana Academy of Science, v. 77, p. 231–235.

STRAW, W. T., GRAY, H. H., AND POWELL, R. L., 1977, Environmental geology of the Evansville area, southwestern Indiana: Bloomington, Indiana Geological Survey Special Report 12, 8 p.

THEISS, C. V., 1922, The geology of Henderson County, Kentucky: Unpublished Ph.D. Thesis, University of Cincinnati, Cincinnati, 215 p.

WALKER, E. H, 1957, The deep channel and alluvial deposits of the Ohio Valley in Kentucky: Washington, D. C., United States Geological Survey Water-Supply Paper 1411, 25 p.

WAYNE, W. J., 1952, Pleistocene evolution of the Ohio and Wabash valleys: Journal of Geology, v. 60, p. 575–585.

WAYNE, W. J., 1963, Glacial geology of Indiana: Bloomington, Indiana Geological Survey, Atlas of Mineral Resources of Indiana Map 10.

WEBB, W. M., 1970, Sand and gravel resources of the Ohio River valley-Lawrenceburg to Jeffersonville, Indiana: Harrisburg, Pennsylvania Geological Survey Mineral Resources Report M-64, p. 23–42.

HIGH-FREQUENCY SEQUENCES AND THE NATURE OF INCISED-VALLEY FILLS IN FLUVIAL SYSTEMS OF THE BREATHITT GROUP (PENNSYLVANIAN), APPALACHIAN FORELAND BASIN, EASTERN KENTUCKY

JOHN F. AITKEN AND STEPHEN S. FLINT

Department of Earth Sciences, Jane Herdman Laboratories, University of Liverpool, Liverpool, L69 3BX, United Kingdom

ABSTRACT: The fluvio-deltaic Pikeville, Hyden, and Four Corners Formations of the Breathitt Group in eastern Kentucky represent three superimposed 3rd-order composite sequences comprising stacked aggradational, progradational, and retrogradational 4th-order sequences. These define lowstand, transgressive, and highstand sequence sets. Incised-valley fill (IVF) deposits overlie the sequence boundaries and are predominantly characterised by fluvial sandstone fill with only limited fine-grained partings. Third-order IVF's are thicker and more laterally extensive than 4th-order variants and also contain parasequences related to 4th-order cyclicity. IVFs were deposited during aggradation when the accommodation rate was in equilibrium with sediment supply.

Each sequence set has a distinctive stacking pattern of 4th-order IVFs in terms of the degree of incision and the amount of transgressive and highstand deposits preserved between, 4th-order sequence boundaries. The lowstand sequence set contains the most amalgamated IVFs while the transgressive sequence set contains the least amalgamated.

The position of 4th-order sequences on a 3rd-order relative sea-level curve is critical in controlling both the fill and stacking of IVFs. The stacking of 4th-order sequences into sequence sets has important implications for hydrocarbon exploration and production. The number of individual sandstone beds within 4th-order sequences offers multiple stacked reservoir targets, especially within the lowstand sequence set, which contains the greatest proportion of sandstone.

INTRODUCTION

Previous sequence-stratigraphic research has largely been concentrated on shallow and marginal-marine strata (e.g., Jervey, 1988; Van Wagoner and others, 1990). Apart from the conceptual framework of Posamentier and Vail (1988) and the field-based studies of Shanley and McCabe (1991a, b, 1993) few attempts have been made to apply sequence-stratigraphic concepts to fluvial successions. The aim of this study is to describe the internal architecture and stacking pattern of incised-valley fills of fluvio-deltaic deposits from the Pennsylvanian Breathitt Group of eastern Kentucky within the context of high-frequency sequences.

Sequence-stratigraphic principles provide guidelines from which to ascertain sand-body stacking patterns and, thus, the areal distribution of genetic facies units within the successions. Four, 3rd-order sequence boundaries and 11, 4th-order sequence boundaries have been identified. The identification of these sequence boundaries, their related incised-valley fills and the sets into which the sequences stack, provides a tool to handle stratigraphic complexity and has important implications for reservoir exploration and prediction.

In the Appalachian Basin of eastern Kentucky, the studied portion of the Breathitt Group is well exposed in a series of roadcuts for circa 110 km NNE-SSW along US Highway 23 (US 23), between Louisa and Pikeville and for circa 67.5 km ENE-WSW along Kentucky Highway 80 (Ky 80), between Prestonsburg and Hazard (Fig. 1). The sinuous nature of the roads permits (limited) three-dimensional analysis of stratal surfaces and sand-body geometry. The excellent exposure and well-established lithostratigraphy of the road outcrops were prerequisite to choosing this area for high-resolution sedimentological and stratigraphic analysis. The fluvio-deltaic deposits of the Breathitt Group provide a good test for the high-frequency sequence-stratigraphic concepts of Van Wagoner and others (1990) and Mitchum and Van Wagoner (1991), and the conceptual model of the sequence stratigraphy of fluvial deposits of Posamentier and Vail (1988). Furthermore, the maximum glaciation of Gondwanaland occurred in the middle to late Pennsylvanian period (Veevers and Powell, 1987), and relative changes of sea level have been variously estimated to be a minimum of 50–70 m (e.g., Adlis and others, 1988; Crowley and Baum, 1991) and a maximum of 100–200 m (e.g., Heckel, 1977). Donaldson and Eble (1991) compared Appalachian Basin allocycles with Veevers and Powell's (1987) inferred Gondwanaland ice volume and global sea-level curve, which indicated that at least some of the Appalachian allocycles may be glacioeustatic in origin.

STRATIGRAPHY

The Pennsylvanian deposits of eastern Kentucky crop out in an area of about 27,000 km^2 and occupy the central part of the Appalachian foreland basin that extends from New York to Alabama (Fig. 1). The rocks form a clastic wedge that thickens south-eastward towards the axis of the Appalachian Basin and attain a maximum thickness of 1400 m along the Kentucky-West Virginia border (Rice, 1981). These sediments originated as siliciclastic debris eroded from highlands along the southeastern margin of the basin during the early stages of the Alleghenian orogeny (Tankard, 1986; Englund and Thomas, 1989). Northwestward-prograding delta lobes and fluvial systems deposited sediment in a slowly subsiding foreland basin. Simultaneously, marine deposition encroached from the northwest in a shallow epicontinental sea which covered an unstable cratonic shelf (Englund and Thomas, 1989).

The Breathitt Group (Chesnut, pers. commun., 1992) comprises eight lithostratigraphic units, as proposed by Chesnut (1988a, b), of which three, the Pikeville, Hyden, and Four Corners Formations, are considered here (Fig. 2). The Breathitt Group, up to 950 m thick in eastern Kentucky, comprises delta-plain facies of siltstone, clay-rich shale, sandstone, coal, siderite, and rare limestone. Chesnut (pers. commun., 1992) calculated the average ages of the top and the base of the Breathitt to be circa 303 Ma (Westphalian-Stephanian boundary) and circa 323 Ma (Namurian A-B boundary), respectively. Consequently, each

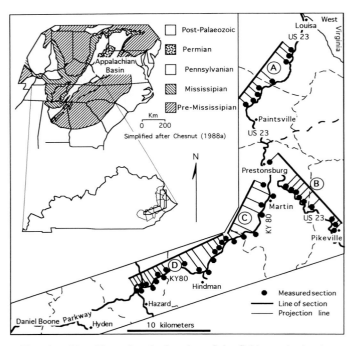

FIG. 1.—Map illustrating the location of the field area in the Appalachian basin, the distribution of measured sections in eastern Kentucky and the lines of section.

Formation (Chesnut, 1988a, 1988b)	Coal beds (Rice & Smith, 1980; Chesnut, 1988b)	Marine strata (Chesnut, 1991a)
Princess Formation		Stoney Fork
Four Corners Formation	Hindman Coal	Bulan Shale Member
	Francis Coal	Member O
	Hazard No. 7 coal	Cowcreek Shale Member
	Hazard Coal	Member N
	Haddix Coal	Magoffin Member
Hyden Formation	Taylor Coal	Member M
	Hamlin Coal	Member L
	Fire Clay Rider Coal	Member K
	Fire Clay Coal	Member J
	Upper Whitesburg Coal	Member I
	Lower Whitesburg Coal	Kendrick Shale Member
Pikeville Formation	Amburgy Coal	Elkins Fork Shale
	Darby Coal	Dwale Shale
	Upper Elkhorn No. 3 Coal	Member H
	Upper Elkhorn No. 2 Coal	Member G
	Upper Elkhorn No. 1 Coal	Crummies Shale Member
	Lower Elkhorn Coal	Member F
	Little Blue gem Coal	Betsie Shale Member
Grundy Formation	Manchester Coal	

(BREATHITT GROUP)

FIG. 2.—Lithostratigraphy of the Pikeville, Hyden and Four Corners Formations.

Formation within the Breathitt Group was deposited in an average of circa 2.5 Ma (Chesnut, 1989).

The traditional model of deposition for the Carboniferous in eastern Kentucky equates all the units from late Mississippian to middle Pennsylvanian age as a series of penecontemporaneous lateral facies associations (e.g., Horne and others, 1978). All adjacent lithologies within this stratigraphic interval were thought to represent separate facies in a single environmental continuum. This model included strata deposited in open marine and fully continental environments separated by barrier bar, lagoonal and delta-plain environments (Ferm and others, 1971; Ferm and Horne, 1979). The Breathitt Group was placed in the lower, transitional and upper delta-plain depositional environments (Ferm and Horne, 1979).

The majority of traditional lithostratigraphic analyses, however, failed to recognise regionally significant unconformities similar to those described by Van Wagoner and others (1990). Such surfaces have been identified in the present study in the Pikeville, Hyden, and Four Corners Formations. Four, 3rd-order sequence boundaries have been identified overlying the Betsie, Kendrick, Magoffin, and Stoney Fork marine members. Between these sequence boundaries are 11, 4th-order sequences which stack into aggradational, progradational, and retrogradational patterns, hence defining sequence sets (Figs. 3, 4, 5, 6) (see below). The lithostratigraphic formation boundaries of Chesnut (1988a, b) correspond with the maximum flooding surfaces of the 3rd-order sequences.

METHODS

Sections were logged at the centimeter scale, where possible at spacings of between 0.5–1.5 km. To obtain detailed data on sediment bodies, large-scale photo-mosaics were constructed. Outcrops were then mapped with the aid of binoculars, involving annotation of transparent overlays on the photomosaics. Surfaces identified on the logs were walked out along the outcrop and correlated between outcrops. Stratigraphic correlation was based on the coal correlation framework of Horne (1978, 1979a, b), Baganz and Horne (1979) and Ferm (pers. commun., 1991), and the lithostratigraphic correlation of Chesnut (1991b).

TERMINOLOGY

The sequence-stratigraphic terminology used throughout this paper is that defined by Mitchum (1977), Van Wagoner and others (1988), and Mitchum and Van Wagoner (1991). Mitchum (1977) defines a sequence as a "relatively conformable, genetically related succession of strata bounded by unconformities or their correlative conformities." This definition holds true whatever the sequence's frequency, duration, or stratigraphic thickness. "A sequence set is a set of sequences arranged in a distinctive progradational, aggradational, or retrogradational stacking pattern. A composite sequence is a succession of genetically related sequences in which the individual sequences stack into lowstand, transgressive and highstand sequence sets. Sequence sets in a composite sequence are analogous to systems tracts in sequences" (Mitchum and Van Wagoner, 1991, p. 142).

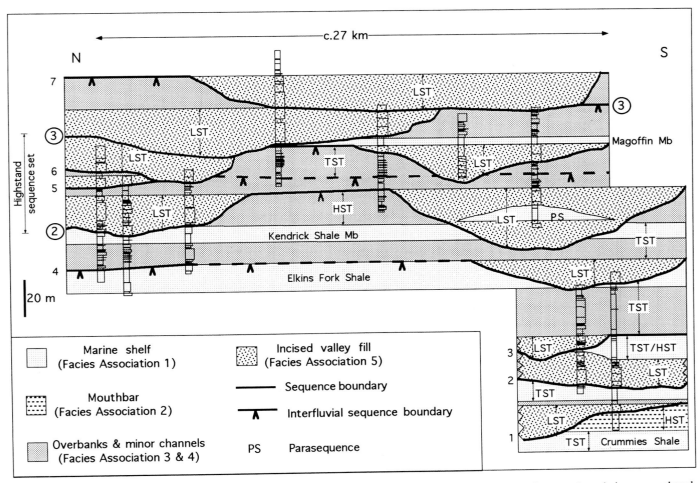

Fig. 3.—Simplified, oblique strike section along US 23 between Louisa and Paintsville (section A, Fig. 1). Sequence boundaries are numbered. Third-order sequence boundaries are circled numbers. LST, TST and HST refer to lowstand, transgressive, and highstand systems tracts, respectively.

Due to the non-exposure of the deeper basin to the west and south west, no lowstand fan or wedge deposits were found associated with any of the sequence boundaries in the study area. Although incised-valley fills (IVFs) are deposited during transgression in the late lowstand and early transgressive systems tracts (Posamentier and Vail, 1988; Posamentier and others, 1988; Van Wagoner and others, 1990; Miall, 1991; Shanley and McCabe, 1991b, 1993), in eastern Kentucky, it is impossible to distinguish the lowstand from the transgressive infill. Consequently, Exxon terminology (Van Wagoner and others, 1988) is followed here, and IVFs (see below) are assigned to the lowstand systems tract (LST). Additionally, this enables the incised-valley deposits to be distinguished from the later, predominantly fine-grained, transgressive systems tract deposits (TST) which overlie both incised valleys and interfluves.

FACIES ASSOCIATIONS: DESCRIPTION AND INTERPRETATION

Five major Facies Associations, namely offshore, mouthbar, overbank, minor channels, and stacked major fluvial bodies, along with numerous sub-facies associations, have been identified in the Breathitt Group. Facies Associations

were defined on the basis of lithological and geometric criteria, and lateral facies relationships and are summarised in Table 1.

1. Offshore Deposits

Offshore deposits (Facies Association 1) are composed of bioturbated to laminated, dark grey to black siltstones ranging from 1–35 m in thickness with both rare to abundant marine to brackish-water fossils and thin (generally <20 cm), discontinuous, micritic, and fossil-rich limestones. This facies association is interpreted as marine shelf sediments.

2. Mouth Bar Deposits

Coarsening-upward successions of rhythmically bedded, sharp-based sandstone and siltstone up to 30 m thick and up to 25 km wide (Facies Association 2) gradationally overlie, pass laterally and downdip into Facies Association 1. Current ripple lamination, wavy and flaser bedding are common with rare occurrences of lenticular bedding. Both vertical and horizontal trace fossils occur. Many vertical

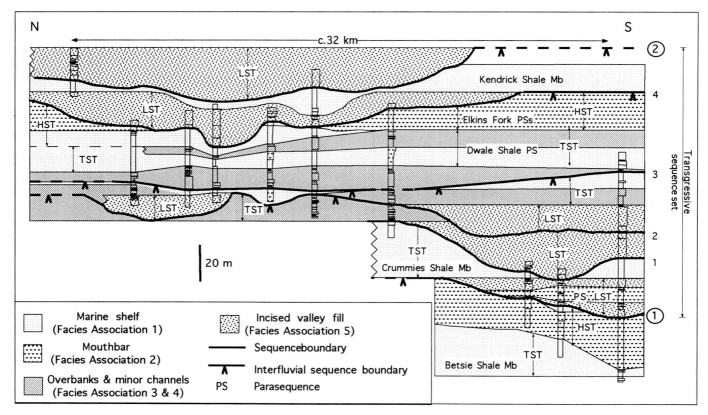

FIG. 4.—Simplified, oblique strike section along US 23 between Prestonsburg and Pikeville (section B, Fig. 1). Sequence boundaries are numbered. Third order sequence boundaries are circled numbers. LST, TST and HST refer to lowstand, transgressive and highstand systems tracts respectively.

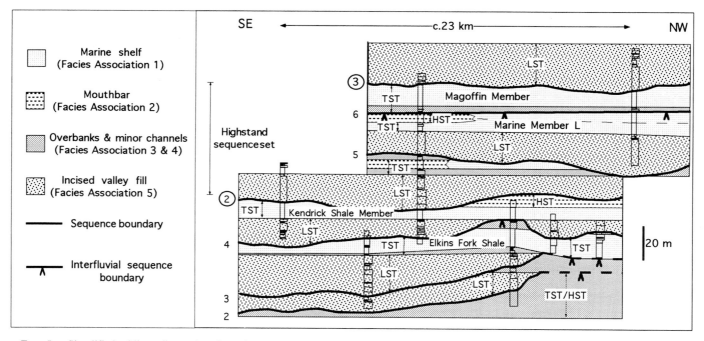

FIG. 5.—Simplified, oblique dip section along the northern section of Ky 80 (section C, Fig. 1). Sequence boundaries are numbered. Third-order sequence boundaries are circled numbers. LST, TST and HST refer to lowstand, transgressive, and highstand systems tracts, respectively.

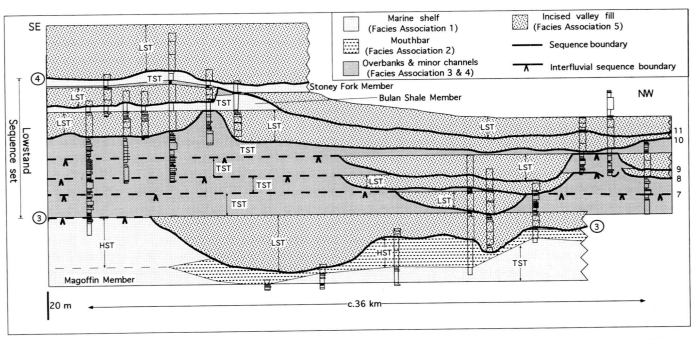

FIG. 6.—Simplified, oblique dip section along the southern section of Ky 80 (section D, Fig. 1). Sequence boundaries are numbered. Third-order sequence boundaries are circled numbers. LST, TST and HST refer to lowstand, transgressive, and highstand systems tracts, respectively.

TABLE 1

Facies Association	Interpretation	Lithology	Sedimentary Structures	Geometry	Fossils
1	Marine shelf	Grey to black siltstone	Laminated and bioturbated	Sheet	Marine bivalves, brachiopods, crinoids, amonoids, rare goniatites, *Lingula*, trace fossils, plant fragments
2	Distributary mouthbar	Fine- to coarse-grained "pin-striped" sandstone with minor siltstone partings	Parallel bedding, current ripples, dewatering structures	Unknown, probably lobate sheet	Trace fossils, plant fragments
3A	Crevasse splay	Sharp-based interbedded sandstone and siltstone	Sole marks, trough cross-bedding, climbing ripples, current ripples, parallel lamination, dewatering structures	Ribbon-lobate	Leaves, plant fragments, *in situ Lepidodendron & Calamites*
3B	Lake fill	Pale grey to grey siltstone	Parallel & wavy laminated	Sheet	Plant fragments
3C	Peat bog	Coal, rooted seat earth		Sheet	Plant fragments
4	Crevasse channels, distal feeder channels, distributary channels of the TST & HST	Siltstone, fine- to medium-grained sandstone, interbedded sandstone & siltstone, coal	Trough cross-bedding, current ripples, lateral accretion	Ribbon	Plant fragments
5A	Incised-valley fill	Fine to coarse sandstone with minor siltstone partings	Massive, parallel lamination, trough and planar tabular cross-bedding, current ripple cross-lamination	Ribbon	Few plant fragments
5B	Incised-valley fill	Fine to coarse sandstone with siltstone & coal partings	Massive, parallel lamination, trough and planar tabular cross-bedding, current ripple cross-lamination	Ribbon	Few plant fragments
5C	Incised-valley fill (tidally influenced)	Fine to coarse sandstone with minor siltstone partings	Sigmoidal cross-bedding, current ripple cross-lamination	Ribbon	Trace fossils
5D	Incised-valley fill	Fine to medium sandstone commonly with siltstone drapes	Lateral accretion, current ripple cross lamination	Ribbon	None
5E	Abandoned incised-valley fill	Siltstone, coal, minor sandstone	Laminated, current ripple cross lamination, wavy bedded, scour	Ribbon	Trace fossils, plant fragments, *in situ* tree stumps

traces cut through individual laminae. Bedsets of rhythmically bedded sandstone and siltstone are sometimes separated by relatively thin (1–2 m thick), dark grey to black siltstones, occasionally with scattered siderite beds. Chesnut and Cobb (1989) reported *Lingula* fossils from one such finer-grained interval near Pikeville. This facies association is interpreted as a prograding distributary mouth bar. The thick siltstone deposits (with marine fauna), which episodically separate bedsets of rhythmically deposited strata from one another, are interpreted as offshore siltstones deposited during minor transgressions.

3. Overbank Deposits

Facies Association 3A comprises vertical successions up to 10 m thick of complexly interbedded fine- to medium-grained sandstone and laminated siltstone. Internal sedimentary structures within sandstones of this association include abundant small-scale trough cross-bedding, climbing-ripple cross-lamination, current ripples, parallel lamination, dewatering structures, and rare internal erosion surfaces. This association was deposited by a variety of processes ranging from settling from suspension (laminated siltstone) to high-energy, tractional flows (cross-bedded and parallel-laminated sandstone). From the above and the lateral relationships with other Facies Associations, Facies Association 3A is interpreted as the deposits of crevasse splays. Facies Association 3B comprises parallel- and wavy-laminated, pale grey to grey siltstone deposited by settling from suspension in lacustrine settings.

Facies Association 3C comprises seams of coal underlain by root-penetrated sediments. Heavily mottled seat earths are common beneath the coals. Individual seams generally have variable ash contents but are generally relatively low in ash (e.g., Brant and Hester, 1980) and are commonly split by a variety of siltstone and sandstone deposits. Three major types of coal seam have been identified:

i. Thick (up to 2 m thick), sharp-based seams which are laterally continuous over tens of kilometers and drape underlying topography.
ii. Thin (generally less than 0.4 m) seams which are laterally restricted (less than 2–3 km traceable extent) and occur within other overbank deposits.
iii. Seams which drape the base of channel fills, thickening into the axis of the channels and pinching out over the channel margins.

The relatively low ash contents in the thick, laterally continuous coals (Type i) suggests that these seams developed in raised mires (McCabe, 1984, 1991) on abandoned sections of the delta plain, at times when base level was sufficiently high to raise the water table to ground level. Type ii coals are interpreted to have been deposited in backswamps close to active fluvial systems which introduced clastic material to the peat swamp during floods, producing the splits (cf. Gersib and McCabe, 1981). Finally, Type iii coals are interpreted to have developed in abandoned channels (oxbows?) prior to infilling.

4. Minor Channel Fills

Minor channel fills (Facies Association 4) (Table 1) comprise successions which occupy single-storey, channelized depressions up to 563 m wide and 13 m thick but are more commonly less than 100 m wide and 5 m thick. Channels cut into marine siltstones, mouthbars, and overbank facies associations. These units commonly contain a basal coal within the depressions and have three major fill types: siltstone, fine- to medium-grained sandstone, and interbedded sandstone and siltstone, the latter being the most common. Trough cross-bedding, current ripple lamination, low angle lateral-accretion surfaces, and internal erosion surfaces are all abundant. Paleocurrent measurements taken from trough cross beds indicate unidirectional flow oriented along the axis of the channel. Locally, the sediments are bioturbated, displaying a restricted ichnofabric. Facies Association 4 represents a variety of channel types including major and minor distributary channels (of the transgressive and highstand systems tracts; see below), distal feeder channels, and crevasse channels. The bioturbation within some isolated instances indicates a tidal influence during deposition (cf. Greb and Chesnut, 1992).

5. Major Stacked Fluvial Bodies

Major stacked fluvial bodies (Facies Association 5) (Table 1) comprise elongate units many tens of kilometers in length and 5 to 20 km in minimum width. These bodies are generally 10–15 m thick but can exceed 20 m and are incised into marine siltstones, mouthbars, and overbank deposits. They are multilateral and multistorey in nature and are separated into depositional units by erosive bounding surfaces (see below). Five dominant associations have been recognized on the basis of geometry and internal characteristics.

Homogeneous and heterolithic (Facies Associations 5A and 5B).—

Facies Associations 5A and 5B are predominantly composed of fining-upward sandstone with minor, fine-grained partings (Facies Association 5a) (Figs. 7, 8). Less commonly, siltstone partings up to 20 m long and 3 m thick occur along stacking surfaces within this association (Facies Association 5B). Rarely these siltstone partings contain rooted coals (Figs. 9A, 10).

Coal stringers, larger coal rafts up to 3 m long and 1 m wide, concentrations of heavy minerals along laminae, and laterally discontinuous pockets of matrix-supported, pebble conglomerate occur solely towards the base of Associations 5A and 5B. Clasts are generally of siderite and siltstone, although very rare quartzite clasts have also been identified. Transported plant stems, tree trunks, and disseminated carbonaceous to coaly streaks of plant debris are commonly preserved. No other fossils have been found.

Facies Associations 5A and 5B sandstones are medium- to coarse-grained and are separated into depositional units by erosive bounding surfaces (see below). Although a large proportion of the sandstones within these facies associations are massive, they also display uneven and flat lamination, generally poorly developed cross-bedding, com-

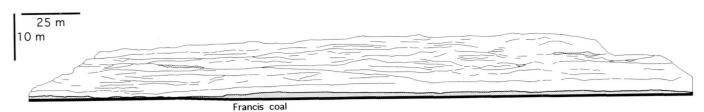

Fig. 7.—Example of the dominantly sandstone (Facies Associaton 5A) IVF internal architectural style, traced from a photo mosaic. Coal is shaded black, siltstone with a light shade; sandstone is unshaded. The outcrop lies at the junction of Ky 80 and the Daniel Boone Parkway, immediately north of Hazard (Fig. 1).

Fig. 8.—Photograph of the homogeneous IVF Facies Association 5A. Note the channelised erosion surfaces, large tabular cross beds and absence of siltstone partings. Staff is 2 m tall.

monly with asymptotic toesets (dominantly trough and irregular trough with generally minor planar, tabular cross-bedding), and current ripple cross-lamination. Cross-beds, generally between 0.5 and 1.0 m thick, occur either singly or in sets up to 3 m thick. Larger trough cross-beds (up to 4 m thick) also occur in cross-cutting relationships. Super-imposition of small-scale structures on larger ones is common.

Paleocurrent data taken from trough and planar cross-beds generally show low to moderate dispersion about a vector mean for a specific outcrop. On a regional scale, however, paleoflow shows a wide spread, with a predominantly north-westerly trend.

Massive sandstones are interpreted as the result of rapid sedimentation from high-energy flows which were capable of entraining water-logged trees and rafts of peat. The almost complete absence of lateral-accretion surfaces and overbank deposits in the main body of Facies Associations 5A and 5B in the Breathitt Group suggests that infill was mainly by vertical accretion in non-migrating rivers of low sinuosity. Similar channel deposits have been described by Campbell (1976) from Jurassic deposits in New Mexico, by Allen (1983) from Devonian successions in Wales, and by Haszeldine (1983) from Westphalian B sediments in north-east England. Haszeldine (1983) interpreted these deposits as the product of deposition in large, low-sinuosity to braided channels. However, the palaeochannel pattern of the rivers that deposited the multistorey, multilateral deposits in the Breathitt Group may have varied considerably in space.

Stable river courses may be either straight (low-sinuosity, single channel) or anastomosed (high to variable sinuosity, multiple channel) (Schumm, 1977; Rust, 1978). Channels of the former type are commonly dominated by rapid vertical infilling after incision into fine-grained sediment (Meckel, 1972; Coleman and Prior, 1982; Haszeldine, 1983). Straight channels frequently shift position in response to changes in gradient on the delta plain but remain stable in their positions between shifts (fixed channels of Friend, 1983). Anastomosed rivers are similarly dominated by rapid vertical filling (Smith and Smith, 1980; Smith, 1986). Mapping of the major fluvial bodies in the Breathitt Group by means of combined outcrop and borehole studies (Davies and Burn, 1991; Davies and others, 1992) indicates a complex range of geometries. Fine-grained intervals encased within major, stacked-sandstone successions are interpreted as slough channel or abandonment deposits within channel belts.

Tidally influenced (Facies Association 5C).—

Facies Association 5C is characterised by sigmoidal sets of sandstone, in beds up to 30 cm thick and 2 m long, displaying current ripple lamination and sudordinate, ripple-scale trough cross-beds and wavy bedding. Bedforms thin upwards and a few, scattered burrows are present. The sandstone is clean but regularly draped by thin (mm to cm

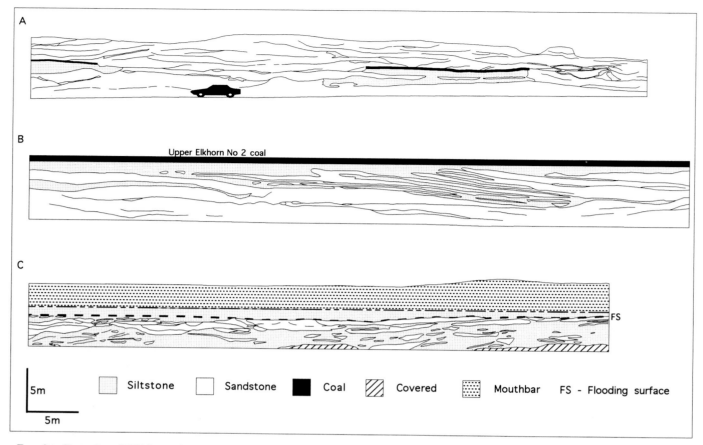

A

B

Upper Elkhorn No 2 coal

C

FS

| 5m | ▦ Siltstone | ☐ Sandstone | ■ Coal | ▨ Covered | ⠿ Mouthbar | FS - Flooding surface |

5m

FIG. 9.—Examples of IVF internal architecture, traced from photo mosaics. (A) Heterolithic IVF Facies Association 5B from an outcrop on the Ky 80 circa 10 km from Hazard. (B) Portion of the draped, laterally accreted IVF Facies Association 5D from an outcrop on the US 23 near Banner. (C) Portion of the IVF abandonment Facies Association 5E from an outcrop on the US 23 near Ivel.

FIG. 10.—Photograph of the heterolithic IVF Facies Association 5B. Note the relatively thick siltstone partings. Outcrop is circa 6 m high.

scale) siltstones which can be traced from the upper part of a sandstone bed along inclined surfaces to the base (Fig. 11). Ripple cross-lamination clearly indicates a dominant north-westerly trend to paleoflow, while paleocurrents from the trough cross-beds indicate a subordinate southerly (landward) paleoflow. Similar bimodal paleocurrent trends have been recorded from planar cross-beds in rare examples of Facies Associations 5A and 5B.

Within a number of the stacked-sandstone bodies, discrete units can be identified which contain some of the most diverse ichnofabrics observed in the study area. These units are often associated with sandstone containing abundant draped ripple and draped, climbing-ripple cross-lamination. Association 5C is interpreted as tidally-influenced deposits (cf. Shanley and McCabe, 1991a, b, 1993). The absence of tidal bundles or rhythmites suggests that these deposits do not reflect the effects of daily tidal processes or spring-neap cycles. Following Rahmani's (1988) and Shanley and McCabe's (1993) interpretations for similar heterolithic facies in Cretaceous units of Alberta and Utah, respectively, we believe these deposits reflect the interaction of tidal processes, channel and valley morphology and variations in seasonal runoff. The presence of these tidal deposits may be indicative of an upper estuarine depositional setting (Allen, 1991; Reinson, 1992).

Draped laterally accreted (Facies Association 5D).—

Large-scale, lateral-accretion surfaces up to 50 m long are common towards the top of the major stacked fluvial bodies; these are often draped by laminated siltstones (Figs. 9B, 12), with rare current ripple structures. Paleocurrents from the current ripples appear to be at a high angle to the dip of lateral-accretion surfaces. Association 5D is clearly indicative of an increase in sinuosity, probably related to a decrease in discharge and/or a reduction in gradient as the channel complex neared abandonment.

Abandonment facies (Facies Association 5E).—

The uppermost portions of major stacked fluvial bodies are commonly heterolithic, often becoming dominated by siltstone and resembling overbank deposits (Facies Association 3). These comprise crevasse splays and complicated deposits of small-scale scour channels in a siltstone framework, with *in situ* rooted tree stumps and poorly developed coals (Figs. 9C, 13). Association 5E is interpreted as abandonment and partial abandonment facies. These sediments were probably deposited by suspension and occasional tractional flows (rippled facies).

SEQUENCE-STRATIGRAPHIC FRAMEWORK

Posamentier and Vail (1988) used the concept of a graded-stream profile to define an equilibrium surface that controls

FIG. 11.—Photograph of siltstone draped, sigmoidal cross beds interpreted as tidal deposits within an IVF (Facies Association 5C). Key circa 7 cm long.

FIG. 12.—Photograph of draped, lateral-accretion surfaces at the top of an IVF (Facies Association 5D) exposed in an outcrop on US 23 near Banner. Exposure is circa 5 m high.

FIG. 13.—Outcrop photograph of the IVF abandonment Facies Association 5E (car for scale).

and defines subaerial accommodation space in fluvial settings. From this they developed a conceptual model which relates fluvial deposition to changes in relative sea level. However, they overlooked many modern geomorphological concepts so that many of the conclusions with respect to base level changes, slope of the fluvial system, and the fluvial response to base level changes are oversimplified (e.g., Miall, 1991; Shanley and McCabe, 1991b). Nonetheless, the geometrical relationships resulting from flume studies investigating the fluvial response to base level changes (e.g., Koss and others, 1990; Wood and others, 1990, 1991) reproduced geometrical relationships similar to those found in ancient stratigraphic studies; hence, the Posamentier and Vail (1988) model can be used as a first approximation to the response of fluvial systems, especially in the lower reaches, to base level changes.

Posamentier and Vail (1988, p. 132–133) suggest that during the transgressive systems tract and early highstand systems tract the rate of creation of accommodation space (represented by an updip shift in the equilibrium profile) is high so that rapid aggradation, characterized by vertical stacking of poorly interconnected fluvial deposits, will occur as the river attempts to return to grade. However, as the river's grade nears the final equilibrium profile in the later highstand systems tract, the rate of creation of accommodation space falls and approaches zero. Vertical stacking grades into lateral amalgamation resulting in the deposition of interconnected sheet sandstones in the late highstand systems tract. This paper tests this conceptual model using field data.

Sequence Boundaries

Recognition of sequence-bounding unconformities in predominantly alluvial strata can be difficult because basinward shifts in facies tracts and related incision can easily be confused with more local channel scour. Sequence boundaries can be identified by an abrupt facies-tract dislocation, an abrupt increase in vertical sandstone amalgamation, and an increase in mean grain size and/or change in petrographic composition (cf. Shanley and McCabe, 1991a, b, 1993). Such criteria, however, can only be used to identify sequence boundaries if the changes are of regional (mappable) extent, such that there is incision in many places at the same stratigraphic level.

In the Breathitt Group, facies-tract dislocations are associated with the unconformable bases of major stacked fluvial bodies (Facies Association 5) (Figs. 2, 3, 4, 5, 6). Locally these unconformities separate fluvial deposits from underlying marine or mouthbar deposits, but over large distances they separate overlying, fine- to medium-grained, multilateral and multistorey fluvial sandstones from subjacent lacustrine siltstones, coals, crevasse splay packages, and single-storey, laterally-accreted, channel sandstone bodies. A number of these unconformities are traceable at each stratigraphic level throughout the study area. It is (a) the degree of facies jump, (b) the marked contrast in grain size, (c) the depth of incision, (d) the contrast in depth of individual channels (maximum of circa 3–4 m) in relation to the depth of incision (15–20 m), and (e) the regional, mappable extent of the surfaces that indicates that fluvial incision was related to a significant fall in base level, rather than simple channel switching or other 'normal progradation' phenomena. The abrupt transition from predominantly fine-grained strata to medium- and coarse-grained strata indicates a change in the rate of fluvial aggradation (Bridge and Leeder, 1979) and/or a change in accommodation potential (Posamentier and Vail, 1988). Similarly, the abrupt

changes in the degree of fluvial stacking and sand:shale (net:gross) ratio across erosional surfaces with regional extent suggest a marked alteration in hydraulic character and rates of alluvial aggradation. Taken together all these factors support the interpretation of these incision surfaces as sequence-bounding unconformities. Hence the multistorey, multilateral fluvial deposits (Facies Association 5) are interpreted as incised-valley fills.

Interfluvial sequence boundaries are associated with thin coals, carbonaceous siltstones, seat earths, rooted surfaces, and/or slight bleaching and mottling. However, taken in isolation, these deposits are difficult to distinguish from similar sediments deposited in the lowstand and highstand systems tracts and are only clearly defined by mapping their relationship with incised-valley fills along strike. However, by careful correlation and by estimation of the vertical position of such surfaces with respect to the transgressive surface and maximum flooding zone (see below), it is possible to identify interfluvial sequence boundaries. Although other workers have identified well-developed paleosols on interfluves (e.g., Leckie and others, 1989 in the Cretaceous strata of British Columbia and Krystinik and Blakeney-Dejarnett, 1991 in Pennsylvanian deposits of eastern Colorado), such deposits are rare in the Breathitt Group. Instead interfluvial paleosols are poorly developed and appear to have been saturated for long periods of time as indicated by their mottled, gleyed nature.

Although there is little biostratigraphic control, the four major marine members (the Betsie, Kendrick, Magoffin, and Stoney Fork members) are estimated to occur at 2.5 Ma intervals (Chesnut, 1989; pers. commun., 1992), which equates with the 3rd-order cyclicity of Vail and others (1977). Hence the sequence boundaries overlying these marine members are herein classified as 3rd-order in terms of duration and magnitude, but a eustatic origin is not necessarily inferred. The other sequence boundaries bound coal-clastic cycles which have been estimated to have durations of 400 to 450,000 years in the Breathitt Group (Chesnut, 1989; pers. commun., 1992). Because they equate with the 4th-order cyclicity of Van Wagoner and others (1990) and Mitchum and Van Wagoner (1991) and the long-earth periodicity, which is known to control glacial cycles, these sequence boundaries are classified as 4th-order.

Parasequences

Parasequences and parasequence sets occur rarely in the Breathitt Group because minor changes in sea level are not readily expressed in much of the non-marine strata. However, three types of parasequence, bounded by marine flooding surfaces, have been identified.

First, marine siltstones which separate rhythmically bedded, coastal mouthbar deposits (see above) are indicative of small-scale marine transgressions and delimit parasequence boundaries in these deposits. Second, when the rate of base level rise is at a maximum, in the transgressive sequence set (see below), parasequences and not 4th-order sequences are deposited (see below). These parasequences comprise coarsening-upward successions from basal marine siltstones through mouthbar deposits to fluvial-channel and overbank deposits which are then overlain by another marine siltstone deposit (Figs. 3, 4). These are classic coarsening-upward parasequences (*sensu* Van Wagoner and others, 1990). Finally, parasequences occur within 3rd-order IVFs.

Thick (up to several meters), fine-grained successions are occasionally enclosed within the 3rd-order IVF sandstones. They are of limited extent along strike (traceable for <7 km) and include rooted coal, floodplain siltstone, occasionally with rooted tree stumps, and/or marine siltstone. Even when the deposits in these fine-grained intervals are of terrestrial origin, they invariably occur at stratigraphic levels where marine zones are known to occur down dip (Chesnut, 1991a), namely marine members F, I, J, and N (Fig. 2). The preservation of these fine-grained intervals can be explained by marine flooding and a concomitant increase in accommodation space. The fine-grained deposits are erosively overlain by multistorey, multilateral sandstone. These erosive surfaces could, therefore, be interpreted as 4th-order sequence boundaries. However, they occur solely within the erosional trough of the 3rd-order IVF and, although they will be represented in many of the 3rd-order IVFs at that stratigraphic level, they are not of regional extent and, therefore, do not fulfill the criteria for sequence-boundary definition. Therefore, the fine-grained intervals represent 4th-order parasequence boundaries within 3rd-order IVFs.

Systems Tracts

Although parasequences and parasequence sets are generally not identifiable, it is possible to identify 4th-order systems tracts on the basis of vertical position within a sequence, depositional environments, facies associations, and changes in architectural style. The LST comprises IVFs characterised by multistorey, multilateral, fine- to coarse-grained channel sandstones (Facies Association 5), and the adjacent, conformable interfluve. Incised valleys are bounded above by the transgressive surface (*sensu* Van Wagoner and others, 1988) or initial flooding surface. Such a surface is difficult to identify in the relatively updip alluvial deposits of Kentucky. However, many of the IVFs are capped by thick coals (Figs. 9B, 12) which may have developed in response to base level rise and waterlogging of the substrate as a result of transgression. Updip, the TST, and highstand systems tract (HST) are difficult to distinguish from one another. Although there are tidal deposits within the TST in Kentucky (Greb & Chesnut, 1992), there is no clear tidal horizon to delimit the maximum flooding surface, which separates the TST from the HST, as occurs in the Kaiparowits Plateau, Utah (Shanley and McCabe, 1991a, 1993). In the Breathitt, both the TST and HST are represented by similar, single-storey point bar sandstone (Facies Association 4), large proportions of crevasse splays, thin coals, and thick successions of floodplain siltstone (Facies Association 3). However, it is possible to identify a zone of maximum flooding based on the concept of accommodation potential (Cross, 1988) and its relationship to the development of coal. The thickest, most laterally extensive coals are believed to occur within the TST, because the accom-

modation potential is high. The transition to more laterally restricted, thinner coals represents a marked fall in the accommodation potential, which defines a maximum flooding zone, hence delimiting the TST from the HST. Furthermore, as predicted by Posamentier and Vail's (1988) model, channels in the transgressive and early highstand systems tract tend to be filled with fine-grained or interbedded lithologies, while those in the late HST, although still single-storey, tend to be sandstone-filled.

Sequence Sets

The stacking patterns of the 4th-order sequences define sequence sets (Mitchum and Van Wagoner, 1991). Fourth-order sequences which lie between the Betsie and Kendrick marine members stack in a retrogradational manner (Fig. 4); hence, this interval is interpreted as a transgressive sequence set (TSS). Incision at the base of IVFs is at its least pronounced in the study area, and the maximum amount (circa 50%) of TST and HST deposits is preserved (Fig. 4).

The succession between the Kendrick and Magoffin marine members (Figs. 3, 5) shows a weakly progradational to aggradational stacking pattern of its component 4th-order sequences (Figs. 3, 5) with a relatively high proportion (circa 40%) of TST. Some HST is also preserved. Hence, it has been interpreted as a 4th-order highstand sequence set (HSS).

The succession between the Magoffin and Stoney Fork marine members (Fig. 6) displays an aggradational stacking pattern of 4th-order sequences with the least amount of TST and HST preserved between succeeding 4th-order IVFs. Consequently, this succession is interpreted as a 4th-order lowstand sequence set (LSS).

INTERNAL ARCHITECTURE OF INCISED-VALLEY FILLS

Thickness variations within IVFs depend mainly on the basal erosional surface of the valley. The amount of incision is commonly controlled by the presence or absence of subjacent coals, which are resistant to erosion (McCabe, 1984). Where IVFs sit directly on coal, they are sharp-based; where (rarely) the coal has been incised, there is an abrupt thickening of the IVF.

All observed IVFs contain internal heterogeneities. The greatest proportion of IVF heterogeneities are wide, channelised erosion surfaces and numerous discontinuous siltstone partings (Fig. 7). This represents stacking of several channels where each successive channel has eroded and reworked the underlying fill; hence, the morphology of individual sedimentary bodies is rarely preserved. Identifiable, individual channel fills within IVFs rarely exceed 20 m in width and 6 m in thickness. Nonetheless, sandbody connectivity is high.

The laterally accreted facies (Association 5D) towards the top of IVFs shows epsilon cross-strata with variable orientations and well-developed siltstone partings (Fig. 9B). Abandonment facies at the top of IVFs are complex (Fig. 9C), dominated by variably rooted siltstones with numerous scour channels up to 5 m wide and 1 m thick which erode into one another and also into the siltstone (Fig. 9C). Sandbody connectivity within these facies associations is low.

Stacked channel sandstones within the IVFs were undoubtedly deposited during aggradation when the accommodation rate was in equilibrium with sediment supply (cf. Posamentier and Vail, 1988) during early transgression. A constant accommodation rate accounts for the stacking of single channels to form a more laterally extensive sheet-like form (Eschard and others, 1991). The lateral-accretion units are representative of a change to a meandering channel pattern. This change is interpreted to result from an increase in the rate of relative sea-level rise, which causes a reduction in gradient and a fall in current speeds. Hence, both the architecture and reservoir characteristics of the IVFs are directly controlled by changes in relative sea level.

STACKING PATTERNS OF INCISED-VALLEY FILLS WITHIN SEQUENCE SETS

In the lowstand sequence set, incision at the base of IVFs is at a maximum because the 4th-order sea-level curve is superimposed on the falling limb of the 3rd-order curve, accentuating erosion and downshifts. Consequently, incision associated with successive 4th-order sequence boundaries has commonly removed all of the HST and TST of the underlying sequences, such that IVFs of successive 4th-order sequences are amalgamated (cf. Krystinik and Blakeney-DeJarnett, 1991). A good example of this phenomenon is illustrated at the eastern end of the Ky 80 (Figs. 14, 15), where the IVF above sequence boundary 11 is amalgamated with the valley fill above sequence boundary 10. Sequence boundary 11 is marked by a stacking surface beneath which a considerable amount of siltstone is preserved (Fig. 14). Furthermore, there is a contrast in architectural style between the two IVFs, with the upper IVF (above sequence boundary 11) containing more siltstone partings and internal stacking surfaces (Fig. 14). Hence, IVF interconnectedness is greatest in the lowstand sequence set (LSS).

Conversely, when the 4th-order sea-level curve is superimposed on the rising limb of the 3rd-order curve (i.e. within the transgressive sequence set), incision is suppressed. Consequently, in the transgressive sequence set incision is at a minimum and IVFs tend to stack discretely in a retrogradational manner, with the maximum amount of fine-grained TST and HST preserved between them. Furthermore, there is a change in the nature of the 4th-order cycles towards the top of the transgressive sequence set (TSS). Here, fine-grained marine parasequences are deposited in place of sequences with IVFs. This change is interpreted as the result of the accommodation rate outstripping the rate of sediment supply.

The highstand sequence set is transitional between the LSS and TSS in terms of the amount of transgressive and highstand sediments preserved. Incised valleys tend to stack discretely with an aggradadational to progradational style (Figs. 3, 5). Less fine-grained material is preserved than in the TSS.

APPLICATIONS TO RESERVOIR CHARACTERISATION

Sandstone-filled IVFs offer the best potential reservoir rocks in the Breathitt Group. They are generally sealed at the base by either coal, marine siltstones, or fine-grained overbank facies. At their top, IVFs are sealed by the abandonment subfacies, fine-grained overbank facies, coal, or marine siltstone. Internal heterogeneites make IVFs anisotropic media with respect to fluid flow. The role of internal siltstone partings in permeability compartmentalisation is considered negligible because of their thinness and lack of lateral continuity. However, the distribution of thicker, more laterally continuous fine-grained partings associated with parasequence boundaries in 3rd-order IVFs have important implications for reservoir quality. These fine-grained facies, which are several meters thick and 7 km wide, present significant barriers to fluid flow within otherwise good reservoir sandstones.

The abundance of individual sandstone beds within 4th-order sequences offers multiple stacked reservoir targets. Within this context, the lowstand sequence set offers more possibilities for reservoir development because of its relatively greater proportion of sandstone. However, sediments with different reservoir qualities may be superimposed as

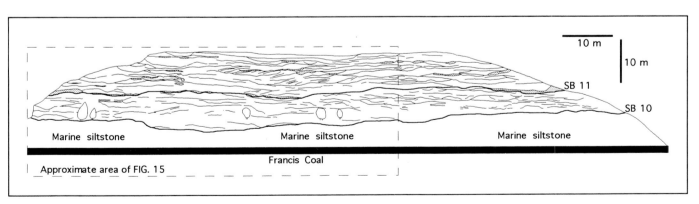

FIG. 14.—Example of the superimposition of IVFs in the lowstand sequence set, traced from a photo mosaic. Coal is shaded black and siltstone with a light shade. Sandstone is unshaded. Bedding planes are drawn as thin lines, whereas sequence boundaries (SB) are represented by thicker lines. Note particularly the distinct change in stacking pattern and architectural style across sequence boundary 11. This is represented by an increase in the number of preserved siltstone partings and internal stacking surfaces in the upper IVF in comparison to the lower. The outcrop is located by milepost 14 on the Ky 80 in Knott County (Fig. 1).

FIG. 15.—Photograph of outcrop illustrated in Figure 14 illustrating the change in architecture and increase in siltstone partings across sequence boundary 11 in the middle of the photograph.

younger valleys incise into or through older valley deposits (e.g., Figs. 14, 15). Incision may cause isolation of reservoir units in some areas, while creating unexpected interzone communication elsewhere. The stratigraphic complexity of sandstone bodies present in the Breathitt Group and similar depositional settings can be clarified by the correlation of high-frequency sequences and by the identification of 3rd-order sequence boundaries which group sandstones into sequence sets.

CONCLUSIONS

In the fluvio-deltaic deposits of eastern Kentucky, IVFs are most commonly characterised by multistorey, multilateral channel sandstones with few, fine-grained partings. However, towards their tops, IVFs become more heterolithic and are commonly characterised by siltstone-draped lateral-accretion surfaces and heterolithic abandonment facies. The thickest and most laterally extensive fine-grained deposits within incised valleys occur as parasequences within 3rd-order IVFs.

Fourth-order sequences stack into progradational, aggradational, and retrogradational patterns that define lowstand, transgressive, and highstand sequence sets. Each of these sequence-set types is distinctive in terms of the degree of incision of 4th-order sequence boundaries and the amount

of transgressive and highstand deposits preserved between 4th-order sequence boundaries. The LSS contain the most amalgamated IVFs while the TSS contain the least amalgamated. The HSS is transitional between the LSS and TSS.

The architecture within systems tracts broadly conforms to Posamentier and Vail's (1988) conceptual model. However, the current research clearly indicates that the position of a 4th-order sequence on a 3rd-order relative sea-level curve is critical in controlling both the fill and stacking of IVFs.

ACKNOWLEDGEMENTS

This research is funded by the Stratigraphic Studies and Reservoir Quality Prediction Groups of British Petroleum, London, whose support is gratefully acknowledged. John Howell commented on the manuscript. The work has profited from discussions with John Ferm (University of Kentucky) and Don Chesnut (Kentucky Geological Survey). This paper has been greatly improved by the comments of the two reviewers, Martin Gibling and Frank Ethridge. The views expressed in this paper are, however, those of the authors.

REFERENCES

ADLIS, D. S., GROSSMAN, E. L., YANCEY, T. E., AND McLERRAN, R. D., 1988, Isotope stratigraphy and paleodepth changes of Pennsylvanian cyclical sedimentary deposits: Palaios, v. 3, p. 487–506.

ALLEN, G. P., 1991, Sedimentary processes and facies in the Gironde estuary: a recent model for macrotidal estuarine systems, *in* Smith, D. G., Reinson, G. E., Zaitlin, B. A., and Rahamani, R. A., eds., Clastic Tidal Sedimentology: Calgary, Canadian Society of Petroleum Geologists Memoir 16, p. 29–40.

ALLEN, J. R. L., 1983, Studies in fluviatile sedimentation: bars, bar-complexes and sandstone sheets (low sinuosity braided streams) in the Brownstones (L. Devonian), Welsh Borderlands: Sedimentary Geology, v. 33, p. 237–293.

BAGANZ, B. B., AND HORNE, J. C., 1979, Geologic cross-section along U.S. Highway 23 between Prestonsburg and Pikeville, Johnson and Floyd Counties, Kentucky (Carolina Coal Group (Geologic Cross-section GCS-4): Columbia, University of South Carolina, 2 sheets.

BRANT, R. A., AND HESTER, N. C., 1980, Coal in Kentucky: Kentucky Geological Survey Series XI, Reprint 7, Lexington, Kentucky Geological Survey, 11 p.

BRIDGE, J. S., AND LEEDER, M. R., 1979, A simulation model of alluvial stratigraphy: Sedimentology, v. 26, p. 617–644.

CAMPBELL, C. V., 1976, Reservoir geometry of a fluvial sheet sandstone: American Association of Petroleum Geologists Bulletin, v. 60, p. 1009–1020.

CHESNUT, D. R., 1988a, Stratigraphic analysis of the Carboniferous rocks of the central Appalachian basin: Unpublished Ph.D. Dissertation, University of Kentucky, Lexington, 297 p.

CHESNUT, D. R., 1988b, Preferred coal bed names for the eastern Kentucky coal field: Lexington, Kentucky Geological Survey Open-File Report OF-88–13, 5 p.

CHESNUT, D. R., 1989, Pennsylvanian rocks of the eastern Kentucky coal field, *in* Cecil, C. B., and Eble, C., eds., Coal and Hydrocarbon Resources of North America, v. 2: Washington, D.C., International Geological Congress Field Trip T143, Carboniferous Geology of the Eastern United States, American Geophysical Union, p. 57–60.

CHESNUT, D. R., 1991a, Paleontological survey of the Pennsylvanian rocks of the eastern Kentucky coal field: Part 1, Invertebrates: Lexington, Kentucky Geological Survey Information Circular 36 (Series XI), Kentucky Geological Survey, 71 p.

CHESNUT, D. R., 1991b, Geologic Highway Cross Section: Kentucky Highway 80, Hazard to Prestonsburg: Lexington, Kentucky Geological Survey Map and Chart Series 2 (Series XI), Kentucky Geological Survey, 1 sheet.

CHESNUT, D. R., AND COBB, J. C., 1989, Pikeville: "Model City" River Diversion Cut, *in* Cecil, C. B., and Eble, C., eds., Coal and Hydrocarbon Resources of North America, v. 2: Washington, D.C., International Geological Congress Field Trip T143, Carboniferous Geology of the Eastern United States, American Geophysical Union, p. 78–80.

COLEMAN, J. M., AND PRIOR, D. B., 1982, Deltaic environments of deposition, *in* Scholle, P. A., and Spearing, D., eds., Sandstone Depositional Environments: Tulsa, American Association of Petroleum Geologists Memoir 31, p. 139–179.

CROSS, T. A., 1988, Controls on coal distribution in transgressive-regressive cycles, Upper Cretaceous, Western Interior, U. S. A., *in* Wilgus, C. K., Hastings, B. S., Kendall, C. G. St. C., Posamentier, H. W., Ross, C. A., and Van Wagoner, J. C., eds., Sea-level Changes: An Integrated Approach: Tulsa, Society of Economic Paleontologists and Mineralogists Special Publication 42, p. 371–380.

CROWLEY, T. J., AND BAUM, S. K., 1991, Estimating Carboniferous sea-level fluctuations from Gondwanan ice extent: Geology, v. 19, p. 975–977.

DAVIES, H., AND BURN, M., 1991, High resolution sequence stratigraphic analyses of fluvio-deltaic cyclothems: the Upper Carboniferous Breathitt Group, east Kentucky (abs.): Edinburgh, British Sedimentology Research Group 30th Annual Meeting Programme and Abstracts, University of Edinburgh.

DAVIES, H., BURN, M., BUDDING, M. C., AND WILLIAMS, H., 1992, High-resolution sequence stratigraphic analysis of fluvio-deltaic cyclothems: the Pennsylvanian Breathitt Group, east Kentucky (abs.): American Association of Petroleum Geologists 1992 Annual Convention Official Programme, p. 27.

DONALDSON, A. C., AND EBLE, C., 1991, Pennsylvanian coals of central and eastern United States, *in* Gluskoter, H. J., Rice, D. D. and Taylor, R. B., eds., Economic Geology, U. S.: Boulder, The Geology of North America, v. P-2, Geological Society of America, p. 523–546.

ENGLUND, K. J., AND THOMAS, R. E., 1989, Late Paleozoic depositional trends in the central Appalchian Basin: United States Geological Survey Bulletin 1839, p. F1-F19.

ESCHARD, R., RAVENNE, C., HOUEL, P., AND KNOX, R., 1991, Three-dimensional reservoir architecture of a valley-fill sequence and a deltaic aggradational sequence: influences of minor relative sea level variations (Scalby Formation, England), *in* Miall, A. D., and Tyler, N., eds., Three-Dimensional Facies Architecture of Terrigeneous Clastic Sediments and its Implications for Hydrocarbon Discovery and Recovery: Tulsa, SEPM (Society for Sedimentary Geology), Concepts in Sedimentology and Palaeontology 3, p. 133–147.

FERM, J. C., HORNE, J. C., SWINCHATT, J. P., AND WHALEY, P. W., eds., 1971, Carboniferous depositional environments in north-eastern Kentucky (roadlog for Geological Society of Kentucky 1971 Field Excursion): Lexington, Kentucky Geological Survey, Series 10, 30 p.

FERM, J. C., AND HORNE, J. C., eds., 1979, Carboniferous Depositional Environments in the Appalachian Region: Columbia, University of South Carolina, 760 p.

FRIEND, P. F., 1983, Towards the field classification of alluvial architecture or sequence, *in* Collinson, J. D., and Lewin, J., eds., Modern and Ancient Fluvial Systems: Oxford, International Association of Sedimentologists Special Publication 6, p. 345–354.

GERSIB, G. A., AND MCCABE, P. J., 1981, Continental coal-bearing sediments of the Port Hood Formation (Carboniferous), Cape Linzee, Nova Scotia, Canada, *in* Ethridge, F. G., and Flores, R. M., eds., Recent and Ancient Nonmarine Depositional Environments: Models for Exploration: Tulsa, Society of Economic Paleontologists and Mineralogists Special Publication No. 31, p. 95–108.

GREB, S. F., AND CHESNUT, D. R., 1992, Transgressive channel filling in the Breathitt Formation (Upper Carboniferous), Eastern Kentucky coal field, USA: Sedimentary Geology, v. 75, p. 209–221.

HASZELDINE, R. S., 1983, Fluvial bars reconstructed from a deep, straight channel, Upper Carboniferous coalfield of northeast England: Journal of Sedimentary Petrology, v. 53, p. 1233–1247.

HECKEL, P. H., 1977, Origin of phosphatic black shale facies in Pennsylvanian cyclothems of mid-continent North America: American Association of Petroleum Geologists Bulletin, v. 61, p. 1045–1068.

HORNE, J. C., 1978, Geologic cross-section along the Daniel Boone Parkway between Hazard and Buckhorn Reservoir, Perry and Leslie Counties, Kentucky (Carolina Coal Group Geologic Cross-Section GCS-1): Columbia, University of South Carolina, 2 sheets.

HORNE, J. C., 1979a, Geologic cross-section along U.S. Highway 23 between Louisa and Paintsville, Lawrence and Johnson Counties, Kentucky (Carolina Coal Group Geologic Cross-Section GCS-2): Columbia, University of South Carolina, 3 sheets.

HORNE, J. C., 1979b, Geologic cross-section along U.S. Highway 23 between Paintsville and Prestonsburg, Floyd and Pike Counties, Kentucky (Carolina Coal Group Geologic Cross-Section GCS-3): Columbia, University of South Carolina, 2 sheets.

HORNE, J. C., FERM, J. C., CARUCCIO, F. T., AND BAGANZ, B. P., 1978, Depositional models in coal exploration and mine planning in Appalachian region: American Association of Petroleum Geologists Bulletin, v. 62, p. 2379–2411.

JERVEY, M. T., 1988, Quantitative geological modelling of rock sequences and their seismic expressions, *in* Wilgus, C. K., Hastings, B. S., Kendall, C. G.St. C., Posamentier, H. W., Ross, C. A., and Van Wagoner, J. C., eds., Sea-Level Changes: An Integrated Approach: Society of Economic Palaeontologists and Mineralogists Special Publication No. 42, p. 39–46.

KOSS, J. E., ETHRIDGE, F. G., AND SCHUMM, S. A., 1990, Effects of base-level change on coastal plain and shelf systems-an experimental approach (abs.): American Association of Petroleum Geologists Bulletin, v. 74, p. 697.

KRYSTINIK, L. F., AND BLAKENEY-DEJARNETT, B. A., 1991, Sequence stratigraphy and sedimentologic character of valley fills, lower Pennsylvanian Morrow Formation, eastern Colorado and western Kansas (abs.): Calgary, Programme, Proceedings, Guidebook, 1991 NUNA Conference on High-Resolution Sequence Stratigraphy, Global Sedimenatry Geology Programme, p. 24–26.

LECKIE, D., FOX, C., AND TARNOCAI, C., 1989, Multiple paleosols of the late Albian Boulder Creek Formation, British Columbia, Canada: Sedimentology, v. 36, p. 307–322.

MCCABE, P. J., 1984, Depositional environments of coal and coal-bearing strata, *in* Rahmani, R. A., and Flores, R. M., eds., Sedimentology of Coal and Coal-bearing Sequences: Oxford, International Association of Sedimentologists Special Publication 7, p. 13–42.

MCCABE, P. J., 1991, Geology of coal: environments of deposition, *in* Gluskoter, H. J., Rice, D. D., and Taylor, R. B., eds., Economic Geology, U. S.: Boulder, The Geology of North America, v. P-2, Geological Society of America, p. 469–482.

MECKEL, L. D., 1972, Anatomy of distributary channel-fill deposits in recent mud-deltas (abs.): American Association of Petroleum Geologists Bulletin, v. 56, p. 639.

MIALL, A. D., 1991, Stratigraphic sequences and their chronostratigraphic correlation: Journal of Sedimentary Petrology, v.61, p. 497–505.

MITCHUM, R. M., 1977, Seismic stratigraphy and global changes of sea level, Part XI: Glossary of terms used in seismic stratigraphy, *in* Payton, C. E., ed., Seismic Stratigraphy-Applications to Hydrocarbon Exploration: Tulsa, American Association of Petroleum Geologists Memoir 26, p. 205–212.

MITCHUM, R. M., AND VAN WAGONER, J. C., 1991, High-frequency sequences and their stacking patterns: sequence-stratigraphic evidence of high-frequency eustatic cycles: Sedimentary Geology, v. 70, p. 131–160.

POSAMENTIER, H. W., AND VAIL, P. R., 1988, Eustatic controls on clastic deposition II-sequence and systems tract models, *in* Wilgus, C. K., Hastings, B. S., Kendall, C. G. St. C., Posamentier, H. W., Ross, C. A., and Van Wagoner, J. C., eds., Sea-Level Changes: An Integrated Approach: Tulsa, Society of Economic Palaeontologists and Mineralogists Special Publication 42, p. 125–154.

POSAMENTIER, H. W., JERVEY, M. T., AND VAIL, P. R., 1988, Eustatic controls on clastic deposition I—conceptual framework, *in* Wilgus, C. K., Hastings, B. S., Kendall C. G. St. C., Posamentier, H. W., Ross, C. A., and Van Wagoner, J. C., eds., Sea-Level Changes: An Integrated Approach: Tulsa, Society of Economic Palaeontologists and Mineralogists Special Publication 42, p. 109–124.

RAHMANI, R. A., 1988, Estuarine tidal channel and nearshore sedimentation of a late Cretaceous epicontinental sea, Drumheller, Alberta, Canada, *in* de Boer, P. L., van Gelder, A., and Nio, S. D., eds., Tide Influenced Sedimentary Environments and Facies: Dordrecht, Reidel Publishing Company, p. 433–471.

REINSON, G. E., 1992, Transgressive barrier island and estuarine systems, *in* Walker, R. G., and James, N. P., eds., Facies Models: Response to Sea Level Change: St. Johns, Geological Association of Canada, p. 179–194.

RICE, C. L., 1981, Introduction: the stratigraphic framework of the Pennsylvanian rocks in eastern Kentucky, *in* Cobb, J.C., Chesnut, D.R., Hester, N.C., and Hower, J.C., eds. Coal and Coal Bearing Rocks of Eastern Kentucky (Annual Geological Society of America Coal Division Field Trip 1981): Lexington, Kentucky Geological Survey, p. 2–5.

RICE, C. L., AND SMITH, J. H., 1980, Correlation of coal beds, coal zones, and key stratigraphic units in the Pennsylvanian rocks of eastern Kentucky: United States Geological Survey Miscellaneous Field Studies Map MF-1188, 1 sheet.

RUST, B. R., 1978, The interpretation of ancient alluvial successions in the light of modern investigations, *in* Davidson-Arnott, R., and Nickling, W., eds., Research in Fluvial Geomorphology, Proceedings of the 5th Guelph Symposium on Geomorphology: Norwich, Geo Abstracts, p. 67–105.

SCHUMM, S. A., 1977, The Fluvial System: New York, Wiley, 338 p.

SHANLEY, K. W., AND MCCABE, P. J., 1991a, Predicting facies architecture through sequence stratigraphy-an example from the Kaiparowits Plateau, Utah: Geology, v. 19, p. 742–745.

SHANLEY, K. W., AND MCCABE, P. J., 1991b, Perspectives on the sequence stratigraphy of continental strata: Calgary, 1991 NUNA Conference on High Resolution Sequence Stratigraphy, White Paper, Global Sedimenatry Geology Programme, 26 p.

SHANLEY, K. W., AND MCCABE, P. J., 1993, Alluvial architecture in a sequence stratigraphic framework-a case history from the upper Cretaceous of southern Utah, U. S. A., *in* Flint, S. S., and Bryant, I. D., eds., Quantitative Description and Modelling of Clastic Hydrocarbon Reservoirs and Outcrop Analogues: Oxford, International Association of Sedimentologists Special Publication 15, p. 21–55.

SMITH, D. G., AND SMITH, N. D., 1980, Sedimentation in anastomosed river systems: examples from alluvial valleys near Banff, Alberta: Journal of Sedimentary Petrology, v. 50, p. 157–164.

SMITH, D. G., 1986, Anastomosing river deposits, sedimentation rates and basin subsidence, Magdalena river, northwestern Colombia, South America: Sedimentary Geology, v. 46, p. 177–196.

TANKARD, A. J., 1986, Depositional response to foreland deformation in the Carboniferous of Eastern Kentucky: American Association of Petroleum Geologists Bulletin, v. 70, p. 853–868.

VAIL, P. R., MITCHUM, R. M., AND THOMPSON, S., 1977, Seismic stratigraphy and global changes of sea level, Part III: Relative changes of sea level from coastal onlap, *in* Payton, C. E., ed., Seismic Stratigraphy-Applications to Hydrocarbon Exploration: Tulsa, American Association of Petroleum Geologists Memoir 26, p. 63–82.

VAN WAGONER, J. C., POSAMENTIER, H. W., MITCHUM, R. M., VAIL, P. R., SARG, J. F. LOUTIT, T. S., AND HARDENBOL, J., 1988, An overview of the fundamentals of sequence stratigraphy and key definitions, *in* Wilgus, C. K., Hastings, B. S., Kendall, C. G. St. C., Posamentier, H. W., Ross, C. A., and Van Wagoner, J. C., eds., Sea-level Changes: An Integrated Approach: Tulsa, Society of Economic Palaeontologists and Mineralogists Special Publication 42, p. 39–46.

VAN WAGONER, J. C., MITCHUM, R. M., CAMPION, K. M., AND RAHMANIAN, V. D., 1990, Siliciclastic sequence stratigraphy in wells, logs, cores and outcrops: Tulsa, American Association of Petroleum Geologists Methods in Exploration Series 7 , 55 p.

VEEVERS, J. J., AND POWELL, C. M., 1987, Late Palaeozoic episodes in Gondwanaland reflected in transgressive-regressive depositional sequences in Euramerica: Geological Society of America Bulletin, v. 98, p. 475–487.

WOOD, L. J., ETHRIDGE, F. G., AND SCHUMM, S. A, 1990, Effects of base level change on coastal plain-shelf-slope systems: an experimental approach (abs.): American Association of Petroleum Geologists Bulletin, v. 74, p. 1349.

WOOD, L. J., ETHRIDGE, F. G., AND SCHUMM, S. A., 1991, Influence of subaqueous shelf angle on coastal plain-shelf slope deposits resulting from a rise or fall in base level (abs.): American Association of Petroleum Geologists Bulletin, v. 75, p. 696.

NEOPROTEROZOIC INCISED VALLEYS OF THE EASTERN GREAT BASIN, UTAH AND IDAHO: FLUVIAL RESPONSE TO CHANGES IN DEPOSITIONAL BASE LEVEL

MARJORIE LEVY
Chevron Petroleum Technology Company, P.O. Box 446, La Habra, California 90633
NICHOLAS CHRISTIE-BLICK
Department of Geological Sciences and Lamont-Doherty Earth Observatory of Columbia University, Palisades, New York 10964
AND
PAUL KARL LINK
Department of Geology, Idaho State University, Pocatello, Idaho 83209

ABSTRACT: Incised valleys associated with sequence boundaries of regional extent are present at two stratigraphic levels in Neoproterozoic siliciclastic rocks of northern and western Utah and southeastern Idaho. In comparison with many Phanerozoic examples, the sedimentary fill of these Neoproterozoic incised valleys is unusually coarse-grained. The most prominent paleovalley system is present along a sequence boundary in the upper part of the Caddy Canyon Quartzite, and may be traced from the Portneuf Range in southeastern Idaho south to the Canyon Range in central Utah and west to the Dugway Range in western Utah. Individual valleys range in depth from several meters to >45 m and in width from a few tens of meters to several hundred meters. Valley fills consist of diffusely to well stratified granule to pebble conglomerate characteristically containing siltstone clasts <1 cm to >2 m across. They are interpreted to have accumulated predominantly in a fluvial environment, and perhaps in part by debris flows in a subaerial or shallow estuarine setting. This paleodrainage system is of significance because it is one of the few documented examples of a widespread incised-valley system that erodes into an underlying fluvial braid plain more than 200 km in width, indicating that the effects of base-level changes were felt far upstream in the more proximal reaches of a braided fluvial system. A second incised valley with more than 60 m of local relief, and located at the sequence boundary at the base of the Geertsen Canyon Quartzite, is developed only locally in the Portneuf Range of southeastern Idaho. It is similar in both geometry and sedimentary fill to the valleys in the Caddy Canyon Quartzite, and is incised into the proximal reaches of a widespread fluvial braid plain. Somewhat shallower, conglomerate-filled valleys associated with higher-order cyclicity have been observed within the upper part of the Caddy Canyon Quartzite and overlying Inkom Formation, and, unlike the other examples, are encased in offshore marine siltstone.

The development of Neoproterozoic sequence boundaries in the western U. S. is probably related to some combination of glacial eustasy (well documented in correlative strata elsewhere) and lithospheric extension, which appears to have preceded the development of the early Paleozoic passive continental margin. The relative roles of these mechanisms cannot yet be distinguished in the absence of more precise geochronology.

INTRODUCTION

Incised valleys are characteristic of subaerial erosion surfaces produced by the lowering of depositional base level (Vail, 1987; van Wagoner and others, 1990, 1991), surfaces that in sequence-stratigraphic terminology are referred to as sequence boundaries. Subaerial erosion surfaces tend to pass laterally both down depositional dip and along strike into surfaces that are approximately concordant with overlying and underlying strata, and in many cases characterized by abrupt upward-*deepening* of sedimentary facies. In the absence of valleys, therefore, it is commonly difficult to establish that base level was in fact lowered prior to subsequent flooding. This is especially the case in depositional ramp settings, where stratal discordance is typically subtle, "lowstand" units are thin to absent, and the stratigraphic record of repeated changes in shoreline position appears to be deceptively continuous.

Since the mid-1980s, there has been increasing interest in the application of sequence-stratigraphic principles to Proterozoic basins, not so much in spite of, but rather because other stratigraphic techniques yield less precise time-correlation than is usually possible in the Phanerozoic (Christie-Blick and Levy, 1985, 1989a; Lindsay, 1987; Link and others, 1987; Christie-Blick and others, 1988, 1990; von der Borch and others, 1988; Grotzinger and others, 1989; Bowring and Grotzinger, 1992; Christie-Blick, 1992). Preferentially preserved among these ancient deposits are sediments that accumulated in shallow intracratonic and foreland basins and the inner parts of passive continental margins,

all of which are primarily ramp settings. The recognition of incised valleys has therefore become vital to the confident interpretation of sequence stratigraphy in Proterozoic rocks. Where the existence of valleys is difficult to establish, owing to the vagaries of deformation, incomplete preservation, or lack of appropriate facies variation, it is quite likely that only a small proportion of the sequence boundaries in a given succession are actually identified.

Proterozoic studies are justified primarily as a way of gaining a longer-term perspective of earth history and geological phenomena than is possible with reference only to modern or younger geological examples. One of the most notable aspects of the few Proterozoic examples of incised valleys that have been documented to date is that they tend to be filled at least in part with relatively coarse-grained facies (Gehling, 1982; Germs, 1983; Eickhoff and others, 1988; Grotzinger and others, 1989; von der Borch and others, 1989; Christie-Blick and others, 1990; McDonald, 1992; Dyson and von der Borch, this volume; J. P. Grotzinger and B. Z. Saylor, pers. commun., 1993, concerning incised valleys in the Nama Group of southern Namibia). This paper describes some unusually conglomeratic incised-valley fills from the Neoproterozoic Brigham Group of the western United States. The sediments are thought to be primarily of fluvial origin, and perhaps in part due to debris flow in subaerial to shallow estuarine settings. Specific examples are now isolated as a result of subsequent deformation, but the valley system at one horizon (upper Caddy Canyon sequence boundary) appears to have incised into a fluvial braid plain palinspastically more than 200 km wide in the direction of flow (Levy and Christie-Blick, 1991a).

REGIONAL FRAMEWORK

The uppermost Neoproterozoic to Middle Cambrian Brigham Group of northern and western Utah and southeastern Idaho was formally defined by Crittenden and others (1971) to include the Caddy Canyon Quartzite, the Inkom, Mutual, and Browns Hole formations, and the Geertsen Canyon Quartzite in Utah (Figs. 1, 2) and the Papoose Creek Formation, Caddy Canyon Quartzite, Mutual Formation, Camelback Mountain Quartzite, and the Gibson Jack Formation in Idaho (Link and others, 1985). The Brigham Group is 3–4 km thick and consists predominantly of quartzite with lesser amounts of siltstone, conglomerate, and volcanic rocks (e.g., Crittenden and others, 1971; Oriel and Armstrong, 1971; Woodward, 1972; Hintze, 1973, 1988; Trimble, 1976; Christie-Blick, 1982; Rodgers, 1984; Link and others, 1987). These strata have been interpreted previously to represent a relatively conformable succession of shallow-marine sandstones and siltstones (Crittenden and others, 1971).

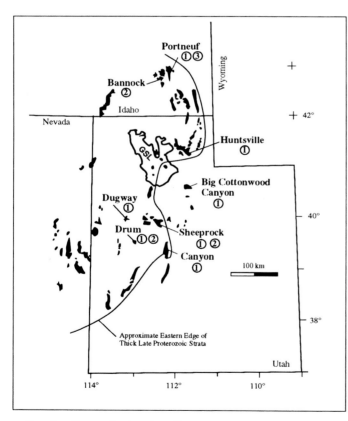

FIG. 1.—Present-day location of Neoproterozoic and Lower Cambrian outcrops of southeastern Idaho, Utah, and eastern Nevada. Ranges in which incised valleys have been observed are labeled. 1.—location of incised valleys associated with the upper Caddy Canyon sequence boundary; 2.—location of incised valleys within the upper Caddy Canyon Quartzite and Inkom Formation; 3.—location of incised valley associated with the base-Geertsten Canyon sequence boundary; and GSL-Great Salt Lake.

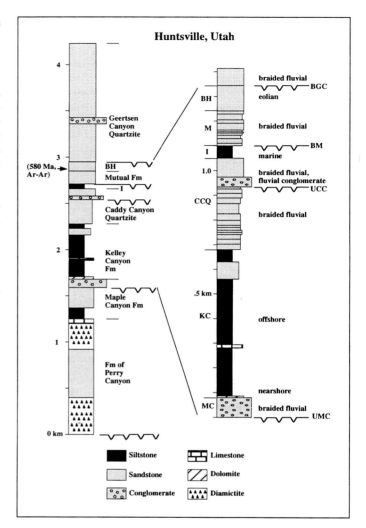

FIG. 2.—Lithostratigraphy, facies interpretation, and sequence stratigraphy, with expanded stratigraphic section of interval of interest, of the Neoproterozoic and Lower Cambrian strata at Huntsville, Utah. Note that lithostratigraphic boundaries and sequence-stratigraphic boundaries are not necessarily coincident. Abbreviations: MC—Maple Canyon Formation, KC—Kelley Canyon Formation, CCQ—Caddy Canyon Quartzite, I—Inkom Formation, M—Mutual Formation, BH—Browns Hole Formation, BGC—base-Geertsen Canyon sequence boundary, BM—base-Mutual sequence boundary, UCC—upper Caddy Canyon sequence boundary, and UMC—upper Maple Canyon sequence boundary. Figure modified from Levy and Christie-Blick (1991a).

However, re-evaluation of facies in a sequence-stratigraphic context have shown this succession to consist of several unconformity-bounded depositional sequences, and to represent a variety of depositional settings including fluvial, shallow-marine, and eolian (Christie-Blick and Levy, 1985, 1989a, 1989b; Levy, 1991; Levy and Christie-Blick, 1991a).

For the most part, these rocks are poorly dated. Over a large area of western Utah and southeastern Idaho, the Brigham Group overlies a thick succession of glacial and glacial-marine strata (Christie-Blick and Levy, 1989a), which although not directly dated are thought to be between 770

Ma and 720 Ma on the basis of dating of correlative glacial successions elsewhere in the Cordillera (Armstrong and others, 1982; Evenchick and others, 1984; Devlin and others, 1985, 1988). Ar-Ar dating of hornblende from volcanic breccia fragments within the volcanic member of the Browns Hole Formation (Fig. 2) yielded an age of 580 Ma (corrected for the new decay constants; Crittenden and Wallace, 1973). The uppermost part of the Geertsen Canyon Quartzite (Fig. 2) contains *Skolithos* burrows and rare trilobite tracks and is considered to be of Early Cambrian age (Crittenden and others, 1971). The Precambrian-Cambrian boundary, considered to be 550–545 Ma on the basis of U-Pb zircon dating of tuff layers from the Avalon terrane and Siberia (Benus, 1988; Conway Morris, 1988, 1989; Samson and Landing, 1992; S. A. Bowring, pers. commun., 1993), is conventionally placed within the lower Geertsen Canyon Quartzite (above the Browns Hole Formation and below the first appearance of *Skolithos* burrows) although it has not been located precisely.

Sequence boundaries have been identified at three horizons in the Brigham Group: (1) in the upper part of the Caddy Canyon Quartzite, (2) at or near the base of the Mutual Formation, and (3) at the base of the Geertsen Canyon Quartzite (Fig. 2; Christie-Blick and others, 1988; Christie-Blick and Levy, 1989a, 1989b; Levy, 1991; Link and others, 1993). Of these, the upper Caddy Canyon and base-Mutual sequence boundaries can be identified with greatest confidence and traced on a regional scale. The base-Geertsen Canyon sequence boundary is confidently identified in northern Utah and southeastern Idaho, but is cryptic elsewhere in Utah. In this paper, we discuss the geometry and fill of incised valleys associated with the upper Caddy Canyon and base-Geertsen Canyon sequence boundaries as well as incised valleys associated with higher-order cyclicity in the upper part of the Caddy Canyon Quartzite and overlying Inkom Formation.

The tectonic setting of the Neoproterozoic and Cambrian quartzites is uncertain. One view is that they are entirely post-rift, and that the rocks may have accumulated on a passive continental margin (Stewart, 1972, 1976, 1982; Stewart and Suczek, 1977; Link, 1984; Link and others, 1987; Hoffman, 1991; Ross, 1991). However, quantitative studies of tectonic subsidence for Cambrian and Ordovician strata in the western U.S. and southern Canada indicate that thermally driven subsidence of the Paleozoic passive margin began in latest Proterozoic or Early Cambrian time (Armin and Mayer, 1983, 1984; Bond and others, 1983, 1985; Bond and Kominz, 1984; Christie-Blick and Levy, 1989b; Levy and Christie-Blick, 1991b), corresponding approximately to the stratigraphic level of the Geertsen Canyon Quartzite (Fig. 2). Our preferred interpretation is that the Brigham Group accumulated predominantly in an intracontinental setting, but we cannot yet eliminate the possibility that a passive margin was already present, dating from the extensional event associated with deposition of the underlying diamictite unit. Whichever tectonic interpretation is correct, the distribution of sedimentary facies in the quartzite unit indicates the existence of a broad, west-facing terrigenous ramp that persisted well into Cambrian time (Levy and Christie-Blick, 1991b).

DISTRIBUTION AND GEOMETRY OF INCISED VALLEYS

Incised valleys are present at three stratigraphic levels in the Brigham Group: (1) along the upper Caddy Canyon sequence boundary, (2) along the base-Geertsen Canyon sequence boundary, and (3) within the sequence between the upper Caddy Canyon Quartzite and base of the Mutual Formation (Fig. 2; Christie-Blick and others, 1988; Christie-Blick and Levy, 1989a, 1989b; Levy, 1991; Link and others, 1993). Incised valleys at the upper Caddy Canyon sequence boundary, recognized in as many as seven ranges from southeastern Idaho to western Utah (Fig. 1), form an extensive paleodrainage system, and are associated with the lowering of depositional base level on a regional scale. In contrast, valley incision associated with the base-Geertsen Canyon sequence boundary is developed only locally near the eastern margin of the basin in southeastern Idaho, and may be enhanced by tectonic activity. Incised valleys present between the upper Caddy Canyon and base-Mutual sequence boundaries are not traceable on a regional scale and are likely associated with higher-order cyclicity.

The upper Caddy Canyon sequence boundary is located at or near the top of the Caddy Canyon Quartzite (Figs. 2, 3). It is identified by an abrupt facies discontinuity, characterized by coarsening and shoaling across the boundary and by onlap and erosional truncation of strata, as well as by the development of incised valleys with as much as several tens of meters of relief. These incised valleys are distinguished on the basis of scale from erosional surfaces produced by autocyclic channel switching. For several hundred meters below the incised valleys, broad shallow channels with low-relief basal erosion surfaces characterize the Caddy Canyon Quartzite. Consistently, along the interpreted sequence boundary, relief is considerably greater, truncating meters to tens of meters of underlying beds. Incised valleys are best developed in the Dugway Range (Fandangle Canyon), Sheeprock Mountains (Horse Valley) and in Big Cottonwood Canyon (Mill B North Fork; Fig. 1). Erosional relief of several meters at the sequence boundary is observed also at Huntsville (South Fork of the Ogden River) and in the Canyon Range (Fool Creek; Fig. 1). No relief has been documented in the Portneuf Range (Green Canyon), Idaho, or in the Drum Mountains (Fig. 1), but this is due at least in part to less favorable outcrop.

Along the upper Caddy Canyon sequence boundary, the thickness of the valley fill varies irregularly, but in general, the coarsest deposits thicken from a few meters near the basin margin in the Portneuf Range and in Big Cottonwood Canyon to a few tens of meters basinward in the Canyon Range, Sheeprock Mountains, Dugway Range, and Drum Mountains. An exception to this is at Huntsville, near the basin margin, where the thickness of the coarsest-grained facies is as much as 30 m. The maximum width of the valleys is difficult to determine with certainty because of discontinuous outcrop, but the preserved lateral extent of individual valleys ranges from a few hundred meters to more than 2 km.

The base-Geertsen Canyon sequence boundary (Fig. 2) is well developed in isolated localities of northern Utah (Huntsville) and southeastern Idaho (Portneuf Range), where

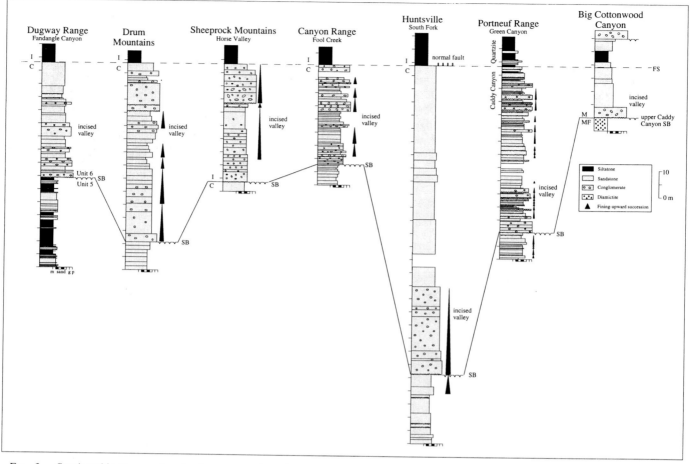

FIG. 3.—Stratigraphic cross-section for the sequence boundary near the top of the Caddy Canyon Quartzite from Big Cottonwood Canyon in the central Wasatch Range to the Dugway Range in western Utah. The datum at the top of the coarse-grained intervals is composite and not necessarily the same surface at each locality Note that in different localities, different criteria have been used for defining the lithostratigraphic boundary between the Caddy Canyon Quartzite and Inkom Formation. Sequence boundaries and flooding surfaces are interpreted on the basis of stratigraphic sedimentology rather than gross lithic character, and do not necessarily coincide with formal stratigraphic units. Notched lines indicate location of sequence boundaries. Abbreviations: C—Caddy Canyon Quartzite, I—Inkom Formation, M—Mutual Formation, MF—Mineral Fork Formation, SB—sequence boundary, FS—flooding surface, m—mudstone, g—granule conglomerate, and p—pebble conglomerate. Figure modified from Levy and Christie-Blick (1991a).

it coincides with the lower boundary of the Geertsen Canyon Quartzite and Camelback Mountain Quartzite, respectively (Fig. 1). In the Portneuf Range, an incised valley with more than 60 m of relief and extending at least several hundred meters laterally is present. Elsewhere (e.g., Canyon Range, Sheeprock Mountains, Dugway Range, Drum Mountains; Fig. 1), the lithostratigraphic contact between the Mutual Formation and Geertsen Canyon Quartzite (and its equivalent units) is gradational, and the sequence boundary is cryptic within a nonmarine succession several hundred meters thick.

Incised valleys associated with higher-order cyclicity are present within the depositional sequence between the upper Caddy Canyon and base-Mutual sequence boundaries (Fig. 2). They have been observed in the Bannock Range in southeastern Idaho and in the Sheeprock and Drum Mountains in western Utah (Fig. 1). Unlike the valleys along the Caddy Canyon sequence boundary, individual valleys can-

not be traced with confidence on a regional scale. In general, these valley have a smaller lateral extent, typically <100 m, and the thickness of the fill ranges from as little as 5 m in the lowermost and uppermost valleys in the Bannock Range to as much as 25–40 m elsewhere.

INCISED-VALLEY FILL

The incised-valley fill is characterized by predominantly medium to very thick-bedded conglomerates and pebbly sandstones commonly having erosional to irregular bases. An overall fining-upward on the scale of channels is observed, although larger-scale grain-size changes are variable. For the most part, the fill is poorly sorted and commonly more feldspathic than underlying strata. The valley fill includes three facies that form a complex array of nested channels—a granule to pebble conglomerate facies, a pebbly sandstone to medium- to coarse-grained sandstone facies, and a siltstone facies.

The granule to pebble conglomerate facies makes up the bulk of the valley fill. Channeling within this facies is common. Beds are typically lenticular (Fig. 4), and scours at the base of beds, with as much as 50 cm of relief, are commonly observed. The conglomerates are typically clast-supported, and clasts are predominantly quartz pebbles and to a varying extent, siltstone clasts, with minor quartzite and jasper pebbles (Fig. 5). Systematic grain-size variations within conglomerate beds range from absent to well-defined fining upward. Crude to well-developed parallel to gently inclined stratification is commonly observed (Fig. 6). Rare well-developed cross-stratification is locally present. Alignment of clasts is rare, but where developed, is commonly parallel to bedding. In some places, this facies is gradationally to abruptly overlain by a poorly-sorted pebbly sandstone to medium- to coarse-grained sandstone facies. The sandstone facies comprises a subordinate com-

FIG. 6.—Subtle horizontal stratification defined by pebbles within the conglomerate facies of the incised-valley fill. This example is from the upper Caddy Canyon Quartzite in the Dugway Range, Utah. Pocket knife for scale.

FIG. 4.—Example of abundant channeling and lenticular bedding typical of the conglomerate fill. This example is from the incised valley at the base of the Camelback Mountain Quartzite in the Portneuf Range (Upper Rock Creek), Idaho. Pocket knife for scale.

ponent of the valley fill. It consists of generally lenticular beds that are poorly sorted and locally feldspathic, and that display diffuse to poorly-developed stratification. Locally, this facies is overlain abruptly by a laterally impersistent, laminated siltstone facies. However, more commonly, siltstone is observed as clasts ranging from a few centimeters to as much as 1–2 m in length in the conglomerate facies. These three facies, where present, are arranged in an overall fining-upward succession on a scale of one to a few meters (Fig. 7).

ASSOCIATED FACIES

The incised valleys associated with the upper Caddy Canyon and base-Geertsen Canyon sequence boundaries consistently erode into a fine- to coarse-grained sandstone

FIG. 5.—Clast-supported pebble conglomerate with predominantly quartz and large siltstone clasts from the incised valley along the upper Caddy Canyon sequence boundary in the Sheeprock Mountains. Pocket knife for scale.

FIG. 7.—Photograph of the fining-upward successions abundant in the incised-valley fill in the Portneuf Range (Upper Rock Creek) where individual conglomerate layers fine upward into poorly-sorted, medium- to very coarse-grained, laminated sandstone and siltstone on a scale of one to a few meters. Pocket knife for scale.

facies. This underlying facies is characterized by broadly lenticular beds with low-relief basal erosion surfaces, typically arranged in nested channels. The beds are generally poorly sorted and contain abundant trough cross-stratification. Subtle fining-upward is observed on the scale of beds as well as bedsets. In marked contrast, incised valleys present between the upper Caddy Canyon and base-Mutual sequence boundaries erode into and truncate a fine-grained laminated siltstone facies. The contact between the valleys and the underlying facies is typically extremely sharp with no soft sediment deformation of the uppermost beds of the underlying facies.

The majority of the incised-valley fills are abruptly overlain by a fine-grained micaceous siltstone unit that contains thin, fine-grained sandstone beds characterized by wavy to even parallel laminae, current ripples, and flaser bedding. In a few localities (Huntsville, and Green Canyon and Upper Rock Creek in the Portneuf Range; Fig. 1), however, the conglomeratic fill of the valleys is overlain gradationally by several tens of meters of a pebbly sandstone to sandstone facies. At Huntsville, the conglomerate fill passes upward into relatively poorly-sorted, poorly-stratified, fine- to very coarse-grained quartzite. In Green Canyon, the overlying facies consists of coarse-grained sandstone characterized by well-developed erosion surfaces, nested channels, and fining-upward successions. In Upper Rock Creek, the valley fill is overlain gradationally by a well-sorted, fine- to coarse-grained quartzite with poorly defined cross-stratification. In these cases, in which the conglomerate is overlain gradationally by a coarse-grained sandstone facies and exposure does not afford the possibility of identifying the lateral pinchout of the channel, the stratigraphic location of the upper boundary of the valley fill is uncertain.

VARIATIONS OF GEOMETRY AND FILL OF INDIVIDUAL VALLEYS

Upper Caddy Canyon Incised Valleys

In the northeastern part of the Dugway Range in west-central Utah, a thick section of Caddy Canyon Quartzite (units 1–6 of Staatz and Carr, 1964), overlain by the Inkom and Mutual Formations (units 7 and 8 of Staatz and Carr, 1964) is well-exposed in several fault blocks (Fig. 1; Staatz and Carr, 1964). Here, the Caddy Canyon Quartzite consists of interstratified quartzite and siltstone. Although generally finer-grained in the Dugway Range than the type Caddy Canyon Quartzite in the Bannock Range of southeastern Idaho (Fig. 1), it is considered correlative on the basis of stratigraphic position (Staatz and Carr, 1964; Crittenden and others, 1971; Christie-Blick, 1982). An incised valley with greater than 40 m of relief is present within unit 6, where a pebble conglomerate can be seen to truncate the underlying sandstone beds near the base of unit 6 (Figs. 8, 9), and can be traced laterally for >200 m. In an adjacent fault block, an incised valley along the upper Caddy Canyon sequence boundary cuts downsection into interbedded siltstones and fine-grained sandstones of unit 5 (Figs. 9, 10). The incised-valley fill is composed of a clast- to matrix-supported conglomerate and pebbly sandstone. Feldspar is rare to absent. Bedding surfaces are commonly obscured by abundant fracturing, and channeling within the valley is

Fig. 8.—Photograph of an incised valley along the upper Caddy Canyon sequence boundary in the Dugway Range (see Figure 9, section B). Arrows indicate the base of the valley. In this fault block, the incised valley truncates tens of meters of well-bedded sandstones of the lower part of unit 6 (uppermost unit of the Caddy Canyon Quartzite) of Staatz and Carr (1964). Recessive outcrops on the left are unit 5 (upper part of Caddy Canyon Quartzite) of Staatz and Carr (1964) and the recessive outcrops on the right are the Inkom Formation (unit 7 of Staatz and Carr, 1964).

difficult to observe. These strata are characterized by common but subtle horizontal to subhorizontal layering (Fig. 6) and rare cross-stratification.

In the southern Sheeprock Mountains in central Utah, the Caddy Canyon Quartzite and Inkom Formation is exposed in an overturned structural block bounded by thrust faults (Fig. 1; Christie-Blick, 1982, 1983a; Christie-Blick and others, 1988; Christie-Blick and Levy, 1989a). An incised valley containing strata up to 45 m thick and about 250 m across is present at the base of the Inkom Formation. Underlying strata of the Caddy Canyon Quartzite, consisting of predominantly cross-stratified fine- to coarse-grained quartzite, are abruptly truncated by pebble conglomerate and pebbly sandstone that fill the incised valley (Fig. 11). The valley fill consists of two distinct units separated by an erosion surface having more than 3 m of relief, with the coarsest deposits being present in the upper unit (Fig. 3). The lower unit consists of matrix-supported conglomerate containing small to large pebbles that are flattened and aligned parallel to bedding, and fines upward to pebbly sandstone containing granule to small-pebble clasts. Poorly-defined cross-stratification is present locally in the pebbly sandstone. The upper unit consists of two stacked channels and fines upward overall. The lower of these channels contains a large pebble to cobble conglomerate at the base overlain by a unit of medium to coarse-grained quartzite. The upper channel consists of pebbly sandstone at the base and fines upward to a muddy sandstone containing scattered granules and small pebbles. Argillite clasts as large as 2 m are locally present, but typically do not exceed 15–20 cm. They likely are derived from the eroded tops of underlying channel successions.

In Big Cottonwood Canyon, in the Wasatch Mountains, a thick succession of Neoproterozoic strata is exposed, con-

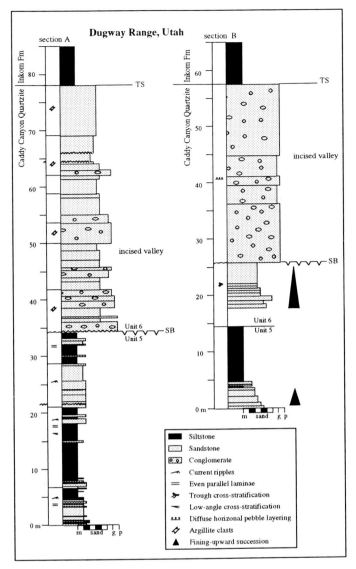

FIG. 9.—Stratigraphic sections from different fault blocks (approximately 500 m apart) of the incised valley in the upper part of the Caddy Canyon Quartzite in the Dugway Range. In section A, the incised valley is eroded into interbedded siltstone and fine-grained sandstone of unit 5 of Staatz and Carr (1964) (see Figure 10). In section B, the valley truncates well-bedded sandstones of the lower part of unit 6 of Staatz and Carr (1964) (see Figure 8). Figure modified from Christie-Blick and others (1989).

FIG. 10.—Photograph of the base of the incised valley (arrows) along the upper Caddy Canyon sequence boundary in the Dugway Range in a fault block adjacent to the valley shown in Figure. 8. Here, the valley erodes through unit 6 (uppermost unit of the Caddy Canyon Quartzite) and into the siltstones of unit 5 (upper part of Caddy Canyon Quartzite) of Staatz and Carr (1964). Stratigraphic column is shown in Figure 9, section A.

FIG. 11.—Photograph of the edge of the incised valley along the upper Caddy Canyon sequence boundary in the Sheeprock Mountains (Horse Valley). Note the abrupt truncation of white sandstone beds (in the lower lefthand corner of the photograph) underlying the valley by grey conglomerate beds within the incised valley. The valley is present in an overturned structural block bounded by thrust faults (Christie-Blick, 1983a).

sisting of the Big Cottonwood, Mineral Fork, and Mutual Formations, and the Tintic Quartzite (Figs. 1, 12; Crittenden and others, 1952; 1971). The Caddy Canyon Quartzite and Inkom Formation have not been mapped at this locality and the Mineral Fork Formation is unconformably overlain by the Mutual Formation. In the vicinity of Mill B North Fork, an incised valley with as much as 15 m of relief is present along the base of the Mutual Formation, truncating grey to black diamictite of the underlying Mineral Fork Formation. Within approximately 1 km to the south, the valley fill thins from 19 m to about 4 m and conglomerate

is absent. The valley fill consists of a few meters of pebble conglomerate overlain by as much as 15 m of fine- to very fine-grained sandstone characterized by parallel laminae, poorly-defined cross-stratification, and minor ripples (Figs. 3, 12). The conglomerate differs from the typical valley fill in that it contains predominantly granitic and quartzite clasts with lesser amounts of gabbro, gneiss, schist, quartz, and carbonate clasts, most likely derived from the underlying diamictite, which contains similar clasts (Christie-Blick, 1983b). Argillite clasts form a very minor component of the conglomerate, and feldspar is not observed. The incised-valley fill is overlain by about 10 m of fine-grained sandstone and siltstone, which in turn is overlain abruptly

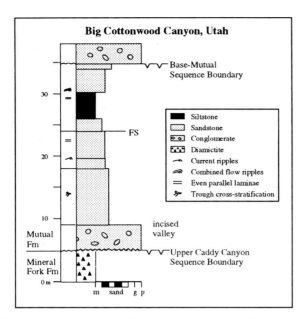

FIG. 12.—Stratigraphy of Neoproterozoic strata in Big Cottonwood Canyon. The incised valley at the base of the Mutual Formation is interpreted to be time-equivalent to upper Caddy Canyon incised valleys elsewhere.

by several tens of meters of pebble to cobble conglomerate and pebbly sandstone infilling a second stratigraphically younger incised valley. The contact between the Mineral Fork and Mutual Formations is interpreted to correlate with the upper Caddy Canyon sequence boundary, and the base of the cobble conglomerate is correlative with the base-Mutual sequence boundary (Figs. 3, 12). Note that in this interpretation, the physical stratigraphic surfaces do not maintain a consistent stratigraphic position with respect to conventional lithic units. The basal Mutual Formation at this locality is a time-equivalent of the uppermost Caddy Canyon Quartzite and Inkom Formation elsewhere, and therefore the incised valley at the base of the Mutual Formation is time-equivalent to upper Caddy Canyon incised valleys.

At Huntsville, a well-exposed section of the Caddy Canyon Quartzite, Inkom Formation, and lowermost Mutual Formation is present (Figs. 1, 3; Crittenden and others, 1971; Crittenden, 1972; Sorensen and Crittenden, 1979). The uppermost 120 m of the Caddy Canyon Quartzite is generally coarser-grained than underlying beds. The basal contact of this uppermost unit of the Caddy Canyon Quartzite is extremely abrupt and overlain by about 30 m of conglomerate. Relief of several meters is observed at the base of the conglomerate, which is interpreted as the upper Caddy Canyon sequence boundary. The full lateral extent of the incised valley is unknown because of structural complications (Christie-Blick and Levy, 1989a; N. Christie-Blick, unpubl. mapping). The incised-valley fill consists of very poorly stratified, granule and small-pebble conglomerate (Christie-Blick and Levy, 1989a; Fig. 3). Argillite clasts are rare to absent in this valley, and little if any feldspar is observed. The conglomerate passes upward into relatively

poorly-sorted, fine- to very coarse-grained quartzite, which is also poorly stratified (Christie-Blick and Levy, 1989a). The uppermost few meters of the Caddy Canyon Quartzite is characterized by broad nested channels and by fining-upward successions on the scale of a few meters (Christie-Blick and Levy, 1989a).

In the upper plate of the Canyon Range thrust sheet on the western side of the Canyon Range, a thick succession of Brigham Group strata is well-exposed (Fig. 1; Higgins, 1982; Millard, 1983; Holladay, 1984). However, a considerable amount of structural deformation is present in this range, including both large-scale and small-scale faulting and folding, as well as structurally overturned beds, making stratigraphic analysis somewhat uncertain (Christiansen, 1952; Higgins, 1982; Millard, 1983; Holladay, 1984). An incised valley as much as 40 m deep is thought to be present at the top of the Caddy Canyon Quartzite just north of Fool Creek. It is at least several hundred meters wide, but owing to structural complications, the full lateral extent and erosional relief of this valley is unknown. The fill consists of granule to small pebble conglomerate and pebbly sandstone, similar to the valley fill described above (Fig. 3). However, the conglomerate is predominantly matrix-supported, and argillite clasts and feldspar are rare to absent. Furthermore, the valley fill forms a recessive unit with bedding geometry poorly preserved; however, where observed, beds tend to be broadly lenticular to wedge-shaped.

As in the Sheeprock Mountains example, the inferred incised valley in the Drum Mountains consists of two distinct units (Fig. 3). The lower unit consists of matrix-supported granule to small pebble conglomerate that grades upward to fine to very coarse-grained pebbly sandstone. Beds are crudely stratified and arranged into abundant nested channels. Fining-upward successions are present on the scale of beds and bedsets. The upper unit consists of pebble to cobble conglomerate at the base with up to several meters of relief, and fines upward to granule conglomerate and pebbly sandstone. The conglomerate is clast-supported at the base and matrix-supported near the top. It is characterized by crudely- to well-developed parallel stratification, minor argillite clasts, and the presence of feldspar. Stacked channels within the upper unit display fining upward on the scale of beds and bedsets. This valley and the one in the Sheeprock Mountains are distinct in that two separate channel systems can be recognized, suggesting two episodes of erosion and fill.

Base-Geertsen Canyon Incised Valleys

At Upper Rock Creek, in the Portneuf Range, an incised valley with more than 60 m of relief is present (Fig. 13). The contact between the incised valley and the underlying Mutual Formation is in places a detachment surface that accommodates disharmonic folding in strata above and below. For the most part, however, the contact is stratigraphic (N. Christie-Blick, unpubl. mapping). Erosional truncation of the underlying strata and onlap at the base of the incised valley is observed. Inasmuch as only the northern edge of the valley is preserved, the minimal lateral extent is at least a few hundred meters. The valley is filled predominantly

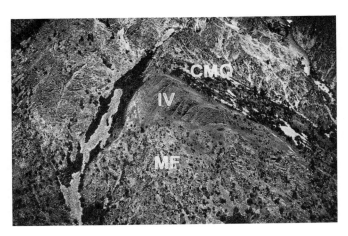

FIG. 13.—Aerial photograph of the large-scale geometry of the incised valley along the base-Geertsen Canyon sequence boundary in the Portneuf Range (Upper Rock Creek), Idaho. The incised valley at the base of the Camelback Mountain Quartzite has more than 60 m of relief and is filled predominantly with pebble conglomerate and pebbly sandstone. It truncates underlying strata of the Mutual Formation. Abbreviations: MF—Mutual Formation, IV—incised valley, CMQ—Camelback Mountain Quartzite.

with pebble conglomerate and pebbly sandstone. The thickness of the fill is uncertain because the conglomerate is only crudely stratified, and was folded probably during Mesozoic time. The fill is characterized by matrix- to clast-supported conglomerate consisting of rounded clasts of predominantly vein quartz with minor jasper and quartzite, together with more angular blocks of sandstone and siltstone in a sandy matrix. Relatively little feldspar is present in the conglomerate. At a scale of one to a few meters, individual layers fine upward into poorly-sorted, medium- to very coarse-grained, laminated sandstone and siltstone (Fig. 7). Beds within the valley fill, arranged in abundant nested channels, appear to be disrupted as a result of later deformation, and rarely are laterally persistent for more than a few meters.

Higher-Order Incised Valleys

An incised valley within the Inkom Formation is present in the northeastern Drum Mountains (Fig. 1). The valley fill is as much as 40 m thick and consists of a small- to large-pebble conglomerate containing abundant quartz and argillite clasts and minor quartzite and jasper pebbles. Beds within the valley are channelized, and fining-upward successions are present on the scale of beds. Minor cross-stratification is observed locally. The basal contact of the incised valley is an erosional surface, truncating underlying siltstone of the lower Inkom Formation, which is characterized by abundant interference ripples and wave-modified current ripples. This valley is unique in that it can be seen to thin to a few cms of fine-grained sandstone within about 100 m laterally. Several hundred meters to the north, at what appears to be approximately the same stratigraphic horizon, additional channels are present displaying the same vertical facies relationships.

In the Sheeprock Mountains, incised valleys are present in both Horse Valley and at Erickson Peak (Fig. 1). In Horse Valley, the incised-valley fill is more than 30 m thick and forms a prominent cliff-forming unit encased in siltstone of the Inkom Formation. The valley fill is characterized by abundant fining-upward successions of granule and pebble conglomerate to medium- to coarse-grained pebbly sandstone. Argillite clasts as much as 25 cm across are abundant at several horizons. Beds are generally wedge-shaped with common, low-relief erosion surfaces. Internally, bedding is poorly developed with only a hint of diffuse parallel laminae defined by the presence of pebble-rich layers. A similar incised valley is observed in the upper Inkom Formation at Erickson Peak in the northern Sheeprock Mountains. The valley fill is more than 40 m thick and consists of granule to small pebble conglomerate and fine- to very coarse-grained sandstone. Argillite clasts up to 20 cm are locally present. Beds are tabular to wedge-shaped, contain horizontal laminae to trough cross-stratification, and display fining upward of individual beds as well as bedsets.

A critical exposure of the uppermost Caddy Canyon Quartzite and Inkom Formation is present in the northern end of the Bannock Range in the vicinity of the West Fork of Mink Creek (Fig. 1; Jansen, 1986; Christie-Blick and others, 1989). Here, four stacked incised valleys are present within a vertical succession approximately 200 m thick, and in each case the base of the valley erodes into and truncates underlying laminted siltstone (Fig. 14). The fill of the valleys is predominantly feldspathic conglomerate and pebbly quartzite. The lowest valley is a lenticular body about 5 m thick and consists of poorly stratified, very fine- to coarse-grained, tan-weathering quartzite with minor feldspar; quartz granules and clasts of siltstone as much as 5–15 cm across are present locally. The overlying valley fill is more than 32 m thick and is composed of tabular to wedge-shaped beds of granule to pebble conglomerate and very fine- to very coarse-grained pebbly sandstone, in places bounded by erosional surfaces. These beds tend to be more feldspathic than the lower valley fill, and are very poorly sorted and poorly stratified. Fining upward is present on a scale of 2–5 m, but larger-scale grain-size trends are not observed. Argillite clasts, as much as 40 cm long, are locally abundant and commonly aligned parallel to bedding. The upper two valleys fills, approximately 25 m and 5 m thick respectively, are composed of similar facies as the underlying valleys. Bedding is broadly lenticular and fining upward is observed on a scale of beds and bedsets.

INTERPRETATION OF FACIES

The interpretation of conglomeratic incised-valley fills is important because it bears directly on the interpretation of both the sequence stratigraphy and the paleogeography. The existence of incised valleys rather than large channels is inferred in part on the basis of scale (the valleys are in many cases considerably deeper than channels in the same succession), and in part from the presence of an abrupt and very marked upward increase in grain size at the interpreted sequence boundary. The interpretation of subaerial erosion is supported by the fact that in many but not all examples

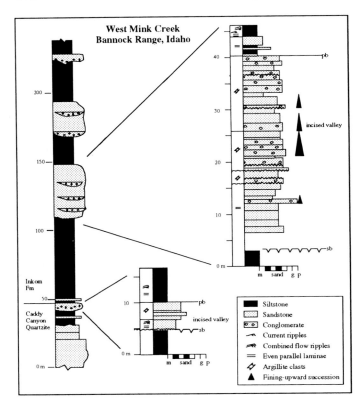

FIG. 14.—Simplified stratigraphic section of the upper Caddy Canyon Quartzite and Inkom Formation at West Mink Creek in the Bannock Range of southeastern Idaho (modified from Jansen, 1986), with detailed measured sections of the lower two incised valleys. Abbreviations: sb—sequence boundary, pb—parasequence boundary.

strata beneath the sequence boundary themselves appear to have accumulated in a fluvial environment. The conglomerates now preserved within the valleys in at least some examples pass upward into sandstones interpreted to have accumulated in a fluvial to shallow marine environment. Taken together, available data support the idea that the conglomerate is primarily of fluvial origin, and perhaps in part due to debris flow in a subaerial to shallow estuarine setting.

The predominance of channelized clast-supported conglomerates containing both parallel and inclined crude to well-defined stratification suggests deposition of gravel bedload from high-energy flows in which finer sand and silt components were transported primarily in suspension (Nemec and Steel, 1984; Rust and Koster, 1984; Collinson, 1986). The abundance of subtle to well-defined fining-upward successions, commonly passing upward into sandstone, is interpreted to indicate waning flood discharge, or in some cases, gradual abandonment of fluvial channels (Nemec and Steel, 1984). Alternations of conglomerate and pebbly sandstones are taken to indicate fluctuations in discharge. Argillite clasts that are locally abundant appear to have been derived at least in part from the erosion of fine-grained sediment deposited during conditions of low flow. The best evidence for this is present in the incised valley at the base of the Camelback Mountain Quartzite in southeastern Idaho, where identical argillites are locally pre-

served as intact layers within the valley fill but are absent from the fluvial sandstones of the underlying Mutual Formation.

Although the bulk of the conglomerate appears to be fluvial, we cannot eliminate the possibility that some of the least stratified beds accumulated from debris flow, and indeed we previously favored that interpretation (Christie-Blick and others, 1989). However, the debris-flow interpretation poses certain paleogeographic difficulties (Christie-Blick and Levy, 1989a) because it appears to require unreasonably large regional paleoslopes. In addition, a systematic re-examination of all of the critical outcrops in 1989 revealed that the conglomerates are considerably more stratified than originally thought and that our initial impressions were influenced strongly by the fact that depositional layering tends to be obscured by the effects of low-grade metamorphism and fracturing. A key outcrop is the one at Mink Creek in the Bannock Range (Fig. 14), where crudely stratified conglomerate is present in four intervals in the upper part of the Caddy Canyon Quartzite and lower Inkom Formation. In each case, contacts against underlying offshore marine siltstone are sharp and in places clearly erosional. This and the fact that no turbidites are present in the siltstone, as might be expected if the conglomerates were simply random sediment gravity flow deposits, suggests strongly that the conglomerate and siltstone are not genetically related facies and supports the interpretation that these incised valleys are filled with fluvial conglomerates.

It is nevertheless possible that some of the conglomerate accumulated in a shallow estuarine rather than strictly fluvial environment. Similar, diffusely to well-stratified conglomerate is present in incised valleys of the Upper Cretaceous Castlegate Formation in southeastern Utah (van Wagoner and others, 1991). In that example, the physical sedimentology is consistent with a fluvial interpretation, but the presence of a displaced low-diversity assemblage of brackish-water molluscs indicates occasional marine incursions. In the absence of a diagnostic fauna, it is not possible to make such distinctions in Proterozoic deposits.

The interpretation of Proterozoic incised-valley fills in Utah and Idaho is relevant to the interpretation of similar conglomeratic facies in other Proterozoic successions. Large-scale incised valleys as much as 1 km deep are present at five horizons in the Neoproterozoic and Lower Cambrian of South Australia (Gehling, 1982; von der Borch and others, 1985, 1989; Eickhoff and others, 1988; Christie-Blick and others, 1990; McDonald, 1992; Christie-Blick, 1993; Dyson and von der Borch, this volume). The origin of these valleys is controversial, with interpretations ranging from mass wasting in a marine environment to fluvial incision as a result of large-scale lowering of base level. Crudely to well-stratified conglomerate and sandstone, remarkably similar to the facies described in this paper, are present at the base of each valley system. The rocks have been interpreted by most authors as a product of sediment gravity flow, in part because well-developed cross-stratification is uncommon to absent and in part because the rocks are associated with and overlain by finer-grained sandstones and siltstones that appear to have accumulated in a marine setting, if of uncertain water depth. The observations presented in this paper, especially the largely non-marine stratigraphic context of the conglomerates, indicates that a fluvial rather than sediment gravity flow interpretation should be entertained also in some or all of the Australian examples (Christie-Blick, 1993).

ORIGIN OF VALLEYS

The primary constraint on the origin of Neoproterzoic valleys in the western U. S. is that they are associated with the regional lowering of depositional base level by a minimum of several tens of meters. It is not known whether this was primarily in response to eustasy or to changes in the rate of tectonic subsidence. Age control is not adequate to make any firm statements, but the succession appears to be broadly coeval with successions elsewhere containing evidence for the Varanger glacial event of northwestern Europe and Australia (Hambrey and Harland, 1981, 1985). In the North American Cordillera, evidence for a second glaciation is present in the upper part of the Neoproterozoic succession only in the Ice Brook Formation of the Mackenzie Mountains (Aitken, 1991). Glacial-marine sediments in the upper part of that unit rest with unconformable contact on platform carbonate rocks of the Keele Formation, one sequence above the main glacial unit (Shezal Formation). We suggest that the sequence boundary in the upper part of the Caddy Canyon Quartzite may represent the same horizon. Support for this view is provided by three observations: (1) The sequence boundary in the Caddy Canyon Quartzite appears to be at an equivalent stratigraphic position with respect to the main glacial unit in Utah and Idaho (Fig. 2). (2) Incised valleys are best developed at this horizon, consistent with the relatively large amplitude in sea-level change anticipated for glacial-eustatic fluctuation. (3) The higher-order valleys documented in the uppermost Caddy Canyon Quartzite and Inkom Formation are in the lower part of the overlying sequence, consistent with the high-frequency base-level changes that tend to characterize glacial intervals (cf. the Oligocene and Miocene record of ice-volume change and sequence stratigraphy of the U. S. Atlantic margin; Miller and others, 1991; Greenlee and others, 1992). Changes in the rate of tectonic subsidence are also likely during the Neoproterozoic, which corresponds in the western U. S. to a time of lithospheric extension prior to the development of a passive continental margin in the Early Cambrian (Christie-Blick and Levy, 1989b; Levy and Christie-Blick, 1991b). Again, it is not possible to resolve the ages of individual tectonic events, which may have led directly to the development of sequence boundaries or perhaps only enhanced the depth of valley incision.

Although the available evidence is equivocal, it bears on the mechanism by which valleys are incised. The generally accepted view (Posamentier and others, 1988) is that valleys are due to the lowering of base level at some break in the depositional profile (e.g., "depositional shoreline break," "depositional shelf edge"), and that once formed in this way, they propagate upstream by headward erosion. In the case of the examples described in this paper from the Caddy Canyon Quartzite and Inkom Formation, the break in slope

would have to be located well within the marine environment. For the higher-order sequences in the Bannock Range, the observed facies discontinuity between offshore siltstone and fluvial conglomerate appears to require rapid lowering of sea level. An alternative view (Christie-Blick, 1991) is that subaerial exposure surfaces and associated incised valleys initially propagate *downstream* from areas near the basin margin where the rate of subsidence is lowest. Breaks in slope are not required for the incision of valleys. This mechanism readily explains why a deep valley is present in proximal fluvial sandstones at the base of the Camelback Mountain Quartzite whereas such features are not observed in more distal paleogeographic settings in spite of appropriate outcrop.

SUMMARY

Incised valleys as much as 60 m deep are present at two main horizons in the Neoproterozoic Brigham Group of northern and western Utah and southeastern Idaho, and associated with higher-order cyclicity at an intervening level. The main valleys are thought to correspond with sequence boundaries of regional extent. The valleys are filled with crudely to well-stratified conglomerate and sandstone, and interpreted to have accumulated for the most part in a fluvial environment. The origin of the valleys is uncertain, but a combination of eustatic effects and lithospheric extension seems likely.

ACKNOWLEDGMENTS

Sequence stratigraphic studies by Levy and Christie-Blick have been supported by the National Science Foundation (EAR 85–17923), by the Donors of the Petroleum Research Fund, administered by the American Chemical Society (PRF 16042-G2 and PRF 19989-AC2), by the Arthur D. Storke Memorial Fund of the Department of Geological Sciences, Columbia University; and by Grants-in-Aid (to M. Levy) from the Geological Society of America, American Association of Petroleum Geologists, and Sigma Xi. Stratigraphic studies by Link have been supported by the Idaho Geological Survey and the Kackley Family Bear River Endowment to Idaho State University. Some of this project represents work done as part of Levy's dissertation, completed at Lamont-Doherty Geological Observatory of Columbia University, New York. We thank C. Fielding, R. W. Schlische, C. Summa, and R. Walker for helpful reviews of this manuscript, and M. A. Anders, M. S. Steckler, A. R. Prave, and W. B. F. Ryan for critical reviews of an earlier version of this manuscript.. We also thank J. P. Grotzinger and B. Z. Saylor for generously sharing unpublished data with us. Lamont-Doherty Earth Observatory contribution number 5080.

REFERENCES

AITKEN, J. D., 1991, Two Late Proterozoic glaciations, Mackenzie Mountains, northwestern Canada: Geology, v. 19, p. 445–448.

ARMIN, R. A., AND MAYER, L., 1983, Subsidence analysis of the Cordilleran miogeocline: Implications for timing of Late Proterozoic rifting and amount of extension: Geology, v. 11, p. 702–705.

ARMIN, R. A., AND MAYER, L., 1984, Reply on "Subsidence analysis of the Cordilleran miogeocline: Implications for timing of Late Proterozoic rifting and amount of extension": Geology, v. 12, p. 699–701.

ARMSTRONG, R. L., EISBACHER, G. H., AND EVANS, P. D., 1982, Age and stratigraphic-tectonic significance of Proterozoic diabase sheets, Mackenzie Mountains, northwestern Canada: Canadian Journal of Earth Sciences, v. 19, p. 316–323.

BENUS, A. P., 1988, Sedimentological context of a deep-water Ediacaran fauna (Mistaken Point Formation, Avalon Zone, eastern Newfoundland), *in* Landing, E., Narbonne, G. M., and Myrow, P., eds., Trace Fossils, Small Shelly Fossils and the Precambrian-Cambrian Boundary: Bulletin of the New York State Museum 463, p. 8–9.

BOND, G. C., CHRISTIE-BLICK, N., KOMINZ, M. A., AND DEVLIN, W. J., 1985, An Early Cambrian rift to post-rift transition in the Cordillera of western North America: Nature, v. 316, p. 742–745.

BOND, G. C., AND KOMINZ, M. A., 1984, Construction of tectonic subsidence curves for the early Paleozoic miogeocline, southern Canadian Rocky Mountains: Implications for subsidence mechanisms, age of breakup, and crustal thinning: Geological Society of America Bulletin, v. 95, p. 155–173.

BOND, G. C., KOMINZ, M. A., AND DEVLIN, W. J., 1983, Thermal subsidence and eustasy in the Lower Paleozoic miogeocline of western North America: Nature, v. 306, p. 775–779.

BOWRING, S. A., AND GROTZINGER, J. P., 1992, Implications of new chronostratigraphy for tectonic evolution of Wopmay orogen, nothwest Canadian shield: American Journal of Science, v. 292, p. 1–20.

CHRISTIANSEN, F. W., 1952, Structure and stratigraphy of the Canyon Range, central Utah: Unpublished Ph.D. Dissertation, University of Utah, Salt Lake City, 145 p.

CHRISTIE-BLICK, N., 1982, Upper Proterozoic and Lower Cambrian rocks of the Sheeprock Mountains, Utah: regional correlation and significance: Geological Society of America Bulletin, v. 93, p. 735–750.

CHRISTIE-BLICK, N., 1983a, Structural geology of the southern Sheeprock Mountains, Utah: regional significance, *in* Miller, D. M., Todd, V. R., and Howard, K. A., eds., Tectonic and Stratigraphic Studies in the Eastern Great Basin: Boulder, Geological Society of America Memoir 157, p. 101–124.

CHRISTIE-BLICK, N., 1983b, Glacial-marine and subglacial sedimentation, Upper Proterozoic Mineral Fork Formation, Utah, *in* Monia, B. F., ed., Glacial-marine Sedimentation: New York, Plenum Press, p. 703–776.

CHRISTIE-BLICK, N., 1992, Sequence stratigraphy: Implications for correlation in Neoproterozoic successions (abs.): 29th International Geological Congress, Kyoto, Japan, Abstracts, v. 1, p. 239.

CHRISTIE-BLICK, N., 1993, Day 5. Saturday, May 15th — Wonoka Canyons, Umberatana Syncline, *in* Jenkins, R. J. F., Lindsay, J. F., and Walter, M. R., eds., Field Guide to the Adelaide Geosyncline and Amadeus Basin, Australia: Adelaide, Australian Geological Survey Organisation Record No. 1993/35, p. 29–31.

CHRISTIE-BLICK, N., GROTZINGER, J. P., AND VON DER BORCH, C. C., 1988, Sequence stratigraphy in Proterozoic successions: Geology, v. 16, p. 100–104.

CHRISTIE-BLICK, N., AND LEVY, M., 1985, A new approach to time correlation in Proterozoic rocks: sequence boundaries in the Brigham Group, Utah (abs.): Geological Society of America Abstracts with Programs, v. 17, p. 546.

CHRISTIE-BLICK, N., AND LEVY, M., 1989a, Concepts of sequence stratigraphy, with examples from strata of late Proterozoic and Cambrian age in the western United States, *in* Christie-Blick, N., and Levy, M., eds., Late Proterozoic and Cambrian Tectonics, Sedimentation, and Record of Metazoan Radiation in the Western United States: Washington, D.C., Field Trip Guidebook T331, American Geophysical Union, p. 23–37.

CHRISTIE-BLICK, N., AND LEVY, M., 1989b, Stratigraphic and tectonic framework of upper Proterozoic and Cambrian rocks in the western United States, *in* Christie-Blick, N., and Levy, M., eds., Late Proterozoic and Cambrian Tectonics, Sedimentation, and Record of Metazoan Radiation in the Western United States: Washington, D.C., Field Trip Guidebook T331, American Geophysical Union, p. 7–21.

CHRISTIE-BLICK, N., MOUNT, J. F., LEVY, M., SIGNOR, P. W., AND LINK, P. K., 1989, Description of stops, *in* Christie-Blick, N., and Levy, M., eds., Late Proterozoic and Cambrian Tectonics, Sedimentation, and Record of Metazoan Radiation in the Western United States: Wash-

ington, D.C., Field Trip Guidebook T331, American Geophysical Union, p. 55–99

CHRISTIE-BLICK, N., VON DER BORCH, C. C., AND DIBONA, P. A., 1990, Working hypotheses for the origin of the Wonoka canyons (Neoproterozoic), South Australia: American Journal of Science, v. 290-A, p. 295–332.

COLLINSON, J. D., 1986, Alluvial sediments, *in* Reading, H. G., ed., Sedimentary Environments and Facies: Boston, Blackwell Scientific Publications, p. 20–62.

CONWAY MORRIS, S., 1988, Radiometric dating of the Precambrian-Cambrian boundary in the Avalon Zone, *in* Landing, E., Narbonne, G. M., and Myrow, P., eds, Trace Fossils, Small Shelly Fossils and the Precambrian-Cambrian Boundary: Bulletin of the New York State Museum, no. 463, p. 53–58.

CONWAY MORRIS, S., 1989, South-eastern Newfoundland and adjacent areas (Avalon Zone), *in* Cowie, J. W., and Brasier, M. D., eds., The Precambrian-Cambrian Boundary: Oxford, Clarendon Press, p. 7–39.

CRITTENDEN, M. D., JR, 1972, Geologic map of the Browns Hole quadrangle, Utah: Washington, D. C., United States Geological Survey, Map GQ-968, scale 1:24,000.

CRITTENDEN, M. D., JR., SCHAEFFER, F. E., TRIMBLE, D. E., AND WOODWARD, L. A., 1971, Nomenclature and correlation of some upper Precambrian and basal Cambrian sequences in western Utah and southeastern Idaho: Geological Society of America Bulletin, v. 82, p. 581–602.

CRITTENDEN, M. D., SHARP, B. J., AND CALKINS, F. C., 1952, Geology of the Wasatch Mountains east of Salt Lake City, Parleys Canyon to Traverse Range, *in* Marsell, R. E., ed., Geology of the Central Wasatch Mountains: Utah Geological and Mineralogical Survey Guidebook to the Geology of Utah, No. 8, p. 1–37.

CRITTENDEN, M. D., JR., AND WALLACE, C. A., 1973, Possible equivalents of the Belt Supergroup in Utah, *in* Belt Symposium, v. 1: Moscow, University of Idaho, Idaho Bureau of Mines and Geology, Special Report 2–3, v. 1, p. 116–138.

DEVLIN, W. J., BOND, G. C., AND BRUECKNER, H. K., 1985, An assessment of the age and tectonic setting of volcanics near the base of the Windermere Supergroup in northeastern Washington: implications for latest Proterozoic-earliest Cambrian continental separation: Canadian Journal of Earth Sciences, v. 22, p. 829–837.

DEVLIN, W. J., BRUECKNER, H. K., AND BOND, G. C., 1988, New isotopic data and a preliminary age for volcanics near the base of the Windermere Supergroup, northeastern Washington, U. S. A.: Canadian Journal of Earth Sciences, v. 25, p. 1906–1911.

EICKHOFF, K. H., VON DER BORCH, C. C., AND GRADY, A. E., 1988, Proterozoic canyons of the Flinders Ranges (South Australia): submarine canyons or drowned river valleys?: Sedimentary Geology, v. 58, p. 217–235.

EVENCHICK, C. A., PARRISH, R. R., AND GABRIELSE, H., 1984, Precambrian gneiss and Late Proterozoic sedimentation in north-central British Columbia: Geology, v. 12, p. 233–237.

GEHLING, J. G., 1982, The sedimentology and stratigraphy of the Late Precambrian Pound Subgroup, central Flinders Ranges, South Australia: Unpublished M. S. Thesis, University of Adelaide, Adelaide, 112 p.

GERMS, G. J. B., 1983, Implications of the stratigraphy and sedimentology of the Nama Group in South West Africa Namibia, *in* The Damara Orogen: Special Publication of the Geological Society of South Africa 11, p. 89–114.

GREENLEE, S. M., DEVLIN, W. J., MILLER, K. J., MOUNTAIN, G. S., AND FLEMINGS, P. B., 1992, Integrated sequence stratigraphy of Neogene deposits, New Jersey continental shelf and slope: Comparison with the Exxon model: Geological Society of America Bulletin, v. 104, p. 1403–1411.

GROTZINGER, J. P., ADAMS, R. D., McCORMICK, D. S., AND MYROW, P., 1989, Sequence stratigraphy, correlations between Wopmay orogen and Kilohigok Basin, and further investigations of the Bear Creek Group (Goulburn Supergroup), District of Mackenzie, *in* Current Research, Part C: Geological Survey of Canada Paper 89–1C, p. 107–120.

HAMBREY, M. M., AND HARLAND, W. B., eds., 1981, Earth's Pre-Pleistocene Glacial Record: Cambridge, Cambridge University Press, 1004 p.

HAMBREY, M. M., AND HARLAND, W. B., 1985, The Late Proterozoic glacial era: Palaeogeography, Palaeoclimatology, Palaeoecology, v. 51, p. 255–272.

HIGGINS, J. M., 1982, Geology of the Champlain Peak quadrangle, Juab and Millard Counties, Utah: Brigham Young University Geology Studies, v. 29, pt. 2, p. 40–58.

HINTZE, L. F., 1973, Geologic history of Utah: Salt Lake City, Brigham Young University Geology Studies, v. 20, Part 3, 181 p.

HINTZE, L. F., 1988, Geologic history of Utah: Salt Lake City, Brigham Young University Geology Studies, Special Publication 7, 202 p.

HOFFMAN, P. F., 1991, Did the breakout of Laurentia turn Gondwanaland inside-out?: Science, v. 252, p. 1409–1412.

HOLLADAY, J. C., 1984, Geology of the northern Canyon Range, Millard and Juab Counties, Utah: Brigham Young University Geology Studies, v. 31, Part 1, p. 1–28.

JANSEN, S. T., 1986, Facies and depositional history of the Brigham Group, northern Banncok and Pocatello Ranges, southeastern Idaho: Unpublished M. S. thesis, Idaho State University, Pocatello, 42 p.

LEVY, M., 1991, Late Proterozoic and Early Cambrian sedimentation, sequence stratigraphy, and tectonic evolution of the eastern Great Basin: Unpublished Ph. D. Dissertation, Columbia University, New York, 380 p.

LEVY, M., AND CHRISTIE-BLICK, N., 1991a, Late Proterozoic paleogeography of the eastern Great Basin, in Cooper, J. D., and Stevents, C. H., eds., Paleozoic Paleogeography of the Western United States-II: Los Angeles, Pacific Section Society of Economic Paleontologists and Mineralogists, v. 67, p.371–386.

LEVY, M., AND CHRISTIE-BLICK, N., 1991b, Tectonic subsidence of the early Paleozoic passive continental margin in eastern California and southern Nevada: Geological Society of America Bulletin, v. 103, p. 1590–1606.

LINDSAY, J. F., 1987, Sequence stratigraphy and depositional controls in Late Proterozoic-Early Cambrian sediments of the Amadeus Basin, central Australia: American Association of Petroleum Geologists Bulletin, v. 71, p. 1387–1403.

LINK, P. K., 1984, Comment on "Subsidence analysis of the Cordilleran miogeocline: Implications for timing of Late Proterozoic rifting and amount of extension": Geology, v. 12, p. 699.

LINK, P. K., CHRISTIE-BLICK, N., STEWART, J. H., MILLER, J. M. G., DEVLIN, W. J., AND LEVY, M., 1993, Late Proterozoic strata of the United States cordillera, in Reed, J. C., Jr., Bickford, M. E., Houston, R. S., Link, P. K., Rankin, D. W., Sims, P. K., and Van Schmus, W. R., eds., Precambrian: Conterminous U. S.: Boulder, Geological Society of America, The Geology of North America, v. C-2, p. 536–558.

LINK, P. K., JANSEN, S. T., HALIMDIHARDJA, P., LANDE, A., AND ZAHN, P., 1987, Stratigraphy of the Brigham Group (Late Proterozoic-Cambrian), Bannock, Portneuf, and Bear River Ranges, southeastern Idaho, in Miller, W. R., ed., The Thrust Belt Revisited: Wyoming Geological Association, 38th Annual Field Conference Guidebook, p. 133–148.

LINK, P. K., LEFEBRE, G. B., POGUE, K. R., AND BURGEL, W. D., 1985, Structural geology between the Putnam thrust and the Snake River Plain, in Kerns, G. L., and Kerns, R. L., eds., Orogenic Patterns and Stratigraphy of North-central Utah and Southeastern Idaho: Utah Geological Association Publication 14, p. 167–174.

McDONALD, C., 1992, Origin and sequence stratigraphic significance of the Uratanna channels, basal Cambrian Uratanna Formation, northern Flinders Ranges, South Australia: Unpublished M. S. Thesis, University of California, Davis, 90 p.

MILLARD, A. W., JR., 1983, Geology of the southwestern quarter of the Scipio North (15 minute) quadrangle, Millard and Juab Counties, Utah: Brigham Young University Geology Studies, v. 30, pt. 1, p. 59–81.

MILLER, K. G., WRIGHT, J. D., AND FAIRBANKS, R. G., 1991, Unlocking the ice house: Oligocene-Miocene oxygen isotopes, eustasy, and margin erosion: Journal of Geophysical Research, v. 96, p. 6829–6848.

NEMEC, W., AND STEEL, R. J., 1984, Alluvial and coastal conglomerates: their significant features and some comments on gravelly mass-flow deposits, in Koster, E. H. and Steel, R. J., eds., Sedimentology of Gravels and Conglomerates: Calgary, Canadian Society of Petroleum Geologists Memoir 10, p. 1–31.

ORIEL, S. S., AND ARMSTRONG, F. C., 1971, Uppermost Precambrian and lowest Cambrian rocks in southeastern Idaho: Washington, D. C., United States Geological Survey Professional Paper 394, 52 p.

POSAMENTIER, H. W., JERVEY, M. T., AND VAIL, P. R., 1988, Eustatic controls on clastic deposition I — conceptual framework, in Wilgus, C. K., Hastings, B. S., Kendall, C. G.St. C., Posamentier, H. W., Ross, C.A ., and van Wagoner, J.C . eds., Sea-level changes—an integrated approach: Tulsa, Society of Economic Paleontologists and Mineralogists Special Publication 42, p. 109–124.

RODGERS, D. W., 1984, Stratigraphy, correlation, and depositional environments of Upper Proterozoic and Lower Cambrian rocks of the southern Deep Creek Range, Utah: Utah Geological Association Publication 13, p. 79–91.

ROSS, G. M., 1991, Tectonic setting of the Windermere Supergroup revisited: Geology, v. 19, p. 1125–1128.

RUST, B. R., AND KOSTER, E. H., 1984, Coarse alluvial deposits, in Walker, R. G., ed., Facies Models: Kitchener, Geoscience Canada Reprint Series 1, p. 53–69.

SAMSON, S. D., AND LANDING, E., 1992, U-Pb zircon geochronology of Precambrian-Cambrian volcanics from the Avalon terrane, New Brunswick (abs.): Geological Society of America Abstracts with Programs, v. 24, p. A113-A114.

SORENSEN, M. L., AND CRITTENDEN, M. D., JR., 1979, Geologic map of the Huntsville quadrangle, Weber and Cache Counties, Utah: Washington, D. C., United States Geological Survey, Map GQ-1503, scale 1:24,000.

STAATZ, M. H., AND CARR, W. J., 1964, Geology and mineral deposits of the Thomas and Dugway Ranges, Juab and Tooele Counties, Utah: Washington, D. C., United States Geological Survey Professional Paper 415, 188 p.

STEWART, J. H., 1972, Initial deposits in the Cordilleran geosyncline: evidence of a Late Precambrian (<850 m.y.) continental separation: Geological Society of America Bulletin, v. 83, p. 1345–1360.

STEWART, J. H., 1976, Late Precambrian evolution of North America: plate tectonics implication: Geology, v. 4, p. 11–15.

STEWART, J. H., 1982, Regional relations of Proterozoic Z and Lower Cambrian rocks in the western United States and northern Mexico, in Cooper, J. D., Troxel, B. W., and Wright, L. A., eds., Geology of Selected Areas in the San Bernardino Mountains, Western Mojave Desert, and Southern Great Basin, California: Shoshone, Geological Society of America Cordilleran Section Meeting, Anaheim, California, Volume and Guidebook, p. 171–186.

STEWART, J. H., AND SUCZEK, C. A., 1977, Cambrian and latest Precambrian paleogeography and tectonics in the western United States, in Stewart, J. H., Stevens, C. H., and Fritschee, A. E., eds., Paleozoic Paleogeography of the Western United States: Society of Economic Paleontologists and Mineralogists, Pacific Section, Pacific Coast Paleogeography Symposium 1, p. 1–17.

TRIMBLE, D. E., 1976, Geology of the Michaud and Pocatello quadrangles, Bannock and Power Counties, Idaho: United States Geological Survey Bulletin 1400, 88 p.

VAIL, P. R., 1987, Seismic stratigraphy interpretation using sequence stratigraphy. Part I: Seismic stratigraphy interpretation procedure, in Bally, A. W., ed., Atlas of Seismic Stratigraphy: Tulsa, American Association of Petroleum Geologists Studies in Geology No. 27, v. 1, p. 1–10.

VAN WAGONER, J. C., MITCHUM, R. M., CAMPION, K. M., AND RAHMANIAN, V. D., 1990, Siliciclastic sequence stratigraphy in well logs, cores, and outcrops: Tulsa, American Association of Petroleum Geologists Methods in Exploration Series, No. 7, 55 p.

VAN WAGONER, J. C., NUMMEDAL, D., JONES, C. R., TALOR, D. R., JENNETTE, D. C., AND RILEY, G. W., 1991, Sequence stratigraphy applications to shelf sandstone reservoirs, outcrop to subsurface examples: Tulsa, American Association of Petroleum Geologists Field Conference, September 21–28.

VON DER BORCH, C. C., GRADY, A. E., ALDAM, R., MILLER, D., NEUMANN, R., ROVIRA, A., AND EICKHOFF, K., 1985, A large-scale meandering submarine canyon: outcrop example from the Late Proterozoic Adelaide Geosyncline, South Australia: Sedimentology, v. 32, p. 507–518.

VON DER BORCH, C. C., CHRISTIE-BLICK, N., AND GRADY, A. E., 1988, Depositional sequence analysis applied to upper Proterozoic Wilpena Group, Adelaide Geosyncline, South Australia: Australian Journal of Earth Science, v. 35, p. 59–71.

VON DER BORCH, C. C., GRADY, A. E., EIKHOFF, K. H., DIBONA, P., AND
   CHRISTIE-BLICK, N., 1989, Late Proterozoic Patsy Springs Canyon,
   Adelaide Geosyncline: submarine or subaerial origin?: Sedimentology,
   v. 36, p. 777–792.

WOODWARD, L. A., 1972, Upper Precambrian stratigraphy of central Utah,
   in Baer, J. L., and Callaghan, E., eds., Plateau-Basin and Range transition zone, central Utah: Utah Geological Association Publication 2,
   p. 1–5.

SUBJECT INDEX

SUBJECT INDEX